Mission Handbook
U.S. and Canadian Protestant Ministries Overseas
2004-2006
(19th Edition)

Edited by Dotsey Welliver
and Minnette Northcutt

emis
Evangelism and Missions Information Service
P.O. Box 794, Wheaton, IL 60189

BILLY GRAHAM CENTER
WHEATON COLLEGE

Mission Handbook

U.S. and Canadian Protestant Ministries Overseas (2004-2006)
(19th edition)

Edited by Dotsey Welliver and Minnette Northcutt
Executive Editor, Kenneth D. Gill

Published by EMIS, a division of the Billy Graham Center, Wheaton College,
Wheaton, Ill.

Printed in the United States of America.
Cover design and layout: Dona Diehl.

For information about other publications or resources of EMIS or the Billy
Graham Center:
Phone: (630) 752-7158
E-mail: emis@wheaton.edu
Web site: www.billygrahamcenter.org/emis

ISBN 0-9617751-9-X

To be included in the next edition of the *Mission Handbook*, to update
your agency's information or to check on current updates for mission
agencies go to: **www.missionhandbookonline.com**

Contents

Abbreviations

Admin.	Administrative, Administrator	Min(s).	Ministry(ies)
Am.	America, American	Msn(s).	Mission(s)
Apt.	Apartment	Mtg.	Meeting
Assoc.	Associate, Association	N.	North
Ave.	Avenue	NA	Not Applicable
Bd.	Board	NASB	New American Standard Bible
Blvd.	Boulevard	Natl.	National
Cen.	Central	NE	Northeast
CEO	Chief Executive Officer	NIV	New International Version
Ch(s).	Church(es)	NR	Not Reported
Co.	Company	NW	Northwest
Comm.	Community, Commission	Org.	Organization
Conf.	Conference	Pres.	President
Cong.	Congregational	P.O.	Post Office
Conv.	Convention	Rd.	Road
COO	Chief Operating Officer	Rep.	Republic
Coord.	Coordinator, Coordination	Rev.	Reverend
Ctr.	Center	Rm.	Room
Dept.	Department	S.	South
Dev.	Development	SE	Southeast
Dir.	Director	Secty.	Secretary
Div.	Division	Soc.	Society
Dr.	Doctor, Drive	St.	Saint, Street
E.	East	Sta.	Station
Ed.	Education	Supt.	Superintendent
Exec.	Executive	Ste.	Suite
Frgn., Frn.	Foreign	SVC(s).	Services
Gen.	General	SW	Southwest
Govt.	Government	TEE	Theological Education by Extension
Hdq.	Headquarters	Theol.	Theology, Theological
Hts.	Heights	U., Univ.	University
Hwy.	Highway	VP	Vice President
Inc.	Incorporated	W.	West
Inst.	Institute	Wld.	World
Intl.	International		
Is(Is).	Island(s)		
Lit.	Literature		
Mgr.	Manager		

Canada

AB	Alberta
BC	British Columbia
MB	Manitoba
NB	New Brunswick
NF	Newfoundland
NS	Nova Scotia
NT	Northwest Territories
ON	Ontario
PE	Prince Edward Island
PQ	Quebec
SK	Saskatchewan
YT	Yukon Territory

United States

AK	Alaska
AL	Alabama
AR	Arkansas
AZ	Arizona
CA	California
CO	Colorado
CT	Connecticut
DE	Delaware
DC	District of Columbia
FL	Florida
GA	Georgia
HI	Hawaii
IA	Iowa
ID	Idaho
IL	Illinois
IN	Indiana
KS	Kansas
KY	Kentucky
LA	Louisiana
MA	Massachusetts
MD	Maryland
ME	Maine
MI	Michigan
MN	Minnesota
MO	Missouri
MS	Mississippi
MT	Montana
NC	North Carolina
ND	North Dakota
NE	Nebraska
NH	New Hampshire
NJ	New Jersey
NM	New Mexico
NV	Nevada
NY	New York
OH	Ohio
OK	Oklahoma
OR	Oregon
PA	Pennsylvania
PR	Puerto Rico
RI	Rhode Island
SC	South Carolina
SD	South Dakota
TN	Tennessee
TX	Texas
UT	Utah
VA	Virginia
VT	Vermont
WA	Washington
WI	Wisconsin
WV	West Virginia
WY	Wyoming

Introduction

The purpose of the *Mission Handbook* is to provide the reader with ready access to vital and current information about Protestant mission agencies based in the U.S. and Canada that are engaged in overseas (all countries beyond the U.S. and Canada) ministries. As such, it provides the user with the most complete information available in a single publication. The term "agency" is used in the broad sense referring to all denominational boards, nondenominational societies, and other organizations involved in overseas mission.

The United States, Canada, and the Rest of the World

Including only U.S. and Canadian agencies with overseas mission activities has over the years given manageable boundaries to this survey and publication effort. Some of the agencies are also involved in ministries in the U.S. and Canada but home mission data by definition is not included.

Mission agency activity for much of the rest of the world is provided in other publications. For example, non-Western world mission agency information is given in *From Every People: A Handbook of Two-Thirds World Missions (1989)*. A continuing series of Christian handbooks with mission sections have been published for Britain and parts of Europe. At various times mission agency information for countries in Africa, Asia, South America, and Oceania has been published in those countries. (See the bibliography for a list of some of these publications.)

The last worldwide publication from the perspective of mission agencies was *The Encyclopedia of Modern Christian Missions: The Agencies (1967)* with Burton L. Goddard as editor. *The World Christian Encyclopedia (2001)* edited by David B. Barrett, George T. Kurian and Todd M. Johnson and *Operation World (2001)* by Patrick Johnstone give overall country totals for missionary sending and receiving.

This Edition of the *Mission Handbook*

The information about the agencies and their fields of service was obtained via a mailed or e-mailed questionnaire shown in the Appendix. In a few cases it was obtained by fax or phone. In the past decade the questionnaire has changed some from survey to survey as the times and mission agencies themselves have changed. Key questions, however, have stayed the same over extended periods of time. For example, questions relating to financial data have used the same definitions since the late 1970s. The countries of service and field personnel questions have remained the same since the early 1990s when the "more than 4 years" definition for long-term personnel was instituted. These definitions were determined in consultation with editors of other mission directories from several countries and the heads of two national mission associations.

Dr. Scott Moreau, who served as a missionary in Africa before taking up his current teaching post at the Wheaton College Graduate School, used his research and computer expertise to analyze the survey database and come up with a variety of ways to view the data.

Brief History of the *Mission Handbook*

The direct antecedent of the *Mission Handbook* first appeared in 1953 with the title *Foreign Missionary Agencies in the United States: A Check List*. It was compiled and mimeographed by the Missionary Research Library (MRL) in New York under director R. Pierce Beaver. The MRL had been founded in 1914 at the initiative of John R. Mott who chaired the World Missionary Conference at Edinburgh, Scotland, in 1910 and headed its continuation committee.

The 1960 edition was spiral bound and typeset with the title *Directory of North American Protestant Foreign Missionary Agencies* as MRL directors Frank W. Price and Herbert C. Jackson expanded and enhanced the publication.

In 1968 the publication became a cooperative effort of MRL and the Missions Advanced Research and Communication (MARC) Center, a division of World Vision International near Los Angeles. The title became *North American Protestant Ministries Overseas Directory*. Under MARC director Edward R. Dayton, the information was placed in electronic storage and processed by a computer for the first time in 1968.

In 1973 the title included "Mission Handbook" as the publication continued to be enhanced with related articles and expanded analyses of the survey data. In 1976 MARC became the sole publisher and in 1979 Samuel Wilson became director of MARC.

The *Mission Handbooks* of the 1990s contained chapters by MARC director Bryant L. Myers that brought together information from various sources displayed as maps, charts, graphs, pictures and other forms to give a global perspective of evangelism and missions. Also in the 1990s, chapters from the Catholic and Orthodox mission communities were added and "Protestant" in the title was changed to "Christian." In this present edition, because of the increased usage of Web sites, readers are referred to the Web pages of those two groups for their mission data.

For nearly two decades, editor John A. Siewert of MARC had, with dedication and great attention to detail, used his unique editorial skills in the production of the volume. Near the end of the century, production of the *Handbook* was transferred from MARC's auspices to find a new home at the Evangelism and Missions Information Service (EMIS) of the Billy Graham Center at Wheaton College near Chicago, Illinois. The 18th edition (copyright 2000) was the first volume to be produced by EMIS, under the transitional leadership of MARC editor John Siewert and the guidance of new EMIS executive editor Kenneth Gill.

agencies reported a 5.5% increase. Since the vast bulk of the data is from 2001, it would not be likely that enough time had transpired since the events of September 11 to have had an impact on the turn-around increase in long-term workers being deployed. Additionally, the new organizations accounted for 162 less long-term workers than the previously listed agencies that were dropped in this edition, so none of the gains in long-term personnel were the result of the new agency listings.

Table 2: Summary of Changes in Reported US Missions Statistics, 1992-2001

Personnel from the US	1992	1996	1998	2001	Change 1998-2001	Change 1992-2001
Fully supported US Personnel Serving Overseas						
Long-term (overseas more than 4 years)	32,634	33,074	32,957	34,757	5.5%	6.5%
Short-term (overseas from 1 to 4 years)	5,115	6,562	6,930	8,030	15.9%	57.0%
Nonresidential fully supported	626	507	1,815	1,599	-11.9%	155.4%
Total fully supported US prsonnel serving overseas	38,375	40,143	41,702	44,386	6.4%	15.7%
Other US Personnel Serving Overseas						
Short-term of 2 weeks up to one year (1996 and 1999)	NA	63,995	97,272	346,270	256.0%	
Bivocational associates sponsored or supervised	1,040	1,336	3,220	1,748	-45.7%	68.1%
Nonresidential partially supported	80	215	310	506	63.2%	532.5%
Non-US Personnel Directly Supported						
Those serving in their home country	NA	28,535	71,150	59,843	-15.9%	
Those serving in a country other than their home country	1,898	1,791	3,179	5,029	58.2%	165.0%
US Ministry and Home Office Staff						
Full-time paid staff	14,694	19,399	21,758	22,462	3.2%	52.9%
Part-time staff/associates	1,742	2,850	2,946	2,962	0.5%	70.0%
Volunteer (ongoing) helpers	37,452	59,332	196,528	638,907	225.1%	1605.9%

Financial Support Raised in the US—Income for Overseas Ministries (Adjusted for Inflation)					
1992	1996	1998	2001	Change 1998-2001	Change 1992-2001
$2,587,013,186	$2,626,008,218	$3,199,249,115	$3,752,306,193	17.3%	45.0%

There was also a healthy increase for those U.S. nationals serving overseas for 1 to 4 years (15.9%), which is a hopeful sign for the ongoing longevity of long-term U.S. missionaries. Perhaps the short-term boom is starting to produce some results, though it is still too early to tell and no correlation can be established between the short-term increase and the long-term increase reported in this edition. The newly listed agencies only added 1 worker more than lost through the de-listed agencies, so they did not affect the 1 to 4 year totals.

Those who serve as non-residential fully supported by an agency dropped 11.9%. While the drop looks significant, the entire loss came from one organization. In the previous edition they reported 722 workers in this category, and in this edition they reported 0. When this agency is factored out, the remaining 176 agencies that reported workers in this category gained 504 over the previous edition (a 27.8% increase).

The largest increase between the two editions is the enormous short-term (two weeks to 1 year) personnel gain (from 97,272 to 346,270, which is 256% in the three-year span). It is most likely that the sheer size of the gain is due to changes in reporting rather than actual growth. Two agencies alone accounted for 62.7% of the total short-term reported number. If they are factored out, the growth rate between the two editions was still an impressive 48%.

Table 3 shows the 22 agencies with 1,000 or more short-term missionaries reported (in the previous edition 10 agencies reported 1,000 or more short-term missionaries). Thus, there is no doubt that the number of short-term mission opportunities have almost exploded over the past decade. It is interesting to note that only one agency which was in the top ten in the last edition made it into this edition's top ten short-term sending list. The organizations newly listed in this year's edition only accounted for 7,841 short-term workers, and those de-listed from this edition accounted for 1,926. Thus, while there was a gain of almost 6,000 due to the changes resulting from the new listings, the bulk of the gains in this area were the result of higher numbers reported by the continuing agencies.

The drop in the number of reported tentmakers ("bivocational associates sponsored or supervised,"—1,472 or 45.7%) was almost entirely the result of one agency's reported loss of 1,367 tentmakers between the editions.

Nationals serving in their home country dropped significantly (11,307; 15.9%). In this case all of the decrease is attributable to the reporting of a single agency, which dropped just under 14,936 national workers. In other words, the other 267 agencies that reported national workers showed a net gain of almost 3,629 (or 6.9%). Table 4 shows the U.S. agencies that reported 500 or more national workers.

Non-North Americans serving in a country other than their own increased significantly (58.2%). The increase appears to be rather narrowly based. While the number of agencies reporting more than 50 such workers increased from 16 to 20 (see Table 5), the top five agencies reported 1,542 more such personnel than the top five in the last edition, which accounted for almost 70% of the total in-

Table 3: Agencies with 1,000 or More Short-Term Workers Sent

Rank	Agency	No. Sent
1	United Methodist Church, General Board of Global Ministries	117,000
2	Youth With A Mission (YWAM), North American Office	100,000
3	Southern Baptist Convention International Mission Board	33,963
4	Assemblies of God World Missions	12,694
5	Church of the Nazarene, World Mission Department	9,423
6	Church of God (Cleveland, TN) World Missions	8,131
7	Churches of Christ	7,765
8	Mission to the World (PCA), Inc.	6,010
9	Adventures in Missions	6,000
10	Campus Crusade for Christ, Intl.	4,004
11	Foursquare Missions international	2,041
12	Christian Churches/Churches of Christ	2,000
13	Seventh-day Adventists General Conference	1,524
14	Evangelical Covenant Church, Board of World Mission	1,500
15	Christian and Missionary Alliance	1,352
16	American Baptist Churches in the U.S.A., International Ministries	1,231
17	Habitat for Humanity International	1,200
18	Wesleyan World Missions	1,110
19	MercyShips	1,100
20	Youth for Christ/USA, World Outreach Division	1,011
21	On the Go Ministries/Keith Cook Evangelistic Association	1,000
22	Teen Missions International	1,000

crease. Even so, this may be a hopeful sign that more non-North Americans working for North American agencies are actually crossing cultures for their ministry rather than simply working within their home country. However, we do not know if they are actually serving cross-culturally in their new setting rather than ministering among same-culture pockets of people who also live in the countries where these reported workers minister.

The reported number of volunteers soared by 442,379 (or 225.1%) between the editions. The reported increase was almost entirely due to the reports of five agencies,[10] which together accounted for 631,097 (98.8%) of the total reported volunteer force.

In light of the drop in the stock market and the shift in charitable giving after September 11, 2001, it would be expected that giving to overseas ministries might not show the same robust growth in this edition that it did in the previous. In-

Table 4: Agencies with 500 or More National Workers

Rank	Agency	No. of Nationals
1	Campus Crusade for Christ, Intl.	13,628
2	Gospel for Asia	13,500
3	Partners International	4,700
4	Christian Aid Mission	3,873
5	World Missions Far Corners, Inc.	1,661
6	Final Frontiers Foundation, Inc.	945
7	International Needs—USA	804
8	Every Home for Christ International	765
9	OMF International	736
10	World Concern	616
11	Word of Life Fellowship	608
12	Bible League, The	586
13	Global Fellowship	583
14	Compassion International, Inc.	558
15	Holt International Children's Services, Inc.	552
16	India Evangelical Mission, Inc.	525
17	Churches of God General Conference	510
18	Habitat for Humanity International	509

deed, in the previous edition, the inflation adjusted income growth over the three-year span was 21.8%, and in this edition it was 17.3%. We will return to this later in the chapter.

Denominationalism

As we noted in the previous edition, agencies were asked to choose their orientation towards denominationalism from among six categories: denominational, interdenominational, non-denominational, transdenominational, prefer that no orientation be used, and other. The frequency of responses is shown in Figure 1, which combines the last two categories as "No Category." As we noted in the previous edition, "Some are very intentional in distinguishing nondenominational from interdenominational, while others change from edition to edition of the *Handbook*. Despite the nomenclature, the most significant issue is whether an agency considers itself to be a denominationally related one or not. To distinguish the latter from the category 'nondenominational,' in the following discussion we refer to them as 'not-denominational' agencies."[11]

Figure 1 shows a slight shift in orientation away from denominationalism

**Table 5: U.S. Agencies with More than 50 Nationals
Serving in Another Country**

Rank	Agency	No.
1	WEC International	1,189
2	Seventh-Day Adventists General Conference	539
3	Campus Crusade for Christ, Intl.	506
4	CAM International	181
5	International Teams, USA	132
6	New Tribes Mission	129
7	Latin America Mission	114
8	Elim Fellowship, International Dept.	104
9	Word of Life Fellowship	97
10	South America Mission	94
11	Church of the Nazarene, World Mission Department	85
12	Navigators, US International Missions Group	84
13	International Missionary Center	78
14	Cadence International	69
15	Middle East Christian Outreach	66
16	Evangelism Explosion International	64
17	Church of God (Cleveland, TN) World Missions	59
18	Calvary International	59
19	Greater Grace World Outreach	58
20	General Conf. Mennonite Ch., Commission on Overseas Mission	52

among the agencies between this edition and the previous. Even with the replacement of 74 agencies by 71 new ones, the ratios are relatively stable between the two editions.[12] Only 3 (4.2%) of the newly listed agencies were denominational, while 13 of the dropped agencies (14.1%) were denominational. Generally the newer listed agencies tended to be nondenominational (27, or 38.0%) or no category (15, or 21.1%). The net result was that the agencies reporting themselves as denominational decreased the most (8.7%) and those not indicating a category increased the most (23.6%). The overall percent of denominational agencies dropped from 18.2% to 16.7%.

The 20th century shift from denominational agencies to not-denominational agencies is illustrated in Figure 2, which shows the total number of each type of agency listed in this edition of the *Handbook* over the course of the century. Because of the agencies that were dropped, the graph has shifted slightly from our last edition. It still clearly shows that at the turn of the century denominational agencies were more numerous (39) than those agencies which were not denominational (23). By the 1930s they were roughly even, but by the end of the 1990s

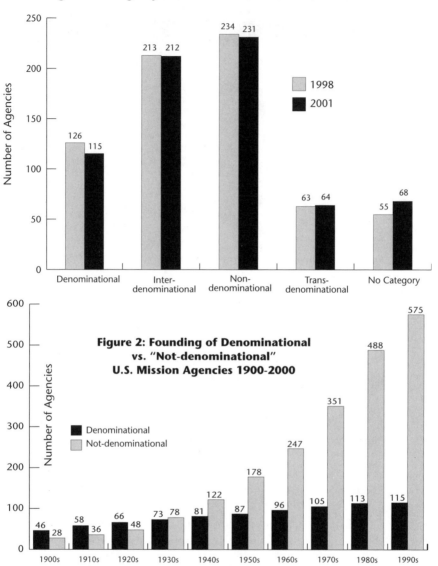

Figure 1: US Agency Orientations towards Denominationalism

Figure 2: Founding of Denominational vs. "Not-denominational" U.S. Mission Agencies 1900-2000

the not-denominational agencies outnumbered their denominational counterparts by a ratio of 5 to 1.

Figure 3 shows the relative shift in resources between the two editions. Not only was the percentage of denominational agencies lower in 2001, they also received a smaller percentage of the income for overseas missions than they had in 1998 (from 36.9% to 28.3% of the total). At the same time, however, they gained in the relative number of national workers serving in a country other than their own (from 13.5% to 19.8% of the total). The other ratios remained relatively stable.

As reported in the previous edition, we can see that denominational agencies

Figure 3: Comparisons by Denominational Orientation of US Agencies

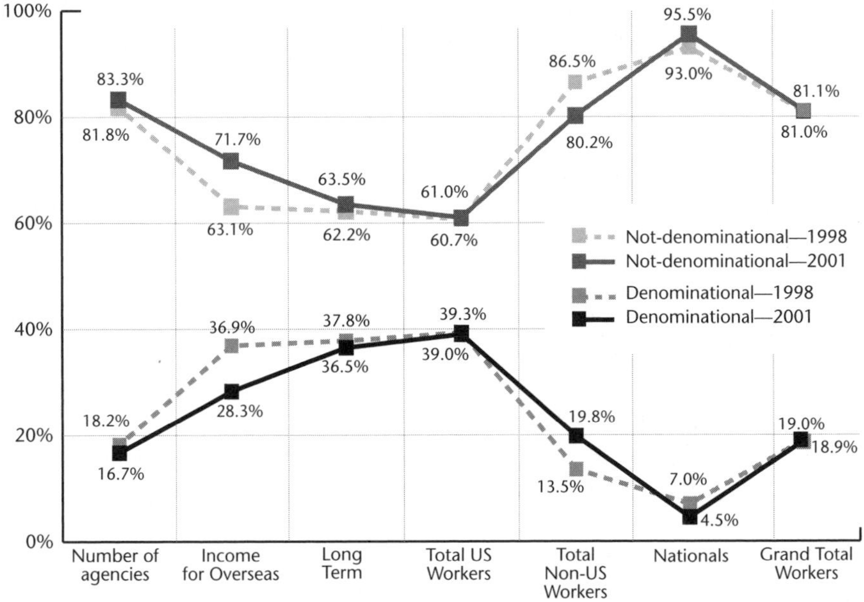

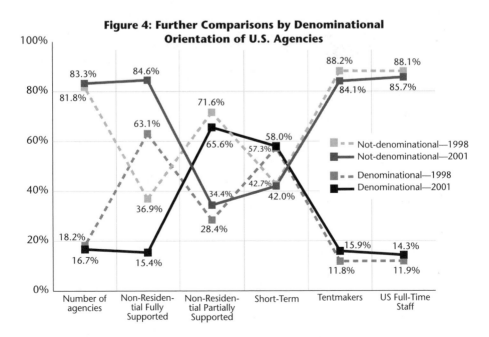

reported proportionately greater overseas income, long-term U.S. missionaries and U.S. full-time missionaries than the not-denominational agencies. The not-denominational agencies, on the other hand, reported relatively more nationals working in their own country. Figure 4, on the other hand, shows significant shifts in the proportions from the last edition. In it we see that denominational

Figure 4: Further Comparisons by Denominational Orientation of U.S. Agencies

agencies reported a proportionate gain in non-residential partially supported missionaries and in their reported numbers of short-term missionaries. The not-denominational agencies reported a gain in non-residential fully supported missionaries, and maintained their proportional emphasis on tentmakers and U.S. full-time staff.

Activities of U.S. Agencies

The survey included a list of fifty-two activities, including an "other" category with a blank to indicate what the "other" activities were. Agencies were asked to indicate what they considered to be their primary activity as well as up to five other activities in which they were engaged. We then examined the activities that the agencies listed as "other" and added seven more categories to the activity list based on their additions: adoption, apologetics, discipleship, justice & related, tentmaking & related, TESOL and urban ministry.

As with the previous survey, church planting/establishing was by far the most frequently chosen primary activity (138, 20%). Table 6 shows this is contrasted with the previous edition of the *Handbook* in which 158 of the agencies indicated that church establishing/planting was their primary activity (a drop of 12.7%). Does this indicate a drop in emphasis among U.S. agencies on church planting? Three considerations help answer this question.

First, of the 74 agencies de-listed in this edition, 15 had indicated in the previous survey that church establishing/planting was their primary activity. Only 3 of the 70 newly added agencies listed church establishing/planting as their primary activity, resulting in a net loss of 12 due to adds/drops. This means that 8 out of

Table 6: Primary Activities: Comparing 1998 and 2001 Top Ten Survey Results

Activity	2001 No.	1998 No.	Change	% Change	2001 Rank	1998 Rank	Change
Church establishing/planting	138	158	-20	-12.7%	1	1	0
Evangelism, personal & group	55	60	-5	-8.3	2	2	0
Leadership development	35	30	5	16.7%	3	4	1
National church nurture/support	34	40	-6	-15.0%	4	3	-1
Evangelism, mass	29	20	9	45.0%	5	7	2
Support of national workers	24	26	-2	-7.7%	6	5	-1
Education, theological	21	17	4	23.5%	7	13	6
Medicine, incl. dental & pub. health	20	18	2	11.1%	8	10	2
Training/Orientation, missionary	20	20	0	0.0%	8	8	0
Broadcasting, radio and/or TV	19	15	4	26.7%	10	16	6
Short-term programs coordination	19	18	1	5.6%	10	10	0
Training, other	19	18	1	5.6%	10	10	0

158 agencies (5.1%) switched their primary listing between surveys. Thus, the change was not as much attributable to agencies *changing* primary emphasis as it was on agencies being removed from this edition's database.

Second, Table 7 shows all of the primary activities grouped into major categories for 1998 and 2001. While it is true that all "evangelism/discipleship" related activi-

Table 7: Primary Activities by Major Categories

	2001		1998	
	No.	%	No.	%
Evangelism/Discipleship Activities	**424**	**61.5%**	**434**	**63.0%**
Church establishing/planting	138	20.0%	158	22.9%
Evangelism, personal and small group	55	8.0%	60	8.7%
Leadership development	35	5.1%	30	4.3%
National church nurture/support	34	4.9%	40	5.8%
Evangelism, mass	29	4.2%	20	2.9%
Support of national workers	24	3.5%	26	3.8%
Broadcasting, radio and/or TV	19	2.8%	16	2.3%
Literature distribution	15	2.2%	13	1.9%
Bible distribution	14	2.0%	15	2.2%
Evangelism, student	11	1.6%	9	1.3%
Children's programs	10	1.5%	8	1.2%
Literature production	6	0.9%	9	1.3%
Translation, Bible	6	0.9%	6	0.9%
Video/Film production/dist.	6	0.9%	8	1.2%
Audio recording/dist.	4	0.6%	3	0.4%
Church construction	4	0.6%	4	0.6%
Youth programs	4	0.6%	3	0.4%
Translation, other	3	0.4%	4	0.6%
Literacy	2	0.3%	2	0.3%
Tentmaking & related	2	0.3%	0	0.0%
Apologetics	1	0.1%	0	0.0%
Camping programs	1	0.1%	0	0.0%
Discipleship	1	0.1%	0	0.0%
Education/Training Activities	**57**	**8.3%**	**56**	**8.1%**
Education, theological	21	3.0%	17	2.5%
Training, other	19	2.8%	18	2.6%
Education, ch/schl gen Christian	8	1.2%	11	1.6%

Continued on page 22

Table 7: Continued

	2001		1998	
	No.	%	No.	%
Education (TEE)	4	0.6%	4	0.6%
Correspondence courses	3	0.4%	3	0.4%
Education, extension (other)	1	0.1%	0	0.0%
Education, missy (cert/deg)	1	0.1%	3	0.4%
Mission Agency Support Activities	**102**	**14.8%**	**91**	**13.2%**
Training/Orientation, missionary	20	2.9%	20	2.9%
Short-term programs coordination	19	2.8%	18	2.6%
Recruiting/Mobilizing	14	2.0%	12	1.7%
Information services	7	1.0%	10	1.4%
Partnership development	7	1.0%	1	0.1%
Aviation services	6	0.9%	5	0.7%
Technical assistance	6	0.9%	6	0.9%
Services for other agencies	5	0.7%	5	0.7%
Furloughed missionary support	4	0.6%	3	0.4%
Member care	4	0.6%	2	0.3%
Association of Missions	3	0.4%	4	0.6%
Management consulting/training	3	0.4%	1	0.1%
Psychological counseling	2	0.3%	2	0.3%
Purchasing services	2	0.3%	2	0.3%
Relief and Development Activities	**81**	**11.8%**	**81**	**11.7%**
Medicine, incl. dental and pub. health	20	2.9%	18	2.6%
Development, community	17	2.5%	18	2.6%
Childcare/orphanage	16	2.3%	16	2.3%
Relief and/or rehabilitation	13	1.9%	14	2.0%
Supplying equipment	4	0.6%	3	0.4%
Disability assistance programs	3	0.4%	4	0.6%
Medical supplies	3	0.4%	6	0.9%
Agricultural programs	2	0.3%	2	0.3%
Justice and related	2	0.3%	0	0.0%
Adoption	1	0.1%	0	0.0%
Other activities	**26**	**3.8%**	**29**	**4.2%**
Funds transmission	11	1.6%	22	3.2%
Other	9	1.3%	4	0.6%
Research	5	0.7%	3	0.4%
TESOL	1	0.1%	0	0.0%

ties were down by 1.5%, that decrease is not as marked as the church establishing/planting decrease. In other words, agencies still had as their primary focus activities related to evangelism, discipleship and church planting. Several agencies had, however, redistributed within that broad category their primary activity focus.

Table 8: All Activities: Comparing 1998 and 2001 Top Ten Survey Results

Activity	2001 No.	1998 No.	% Change	2001 Rank	1998 Rank	Change
Church establishing/planting	267	271	-1.5%	1	1	0
Leadership development	218	169	29.0%	2	3	1
Evangelism, personal and small group	217	264	-17.8%	3	2	-1
Education, theological	145	120	20.8%	4	6	2
National church nurture/support	142	159	-10.7%	5	4	-1
Evangelism, mass	136	104	30.8%	6	8	2
Support of national workers	123	113	8.8%	7	7	0
Literature distribution	122	124	-1.6%	8	5	-3
Short-term programs coordination	108	87	24.1%	9	11	2
Training, other	104	80	30.0%	10	13	3

Finally, and paralleling what is seen in Table 7, Table 8 shows the most frequently indicated activities of all U.S. agencies. While there was a 12.7% drop in those listing church establishing/planting as their *primary* activity, there was only a 1.5% drop in those who listed it as *one* of their regular activities.

Table 7 can be used to see the shifts of primary focus within each activity. For example, as in the previous edition, personal and small group evangelism was the second most frequently chosen primary activity. However, the number of agencies that considered it their primary activity dropped from 60 to 55. This was offset, however, by the number of agencies indicating mass evangelism as their primary activity, which increased from 20 to 29. Other activities that were more frequently listed as primary for an agency included theological education (from 17 to 21) and leadership development (from 30 to 35). The largest drop of primary activity was in funds transmission (from 22 to 11). This could possibly be an early indicator of how the changing U.S. economy affected agency activities. However, a few agencies have stopped reporting funds transmission activities for various reasons.

Figure 5 illustrates a comparison of the percent of activities listed as primary (Table 7) to the percent of all activities (Table 9). As it shows, in relation to the primary activities, when all activities are seen there is a shift away from evangelism/discipleship activities (from 61.5% to 54.1%; a drop of 11.9%) towards educational (from 8.3% to 13.7%; a gain of 65.8%) and relief and development ones

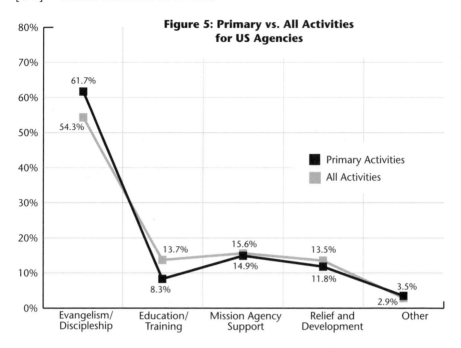

Figure 5: Primary vs. All Activities for US Agencies

Table 9: Comparison of 2001 vs. 1998 US Agency Activities by Major Category

	2001		1998	
	No.	%	No.	%
Evangelism/Discipleship Activities	**1822**	**54.3%**	**1777**	**57.7%**
Church establishing/planting	267	38.8%	271	39.1%
Leadership development	218	31.6%	169	24.4%
Evangelism, personal and small group	219	31.8%	264	38.1%
National church nurture/support	143	20.8%	159	22.9%
Evangelism, mass	138	20.0%	104	15.0%
Literature distribution	122	17.7%	124	17.9%
Support of national workers	124	18.0%	113	16.3%
Bible distribution	93	13.5%	79	11.4%
Literature production	72	10.4%	70	10.1%
Broadcasting, radio and/or TV	68	9.9%	64	9.2%
Children's programs	50	7.3%	39	5.6%
Youth programs	46	6.7%	46	6.6%
Church construction	44	6.4%	44	6.3%
Evangelism, student	40	5.8%	41	5.9%
Translation, Bible	32	4.6%	22	3.2%
Audio recording/distribution	28	4.1%	32	4.6%

Continued on page 25

Table 9: Continued

	2001		1998	
	No.	%	No.	%
Camping programs	28	4.1%	52	7.5%
Video/Film prod./distrib.	29	4.2%	37	5.3%
Literacy	20	2.9%	19	2.7%
Translation, other	14	2.0%	16	2.3%
Linguistics	9	1.3%	12	1.7%
Discipleship	7	1.0%	0	0%
Urban ministry	4	0.6%	0	0%
Bible memorization	3	0.4%	0	0%
Apologetics	2	0.3%	0	0%
Tentmaking and related	2	0.3%	0	0%
Education/Training Activities	**460**	**13.7%**	**382**	**12.4%**
Educational, theological	145	21.0%	120	17.3%
Training, other	107	15.5%	80	11.5%
Education, ch/schl gen Christian	83	12.0%	73	10.5%
Education (TEE)	45	6.5%	44	6.3%
Correspondence courses	30	4.4%	31	4.5%
Education, extension (other)	28	4.1%	19	2.7%
Education, missy (cert/deg.)	22	3.2%	15	2.2%
Mission Agency Support Activities	**524**	**15.6%**	**420**	**13.6%**
Short-term programs coordination	108	15.7%	87	12.6%
Training/Orientation, missionary	93	13.5%	90	13.0%
Recruiting/mobilizing	77	11.2%	65	9.4%
Services for other agencies	57	8.3%	47	6.8%
Information services	40	5.8%	33	4.8%
Technical assistance	40	5.8%	36	5.2%
Management consulting/training	34	4.9%	24	3.5%
Partnership development	20	2.9%	1	0.1%
Furloughed missionary support	17	2.5%	11	1.6%
Aviation services	14	2.0%	11	1.6%
Association of Missions	8	1.2%	4	0.6%
Member care	8	1.2%	2	0.3%
Purchasing services	5	0.7%	5	0.7%
Psychological counseling	3	0.4%	4	0.6%
Relief and Development Activities	**452**	**13.5%**	**423**	**13.7%**
Development, comm. or other	102	14.8%	99	14.3%

Continued on page 26

Table 9: Continued

	2001		1998	
	No.	%	No.	%
Medicine, incl. dental and pub. health	96	13.9%	82	11.8%
Relief and/or rehabilitation	76	11.0%	75	10.8%
Childcare/orphanage	74	10.7%	66	9.5%
Medical supplies	34	4.9%	39	5.6%
Agricultural programs	30	4.4%	30	4.3%
Supplying equipment	25	3.6%	20	2.9%
Disability assistance programs	10	1.5%	12	1.7%
Justice and related	4	0.6%	0	0.0%
Adoption	1	0.1%	0	0.0%
Other activities	**96**	**2.9%**	**109**	**3.5%**
Funds transmission	35	5.1%	60	8.7%
Research	33	4.8%	37	5.3%
Other	27	3.9%	12	1.7%
TESOL	1	0.1%	0	0.0%

(from 11.8% to 13.5%; a gain of 14.6%). This shift parallels the shift seen in the previous edition, though is somewhat stronger.

Tables 10 and 11 offer comparisons related to the activities when sorted by the master categories shown in Table 7. Evangelism/discipleship activities commanded 93.5% of the human resources but only 58.7% of the financial resources. Not surprisingly, given the expensive nature of relief work, relief and development activities deployed 2.9% of the human resources while consuming 35.1% of the financial resources. It is encouraging to note that educational/training activities deployed 1.9% of all U.S. workers, but 2.7% of the national workers (Table 11). It cannot be stated with certainty, but it gives the impression that those agencies involved in education/training may be relatively more indigenized in their work than the agencies whose primary activities are in the other master

Table 10: Resources Used by Primary Activity

Primary activity	No. of Agencies		Income for Overseas		Total Workers	
Education/training	57	8.3%	$49,045,933	1.3%	3,574	0.8%
Evangelism/discipleship	425	61.6%	$2,204,196,185	58.7%	426,070	93.5%
Mission agency support	202	14.8%	$159,227,593	4.2%	12,192	2.7%
Relief and development	81	11.7%	$1,316,848,541	35.1%	13,331	2.9%
Other	25	3.6%	$22,987,941	0.6%	510	0.1%

Table 11: People Resources Used by Primary Activity

Primary Activity	Ed./Train.		Evang./Disc.		Mission Agency Support		Relief & Dev.		Other	
US Short Term	1,049	0.3%	328,123	94.8%	9,984	2.9%	6,980	2.0%	134	0.0%
Tentmakers	36	2.1%	1,446	82.7%	169	9.7%	89	5.1%	8	0.5%
US Long Term	476	1.4%	31,915	91.8%	975	2.8%	1,341	3.9%	50	0.1%
All US Workers	811	1.9%	37,800	88.4%	1,296	3.0%	2,829	6.6%	51	0.1%
Nonnationals	52	1.0%	4,526	90.0%	214	4.3%	222	4.4%	15	0.3%
Nationals	1,626	2.7%	54,175	90.5%	529	0.9%	3,211	5.4%	302	0.5%

Table 12: Comparison of US Agency Activities by Selected Doctrinal/Ecclesiastical Stances

	Evang./Disc.	Ed./Train	Mission Agency Support	Relief & Dev.	Other
Primary Activity					
All Agencies	61.5%	8.3%	14.8%	11.6%	3.8%
Evangelical	58.4%	8.3%	19.9%	11.1%	2.2%
Baptist	76.1%	3.0%	7.5%	7.5%	6.0%
Charis./Pentecostal	64.5%	12.9%	9.7%	8.1%	4.8%
All activities					
All Agencies	54.4%	13.7%	15.6%	13.4%	2.9%
Evangelical	53.0%	13.6%	17.6%	13.0%	2.8%
Baptist	62.7%	13.3%	10.8%	10.8%	2.4%
Charis./Pentecostal	60.9%	14.5%	11.2%	11.2%	2.1%

categories.

It is also interesting to note the results when we compare the reported activities of agencies by doctrinal or ecclesiastical stance. Table 12 shows summaries of these comparisons for three of the stances.

First are the 361 agencies describing their primary doctrinal or ecclesiastical stance as Evangelical. They comprise 52.3% of all agencies and reported 52.8% of all activities reported. In terms of *primary* activity, evangelism/church planting types of activities were by far (58.4%) the most frequently chosen.

However, these agencies were *proportionately* more likely to report activities related to mission agency support[13] and slightly less likely to indicate activities related to evangelism/discipleship[14] or relief and development[15] than agencies that chose different doctrinal or ecclesiastical orientations. In terms of all activities, they were more likely to be involved in mission agency support.[16]

Second are the 67 agencies that reported their primary doctrinal or ecclesiastical stance as Baptist. Altogether they comprise 9.7% of all agencies and reported 9.9% of all activities reported. In terms of *primary* activities they were most likely to report activities related to evangelism/discipleship (76.1%) than agencies of either of the other two doctrinal/ecclesiastical stances in Table 12.

Additionally, they were *proportionately* more likely to report activities related to evangelism/discipleship[17] and much less likely to indicate activities related to education/training,[18] mission agency support,[19] or relief and development[20] than agencies that chose different doctrinal or ecclesiastical orientations. In terms of *all* activities, they were proportionally more likely to be involved in activities related to evangelism/discipleship[21] and proportionally much less likely to indicate activities related to mission agency support[22] or relief and development[23] than agencies that chose different doctrinal or ecclesiastical orientations.

Third are the 62 agencies that described their *primary* doctrinal or ecclesiastical stance as either charismatic or Pentecostal. They comprise 9.0% of all agencies and reported 9.9% of all activities reported. In terms of primary activities, they were more likely to choose activities related to evangelism/discipleship, though they were between the Evangelical and Baptist agencies in this emphasis (64.5%).

In contrast, they were *proportionately* more likely to report activities related to education/training[24] and much less likely to indicate activities related to mission agency support[25] and relief and development[26] than agencies that chose different doctrinal or ecclesiastical orientations. In terms of *all* activities, they were proportionally more likely to be involved in activities related to evangelism/discipleship[27] and proportionally much less likely to indicate activities related to mission agency support[28] or relief and development[29] than agencies that chose different doctrinal or ecclesiastical orientations.

In sum, agencies of all three doctrinal/ecclesiastical blocks placed their emphasis on evangelism/discipleship activities. However, in proportion to what might be expected given their numbers, self-described Evangelical agencies were more active in mission agency support, Baptist agencies were more active in evangelism/discipleship, and charismatic and Pentecostal agencies were more active in education and training.

Overseas Income for US Agencies

The total reported income for overseas mission in this edition for all U.S. agencies was $3,752,306,193. Adjusting for inflation, this represents a 17.3% increase over the previous survey results. Even though less than reported in the last edition, an average growth of 5.7% per year from 1998 to 2001 is still an indicator of the relative financial health of U.S. mission agencies in spite of a slowing economy, a bubble-burst stock market and a national disaster. That this was relatively broadly based can be seen in four factors.

First, Table 13 lists the U.S. agencies whose reported overseas income was $10,000,000 or more. To make the equivalent of the last edition's Table 4.6 list,

Table 13: US Agencies with $10,000,000 or More Income for Overseas Ministries

Rank	Agency	Overseas Income
1	World Vision, Inc.	$358,703,000
2	Southern Baptist Convention International Mission Board	$197,866,000
3	Assemblies of God World Missions	$177,262,833
4	MAP International	$151,751,257
5	Christian Aid Ministries	$132,988,645
6	Campus Crusade for Christ, Intl.	$123,279,000
7	Samaritan's Purse	$111,797,883
8	Compassion International, Inc.	$90,329,583
9	Wycliffe Bible Translators USA	$82,457,000
10	Mission Agency A[30]	$70,000,000
11	Food for the Hungry, Inc.	$69,896,261
12	International Aid	$67,125,062
13	Seventh-Day Adventists General Conference	$62,973,862
14	Church World Service & Witness, Unit of the National Council of Churches of Christ in the USA	$57,998,444
15	Christian Churches/Churches of Christ	$52,000,000
16	Gideons International, The	$50,000,000
17	Church of the Nazarene, World Mission Department	$48,766,310
18	Christian Broadcasting Network, The	$47,646,521
19	Interchurch Medical Assistance	$46,050,979
20	Larry Jones International Ministries (Feed the Children)	$45,178,413
21	Mennonite Central Committee	$41,560,475
22	Presbyterian Church (USA), Worldwide Ministries	$40,107,046
23	Baptist Bible Fellowship, Intl.	$36,000,000
24	ABWE (Association of Baptists for World Evangelism)	$35,000,000
25	Northwest Medical Teams	$34,548,705
26	World Concern	$34,325,723
27	Mission to the World (PCA), Inc.	$34,149,834
28	New Tribes Mission	$32,200,000
29	Church of God (Cleveland, TN) World Missions	$30,137,862
30	Trans World Radio	$29,383,223
31	Evangelical Lutheran Church in America, Div. for Global Mission	$29,172,306
32	Mission Aviation Fellowship	$27,041,701
33	Heifer International	$26,880,000
34	Baptist International Missons, Inc. (BIMI)	$26,400,000

Continued on page 30

Table 13: Continued

35	SIM USA	$26,392,453
36	Christian and Missionary Alliance	$24,743,649
37	TEAM (The Evangelical Alliance Mission)	$23,500,000
38	Lutheran World Relief	$22,598,621
39	Voice of the Martyrs, The	$21,364,009
40	Christian Blind Mission, Intl.	$20,482,603
41	Bible League, The	$20,313,216
42	HCJB World Radio	$20,000,000
43	Salvation Army, USA	$20,000,000
44	Mercy Ships	$19,682,881
45	Opportunity International and the Women's Opportunity Fund	$19,400,000
46	United Pentecostal Church Intl., Foreign Missions Division	$19,352,247
47	CBInternational	$19,155,068
48	Baptist Mid-Missions	$19,000,000
49	Gospel for Asia	$17,297,000
50	World Relief Corporation	$17,083,313
51	Habitat for Humanity International	$17,081,351
52	Evangelical Free Church Mission	$16,847,282
53	American Bible Society	$16,676,371
54	Blessings International	$16,443,449
55	Lutheran Church—Missouri Synod, Board for Mission Services	$15,882,554
56	Navigators, USA International Missions Group	$15,867,000
57	American Baptist Churches in the USA, International Ministries	$15,398,251
58	OMS International, Inc.	$15,311,000
59	Africa Inland Mission International	$15,000,000
60	United Church Board for World Ministries	$13,379,044
61	Christian Missions in Many Lands	$12,800,000
62	Childcare International	$12,333,763
63	Greater Europe Mission	$11,997,671
64	Episcopal Church, Domestic and Foreign Missionary Society	$11,915,649
65	SEND International	$11,458,957
66	World Gospel Mission	$11,322,529
67	Overseas Council International	$11,237,016
68	Operation Mobilization, Inc.	$11,000,000
69	Mission of Mercy	$10,863,810
70	Shelter for Life International, Inc.	$10,753,000

the agency needed an income of $10,908,598. By that criterion, 68 of this edition's agencies would have made the equivalent of last edition's list (which had 58 agencies).

Second, in the previous edition of the *Handbook* we noted that the agency ranked 100th in income for overseas giving reported an income of $4,791,154. Adjusting for inflation, this would be $5,226,473 in 2001 dollars. In this edition, the agency ranked 100th had an income of $5,686,027, which is an 8.8% increase over the previous edition.[31]

Third, in this edition, 117 organizations did not report any income for overseas mission. In the previous edition 91 agencies did not report an income for overseas mission, so the reported increase comes in spite of 31 (about 5%) fewer agencies[32] reporting any income in this edition.

Finally, the total of the newly reported money was $59,592,654, and the total no longer reported by the de-listed agencies was an inflation-adjusted $28,864,983. Thus, the net newly reported income was $30,727,671, which represents only 5.2% of the *total* inflation-adjusted gain reported. Thus the bulk of the financial gain reported here was not due to the increase coming from the changes in agencies listed in this edition. This good news needs to be tempered with the fact that the full impact of the stock market drop and slowing U.S. economy was only beginning to be felt in 2001, which is the year represented by our data.

Deployment of U.S. Agencies and Missionaries

Figures 6 through 8 depict the deployment of U.S. agencies and their person-

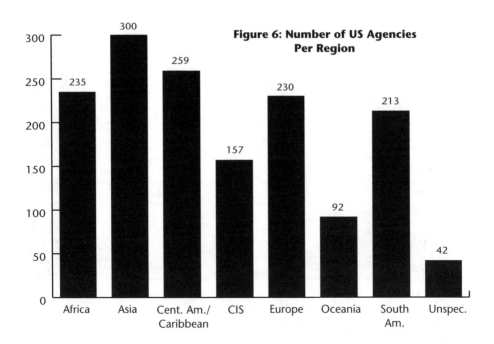

Figure 6: Number of US Agencies Per Region

Figure 7: Number of Full-time US Missionaries by Region

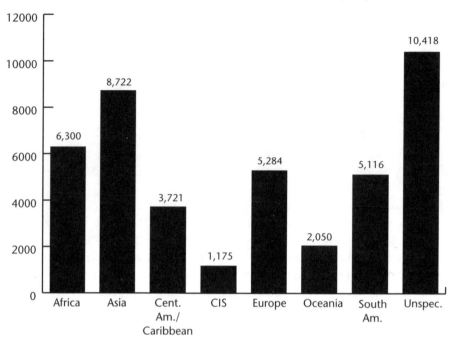

Figure 8: Number of Full-time Workers Deployed by US Agencies

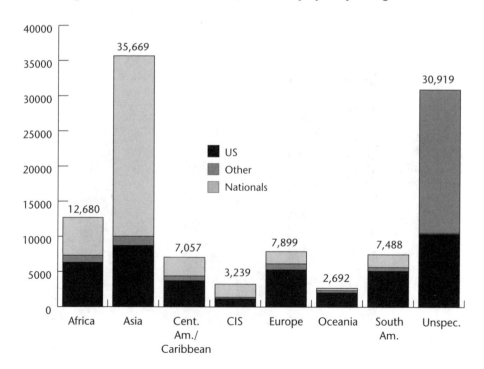

nel by region of the world. The country categories are slightly different than in the last edition;[33] for this edition it was decided to use UN categories to ensure consistency from one edition to the next in the future. Additionally, while Table 14 indicates countries with the most agencies deployed, the numbers given represent the minimum number of agencies per country, since several agencies did not give specific countries of deployment. In this edition 42 agencies reported a total of 30,919 workers in "unspecified countries."[34] This is 28.7% of all U.S. agency deployment. It is apparent that agencies are becoming increasingly reluctant to indicate countries, and in some cases even regions, where they deploy their personnel. Security concerns are the primary issue, and we anticipate that in the future it will be increasingly difficult to obtain hard data on deployment more specific than the regional level.

Table 14: Countries with More than 50 US Agencies Reported

Country	# of Agencies	Country	# of Agencies
Mexico	159	Honduras	69
India	155	Peru	68
Philippines	133	Romania	64
Brazil	112	Ghana	64
Kenya	106	China	64
Russia	96	Asia—General	63
United Kingdom	89	Colombia	62
Japan	86	Uganda	61
Ukraine	77	Bolivia	60
Germany	76	Ecuador	57
Spain	73	Nigeria	57
South Africa	73	Costa Rica	55
France	72	Argentina	55
Thailand	72	Australia	52
Haiti	72	Hungary	51
Indonesia	71	Taiwan	51
Guatemala	70		

Finally, it should be noted that we do not collect data on the locations of deployment for short-term missionaries with less than 1 year of service commitment. Therefore the graphs do not include these short-term workers. Tables 15 and 16 offer further perspective by listing agencies with more than 500 total workers and those with more than 500 full-time U.S. workers respectively.

Short-Term Activity and Support by U.S. Agencies

United States mission agencies reported a total of 346,225 short-term workers (two weeks to one year) sent out during 2001, a 255% increase over the previous edition of the *Handbook*. As with the last edition, we assume that this still represents only a small fraction of the total U.S. short-term workers, since it does not include those who went under the auspices of local churches or on their own. It also does not include many who go for less than two weeks.

Figure 9 shows the number of people whose job to some extent involves sup-

Table 15: US Agencies with More than 500 Total Workers

	# Countries	US Workers	Non US Workers	National Workers	Total
Campus Crusade for Christ, Intl.	113	1,096	506	13,628	15,230
Gospel for Asia	9	0	0	13,500	13,500
So. Bapt. Convention Intl. Msn. Bd.	7	5,437	0	0	5,437
Partners International	39	0	0	4,700	4,700
Christian Aid Mission	53	0	0	3,873	3,873
Assemblies of God World Missions	119	1,708	0	0	1,708
World Missions Far Corners, Inc.	16	36	4	1,661	1,701
New Tribes Mission	22	1,496	129	19	1,644
Christian Churches/Chs. of Christ	66	1,015	0	422	1,437
WEC International	43	135	1,189	0	1,324
Churches of Christ	91	816	0	364	1,180
Seventh-Day Adventists Gen. Conf.	106	573	539	3	1,115
Baptist Intl. Missions, Inc. (BIMI)	1	1,040	0	0	1,040
Final Frontiers Foundation, Inc.	7	0	0	945	945
OMF International	11	187	0	736	923
Mennonite Central Committee	4	874	0	0	874
Word of Life Fellowship	40	133	97	608	838
Baptist Bible Fellowship, Intl.	69	819	0	0	819
United Meth. Ch., Bd. of Global Min.	1	481	22	308	811
International Needs—USA	18	0	0	804	804
Presbyterian Ch. (USA), Worldwide Min.	66	772	0	0	772
Every Home for Christ International	62	0	0	765	765
Christian and Missionary Alliance	46	722	0	0	722
Mercy Ships	1	700	0	0	700
ABWE	39	695	0	0	695
World Concern	19	54	6	616	676
TEAM (The Evangelical Alliance Msn.)	37	675	0	0	675
Habitat for Humanity International	43	119	29	509	657
Global Fellowship	13	0	20	583	603
Bible League, The	43	0	2	586	588
Compassion International, Inc.	23	2	5	558	565
Mission to the World (PCA), Inc.	49	562	0	0	562
CBInternational	55	558	0	0	558
SIM USA	38	557	0	0	557

Continued on page 35

Table 15 continued

	# Countries	US Workers	Non US Workers	National Workers	Total
Holt Intl. Children's Services, Inc.	1	0	0	552	552
Far East Broadcasting Company, Inc.	8	33	0	492	525
India Evangelical Mission, Inc.	1	0	0	525	525
Churches of God, Gen. Conf.	4	9	0	510	519
Baptist Mid-Missions	45	495	2	15	512
BCM International	40	42	0	462	504

Table 16: US Agencies with More than 500 US Workers

	# of Countries	US Workers
Southern Baptist Convention International Mission Board	7	5,437
Assemblies of God World Missions	119	1,708
New Tribes Mission	22	1,496
Campus Crusade for Christ, Intl.	113	1,096
Baptist International Missions, Inc. (BIMI)	1	1,040
Christian Churches/Churches of Christ	66	1,015
Mennonite Central Committee	4	874
Baptist Bible Fellowship Intl.	69	819
Churches of Christ	91	816
Presbyterian Church (USA), Worldwide Ministries	66	772
Christian and Missionary Alliance	46	722
Mercy Ships	1	700
ABWE (Association of Baptists for World Evangelism)	39	695
TEAM (The Evangelical Alliance Mission)	37	675
Seventh-Day Adventists General Conference	106	573
Mission to the World (PCA), Inc.	49	562
CBInternational	55	558
SIM USA	38	557

Figure 9: US Short-Term Mission Support Personnel (1996-2001)

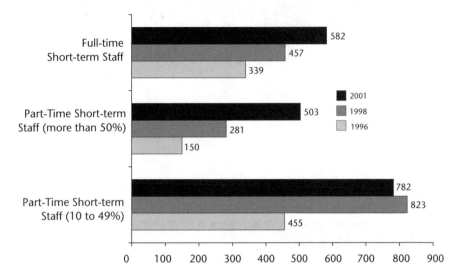

port of short-term efforts from the U.S. agencies, and offers comparison with the previous survey results. To handle the 255% increase in reported short-term workers, as was seen in Table 9, the number of agencies which reported as one of their activities support of short-term mission work jumped from 87 in the previous edition to 107 in this one, an increase of 23%. Additionally, 27.4% full-time staff (last edition: 34.8%) and 79.0% half-time or more staff were added (last edition: 87.3%). However, there was a reduction in part-time staff of 5.0% (in the last edition there was an 80.9% increase). As we reported in the previous edition, the ongoing growth in personnel devoted to servicing short-term missions work

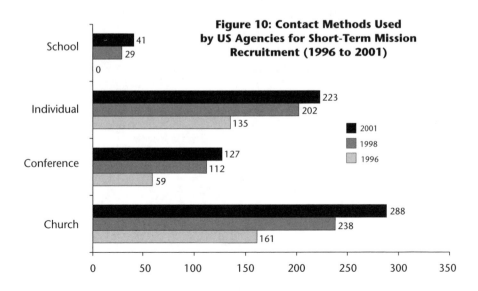

Figure 10: Contact Methods Used by US Agencies for Short-Term Mission Recruitment (1996 to 2001)

indicates a need for further research into the total cost of such work for mission agencies and the benefits that accrue from short-term missions projects.

How did the agencies find people for their short-term projects? Figure 10 indicates the primary methods of initial contact as well as the changes from 1996 to 2001. It should be noted that the category "school" was added in the 1999 survey, and thus no number is available for 1996.

The largest relative increase in the initial contacts for short-term missions was through schools (up 41.4%), though the largest actual number gain belonged to contacts coming through local churches (up by 50 agencies, a 21.0% gain). The large gains seen in the previous edition of making contacts through schools and individuals diminished, though the number of agencies using both areas continued to increase.

U.S. Agency Home Staff

Figure 11 depicts those who work behind the scenes to ensure the deployed field missionaries are able to accomplish their work. From 1998 to 2001, the number of full-time agency home staff increased by 3.2% and the part-time home staff by 0.5%. Both are significantly smaller gains than reported in the previous edition. Perhaps this reflects the change in economy and an early "belt-tightening"; on the other hand it might also indicate a greater efficiency in the use of home staff. Without further data it is not possible to know which.

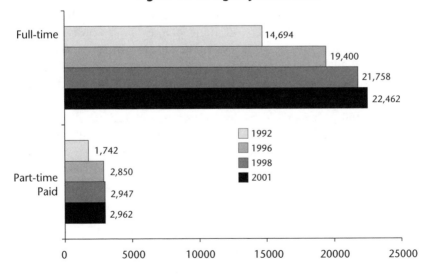

Figure 11: US Agency Home Staff

Canadian Agencies

Geoff Tunnicliffe, Chair, Global Mission Roundtable, Evangelical Fellowship of Canada

Table 17 presents a summary of some of the major personnel changes since the last handbook. The Canadian agencies mobilize a total on-location missionary force of 4,831 (2,830 Canadians, 873 non-Canadians and 1,128 nationals) working in 145 countries. Roughly speaking, for every three Canadians working with Canadian agencies there are two non-Canadians working with Canadian agencies. This is a significant increase in the ratio of non-Canadians to Canadians compared to the previous edition.[35]

Table 17: Canadian General Statistics and Changes from 1998 to 2001

	1998	2001	% Change
Total on-location Canadian mission force	5,003	4,831	-3.4%
Canadians	3,034	2,830	-6.7%
Non-Canadians working in country other than their own	244	873	257.8%
Non-Canadians working in their own country	1,725	1,128	-34.6%

It must also be noted that the significant change in the number of national personnel reported might be a result of changes in how a few major agencies report their numbers. This can be seen in the reporting of three agencies. One agency reported an increase from 220 to 804. Another agency, which in the previous edition split its personnel between Canada and U.S., is now reporting all their missionaries under the U.S. This resulted in a net loss in 25 Canadian long-term workers and 627 nationals. Third, yet another agency indicated a decline from 500 to 4 even though their income for overseas mission doubled between the editions.

In Table 18 a full summary is provided of the personnel changes taking place in the Canadian mission movement. One of the most dramatic, and some would say most sobering, statistics is the 18.9% decline in the long-term Canadian missionary force over the past decade. However, in the same decade there has been a large increase of non-residential workers serving the Canadian missionary enterprise, from 72 in 1992 to 385 in 2001. It may be also important to point out that the number of short-termers serving from 1 to 4 years dropped by 20.0% since the last edition, which is especially troubling given the long-term losses.

Additionally, the major increase in full-time home staff (36.8% higher than in 1999) is a further indication of profound changes taking place in the Canadian missionary movement. Given the growing multicultural nature of Canada, agencies are beginning to assign more workers to serve at home, even as they have less making long-term commitments internationally.

The inflation adjusted 21.1% increase in income for overseas missions is in-

Table 18: Summary of Changes in Reported
Canadian Missions Statistics, 1992-2001

	1992	1996	1998	2001	Change 1998-2001	Change 1992-2001
Fully supported Canadian Personnel Serving Overseas						
Long-term (overseas more than 4 years)	3,075	2,961	2,613	2,493	-4.6%	-18.9%
Short-term (overseas from 1 to 4 years)	304	416	421	337	-20.0%	10.9%
Nonresidential fully supported	72	120	294	385	31.0%	434.7%
Total fully supported US personnel serving overseas	3,451	3,497	3,328	3,215	-3.4%	-6.8%
Other Canadian Personnel Serving Overseas						
Short-term of 2 weeks up to 1 year (1996 and 1999)	NA	2,470	3,186	3,395	6.6%	
Bivocational associates sponsored or supervised	84	140	144	154	6.9%	83.3%
Nonresidential partially supported	13	17	38	27	-28.9%	107.7%
Non-Canadian Personnel Directly Supported						
Those serving in their home country	NA	707	1,725	1,128	-34.6%	59.5%
Those serving in a country other than their home country	36	77	244	873	257.8%	2325.0%
Canadian Ministry and Home Office Staff						
Full-time paid staff	1,412	1,622	1,838	2,515	36.8%	78.1%
Part-time staff/associates	249	389	496	431	-13.1%	73.1%
Volunteer (ongoing) helpers	2,124	3,154	2,374	2,893	21.9%	36.2%

Financial Support Raised in Canada—Income for Overseas Ministries (Adjusted for Inflation)

1992	1996	1998	2001	Change 1998-2001	Change 1992-2001
$260,069,319	$258,926,843	$355,278,092	$426,585,853	20.1%	64.0%

dicative of the fact that Canadian Christians do want to invest in global mission initiatives. However, as discussed below, the giving patterns of Canadians reflects a certain bent for specific ministries.

As the Canadian mission movement undergoes some profound changes there seem to be several overarching issues that are being faced by mission sending agencies. These include:

• A plateauing or declining missionary force
• An aging donor base

• A lack of organizational or denominational loyalty by those who are 50 years and younger

• Leadership transition challenges to the younger leaders

• Local churches asking for greater accountability and partnership

• The need to find appropriate ways to motivate the emerging postmodern generation

Based upon his experience in the corporate world, Jack Welch, Chairman of GE relates, "When the rate of change inside the company is exceeded by the rate of change outside the company, the end is near." Is the same true among the community of mission agencies in Canada?

In the last 25 years Canada has seen relatively few new mission agencies. Is now the time for the younger generation to step up to the plate and launch some new structures or communities that will engage in mission? One must also ask when the growing number of people taking early retirements from the market-place will begin to show up in significant numbers on the statistical data of mission agencies as they take on new careers in the mission enterprise.

What Are the Canadian Agencies Orientations toward Denominationalism?

Fewer than one in four Canadian agencies describe themselves as denominational (Figure 12). While the growth in denominational agencies has been steady over the century, the shift from denominational agencies to not-denominational ones[36] during the last century is illustrated on Figure 13.

Canadian agencies never had the denominational vs. not-denominational ratio seen in the U.S., though the proliferation of agencies that are not-denominational parallels the shift in the U.S. In 1930 the ratio was 1:1, but by 2001 it had shifted to 3.1:1 in favor of the not-denominational agencies.

Figure 12: Canadian Agency Orientations towards Denominationalism 1998 vs. 2001

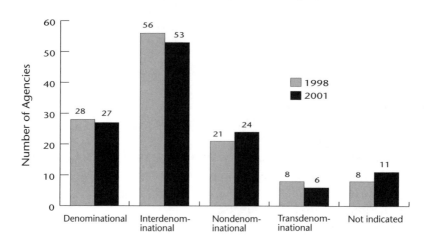

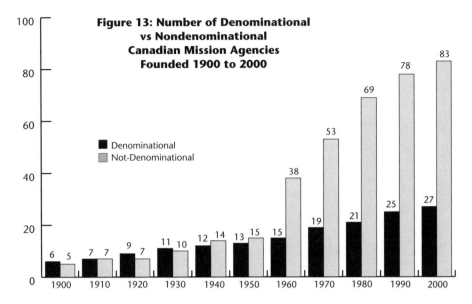

Figure 13: Number of Denominational vs Nondenominational Canadian Mission Agencies Founded 1900 to 2000

For all Canadian agencies, Figures 14 and 15 depict differences in denominational orientation. The most significant shift between 1999 and 2001 appears to be in denominational support for nationals. While denominational agencies represent only 22.3% of the number of agencies in Canada they do manage 34.4%

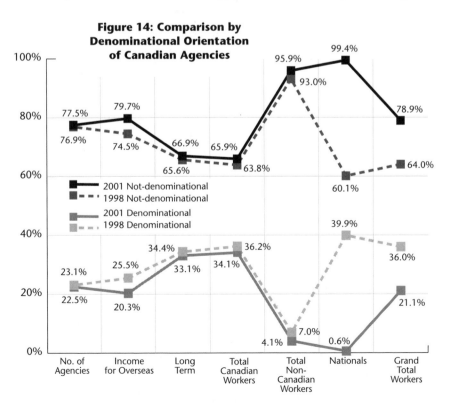

Figure 14: Comparison by Denominational Orientation of Canadian Agencies

**Figure 15: Further Comparisons by Denominational Orientation
of Canadian Agencies**

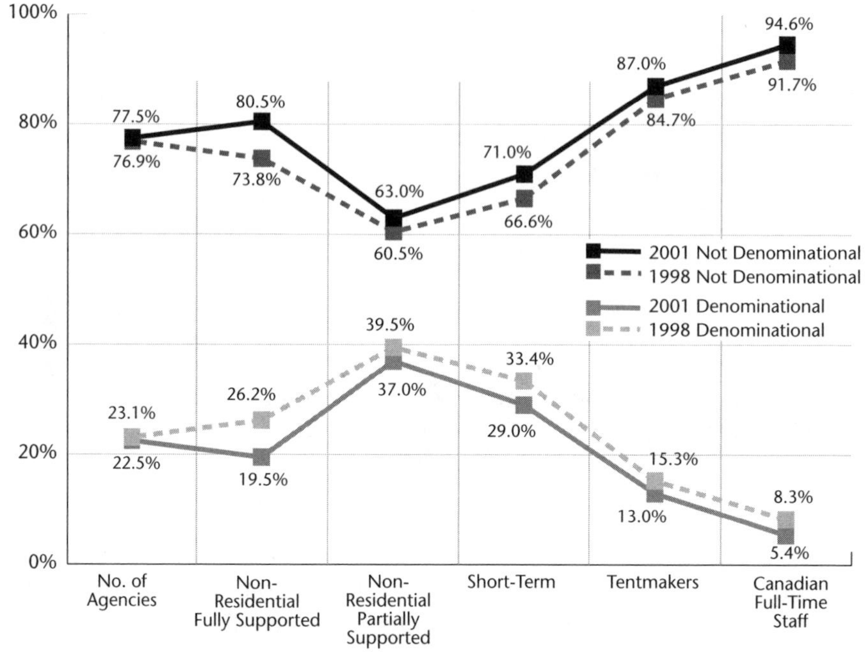

of the long-term missionaries. However, it appears that the support of non-Canadian personnel is now almost exclusively managed by the not-denominational agencies.

Activities of Canadian Agencies

Table 19 depicts the ranking of primary activities of Canadian agencies. While the number one activity of Canadian agencies continues to be church planting there has been some significant changes in other activity categories. While personal and small group evangelism continues to be ranked as the number two activity there was a decline of 35.7% over 1998. The number of agencies indicating their primary activity as relief and development grew 166.7% (from 3 agencies to 8) from 1998. This became the third primary ranked activity of Canadian agencies, up from a ranking of tenth in 1998.

However, when you look at all the activities of the Canadian agencies (Tables 19 through 25) a clearer picture begins to emerge. Almost half of all agencies indicated they are involved in church planting activities. This is an increase of 16.3% over 1998 (Table 21). It is also evident that more agencies are now including development related activities (up 33.3% since 1998; Table 21) and relief work (up 14.3% since 1998; Table 21) in their ministry activities. The combined rate of increase of all relief and development activities was up 25.3% over 1998 (Table 23).

Table 23 compares the major activity categories between 1998 and 2001. One

Table 19: Primary Activities: Comparing 1998 and 2001 Top Ten Survey Results

Activity	2001 No.	1998 No.	Change	% Change	2001 Rank	1998 Rank	Change
Church establishing/planting	34	31	3	9.7%	1	1	0
Evang., personal & small group	9	14	-5	-35.7%	2	2	0
Relief and/or development	8	3	5	166.7%	3	10	7
Development, commun./other	7	9	-2	-22.2%	4	3	-1
Support of national workers	7	6	1	16.7%	4	4	-
Broadcast, radio and/or TV	5	3	2	66.7%	6	10	4
Literature distribution	5	6	-1	-16.7%	6	4	-2
Bible distribution	4	5	-1	-20.0%	9	6	-3
National church nurture/support	4	3	1	33.3%	9	10	1
Education, theological	4	3	1	33.3%	9	10	1
Evangelism, mass	4	5	-1	-20.0%	9	6	-3

Table 20: 2001 Primary Activities by Major Category

	2001		1998	
	No.	%	No.	%
Evangelism/Discipleship Activities	**82**	**68.3%**	**83**	**68.6%**
Church establishing/planting	34	28.3%	31	25.6%
Support of national workers	7	5.8%	6	5.0%
Evangelism, personal and small group	9	7.5%	14	11.6%
Broadcasting, radio and/or TV	5	4.2%	3	2.5%
Literature distribution	5	4.2%	6	5.0%
Bible distribution	4	3.3%	5	4.1%
Evangelism, mass	4	3.3%	5	4.1%
National church nurture/support	3	2.5%	3	2.5%
Evangelism, student	2	1.7%	2	1.7%
Leadership development	2	1.7%	2	1.7%
Translation, Bible	2	1.7%	2	1.7%
Audio recording/distribution	1	0.8%	1	0.8%
Childrens programs	1	0.8%	1	0.8%
Church construction	1	0.8%	0	0.0%
Literature production	1	0.8%	1	0.8%
Youth programs	1	0.8%	1	0.8%
Education/Training Activities	**7**	**5.8%**	**6**	**5.0%**
Education, theological	4	3.3%	3	2.5%

Continued on page 44

Table 20: Continued

	2001		**1998**	
	No.	%	No.	%
Education, church/sch. Gen. Christian	2	1.7%	2	1.7%
Education, extension (other)	1	0.8%	1	0.8%
Mission Agency Support Activities	**8**	**6.7%**	**9**	**7.4%**
Training/Orientation, missionary	3	2.5%	2	1.7%
Recruiting/Mobilizing	2	1.7%	1	0.8%
Short-term programs coordination	2	1.7%	1	0.8%
Aviation services	1	0.8%	1	0.8%
Information services	0	0.0%	2	1.7%
Services for other agencies	0	0.0%	1	0.8%
Technical assistance	0	0.0%	1	0.8%
Relief and Development Activities	**20**	**16.7%**	**19**	**15.7%**
Relief and/or rehabilitation	8	6.7%	3	2.5%
Development, community and/or other	7	5.8%	9	7.4%
Childcare/orphanage	2	1.7%	5	4.1%
Medicine, incl. dental & public health	2	1.7%	1	0.8%
Disability assistance programs	1	0.8%	1	0.8%
Other activities	**3**	**0.5%**	**4**	**3.3%**
Funds transmission	2	1.7%	4	3.3%
Other	1	0.8%	0	0.0%

Table 21: All Activities: Comparing 1998 and 2001 Top Ten Survey Results

Activity	2001 #	1998 #	Change	% Change	2001 Rank	1998 Rank	Change
Church establishing/planting	50	43	7	16.3%	1	2	1
Evangelism, personal & sml. group	49	58	-9	-15.5%	2	1	-1
Develop., commun. and/or other	36	27	9	33.3%	3	4	1
Leadership development	31	25	6	24.0%	4	5	1
Education, theological	28	23	5	21.7%	5	6	1
National church nurture/support	27	34	-7	-20.6%	6	3	-3
Relief and/or rehabilitation	24	21	3	14.3%	7	9	2
Literature distribution	21	23	-2	-8.7%	8	6	-2
Medicine, incl. dental & public health	20	22	-2	-9.1%	9	8	-1
Support of national workers	20	17	3	17.6%	9	10	+1

**Table 22: 2001 Canadian Agencies by Major Category
(actual numbers; total activities listed is 586)**

	2001		1998	
	No.	%	No.	%
Evangelism/Discipleship Activities	**311**	**53.1%**	**307**	**57.1%**
Church establishing/planting	50	8.5%	43	8.0%
Evangelism, personal & small group	49	8.4%	58	10.8%
Leadership development	31	5.3%	25	4.6%
National church nurture/support	27	4.6%	34	6.3%
Literature distribution	21	3.6%	23	4.3%
Support of national workers	20	3.4%	17	3.2%
Evangelism, mass	19	3.2%	17	3.2%
Broadcasting, radio and/or TV	14	2.4%	12	2.2%
Bible distribution	10	1.7%	9	1.7%
Literature production	10	1.7%	15	2.8%
Youth programs	10	1.7%	9	1.7%
Camping programs	9	1.5%	8	1.5%
Children's programs	8	1.4%	10	1.9%
Literacy	7	1.2%	5	0.9%
Translation, Bible	6	1.0%	8	1.5%
Evangelism, student	5	0.9%	4	0.7%
Linguistics	4	0.7%	4	0.7%
Audio recording/distribution	3	0.5%	2	0.4%
Church construction	3	0.5%	3	0.6%
Video/film production/distribution	3	0.5%	1	0.2%
Translation, other	2	0.3%	0	0.0%
Education/Training Activities	**64**	**10.9%**	**64**	**11.9%**
Education, theological	28	4.8%	23	4.3%
Training, other	10	1.7%	8	1.5%
Correspondence courses	7	1.2%	7	1.3%
Education, ch./schl. gen. Christ.	7	1.2%	9	1.7%
Education (TEE)	6	1.0%	13	2.4%
Education, extension (other)	4	0.7%	3	0.6%
Education, missionary (cert./deg.)	2	0.3%	1	0.2%
Mission Agency Support Activities	**70**	**11.9%**	**54**	**10.1%**
Short-term programs coordination	14	2.4%	8	1.5%
Recruiting/mobilizing	12	2.0%	11	2.0%

Continued on page 46

Table 22: Continued

	2001		1998	
	No.	%	No.	%
Training/orientation, missionary	11	1.9%	12	2.2%
Partnership development	8	1.4%	0	0.0%
Technical assistance	8	1.4%	10	1.9%
Information services	4	0.7%	6	1.1%
Management consulting/training	4	0.7%	3	0.6%
Services for other agencies	4	0.7%	1	0.2%
Aviation services	3	0.5%	1	0.2%
Furloughed missionary support	1	0.2%	2	0.4%
Member care	1	0.2%	0	0.0%
Relief and Development Activities	**119**	**20.3%**	**95**	**17.7%**
Development, community or other	36	6.1%	27	5.0%
Relief and/or rehabilitation	24	4.1%	21	3.9%
Medicine, incl. dental & pub. health	21	3.6%	22	4.1%
Agricultural programs	14	2.4%	10	1.9%
Childcare/orphanage	14	2.4%	7	1.3%
Medical supplies	6	1.0%	4	0.7%
Disability assistance programs	4	0.7%	2	0.4%
Supplying equipment	0	0.0%	2	0.4%
Other activities	**22**	**3.8%**	**18**	**3.3%**
Other	12	2.0%	2	0.4%
Funds transmission	8	1.4%	13	2.4%
Research	2	0.3%	3	0.6%

**Table 23: Comparison of Total Canadian
Activities Reported for 2001 vs. 1998**

	2001		1998		# gain/ loss	% gain/ loss
	#	%	#	%		
Evangelism/Discipleship	311	53.1%	307	57.1%	4	1.3%
Education/training	64	10.9%	64	11.9%	0	0.0%
Missionary Agency Support	70	11.9%	54	10.0%	16	29.6%
Relief and Development	119	20.3%	95	17.7%	24	25.3%
Other Activities	22	3.8%	18	3.3%	4	22.2%
Total activities reported	586	100.0%	538	100.0%	48	8.9%

of the major increases in activity categories is in mission agency support activities (up 29.6%). The activity with the largest increase was partnership development, with 0 agencies reporting this in 1998 and 8 agencies in 2001. Another area of significant increase in the number of agencies reporting was short-term mission coordination (up 75.0%). Together they seem to indicate a growing trend among Canadian agencies towards partnership and collaboration.

While 11.9% of the reported activities revolve around educational ministries it appears that the delivery avenues for these ministries are changing. In the data from 2001 there was an increase of 21.7% in theological education (from 23 to 28) and a decrease in TEE of 53.8% (from 13 to 6; see Table 22).

In reviewing the evangelism/discipling category the reader will note several substantive changes in this category from 1998 (Table 21). Leadership development saw a very significant increase (24.0%) and literature distribution saw a sharp decline (-8.7%).

Tables 24 and 25 show the relative proportion of resources marshaled by Canadian agencies in each of the major activity areas. Activities related to evangelism account for the primary focus of 68.3% of the agencies and 82.0% of the total workers, though they receive only 31% of the income. Activities related to development, on the other hand, are the primary focus of 16.7% of the agencies

Table 24: Canadian Resources Used by Primary Activity

Primary activity	No. of Agencies		Income for Overseas		Total Workers	
Ed./training	7	5.8%	$4,483,829	1.1%	151	1.1%
Evang./discipleship	82	68.3%	$132,084,202	31.0%	10,958	82.0%
Mission agency support	8	6.7%	$5,939,031	1.4%	1,125	8.4%
Relief and dev.	20	16.7%	$283,965,987	66.6%	1,120	8.4%
Other	3	2.5%	$112,804	0.0%	7	0.1%

Table 25: Canadian People Resources by Primary Activity

	Ed./Train.		Evang./Disc.		Mission Agency Support		Relief & Dev.		Other	
Short-Term	38	1.1%	2,367	69.7%	631	18.6%	355	10.5%	4	0.0%
Tentmakers	0	0.0%	120	77.9%	27	17.5%	7	4.5%	0	0.0%
Long-Term	31	1.2%	2,114	84.8%	139	5.6%	208	8.3%	1	0.0%
Total Canadian	34	1.2%	2,375	83.9%	188	6.6%	232	8.2%	1	0.0%
Non-nationals	0	0.0%	852	98.2%	0	0.0%	16	1.8%	0	0.0%
Nationals	17	1.5%	1,016	90.1%	1	0.1%	94	8.3%	0	0.0%
Total Workers	151	1.1%	10,958	82.0%	1,125	8.4%	1,120	8.4%	7	0.1%

that employ 8.4% of the total workers, but they account for 66.6% of the total income.

What do all these activities trends mean for the Canadian mission movement? While these major shifts do beg for further research and study they also raise some profound questions:

• Are Canadian agencies developing a more holistic view of mission?

• Are Canadian agencies simply responding to the funding realities of the Canadian Christian community which seems more inclined to give to relief and development activities?

• Are Canadian agencies making these shifts because they reflect the changing role of the Canadian church in globalized community of faith?

Overseas Income for Canadian Agencies

The total reported income for all Canadian agencies was $426,585,853 (Table 18). After adjusting for inflation, this is an increase of 20.1% over the last handbook. Fifty-one organizations reported an income of $1,000,000 or more. This is actually down from sixty-one agencies reporting more than $1,000,000 in 1999. As you evaluate the giving patterns for Canadian agencies you see the following picture:

• The top 10 agencies received 69.5% ($296,440,578) of the total income.

• Organizations focused on relief and development received 66.7% ($289,211,445) of the total income. (This income does not reflect the relief and development divisions of denominations and other agencies. If these figures are factored into the equation a conservative estimate would mean that at least 75% of the income is given to relief and development activities.)

• The top 20 agencies received 82.5% ($351,974,915) of the total income.

• While the overall income from 1998 was increased to $90,052,660, the top 5 relief and development organizations increased their income for the same period by $80,281,271.

Table 26 gives the reported income for overseas mission work for all Canadian agencies with $3,000,000 or more. To compare this with the 24 agencies listed with over $3,000,000 in the previous edition, we have to adjust for inflation. Doing so, to make the same list in 2001 would require an income of $3,167,100, which was met by only 22 agencies in this edition.

Where Are the Canadian Agencies and Missionaries Active?

Figure 16 maps the distribution of Canadian agencies around the world. Figures 17 and 18 show that the largest number of full-time Canadian-supported missionaries (both Canadian citizens and non-Canadians) is in Asia. However, if you look at the number of Canadian missionaries deployed you discover they are almost equally involved in Asia and Africa (Figure 17).

Table 26: Canadian Agencies with Income of $3,000,000 or More

Rank	Agency	Income
1	World Vision Canada	$150,000,000
2	Samaritan's Purse—Canada	$35,989,859
3	Canadian Food for the Hungry	$20,543,000
4	Mennonite Central Committee Canada	$17,645,000
5	Pentecostal Assemblies of Canada	$14,732,000
6	HOPE International Development Agency	$14,512,985
7	Christian and Missionary Alliance in Canada, The	$14,000,000
8	Wycliffe Bible Translators of Canada	$9,800,000
9	United Church of Canada, Justice, Global & Ecumenical Relations	$9,688,000
10	SIM Canada	$9,529,234
11	Canadian Baptist Ministries	$7,763,105
12	Christian Blind Mission International (Canada)	$7,334,000
13	Compassion Canada	$6,640,000
14	Christian Reformed World Relief Committee of Canada	$6,604,644
15	Campus Crusade for Christ of Canada	$6,202,000
16	Mennonite Economic Development Associates	$4,637,128
17	MSC Canada	$4,419,551
18	Salvation Army Canada and Bermuda Territory, The	$4,170,000
19	New Tribes Mission of Canada	$3,943,909
20	Canadian Bible Society / La Societe Biblique Canadienne	$3,820,000
21	Bible League of Canada, The	$3,655,000
22	FEBInternational	$3,200,000
23	Youth with a Mission (Canada)	$3,000,000

Short-Term Activity

Canadian mission agencies reported a total of 3,395 short-term workers (two weeks to one year), an increase of 6.6% over the previous edition of the *Handbook*. This number does not reflect the thousands of people who serve in short-term mission who are sent out directly from their church as opposed to going though a mission agency. It also does not reflect some who go for periods of time less than 2 weeks.

While there was only a modest increase in the number of short-term workers, there was a gigantic leap of 338.9% in full-time staff devoted to short-term ministry (Figure 19). It seems obvious that Canadian agencies are taking the role of short-term mission very seriously and seem to be gearing up for a major expansion in this activity.

Figure 16: Distribution of Canadian Agencies by Region

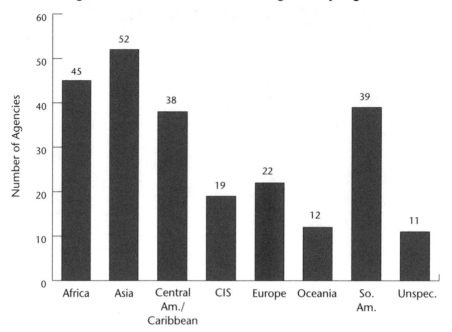

Figure 17: Number of Full-Time Canadian Missionaries by Region

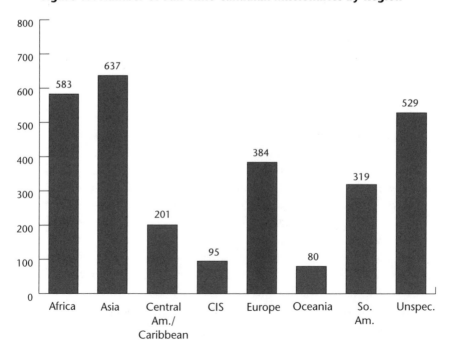

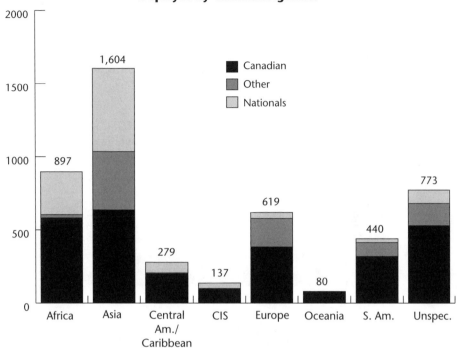

**Figure 18: Number of Full-Time Workers
Deployed by Canadian Agencies**

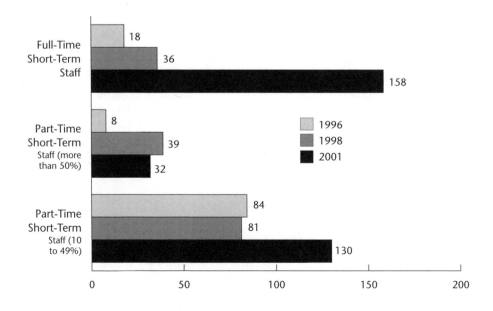

Figure 19: Canadian Short-Term Mission Support Personnel

Another indication that agencies are attempting to increase the positive impact of short-term mission activity is that many of them have now adopted the Code of Best Practice for Short-Term Mission developed cooperatively through the Evangelical Fellowship of Canada in 2000.

How did the agencies find their people for their short-term mission projects? Figure 20 depicts the primary methods of initial contact as well as the changes from 1996. Churches and individual contacts seem to be the primary source of these contacts. The 22% increase in contacts through churches seems to reflect

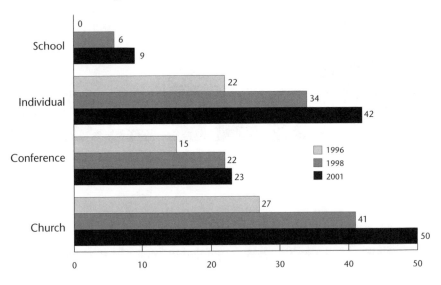

Figure 20: Contact Methods Used by Canadian Agencies for Short-term Mission Recruitment

the growing desire of many agencies to connect more closely with the local church.

Canadian Home Staff

Figure 21 indicates the number of people who make it possible for the missionaries to work and the international programs facilitated. The full-time home staff increased by a massive 36.8%. The part-time staff declined by 13.1%, while the volunteers increased by 21.9%. This means that for every 2 on-location missionaries (Canadian and non-Canadian personnel), there is one full-time home staff person.

Conclusion

At the early part of the 21st century the Canadian mission enterprise finds itself at a crossroads. Some voices both within and outside the churches predict the Canadian missionary movement will be marginalized. Others argue mission organizations will adapt to a changing world. As evangelicals committed to tak-

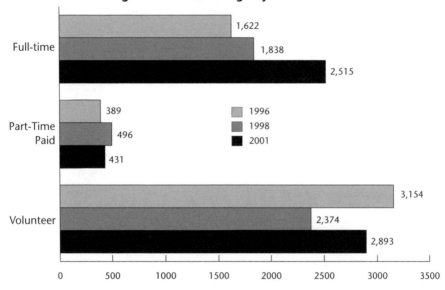

Figure 21: Canadian Agency Home Staff

ing God's Good News to the world, the Canadian mission community must find new ways of overcoming these challenges and working together. Mission organizations, denominations, churches and individuals with a passion for mission must be united in envisioning and equipping the Canadian church to utilize its strength, vitality and commitment to serve the least-reached people at home and beyond Canada's borders.

The Top 50 Agencies Compared 1984 to 2001

MARC conducted surveys of Protestant mission agencies with overseas ministries in 1984, 1988, 1992 and 1996. EMIS conducted the survey with assistance from MARC in 1999 and on its own in 2002. See the appendix for the 2002 survey questionnaire.

The historical data collected from the fifty largest agencies in the U.S. introduced in the 1996 version of the *Handbook* continues to facilitate analyses of trends, now stretching from 1984 through 2001. In the 2002 survey of 2001 data, these agencies accounted for approximately 58.1% of the long-term mission overseas personnel and 39.3% of the giving for overseas missions.

The following six graphs show the number of long-term overseas mission personnel and income for overseas ministries in relation to three different characteristics of mission agencies.[37] These basic charts indicate the occurrence of some definite trends. Most are gradual but cumulatively several are significant.

Figures 22 and 23 show long-term personnel and financial support for overseas ministries in terms of the denominational orientation of the sending agency. The category "No Reference" shows agencies that preferred not to use the term denomination as a reference in describing themselves. In recent years the survey

**Figure 22: Long-term Overseas Personnel
by Denominational Orientation of Agency**

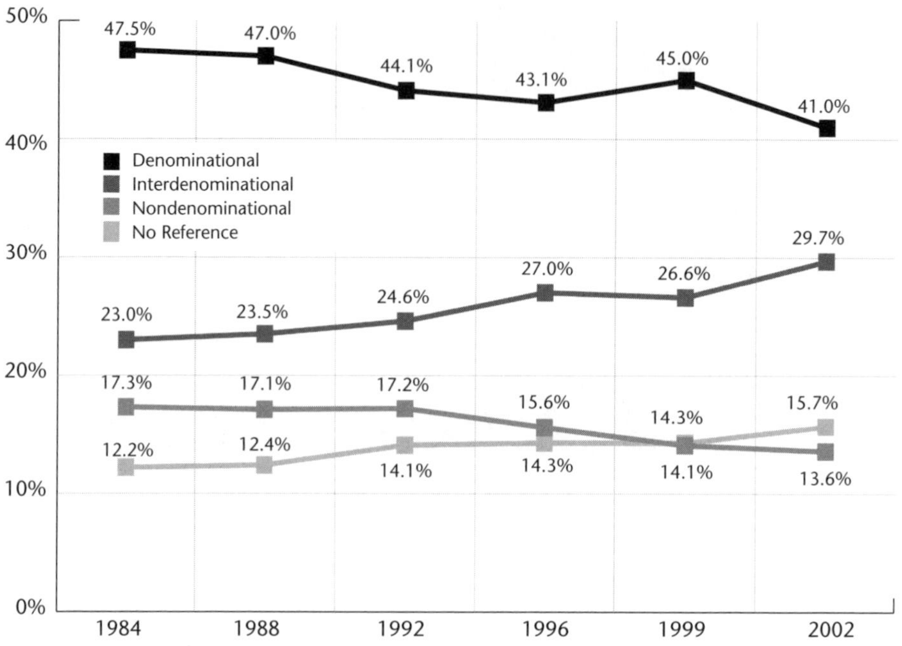

questionnaire also included "transdenominational" as a category, but none of the larger agencies have so far used that term to describe their denominational orientation.

The two figures show small changes in the percentages for this period, but no shifts between the given categories. An important trend across the 17 years is a 6.5% decrease in the proportion of long-term personnel and an 8.7% decrease in the proportion of income for overseas ministries for those agencies describing themselves as denominational.[38] In this survey the trend accelerated. Of the four categories depicted in Figures 22 and 23, only the denominational agencies lost both personnel (4.9%) and income for overseas mission (3.9%).

Over the 17-year span, it was the interdenominational agencies that saw the largest total increases in personnel (35.3%) and income for overseas missions (212.2%). The nondenominational agencies reported the greatest loss in personnel (17.8%), and the denominational agencies the smallest gain in income for overseas missions (85.7%).

The agencies describing themselves as interdenominational picked up the corresponding percentage increases for the most part. However, in 2001 the denominational agencies still led in income for overseas ministries, with 59.5% to the combined 42.5% for the other three categories. The proportional 4% loss in personnel and 8.7% decrease in income seen between this survey and the previous one were the largest ever seen between the surveys. In fact, this decrease was less-

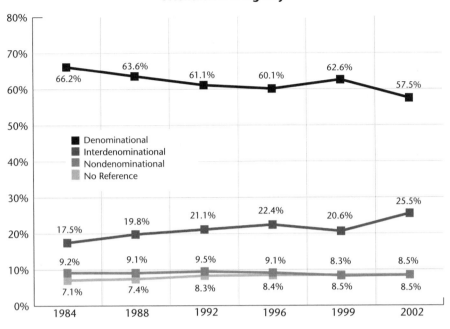

Figure 23: Income for Overseas Ministries by Denominational Orientation of Agency

ened because two "no reference" and one non-denominational agency did not supply an overseas income figure. Together these three accounted for almost $30 million in giving for overseas missions in the previous edition, and had they reported the same income in this edition their inclusion would have made the proportional denominational decline even worse.

Figures 24 and 25 show long-term personnel and financial support for overseas ministries in terms of the era in which the agency was founded in the U.S. For agencies that are the result of mergers, the founding date of the oldest agency was used. In the relatively few cases where mergers took place during the 14-year period covered by the figure,[39] combined totals of the previously separate agencies were used for the years before the merger. For denominations that may have been formed before their overseas mission program was in operation, the date used was the first year that missionaries were sent overseas. All of these agencies were founded before 1984 so that statistics were available for all of the survey years for each agency.

The eras used in the charts are those that social historians have noted were times when basic changes took place in U.S. history. These periods are bounded by the U.S. Civil War of the 1860s and the World Wars of the twentieth century. Overseas mission work for the most part stood still or stopped during those wars. After the wars much of the world experienced some basic change and the mission agencies founded after those times of transition tended to reflect the new realities more quickly than those established earlier.

Figure 24: Long-term Overseas Personnel by Founding Era of Agency

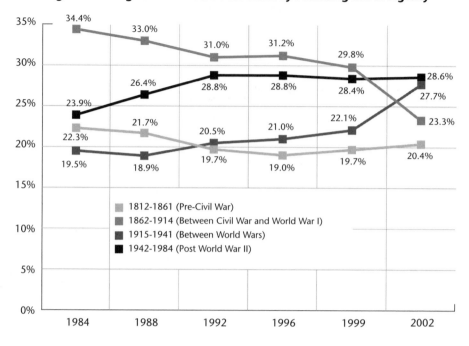

Figure 25: Income for Overseas Ministries by Founding Era of Agency

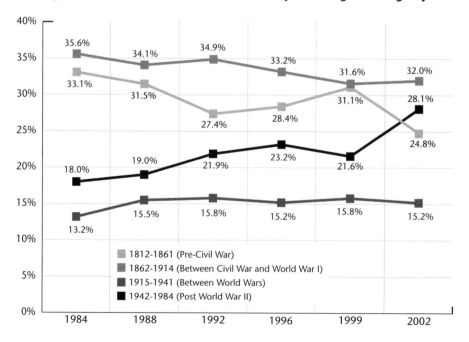

The trends for missionary sending and financial support in Figures 24 and 25 are identifiable and, in the case of income for overseas mission, relatively distinct. One might expect that the "older" agencies (founded before 1915) might show decreases in the percentage of personnel and financial support compared to the "newer" agencies (founded after 1915). This is indeed the case (Figure 24). There was a 5.8% shift between 1984 and 2001 to the newer agencies in personnel and a 5.9% shift in financial support. But while the newer agencies had roughly 56.3% of the long-term personnel in 2001, the older agencies still had 56.8% of the reported income for overseas work, though the gap had narrowed significantly as Figure 25 shows.

Figure 24 reveals an important shift. For the older agencies (pre-1914) in general, their growth rate is slowing or their statistics are decreasing. For long-term personnel, the largest shift was seen among those agencies founded between

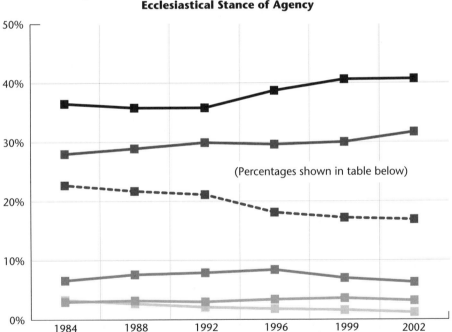

Figure 26: Long-term Overseas Personnel by Doctrinal/ Ecclesiastical Stance of Agency

(Percentages shown in table below)

		1984	1988	1992	1996	1999	2002
■	Evangelical	36.5%	35.8%	35.8%	38.7%	40.6%	40.7%
■	Baptist	28.0%	28.9%	29.9%	29.6%	30.0%	31.7%
■	Pentecostal	6.6%	7.6%	7.9%	8.4%	7.0%	6.3%
■	Presbyterian	3.0%	3.2%	3.0%	3.4%	3.6%	3.2%
■	Lutheran	3.3%	2.7%	2.1%	1.8%	1.6%	1.2%
■■■	Other	22.7%	21.7%	21.1%	18.1%	17.2%	16.9%

1862 and 1914, which dropped by 6.5%. They were the only group of agencies in this figure that saw an actual decrease in personnel, and that decrease was large (18.3%). In reported personnel, they are now surpassed by both sets of the newer agencies (those founded after 1915; Figure 24). Over the entire 17-year span covered in Figures 24 and 25, those agencies founded from 1915 to 1941 saw the greatest total increase in long-term workers (48.9%), and the agencies founded from 1862 to 1914 saw the greatest total decrease (29%). The agencies founded between 1942 and 1984 reported the greatest gain in total income for overseas work (233.5%) and those founded between 1812 and 1861 the smallest (59.8%).

The final figures comparing the top 50 agencies are Figures 26 and 27, which show long-term personnel and financial support for overseas ministries in terms

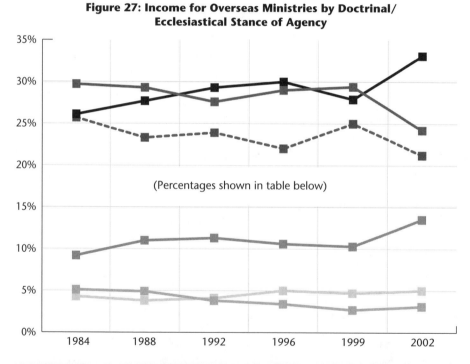

Figure 27: Income for Overseas Ministries by Doctrinal/ Ecclesiastical Stance of Agency

(Percentages shown in table below)

	1984	1988	1992	1996	1999	2002
■ Evangelical	26.1%	27.7%	29.3%	30.0%	27.9%	33.1%
■ Baptist	29.7%	29.3%	27.6%	29.0%	29.4%	24.2%
■ Pentecostal	9.2%	11.0%	11.3%	10.6%	10.3%	13.5%
■ Presbyterian	4.3%	3.8%	4.1%	5.9%	4.7%	5.0%
■ Lutheran	5.1%	4.9%	3.8%	3.4%	2.7%	3.1%
■■■ Other	25.7%	23.3%	23.9%	22.0%	25.0%	21.2%

of the doctrinal and/or ecclesiastical stance of the agencies. Five identifiable categories are shown with the remaining agencies summarized under "other." The 2001 survey questionnaire lists the twenty-two doctrinal/ecclesiastical groups used in the survey. This list has been refined over time with the core categories remaining the same. There are five generic categories (ecumenical, evangelical, etc.) and seventeen denominational families (Adventist, Baptist, etc.). In cases where agencies indicated more than one category, their primary historical group is used.

The trends for missionary sending and financial support in Figures 26 and 27 are easily identifiable. Figure 27 reveals another instance where an important shift has taken place. Income for overseas ministries among agencies that use the generic term "evangelical" as their primary term moved into first place for income in 1992, passing the Baptist denominational family. By 1999 the Baptist family had moved back into first place. In 2001, however, the "evangelical" agencies surged by 5.2% in income while the Baptist ministries dropped by the same amount.[40] Pentecostal agencies gained a proportional 3.2%, while those in the "other" category dropped 3.8%.

Over the 17-year span depicted in Figures 26 and 27, the Baptists gained the most long-term workers (18.6%), and the Lutherans reported the greatest loss (a 62.3% decline). Pentecostal agencies reported the largest growth in total income for overseas missions (214.0%), and Lutherans the smallest (26.7%).

Table 27: Agencies No Longer Listed

Agency	Reason for not being listed
Africa Community Technical Service (Canada)	Overseas data not available
African Meth. Episcopal Zion Ch., Dept. of Overseas Msns.	Overseas data not available
Agape Gospel Mission	Overseas data not available
American Baptist Association Missionary Committee	Overseas data not available
American Tract Society	Overseas data not available
American Waldensian Society	Overseas data not available
Baptist Faith Missions	Overseas data not available
Baptist Missionary Association of America	Overseas data not available
Barnabas Ministries, Inc.	Overseas data not available
Bethany Missionary Association	Overseas data not available
Big World Ventures Inc.	Overseas data not available
Blossoming Rose	Overseas data not available
Children of India Foundation	Overseas data not available
Children of Promise International	Overseas data not available
Children's Hunger Relief Fund	Overseas data not available
China Campus Outreach	Overseas data not available
China Partner	Overseas data not available
Christian Dynamics	Overseas data not available
Christian Services, Inc.	Overseas data not available
Church of God, The	Overseas data not available
Cooperative Baptist Fellowship	Overseas data not available
Door of Hope International	Now considered non-mission
Door of Hope International (Canada)	Now considered non-mission
Educational Services International	Overseas data not available
Episcopal World Mission	Overseas data not available
Europe Missions Outreach	Overseas data not available
Eurovangelism (Canada)	Overseas data not available
Evangelical Lutheran Synod	Overseas data not available
Evangelize China Fellowship, Inc.	Overseas data not available
Franconia Mennonite Conference	Overseas data not available
Friends in the West	Overseas data not available
Friendship Ministries	Overseas data not available
Gospel Outreach	Disbanded
Harvest International Christian Outreach / Target Teams	Overseas data not available
Harvesting in Spanish	No office in USA at present

Table 27: Continued

Agency	Reason for not being listed
HOPE Bible Mission, Inc.	Overseas data not available
Institute of Hindu Studies	Inactive at present
International Children's Care	Overseas data not available
International Children's Haven (Canada)	Overseas data not available
International Christian Literature Distributors, Inc.	Overseas relationship unknown
International Crusades, Inc.	Overseas data not available
International Discipleship Mission	Overseas data not available
International Gospel League	Overseas data not available
Island Missionary Society	Overseas data not available
ISOH/Impact	Overseas data not available
Issachar Frontier Missions Strategies	Disbanded
Japan - N. American Commission on Coop. Mission	Overseas data not available
Liberia Christian Mission	Overseas data not available
Lion and Lamb Outreach	Inactive at present
Lott Carey Baptist Mission Convention	Overseas data not available
Maranatha Baptist Mission	Overseas data not available
Mazahua Mission	Overseas ministries autonomous
Message of Life, Inc.	Overseas data not available
Messenger Films, Inc.	Overseas data not available
Mexican Border Missions	Disbanded
Mexican Christian Mission	Overseas data not available
Middle East Christian Outreach — Canada	Overseas data not available
Ministry of Jesus, Inc.	Overseas data not available
Mission Aides, Inc.	Overseas data not available
Missionary Health Institute, Inc.	Overseas data not available
Moody Institute of Science Div. of Moody Bible Inst.	Overseas data not available
NEED, Inc.	Overseas data not available
Open Bible Ministries	Overseas data not available
ORA International	Overseas data not available
Overcomer Press, Inc.	Overseas data not available
Reformed Presby. Church, Bd. of Foreign Missions	Overseas data not available
Romanian Mission of Chicago	No Financial Information
Scripture Union, USA	Overseas data not available
Society for Europe's Evangelization	Overseas data not available
Spiritual Overseers Service International Corp.	Overseas data not available

Table 27: Continued

Agency	Reason for not being listed
TAM-ICCC (The Associate Missions of the Intl. Council of Christian Churches)	Overseas relationship unknown
Trinitarian Bible Society (Canada)	Overseas data not available
Witnessing Ministries of Christ	Overseas data not available
World In Need — USA	Overseas data not available
World Missions Fellowship	Overseas ministries autonomous
World Neighbors	Now considered non-mission

Endnotes

1. Eight agencies are listed in the *Handbook* but are not included in this survey, since we received the information too late in the data analysis period to include it: Citireach International; European Christian Mission International/USA; Federation Missionaire Francaise; Janz Team Ministries USA; Jusqu'aux Extremities de la Terre (JET-Canada); United World Mission, Inc.; White Fields, Inc. (USA); and White Fields Missionary Society, Canada.

2. By full-time we mean those who are in service for one year or longer.

3. Throughout the analysis we refer to "reported" totals, since they are only as valid as the numbers received from each agency. Several factors contribute a certain "softness" to the numbers, including 1) the real numbers fluctuate during the year, 2) agencies use different methods for counting their personnel, 3) some agencies report painstakingly exact numbers for the month the survey is completed, while others provide either highs or averages for the year, and some provide estimates, especially for categories such as volunteers and nationals.

4. There is important anecdotal evidence that this number, while representative, is likely significantly below the actual number of missionaries deployed out of North America. In addition to agencies that send primarily Christian professionals and do not want to be labeled "mission" agencies, uncounted individuals are sent as partial or fully supported cross-cultural workers by churches and other organizations that are not included in the totals given here.

5. The vast bulk of the agencies supplied data from 2001; several submitted data from 2002. Some organizations run on a calendar year; others on a fiscal year with various ending dates. Throughout this chapter we represent the data as 2001. In all cases the data is reported for a single year only.

6. Throughout this chapter we will use the terms missionary, worker and personnel interchangeably.

7. The numbers reported on country totals will always be the minimum confirmable number. There are two factors involved. First, this does not include countries of nonresidential personnel, short-term workers, tentmakers, or where agencies have ongoing programs they support financially but without personnel. Second, several agencies report a general region but not specific countries for their missionary personnel. As agencies continue to evaluate security concerns, it seems likely that country statistics will become increasingly hard to report reliably.

8. 451 in this edition versus 477 in the previous edition.

9. This is tempered by the fact that almost the entire increase is due to the upsurge in

reported short-term personnel (2-weeks to 1-year) and volunteers.

10. Campus Crusade for Christ (432,223), Awanas International (165,000), International Aid (16,278), International Students, Inc (14,596), and World Relief (3,000).

11. p. 38., previous edition.

12. The reader may notice that the number of agencies for 1998 adds up to 691 rather than 693. This is because two of the agencies listed in the last edition sent the information in too late to be included in the statistics that were used in that edition.

13. They reported 52.4% of the primary activities, and were 69.9% of the agencies that reported their primary activity as some type of mission agency support. This is 33.6% higher than would be proportionally anticipated.

14. They reported 52.4% of the primary activities, and were 49.6% of the agencies that reported their primary activity as some type of evangelism/discipleship. This is 5.1% lower than would be proportionally anticipated.

15. They reported 52.4% of the primary activities, and were 49.4% of the agencies that reported their primary activity as some type of relief and development. This is 5.6% lower than would be proportionally anticipated.

16. They reported 52.8% of all activities, and were 59.6% of the agencies that reported activities related to mission agency support. This is 12.9% higher than would be proportionally anticipated.

17. They reported 9.7% of the primary activities, and were 12% of the agencies that reported their primary activity as some type of evangelism/discipleship. This is 23.4% higher than would be proportionally anticipated.

18. They reported 9.7% of the primary activities, and were 3.5% of the agencies that reported their primary activity as some type of education/training. This is 63.9% lower than would be proportionally anticipated.

19. They reported 9.7% of the primary activities, and were 4.9% of the agencies that reported their primary activity as some type of mission agency support. This is 50.1% lower than would be proportionally anticipated.

20. They reported 9.7% of the primary activities, and were 6.2% of the agencies that reported their primary activity as some type of relief and development. This is 36.5% lower than would be proportionally anticipated.

21. They reported 9.9% of all activities, and 11.5% of the agencies that reported their primary activity as some type of evangelism/discipleship. This is 15.2% higher than would be proportionally anticipated.

22. They reported 9.9% of all activities, and 6.9% of the agencies that reported their primary activity as some type of mission agency support. This is 30.4% lower than would be proportionally anticipated.

23. They reported 9.9% of all activities, and 8% of the agencies that reported their primary activity as some type of relief and development. This is 19.3% lower than would be proportionally anticipated.

24. They reported 9% of the primary activities, and 14% of the agencies that reported their primary activity as some type of education/training. This is 56% higher than would be proportionally anticipated.

25. They reported 9% of the primary activities, and 5.8% of the agencies that reported their primary activity as some type of mission agency support. This is 35.3% lower than would be proportionally anticipated.

26. They reported 9% of the primary activities, and 6.2% of the agencies that reported their primary activity as some type of relief and development. This is 31.4% lower than would be proportionally anticipated.

27. They reported 9.9% of all activities, and 11% of the agencies that reported their primary activity as some type of evangelism/discipleship. This is 12% higher than would be

proportionally anticipated.

28. They reported 9.9% of all activities, and 7.1% of the agencies that reported their primary activity as some type of mission agency support. This is 38.1% lower than would be proportionally anticipated.

29. They reported 9.9% of all activities, and 8.2% of the agencies that reported their primary activity as some type of relief and development. This is 16.6% lower than would be proportionally anticipated.

30. This agency preferred not to be identified.

31. By way of contrast, in the previous edition the gain of the 100th ranked agency was an inflation-adjusted 33.7% over the 1996 edition.

32. This survey lists 5 less U.S. agencies than the previous edition.

33. Though in both editions, Middle East numbers were incorporated into the numbers for Asia.

34. Compared to 48 agencies and 5,990 workers in the previous edition; while fewer agencies did not specify countries in this edition, those agencies that chose not to were ones that deployed more people.

35. In the last edition the ratio was four Canadians for every two nationals working for Canadian agencies.

36. See discussion in the U.S. section on Denominationalism for the definition of the term "not-denominational" as used in the *Handbook*.

37. "Long-term" is defined as fully supported personnel with length of service expected to be more than 4 years.

38. It should be noted that these are not absolute decreases, but decreases in the share of the total personnel and giving by agencies which identified themselves as denominational. In real terms, denominational personnel decreased by 9.6% and income for overseas work increased by 85.7% (not adjusted for inflation) over the 17-year period. In relation to what happened in the other agencies, the percent of those long-term missionaries employed by denominational agencies decreased by 6.5% and the percent of overseas income decreased by 8.7% over the same period.

39. For example, between this survey and the last one UFM International merged with Berean Mission.

40. That one Baptist agency did not report income in this survey is offset by the one evangelical agency that likewise did not report an income for overseas mission. Had both agencies reported, it seems likely that the evangelical agencies would have gained even more ground, since in the previous edition of the *Handbook* the evangelical agency reported $4.2 million more than the Baptist agency.

Chapter 2
U.S. Protestant Agencies

T his chapter contains the basic information for U.S. Protestant agencies engaged in Christian mission ministries outside the U.S. and Canada. The comprehensive coverage includes agencies that directly support the work of such ministries or the work of overseas national churches/workers. The agencies supplied the information. The Survey Questionnaire used to gather the information is reproduced in the Appendix.

The *Handbook* covers an agency's overseas ministry and support activities but not its mission work in the U.S. Much cross-cultural mission work takes place in the U.S., but due to the additional complexities of reporting such activities we have not undertaken the task for this publication. Agencies with both overseas and U.S. mission ministries, however, were asked to include U.S.-based ministry personnel in the total that appears in the "home ministry and office staff" line of the "Other Personnel" section.

Each agency will have at least seven of the basic categories of information listed below, with others included as applicable.

Agency Name

Agencies are listed alphabetically. If the article "the" is in an agency's name, it will appear at the end of the name so the agency is in the most commonly referenced alphabetical order. Rare exceptions occur where the Christian public commonly uses the article "the" as the first word in the agency's name.

Agencies that have changed their name since the previous *Handbook* have their prior name listed, with a cross-reference to the current or new name. A subdivision of a larger organization may be listed separately if it is organized to also serve the larger mission community rather than just its parent organization.

Telephone and Fax Numbers

The common format of showing the area code in parentheses is used throughout. Area codes have changed rapidly in the last decade, so some may even have been changed since publication.

E-mail Address

The Internet format and emerging standards for capitalization are used. For example, upper case letters may be used to the left of the @ sign when meaningful, but characters to the right are generally lower case.

In some cases, agencies have a general e-mail address, such as Info@xxxx.org. Others have supplied an individual person's address within the organization. In cases where only a Web address is given, it generally means a Web page provides access to several e-mail addresses so an inquiry can be immediately directed to the relevant department or person.

Instead of providing a general e-mail address, an agency may indicate the format to be used to contact individuals within the agency. This may take the format of something like Firstname.Lastname@xxxx.org and could be used by the sender when the individual is known.

Mission agencies began to use e-mail on a fairly broad scale by 1995, and now nearly all the agencies use e-mail on a regular basis.

Web Address

A request for a Web address was first included in the survey for the 1998-2000 edition. This edition reports even larger numbers of Web addresses, now including most agencies.

Postal Mailing Address

A post office box number usually appears whenever the agency has one, since it is more unlikely to change over time. Exceptions occur when the agency prefers the street address.

Chief Executive Officer

In some cases where there are multiple primary contacts, or due to agency preference, two officers are listed.

Short Descriptive Paragraph

A brief description appears based on the denominational orientation and primary activities information supplied by the agency. It keeps the same general order so the reader is presented with a consistent format across agencies. Additional specific information, such as name changes, mergers, or other unique aspects may also be included.

Purpose Statement

Purpose statements are included when available. Some of the statements are concise and shown in their entirety, straight from the agency or its promotional material. For most, however, because of space considerations, common or similar phrases such as "exists for the purpose of" are replaced by ellipses to present a more concise statement.

Year Founded in USA

This date is the year the agency or overseas mission component of a larger organization was founded or incorporated in the USA. In some cases the denomination or organization may have existed earlier in another country. For some organizations, the founding date of the missionary-sending component may be later than the founding of the larger organization. For organizations that have experienced mergers, the founding date is generally that of the oldest component involved in the merger.

Income for Overseas Ministries

This is the part of an agency's overall income used or budgeted for ministry activities outside the USA and Canada or in activities that directly facilitate overseas ministries. "NA" indicates that income in this sense is not applicable, and usually applies to specialized service agencies or agencies whose income is reported under a sister or parent organization. "NR" indicates that the agency did not report income for overseas ministries for the survey, but may make this information available on request.

Gifts-in-Kind

If applicable, this is the portion of the income received in the form of donated gifts-in-kind commodities and/or services used for overseas ministries. Please note that some agencies do not include gifts-in-kind as part of their financial audit process, so the value of such gifts may not be included in their income for overseas ministries. Gifts-in-kind amounts that were an insignificant percentage (usually 1 percent or less) are not shown as a separate item.

Fully Supported USA Personnel Overseas

Not all agencies have overseas personnel in the following categories, so the above heading will not always appear. If applicable, the following lines will appear with the appropriate numbers:

• "Expecting to serve more than 4 years" for persons from the USA who are fully supported by the agency

• "Expecting to serve 1 up to 4 years" for persons from the USA who are fully supported by the agency

• "Nonresidential mission personnel" for fully supported USA mission personnel not residing in the country or countries of their ministry, but assigned to work and travel overseas at least 12 weeks per year on operational aspects of the overseas ministry

Other Personnel

If applicable for the agency, the following lines will appear:

• "Non-USA serving in own/other country" for persons with either citizenship in their country of service or another non-USA country, who are fully or partially supported from the USA. Such individuals are not included in the specific numbers for individual countries listed under the "Countries" heading at the bottom of many entries.

• "Bivocational/Tentmaker from USA" for persons sponsored or supervised by the agency, but who support themselves partially or fully through non-church/non-mission vocations and live overseas for the purpose of Christian witness and/or encouraging believers

• "Short-Term less than 1 year from USA" for persons who went on overseas projects or mission trips that lasted at least two weeks but less than one year through the agency, either fully or partially supported, or raising their own support.

• "Home Ministry and office staff in USA" for persons assigned to ministry and/or office duties in the USA either as full-time or part-time paid staff/associates

Countries

These are the countries where the agency sends USA personnel or regularly supports national or other non-USA personnel. Following the name of the country is the number of USA personnel with terms of service of four years or more. In some cases a continent or other general region is shown instead of a country. This may be due to several reasons, such as mission personnel whose ministry covers several countries.

Where an agency's work is maintained by nationals of countries other than the U.S. or Canada, or by personnel serving less than four years, the country of activity may be listed without a number. Refer to the chapter entitled "Countries of Activity for U.S. Protestant Agencies" for more detailed country personnel totals.

ABWE (Association of Baptists for World Evangelism)

(See Ad on page 71)
P.O. Box 8585
Harrisburg, PA 17105 USA

Phone: (717) 774-7000
Fax: (717) 774-1919
E-mail: abwe@abwe.org
Web Site: www.abwe.org
Dr. Michael Loftis, President

An independent Baptist sending agency engaged in evangelism, church planting, theological education, leadership development, support of national churches and training.

Year Founded in US: 1927
Income for Overseas Min: $35,000,000
Fully Supported US Personnel Overseas:
   Expecting to serve more than 4 years: 695
   Nonresidential mission personnel: 37

Other personnel:
   Short-term less than 1 year from US: 117
   Home ministry & office staff in US: 82
   Bivocational/Tentmaker from US: 30

Countries: Argentina 9; Australia 13; Bangladesh 56; Bosnia and Herzegovina 1; Brazil 102; Cambodia 8; Chile 30; Colombia 16; Costa Rica 5; Cuba 4; Egypt 1; France 6; Gambia, The 16; Germany 7; Ghana 12; Hong Kong 8; Hungary 30; India 2; Italy 14; Japan 15; Kenya 2; Mongolia 4; Nicaragua 4; Norway 8; Papua New Guinea 21; Paraguay 15; Peru 49; Philippines 43; Portugal 27; Romania 9; Singapore 6; Slovakia 15; South Africa 40; Spain 16; Thailand 2; Togo 44; Ukraine 20; United Kingdom 13; Vietnam 2

ACM International

619 Washington Ave.
Terre Haute, IN 47802 USA

Phone: (812) 238-2883
Fax: (812) 235-6646
E-mail: bjbuell@aol.com

Mr. Edwin Buell, Exec. Director

A nondenominational sending agency of Christian (Restoration Movement) tradition engaged in leadership development, church planting, theological education, medical work, services for other agencies and missionary training. Statistical data from 1998.

Year Founded in US: 1946
Income for Overseas Min: $850,000
Fully Supported US Personnel Overseas:
   Expecting to serve more than 4 years: 22
   Nonresidential mission personnel: 3

Other personnel:
   Home ministry & office staff in US: 4

Countries: Ethiopia 1; Kenya 7; Mali 2; Mozambique 1; Nigeria 3; Philippines 2; South Africa 2; Tanzania 2; United Kingdom 2

ACMC (Advancing Churches in Missions Commitment)

4201 N. Peachtree Rd. #300
Atlanta, GA 30341-1207 USA

Phone: (800) 747-7346
Fax: (770) 455-4822
E-mail: atlanta@acmc.org
Web Site: www.acmc.org

Mr. James Killgore, President

An Association of Missions of Evangelical tradition engaged in church missions mobilization, literature production, leadership development, Christian education, missions information service, management consulting/training and services for other agencies.

Purpose: "...to help Christian congregations mobilize their resources for effective involvement in world evangelization."

Year Founded in US: 1974
Income for Overseas Min: $100,000
Personnel:
   Home ministry & office staff in US: 39

Action Intl. Ministries

P.O. Box 398
Mountlake Terrace, WA 98043-0398 USA

Phone: (425) 775-4800
Fax: (425) 775-0634
E-mail: info@actionintl.org
Web Site: www.actionintl.org

Rex Lee Carlaw, USA Director

An interdenominational sending agency of Evangelical tradition engaged in children's programs, church planting, development, evangelism, camping programs and mobilization for mission. Financial information from 1998.

Purpose: "...to reach the masses for Christ,

help individual Christians mature, and minister to the whole man, especially the poor..."

Year Founded in US: 1975

Income for Overseas Min: $449,757

Fully Supported US Personnel Overseas:
Expecting to serve more than 4 years: 27
Expecting to serve 1 to 4 years: 1

Other personnel:
Non-US serving in own/other country: 12
Home ministry & office staff in US: 10

Countries: Brazil 5; Colombia 1; Ecuador 2; India; Mexico; Philippines 17; Ukraine 2

ACTS Intl. Ministries

P.O. Box 62725
Colorado Springs, CO 80962 USA
Phone: (719) 282-1139
Fax: (719) 528-8718
E-mail: AlvinLow98@yahoo.com

Dr. Alvin Low, President

A transdenominational support agency of Evangelical tradition engaged in theological education, support of national churches and leadership development.

Purpose: "...equipping national Christian leaders in the least evangelized, economically deprived and restricted countries of the world..."

Year Founded in US: 1991

Income for Overseas Min: $100,000

Personnel:
Home ministry & office staff in US: 1

Adopt-A-People Clearinghouse

P.O. Box 28000
Chicago, IL 60628 USA
Phone: (866) 825-4636
Fax: (708) 367-8613
E-mail: AAPC@xc.org
Web Site: www.aapc.net

Rev. Rick Bashta, Director

An interdenominational service agency of evangelical tradition. Adopt-A-People Clearinghouse is a new ministry of the Bible League.

Purpose: "...to envision, impassion and equip local churches and mission organizations worldwide to spiritually adopt all remaining unreached people groups through

prayer, partnership, provision and personnel for the purpose of starting church planting movements."

Year Founded in US: 1989

Income for Overseas Min: NA

Advancing Indigenous Missions

P.O. Box 690042
San Antonio, TX 78269 USA
Phone: (830) 367-3513
Fax: (830) 367-3414
E-mail: coth@a-omega.net

James W. Colley, Exec. Director

A transdenominational support agency of Evangelical and Charismatic tradition engaged in support of national ministries.

Year Founded in US: 1990

Income for Overseas Min: NR

Personnel:
Home ministry & office staff in US: 2

Advancing Native Missions

P.O. Box 5303
Charlottesville, VA 22905 USA
Phone: (434) 823-7777
Fax: (434) 823-7776
E-mail: anm@adnamis.org
Web Site: www.adnamis.org

Mr. Carl A. Gordon, President

An interdenominational support agency of Evangelical tradition that supports national churches, church-planting efforts, missionary training and children's ministries among unreached peoples.

Purpose: "...to help take the Gospel of Jesus Christ to the world's remaining unreached peoples, standing behind 3,500 indigenous missionaries reaching their own people in more than 60 countries."

Year Founded in US: 1990

Income for Overseas Min: $2,200,000

Gifts-in-Kind: $86,000

Personnel:
Short-term less than 1 year from US: 20
Non-US serving in own/other country: 3
Nonresidential mission personnel: 3
Home ministry & office staff in US: 48

Countries: India; Indonesia

MISSION INSURANCE.
NOTHING ELSE.

There's something to be said for insuring with a company that only offers mission-specific policies. For starters, our professionals are really specialists. They know the ins-and-outs of international insurance and travel hazards—and have helped thousands with unforeseen obstacles. That's why you place your trust in an insurance company in the first place, isn't it?

- Property Insurance Programs

- Mission Property & Casualty Program

- Volunteer Missionary Insurance Package

- Accident & Special Risk Insurance

- Group Medical Insurance

- Individual Medical Insurance

- Life Insurance & Related Products

- Automobile Insurance

Adams & Associates®
INTERNATIONAL

803.758.1400 • 800.922.8438 • Fax 803.252.1988
www.aaintl.com

Advancing Renewal Ministries

11616 Sir Francis Drake Dr.
Charlotte, NC 28277 USA
Phone: (704) 846-9355
Fax: (704) 846-9356
E-mail: ARM_INC@compuserve.com
Dr. Arthur M. Vincent, Director

A nondenominational support agency of Lutheran tradition engaged in training, equipping and supporting national workers and Bible and literature distribution. Financial information from 1998.

Year Founded in US: 1982
Income for Overseas Min: $48,600
Personnel:
   Home ministry & office staff in US: 3

Advent Christian General Conf., Dept. of World Missions

P.O. Box 23152
Charlotte, NC 28227 USA
Phone: (704) 545-6161
Fax: (704) 573-0412
E-mail: worldmissions@adventchristian.org
Web Site: www.adventchristian.org
Rev. David E. Ross, Exec. Director

A denominational sending agency of Adventist tradition engaged in church planting, TEE, theological education, evangelism, leadership development and support of national workers.

Purpose: "...to help local Advent Christian congregations to succeed, both individually and collectively, in fulfilling their role in the Great Commission of Christ."

Year Founded in US: 1865
Income for Overseas Min: $406,352

Fully Supported US Personnel Overseas:
   Expecting to serve more than 4 years: 10
Other personnel:
   Short-term less than 1 year from US: 130
   Non-US serving in own/other country: 130
   Home ministry & office staff in US: 2
Countries: Croatia; Ghana; India 2; Japan 2; Malaysia; Mexico 1; New Zealand 2; Philippines 3; South Africa

Adventures in Missions

6000 Wellspring Trail
Gainesville, GA 30506 USA
Phone: (770) 983-1060
Fax: (770) 983-1061
E-mail: info@adventures.org
Web Site: www.adventures.org
Mr. Seth Barnes Sr., Exec. Director

A nondenominational service agency of Evangelical tradition engaged in short-term programs, evangelism and missionary training.

Year Founded in US: 1989
Income for Overseas Min: NA
Personnel:
   Short-term less than 1 year from US: 6,000
   Home ministry & office staff in US: 50

Africa Inland Mission Intl.

P.O. Box 178
Pearl River, NY 10965 USA
Phone: (845) 735-4014
Fax: (845) 735-1814
E-mail: Go@aimint.net
Web Site: www.aim-us.org
Dr. W. Ted Barnett, U.S. Director

An interdenominational sending agency of Evangelical tradition engaged in church planting, Christian education, extension education, evangelism, leadership development and medical work.

Purpose: "...to plant maturing churches... through the evangelization of unreached people groups and the effective preparation of church leaders."

Year Founded in US: 1895
Income for Overseas Min: $15,000,000
Gifts-in-Kind: $62,725

Fully Supported US Personnel Overseas:
   Expecting to serve more than 4 years: 424
   Expecting to serve 1 to 4 years: 32
   Nonresidential mission personnel: 4
Other personnel:
   Short-term less than 1 year from US: 118
   Home ministry & office staff in US: 84
Countries: Africa–General 2; Cambodia; Central African Republic 1; Chad 8; Comoros 8; Congo, Republic of the 4; France 2; Kenya 284; Lesotho 5; Mozambique 21; Namibia 7; South Africa 2; Sudan 1; Tanzania 55; Uganda 24

Africa Inter-Mennonite Mission

59466 County Rd. 113
Elkhart, IN 46517-3644 USA
Phone: (574) 875-5552
Fax: (574) 875-6567
E-mail: aimm@aimmintl.org
Web Site: www.aimmintl.org
Rev. Garry Prieb, Exec. Secretary

A denominational sending agency of Mennonite tradition engaged in church planting, evangelism, leadership development, linguistics, support of national churches and Bible translation.

Purpose: "...to make known the love of God in Jesus Christ to the people of Africa in ministries of word and deed, witness and service that God's people be brought to full stature in Christ."

Year Founded in US: 1912

Income for Overseas Min: $696,591

Fully Supported US Personnel Overseas:
Expecting to serve more than 4 years: 7
Expecting to serve 1 to 4 years: 9

Other personnel:
Non-US serving in own/other country: 12
Home ministry & office staff in US: 7

Countries: Botswana 3; Burkina Faso 4; Democratic Republic of Congo; Lesotho; Senegal; South Africa

African Bible Colleges, Inc.

P.O. Box 103
Jackson, MS 39060 USA
Phone: (601) 923-1679
Fax: (601) 924-6353
E-mail: BuckABC@netdoor.com
Web Site: www.africanbiblecolleges.com
Rev. William L. Mosal, U.S. Director

An interdenominational sending agency of Evangelical tradition engaged in leadership development, Bible distribution, broadcasting, correspondence courses, Christian education and evangelism.

Purpose: "...to further evangelical Christian education through establishment and funding of Bible colleges in Africa and the acquisition of Christian teachers for African schools and colleges."

Year Founded in US: 1977

Income for Overseas Min: $1,007,862

Fully Supported US Personnel Overseas:
Expecting to serve more than 4 years: 14
Expecting to serve 1 to 4 years: 12

Other personnel:
Non-US serving in own/other country: 25
Home ministry & office staff in US: 2

Countries: Malawi 14; Uganda

African Enterprise, Inc.

P.O. Box 727
Monrovia, CA 91017 USA
Phone: (626) 357-8811
Fax: (626) 359-2069
E-mail: aeusa1@cs.com
Web Site: www.africanenterprise.org
Mr. Malcolm Graham, Exec. Director

An interdenominational support agency of evangelical tradition engaged in evangelism, development, leadership development, relief and/or rehabilitation and missionary training.

Purpose: "To evangelize the cities of Africa through Word & Deed in partnership with the Church."

Year Founded in US: 1962

Income for Overseas Min: $707,453

Personnel:
Non-US serving in own/other country: 138
Home ministry & office staff in US: 7
Bivocational/Tentmaker from US: 3

Countries: Democratic Republic of Congo; Ethiopia; Ghana; Kenya; Malawi; Rwanda; South Africa; Tanzania; Uganda; Zimbabwe

African Leadership

P.O. Box 682444
Franklin, TN 37068-2444 USA
Phone: (615) 595-8238
Fax: (615) 595-7906
E-mail: lavonne@africanleadership.org
Web Site: www.africanleadership.org
Mr. Larry Warren, President

A support agency engaged in pastor training, relief and skills training for the unemployed.

Year Founded in US: 2000

Income for Overseas Min: $786,680

Fully Supported US Personnel Overseas:
Nonresidential mission personnel: 20

Other personnel:
  Short-term less than 1year from US: 25
  Non-US serving in own/other country: 21
  Home ministry & office staff in US: 1

African Methodist Episcopal Church, Dept. of Global Witness and Ministries

P.O. Box 20852
Charleston, SC 29413-0852 USA

Phone: (843) 852-2645
Fax: (843) 852-2648
Web Site: www.ameglobalmissions.com

Rev. George F. Flowers, Exec. Director

A denominational support agency of Methodist tradition engaged in Bible distribution, church construction and children's programs.

Purpose: "...ministry, witness and gospel proclamation so that people of God may be liberated spiritually and materially and reconciled to each other through the Holy Spirit."

Year Founded in US: 1844

Income for Overseas Min: $300,000

Personnel:
  Short-term less than 1 year from US: 190

African Mission Evangelism

2313 Bell Dr.
Knoxville, TN 37998 USA

Phone: (865) 579-1467
Fax: (865) 579-2337
E-mail: cbridges@jbc.edu
Web Site: www.ame-gccs.org

Dr. Carl Bridges, President

A nondenominational sending agency of Christian (Restoration Movement) tradition engaged in theological education, church planting and support of national churches.

Year Founded in US: 1968

Income for Overseas Min: $288,018

Fully Supported US Personnel Overseas:
  Expecting to serve more than 4 years: 9

Other Personnel:
  Short-term less than 1 year from US: 10
  Non-US serving in own/other country: 10

Countries: Ghana 9

AIMS (Accelerating International Mission)

P.O. Box 64534
Virginia Beach, VA 23464 USA

Phone: (757) 226-5850
Fax: (757) 226-5851
E-mail: aims@aims-usa.org
Web Site: www.aims.org

Dr. Howard Foltz, President

An agency that mobilizes, equips and networks the global church with the goal of establishing church planting movements among unreached people groups.

Year Founded in US: 1985

Income for Overseas Min: $150,000

Personnel:
  Short-term less than 1 year from US: 12
  Home ministry & office staff in US: 9

Alberto Mottesi Evangelistic Association

P.O. Box 2478
Huntington Beach, CA 92647-0478 USA

Phone: (714) 375-0110
E-mail: info@albertomottesi.org
Web Site: www.albertomottesi.org

Dr. Alberto H. Mottesi, President

An interdenominational service agency of Evangelical tradition engaged in evangelism, broadcasting, leadership development and family restoration in crusades, etc., in Latin America, the USA and Europe.

Year Founded in US: 1977

Income for Overseas Min: NA

Personnel:
  Short-term less than 1 year from US: 12
  Home ministry & office staff in US: 7

All God's Children Intl.

4114 NE Fremont St.
Portland, OR 97212 USA

Phone: (503) 282-7652
Fax: (503) 282-2582
E-mail: agci@usa.net
Web Site: www.allgodschildren.org

Mr. Ron Beazely, President

A nondenominational service agency of Pentecostal tradition engaged in childcare/orphanage programs, literature distribution, providing medical supplies and relief and/or rehabilitation. Statistical data from 1996.

Year Founded in US: 1991

Income for Overseas Min: $568,000

Fully Supported US Personnel Overseas:
Nonresidential mission personnel: 2

Other personnel:
Non-US serving in own/other country: 5
Home ministry & office staff in US: 5

Countries: Bulgaria; China; Guatemala; Romania; Russia

Allegheny Wesleyan Methodist Missions

P.O. Box 357
Salem, OH 44460 USA

Phone: (330) 332-5271
Fax: (330) 337-9700
E-mail: AWMC@juno.com

Rev. William M. Cope, Director

A denominational sending agency of Wesleyan-Arminian and Holiness tradition engaged in evangelism, Bible and literature distribution, church planting and Christian education.

Year Founded in US: 1969

Income for Overseas Min: $377,333

Fully Supported US Personnel Overseas:
Expecting to serve more than 4 years: 14
Other personnel:
Home ministry & office staff in US: 2

Countries: Haiti 9; Peru 2; Ukraine 3

Amazon Focus

(See Ad on page 77)
P.O. Box 5008
Florence, SC 29502 USA

Phone: (843) 676-0659
Fax: (843) 661-7458
E-mail: info@amazonfocus.com
Web Site: www.amazonfocus.com

Mr. Paul C. Johnson, CEO

A nondenominational sending agency of Evangelical tradition engaged in development, leadership development, medical work, support of national churches, support of national workers and short-term programs.

Purpose: "...to empower and equip the indigenous tribes in the Amazon basin to

assume responsibility for their long-term spiritual, economic and survival needs."

Year Founded in US: 1995

Income for Overseas Min: $170,015

Fully Supported US Personnel Overseas:
Expecting to serve more than 4 years: 4
Nonresidential mission personnel: 2

Other personnel:
Short-term less than 1 year from US: 30
Non-US serving in own/other country: 29
Home ministry & office staff in US: 7

Countries: Belize; Bolivia; Peru 4

Ambassadors for Christ Intl.

P.O. Box 470
Tucker, GA 30085 USA

Phone: (770) 621-3604
Fax: (770) 621-9588
E-mail: phanak@afcinternational.org
Web Site: www.afcinternational.org

Rev. Paul Hanak, Intl. Director

A nondenominational support agency of Evangelical tradition engaged in training, support of national workers and evangelism in 40 countries.

Purpose: "...to support spiritually gifted preachers and Bible teachers to reach their homelands for Jesus Christ."

Year Founded in US: 1972

Income for Overseas Min: $630,000

Personnel:
Home ministry & office staff in US: 6

Ambassadors for Christ, Inc.

P.O. Box 280
Paradise, PA 17562 USA

Phone: (717) 687-8564
Fax: (717) 687-8891
E-mail: AFC@afcinc.org
Web Site: www.afcinc.org

Mr. Paul Schultz, Controller

An interdenominational support agency of Evangelical tradition engaged in evangelism and mobilization.

Purpose: "...to evangelize and disciple Chinese students and professionals in the United States, and other parts of the world, to motivate and equip them to impact the culture for the Lord."

Year Founded in US: 1963
Income for Overseas Min: $600,000
Personnel:
Home ministry & office staff in US: 33
Countries: China

American Association of Lutheran Churches

801 W. 106th St., #203
Minneapolis, MN 55420-5603 USA
Phone: (209) 823-1971
Fax: (209) 823-9335
Pastor Bill Moberly, Chair

A denominational support agency of Luth-eran tradition engaged in funds trans-mission, church planting, relief and/or re-habilitation and Bible translation. Financial figure from 1998.

Year Founded in US: 1987
Income for Overseas Min: $35,000

American Baptist Churches in the U.S.A., Intl. Ministries

P.O. Box 851
Valley Forge, PA 19482-0851 USA
Phone: (610) 768-2212
Fax: (610) 768-2115
E-mail: Donna.Anderson@abc-usa.org
Web Site:
www.abc-internationalministries.org
Dr. John A. Sundquist, Exec. Director

A denominational sending agency of Bap-tist tradition engaged in leadership devel-opment, development, theological education, evangelism, support of national churches and mobilization for mission.

Purpose: "...to glorify God in all the earth by crossing cultural boundaries to make disciples of Jesus Christ."

Year Founded in US: 1814
Income for Overseas Min: $15,398,251
Fully Supported US Personnel Overseas:
Expecting to serve more than 4 years: 134
Expecting to serve 1 to 4 years: 4
Nonresidential mission personnel: 1
Other personnel:
Short-term less than 1 year from US: 1,231
Non-US serving in own/other country: 10
Home ministry & office staff in US: 49
Countries: Bahamas 2; Bolivia 2; Brazil 1;

Bulgaria 2; Cambodia 4; Chile 6; China 1; Costa Rica 5; Cuba 1; Czech Republic 2; Democratic Republic of Congo 15; Dom-inican Republic 5; El Salvador 2; Haiti 6; Hong Kong 4; India 6; Japan 12; Latvia 2; Lebanon; Mexico 12; Nicaragua 10; Panama 1; Philippines 8; South Africa 5; Spain; Thailand 20

American Bible Society

1865 Broadway
New York, NY 10023 USA
Phone: (212) 408-1200
Fax: (212) 408-1512
E-mail: webmaster@americanbible.org
Web Site: www.americanbible.org
Dr. Eugene B. Habecker, President

An interdenominational specialized service agency engaged in Scripture translation, publication and distribution in fellowship with 135 members of the United Bible Soci-eties and other Bible Society offices operat-ing in approximately 200 countries and territories. Financial figure from 1998.

Purpose: "...to provide the Holy Scriptures to every man, woman and child in a lan-guage and form each can readily under-stand, and at a price each can easily afford."

Year Founded in US: 1816
Income for Overseas Min: $16,676,371

American Leprosy Missions, Inc.

1 ALM Way
Greenville, SC 29601 USA
Phone: (864) 271-7040
Fax: (864) 271-7062
E-mail: AmLep@leprosy.org
Web Site: www.leprosy.org
Mr. Christopher J. Doyle, President/CEO

A nondenominational specialized agency of Evangelical tradition engaged in disability assistance programs and providing medical supplies.

Purpose: "To serve as a channel of the love of Christ to persons with Hansen's dis-ease (leprosy) ...helping them to be healed in body and spirit and to be restored to lives of dignity and usefulness."

Year Founded in US: 1917

Income for Overseas Min: $5,296,965

Personnel:
Home ministry & office staff in US: 25

American Missionary Fellowship

(See Ad on page 80)
P.O. Box 370
Villanova, PA 19085 USA
Phone: (610) 527-4439
Fax: (610) 527-4720
E-mail: Info@americanmissionary.org
Web Site: www.americanmissionary.org

Dr. Lee K. Iseley, Gen. Director

A nondenominational support agency of Evangelical tradition engaged in church planting and cross-cultural ministry in the USA leading to overseas missions.

Purpose: "...to evangelize, disciple and congregate the yet-unreached peoples of the United States for Jesus Christ."

Year Founded in US: 1817

Income for Overseas Min: NA

Personnel:
Home ministry & office staff in US: 16
Bivocational/Tentmaker from US: 24

American Scripture Gift Mission

P.O. Box 410280
Melbourne, FL 32941-0280 USA
Phone: (877) 873-2746
Fax: (321) 255-8986
E-mail: asgm@asgm.com
Web Site: www.asgm.com

Mr. James R. Powell, Chairman

A nondenominational support agency of Evangelical tradition distributing all-Scripture booklets and tracts in more than 400 languages, primarily for evangelism. The USA branch of SGM Intl., London, England.

Year Founded in US: 1937

Income for Overseas Min: $1,000

Personnel:
Home ministry & office staff in US: 1

AmeriTribes

(See Ad on page 81)
P.O. Box 27346
Tucson, AZ 85726-7346 USA
Phone: (520) 670-9400
Fax: (520) 670-9444
E-mail: info@ameritribes.org
Web Site: www.ameritribes.org

Mr. Timothy C. Brown, Exec. Director

A nondenominational sending agency of Evangelical tradition engaged in community development and church planting among tribal peoples of the Americas.

Purpose: "...facilitating the development of reproducing, indigenous churches among tribal peoples of the Americas."

Year Founded in US: 1944

Income for Overseas Min: NA

Fully Supported US Personnel Overseas:
Expecting to serve more than 4 years: 8
Nonresidential mission personnel: 2

Other personnel:
Home ministry & office staff in US: 17
Countries: Mexico 8

AMF International

P.O. Box 5470
Lansing, IL 60438 USA
Phone: (708) 418-0020
Fax: (708) 418-0132
E-mail: office@amfi.org
Web Site: www.amfi.org

Mr. Wesley N. Taber, Exec. Director

An interdenominational sending agency of Evangelical tradition engaged in evangelism, literature distribution, Bible distribution, short-term programs and missionary training.

Purpose: "Building bridges of understanding between Jewish and Christian communities for over 100 years."

Year Founded in US: 1887

Income for Overseas Min: $183,905

Fully Supported US Personnel Overseas:
Expecting to serve more than 4 years: 2
Nonresidential mission personnel: 1

Other personnel:
Short-term less than 1 year from US: 20
Non-US serving in own/other country: 9
Home ministry & office staff in US: 17
Bivocational/Tentmaker from US: 3

Countries: France; Israel 2; Mexico

And the rest, is **His**tory...

At American Missionary Fellowship, **His** Story is the reason for our history! And the rest is just the beginning for us today. We continue to *evangelize, disciple,* and *congregate* the lost and unreached here in America for Jesus Christ. Find out more about how **His** Story has shaped our history for over 200 years. Visit us online at **www.americanmissionary.org**, or call our Director of Ministry Resources at 610.527.4439.

You can become part of our history today!

The
First
Peoples of
the Americas
shouldn't be
the last to hear!

AMERITRIBES

- closely partnering with sending churches
- team approach to ministry
- focus on tribal peoples of western U.S. and Mexico
- servant evangelism through community development leading to the establishment of indigenous churches

AMG International

P.O. Box 22000
Chattanooga, TN 37422 USA
Phone: (423) 894-6060
Fax: (423) 894-6863
E-mail: missions@amginternational.org
Web Site: www.amginternational.org

Dr. Spiros Zodhiates, President

Mr. Paul Jenks, CEO

An interdenominational sending agency of Evangelical tradition engaged in Bible distribution, relief and/or rehabilitation, childcare/orphanage programs, church planting, theological education and support of national workers.

Year Founded in US: 1942

Income for Overseas Min: $4,919,477

Fully Supported US Personnel Overseas:
  Expecting to serve more than 4 years: 46
  Nonresidential mission personnel: 3

Other personnel:
  Short-term less than 1 year from US: 50
  Non-US serving in own/other country: 326
  Home ministry & office staff in US: 20

Countries: Albania 2; Bangladesh; Bulgaria; Cyprus 2; Ghana; Greece 13; Guatemala 4; Haiti; India 2; Indonesia; Italy 2; Mexico 5; Peru; Philippines 2; Romania; Spain 10; Thailand; Turkey; Uganda 2; Unspecified Country 2; Zimbabwe

AMOR Ministries

1664 Precision Park Lane
San Diego, CA 92713 USA
Phone: (619) 662-1200
Fax: (619) 662-1295
E-mail: missionservices@comebuildhope.com
Web Site: www.comebuildhope.com

Mr. Scott Congdon, President/CEO

A nondenominational sending agency of Christian (Restoration Movement) tradition engaged in relief and/or rehabilitation, support of national churches, short-term programs, missionary training and youth programs. Personnel information from 1998.

Year Founded in US: 1980

Income for Overseas Min: NA

Fully Supported US Personnel Overseas:
  Expecting to serve more than 4 years: 12
  Expecting to serve 1 to 4 years: 13

Nonresidential mission personnel: 1

Other personnel:
  Short-term less than 1 year from US: 36
  Non-US serving in own/other country: 6
  Home ministry & office staff in US: 15

Countries: Mexico 25

Anglican Frontier Missions

P.O. Box 18038
Richmond, VA 23226-8038 USA
Phone: (804) 355-8468
Fax: (804) 355-8260
E-mail: AFM@xc.org
Web Site: www.afm-25.org

Rev. E. A. de Bordenave, Director

An interdenominational sending agency of Episcopal tradition engaged in church planting, mission-related research, support of national churches and missionary training.

Purpose: "...planting indigenous churches among the 25 largest and least evangelized people groups of World A."

Year Founded in US: 1993

Income for Overseas Min: $500,000

Fully Supported US Personnel Overseas:
  Expecting to serve more than 4 years: 8
  Expecting to serve 1 to 4 years: 8
  Nonresidential mission personnel: 6

Other personnel:
  Home ministry & office staff in US: 3

Countries: Asia–General 8

Anis Shorrosh Evangelistic Association, Inc.

P.O. Box 7577
Spanish Fort, AL 36577-0577 USA
Phone: (251) 626-1124
Fax: (251) 621-0507
E-mail: asea777@truth-in-crisis.com
Web Site: www.islamexpose.com

Dr. Anis Shorrosh, Evangelist

An interdenominational support agency of Baptist and Evangelical tradition engaged in evangelism, broadcasting, literature production and video/film production/distribution with special emphasis in Muslims and apologetics. Ministry has been conducted in 76 countries.

Year Founded in US: 1970

Income for Overseas Min: $10,000

Apostolic Christian Church Foundation

1135 Sholey Rd.
Richmond, VA 23231 USA
Phone: (804) 222-1943
Fax: (804) 236-0642
Mr. Jim Hodges, Director

A denominational sending agency of Anabaptist tradition engaged in funds transmission, church construction, relief aid, support of national workers and evangelism. Personnel data from 1998.

Purpose: "...exists to help fulfill Christ's Commission by sending out members of the AC Church who are called by God to become foreign missionaries."

Year Founded in US: 1953

Income for Overseas Min: $763,358

Fully Supported US Personnel Overseas:
Expecting to serve more than 4 years: 31

Other personnel:
Non-US serving in own/other country: 24
Home ministry & office staff in US: 2

Countries: Argentina 1; Australia 2; Brazil 17; Czech Republic 1; Ghana; Indonesia 2; Japan 2; Mexico 1; Papua New Guinea 2; Paraguay 1; Puerto Rico 2

Apostolic Team Ministries, Intl.

6109 W. Bancroft St.
Toledo, OH 43615 USA
Phone: (419) 865-4063
Fax: (419) 865-5468
E-mail: rgking@buckeye-express.com
Web Site: www.atmintel.org
Mr. Ronald G. King, Admin. Director

A nondenominational support agency of Charismatic tradition engaged in church planting and missionary training.

Year Founded in US: 1980

Income for Overseas Min: $200,000

Fully Supported US Personnel Overseas:
Expecting to serve more than 4 years: 15

Other personnel:
Non-US serving in own/other country: 8
Home ministry & office staff in US: 8

Countries: Albania 5; Austria; Bolivia 2; Brazil 2; France 4; Germany; United Kingdom 2

Arab World Ministries

(See Ad on page 84)
P.O. Box 96
Upper Darby, PA 19082 USA
Phone: (800) 447-3566
Fax: (610) 352-2652
E-mail: awmusa@awm.org
Web Site: www.awm.org
Mr. Robert Sayer, U.S. Director

An interdenominational sending agency of Evangelical tradition engaged in church planting, broadcasting, TEE, evangelism, leadership development and literature distribution.

Year Founded in US: 1952

Income for Overseas Min: $3,480,997

Fully Supported US Personnel Overseas:
Expecting to serve more than 4 years: 116
Expecting to serve 1 to 4 years: 6

Other personnel:
Short-term less than 1 year from US: 43
Home ministry & office staff in US: 30

Countries: Asia–General 116

Arabic Communication Ctr.

P.O. Box 1124
Temple City, CA 91780 USA
Phone: (626) 291-2866
Fax: (626) 291-2159
E-mail: acc@accworld.org
Web Site: www.ACCWORLD.org
Dr. Hisham S. Kamel, President

A denominational specialized agency of Presbyterian tradition engaged in translation work, Bible distribution, theological education, evangelism, literature distribution and video/film production/distribution. Financial figures from 1998.

Year Founded in US: 1992

Income for Overseas Min: $30,000

Gifts-in-Kind: $10,000

Fully Supported US Personnel Overseas:
Nonresidential mission personnel: 5

Other Personnel:
Home ministry & office staff in US: 4

Armenian Missionary Association of America, Inc.

31 West Century Rd.
Paramus, NJ 07652 USA
Phone: (201) 265-2607

Fax: (201) 265-6015
E-mail: amaainc@aol.com
Web Site: www.amaainc.org

Rev. Jirair M. Sogomian, Exec. Director

A nondenominational service agency of Evangelical and Congregational tradition engaged in children's programs, Bible distribution, camping programs, church planting, theological education and evangelism.

Year Founded in US: 1918

Income for Overseas Min: $3,285,018

Gifts-in-Kind: $247,023

Fully Supported US Personnel Overseas:
Expecting to serve more than 4 years: 4
Expecting to serve 1 to 4 years: 1
Nonresidential mission personnel: 4

Other personnel:
Short-term less than 1 year from US: 30
Non-US serving in own/other country: 4
Home ministry & office staff in US: 12

Countries: Argentina; Armenia 2; Australia; Belgium; Brazil; Bulgaria; Canada; Cyprus; Egypt; France; Georgia; Greece; India; Iran; Lebanon 2; Mozambique; Nepal; Syria; Turkey; Uruguay

Artists In Christian Testimony

P.O. Box 1649
Brentwood, TN 37024-1649 USA

Phone: (615) 376-7861
Fax: (615) 376-7863
E-mail: ACTnashville@actinternational.org
Web Site: www.actinternational.org

Rev. Byron L. Spradlin, President

A sending agency of evangelical tradition engaged in arts ministry.

Purpose: "...to develop and deploy culture-sensitive arts missionaries and ministries throughout the world to grow and glorify Christ's Kingdom."

Year Founded in US: 1973

Income for Overseas Min: $241,915

Fully Supported US Personnel Overseas:
Expecting to serve more than 4 years: 4
Expecting to serve 1 to 4 years: 4

Other personnel:
Non-US serving in own/other country: 2
Home ministry & office staff in US: 3

Countries: Asia–General; Costa Rica; Japan 2; Kenya; Philippines 2

Asian Outreach U.S.A.

305 NE 192nd Ave.
Vancouver, WA 98684 USA

Phone: (360) 883-2421
Fax: (360) 892-4556
E-mail: AOUSA@earthlink.net
Web Site: www.asianoutreach.org

Rev. James R. Swanson, Exec. Director

A nondenominational support agency of Evangelical and Charismatic tradition engaged in church planting, Bible distribution, correspondence courses, theological education, evangelism, leadership development, literature distribution, literature production, short-term programs and training.

Year Founded in US: 1965

Income for Overseas Min: $790,000

Personnel:
Short-term less than 1 year from US: 40
Home ministry and office staff in US: 1

Countries: Australia; Cambodia; China; Hong Kong; Indonesia; Japan; Malaysia; Mongolia; Myanmar/Burma; Nepal; New Zealand; Philippines; Singapore; South Africa; Taiwan; Thailand; United Kingdom; Vietnam

Assemblies of God World Missions

1445 Boonville Ave.
Springfield, MO 65802 USA

Phone: (417) 862-2781
Fax: (417) 832-8723
Web Site: www.agwm.org

Rev. John Bueno, Exec. Director

A denominational sending agency of Pentecostal tradition engaged in church planting, Bible distribution, children's programs, extension education, theological education, and evangelism.

Purpose: "...proclaiming the message of Jesus Christ to the spiritually lost... establishing churches, following the New Testament pattern...training leaders to proclaim the message of Jesus Christ to their own people and to other nations... touching poor and suffering people with the compassion of Jesus Christ..."

Year Founded in US: 1914

Income for Overseas Min: $177,262,833

Fully Supported US Personnel Overseas:
  Expecting to serve more than 4 years: 1,199
  Expecting to serve 1 to 4 years: 509
  Nonresidential mission personnel: 40

Other personnel:
  Short-term less than 1 year from US: 12,694
  Bivocational/Tentmaker from US: 2
  Home ministry & office staff in US: 184

Countries: Albania 8; Angola 6; Antigua 2; Argentina 16; Asia–General 89; Austria 9; Bahamas; Bangladesh; Belarus 4; Belau 2; Belgium 20; Belize 12; Benin 6; Bolivia 12; Botswana 4; Brazil 15; Bulgaria; Burkina Faso 7; Cambodia 25; Cameroon 6; Cape Verde 4; Central African Republic 4; Chad 4; Chile 20; Colombia 23; Congo, Democratic Republic of the 3; Costa Rica 25; Cote d'Ivoire 6; Croatia 2; Czech Republic 4; Denmark 2; Dominica 2; Dominican Republic 13; Ecuador 28; Egypt; El Salvador 10; Equatorial Guinea 6; Eritrea 4; Ethiopia 11; Fiji 4; Finland 2; France 13; French Polynesia 2; Georgia; Germany 41; Ghana 2; Greece; Guam; Guatemala 14; Haiti 4; Honduras 18; Hungary 6; Iceland 2; Indonesia 19; Ireland 8; Israel; Italy 4; Jamaica 8; Japan 36; Jordan; Kenya 32; Kiribati 2; Korea, South 4; Laos; Latvia 5; Lesotho 2; Lithuania 4; Luxembourg 4; Macedonia; Madagascar 6; Malawi 9; Mali 4; Marshall Islands; Mauritius 2; Mexico 60; Micronesia, Federated States of 2; Mongolia 8; Mozambique 5; Myanmar/Burma 2; Namibia 4; Nepal; Netherlands 4; Netherlands Antilles 2; Nicaragua 15; Niger 4; Nigeria 4; Panama 8; Paraguay 12; Peru 12; Philippines 69; Poland 2; Portugal 9; Romania 12; Russia 24; Rwanda 6; Senegal 6; Singapore 10; Slovakia 3; Slovenia 2; Solomon Islands 6; South Africa 47; Spain 50; Sudan; Suriname 2; Swaziland 4; Taiwan 10; Tanzania 10; Thailand 20; Togo 15; Tonga 2; Ukraine; United Kingdom 2; Unspecified Country 26; Uruguay 12; Vanuatu 6; Venezuela 14; Zambia 9; Zimbabwe 4

ASSIST—Aid to Special Saints in Strategic Times

P.O. Box 2126
Garden Grove, CA 92842-2126 USA
Phone: (714) 530-6598
E-mail: assistcomm@cs.com

Web site: www.assist-ministries.com
Mr. Dan Wooding, President
A transdenominational support agency of Evangelical tradition engaged in Pen Pal ministry, literature distribution, Bible distribution and relief ministries. Also runs ASSIST news service and sponsors "Window on the World."

Purpose: "...encourages and supports believers who, for religious, political or economic reasons, are unable to worship and witness freely for their faith."

Year Founded in US: 1989
Income for Overseas Min: $60,000

Associate Reformed Presbyterian Church
See: World Witness, the Foreign Mission Board of the Associate Reformed Presbyterian Church

Association of Baptists for World Evangelism
See: ABWE

Association of Free Lutheran Congregations World Missions

3110 E. Medicine Lake Blvd.
Minneapolis, MN 55441 USA
Phone: (763) 545-5631
Fax: (763) 545-0079
E-mail: worldmis@aflc.org
Web Site: www.aflc.org
Rev. Del Palmer, Director World Missions
A denominational sending agency of Lutheran tradition engaged in evangelism, aviation services, childcare/orphanage programs, church planting, theological education and support of national workers.

Year Founded in US: 1963
Income for Overseas Min: NR
Fully Supported US Personnel Overseas:
  Expecting to serve more than 4 years: 10
  Expecting to serve 1 to 4 years: 2
Other personnel:
  Short-term less than 1 year from US: 6

Non-US serving in own/other country: 36
Home ministry & office staff in US: 3

Countries: Brazil 6; India; Mexico 4; Portugal

Audio Scripture Ministries
760 Waverly Rd.
Holland, MI 49423 USA

Phone: (616) 396-5291
Fax: (616) 396-5294
E-mail: asm@audioscriptureministries.org
Web Site: www.asmtoday.org

Mr. Tom Dudenhofer, Exec. Director

A nondenominational specialized agency of Evangelical tradition engaged in audio recording/distribution in more than 200 languages, services for other agencies, supplying equipment and technical assistance.

Year Founded in US: 1989

Income for Overseas Min: $379,924

Personnel:
  Non-US serving in own/other country: 13
  Home ministry & office staff in US: 4

Countries: India; Kenya

Audio Scriptures Intl.
(See Ad on page 88)
P.O. Box 460634
Escondido, CA 92046-0634 USA

Phone: (760) 745-8105
Fax: (760) 745-8150
E-mail: asi@audioscriptures.org
Web Site: www.audioscriptures.org

Mr. Mark S. Hoekstra, President

A nondenominational specialized agency of Presbyterian and Reformed tradition engaged in audio recording/distribution and Bible distribution.

Purpose: "A Talking Bible in every language and village...A Talking Bible on Sunday in every church."

Year Founded in US: 1989

Income for Overseas Min: NA

Personnel:
  Short-term less than 1 year from US: 2
  Non-US serving in own/other country: 2
  Home ministry & office staff in US: 7

Countries: India; Mexico

Aurora Mission
P.O. Box 1549
Bradenton, FL 34206 USA

Phone: (941) 746-2572
Fax: (941) 748-2625
E-mail: mission@auroramission.org
Web Site: ww.auroramission.or

Rev. James E. Pike, Director of Missions

A nondenominational support agency of Independent tradition engaged in church planting, theological education, leadership development, Bible distribution, evangelism, literature distribution, literature production, short-term programs and Bible translation.

Purpose: "...planting and strengthening churches and developing church leadership and church training centers in Italy and beyond."

Year Founded in US: 1978

Income for Overseas Min: $380,867

Fully Supported US Personnel Overseas:
  Expecting to serve more than 4 years: 3

Other personnel:
  Short-term less than 1 year from US: 12
  Non-US serving in own/other country: 10
  Home ministry & office staff in US: 3

Countries: Italy 3

Avant Ministries
(See Ad on Page 89)
Formerly Gospel Missionary Union
10000 N. Oak Trafficway
Kansas City, MO 64155 USA

Phone: (816) 734-8500
Fax: (816) 734-4601
E-mail: info@avmi.org
Web Site: www.AvantMinistries.org

Dr. J. Paul Nyquist, President

An interdenominational sending agency of Evangelical tradition engaged in church planting, Christian education, evangelism and leadership development. Twenty-eight missionaries serving in North America with non-English-speaking groups included in home ministry total.

Purpose: "...to touch the unreached millions with the Gospel and to help many enter fields of service."

Year Founded in US: 1892

How

will those from oral cultures be discipled?

They do not read.

Literacy is not embraced by all cultures.

Yet literacy has long been considered the ideal tool for reaching the world with God's Word.

Listening is universal.

God's Word has been translated into thousands of languages. It is our obligation to make these Bibles accessible to those who will never read.

For the oral majority.

The Talking Bible®...

...a self-contained, sealed unit that looks like a Bible but "talks" like a cassette player.

...houses a single cassette tape which holds an entire New Testament in audio (about 25 hours of material).

...is easier to produce, distribute, and use than cassette players.

...costs less to produce than any other audio media.

www.audioscriptures.org

Audio Scriptures International
419 East Grand Avenue
Escondido, CA 92025
(760) 745-8105
asi@audioscriptures.org

Short-Cycle Solutions / for a Lost World

An Old Friend Has a New Name

Gospel Missionary Union Announces New Name and Focus

Gospel Missionary Union, the 112-year-old missionary-sending agency, has announced the renaming of the organization as part of a multi-year revitalization campaign. The new name, **Avant Ministries**, reflects the organization's forward-thinking approach to church planting, while allowing it freedom to operate in sensitive world settings. **Avant Ministries** is focusing its work on short-cycle church planting, reducing the time it takes to develop new churches for unreached peoples. Opportunities for new career missionary teams are opening up around the world.

Get Acquainted Again

Avant Ministries
10000 North Oak Trafficway
Kansas City, MO 64155
2121 Henderson Highway
Winnipeg MB R2G 1P8

www.AvantMinistries.org
info@avmi.org
800.468.1892

Income for Overseas Min: $8,200,000
Fully Supported US Personnel Overseas:
Expecting to serve more than 4 years: 244
Expecting to serve 1 to 4 years: 13
Nonresidential mission personnel: 4

Other personnel:
Short-term less than 1 year from US: 41
Home ministry & office staff in US: 63

Countries: Argentina 17; Austria 4; Bahamas, The 8; Belgium 4; Belize 6; Bolivia 32; Brazil 21; Cote d'Ivoire 2; Ecuador 52; France 8; Germany 4; Greece 5; Italy 12; Mali 17; Mexico 7; Panama 5; Russia 7; Spain 27; United Kingdom 6

Awana Clubs International
One E. Bode Rd.
Streamwood, IL 60107-6658 USA

Phone: (630) 213-2000
Fax: (630) 213-9704
E-mail: awana@awana.org
Web Site: www.awana.org
Rev. Jack D. Eggar, President/CEO

A specialized agency of Evangelical tradition providing Bible-based, Christ-centered weekly club programs and leadership training for local churches around the world. Awana manages 63,000 clubs serving 107 countries.

Purpose: "...partnering with churches and mission organizations to reach children and teens with the gospel of Jesus Christ and to train them for Christian service."

Year Founded in US: 1950

Income for Overseas Min: $5,000,000

Fully Supported US Personnel Overseas:
Nonresidential mission personnel: 10

Other personnel:
Short-term less than 1 year from US: 200
Non-US serving in own/other country: 250
Home ministry & office staff in US: 530

Back to the Bible Intl.
P.O. Box 82808
Lincoln, NE 68501 USA

Phone: (402) 464-7200
Fax: (402) 464-7474
E-mail: info@backtothebible.org
Web Site: www.backtothebible.org
Dr. Woodrow Kroll, President

A nondenominational service agency of Evangelical tradition engaged in broadcasting, support of national workers, literature production and literature distribution.

Purpose: "To lead believers into spiritual maturity and active service for Christ in the local church and the world. To reach unbelievers with the Gospel of Christ by teaching the Bible through media."

Year Founded in US: 1939

Income for Overseas Min: $986,243

Personnel:
Non-US serving in own/other country: 170
Home ministry & office staff in US: 78

Countries: Australia; Brazil; China; Ecuador; Egypt; India; Indonesia; Italy; Jamaica; Philippines; Poland; Russia; Sri Lanka; Turkmenistan; United Kingdom

Baptist Bible Fellowship Intl.
P.O. Box 191
Springfield, MO 65801 USA

Phone: (417) 862-5001
Fax: (417) 865-0794
E-mail: Bobbaird@bbfi-missionoffice.org
Web Site: www.bbfimissions.com
Dr. Bob Baird, Mission Director

An independent sending agency of Baptist tradition engaged in church planting, theological education, evangelism, support of national churches and missionary training.

Year Founded in US: 1950

Income for Overseas Min: $36,000,000

Fully Supported US Personnel Overseas:
Expecting to serve more than 4 years: 662
Expecting to serve 1 to 4 years: 157

Other personnel:
Home ministry & office staff in US: 21

Countries: Albania 2; Argentina 20; Australia 28; Austria; Azores 2; Bahamas, The; Belgium 9; Belize 6; Bolivia 4; Botswana 2; Brazil 33; Bulgaria 2; Burkina Faso 2; Cambodia 4; Chile 11; Colombia 4; Congo, Democratic Republic of the 6; Costa Rica 11; Cote d'Ivoire 2; Denmark 2; Dominican Republic 4; Ecuador 12; Ethiopia 6; France 6; French Polynesia 2; Germany 18; Greece 2; Haiti 1; Honduras 3; Hong Kong 4; Hungary 8; Iceland 1; Ireland 5; Jamaica 6; Japan 20; Kenya 31; Korea, South 15; Lithuania 4; Malta 2; Mexico 63; Netherlands 2; New Zealand 10; Nicaragua 2; Nigeria 4; Panama 8; Papua New Guinea 16; Paraguay 2; Peru 12; Philippines 41; Poland; Portugal 6; Puerto Rico 5; Romania 12; Singapore 6; South Africa 16; Spain 16; Sweden; Taiwan 10; Tanzania 13; Thailand 8; Trinidad and Tobago 2; Uganda 2; Ukraine 2; United Kingdom 36; Unspecified Country 46; Uruguay 2; Vanuatu 2; Venezuela 6; Zambia 12

Baptist Bible Translators Institute

P.O. Box 1450
Bowie, TX 76230 USA

Phone: (940) 872-5751
E-mail: bbti@morgan.net
Web Site: www.morgan.net/~bbti

Dr. Charles V. Turner, Exec. Director

A denominational service agency of independent Baptist tradition engaged in church planting, Bible distribution, missionary education, linguistics, literacy work, mobilization for mission and Bible translation.

Purpose: "...missionaries training missionaries to plant New Testament Baptist churches in every bibleless nation and translate the Scriptures into every bibleless language."

Year Founded in US: 1973
Income for Overseas Min: NA

Baptist General Conference

2002 S. Arlington Hts. Rd
Arlington Hts., IL 60005 USA

Phone: (847) 228-0200
Fax: (847) 228-5376
Web Site: www.bgcworld.net

Dr. Robert S. Ricker, President

A denominational sending agency of Baptist tradition engaged in church planting, development, theological education, evangelism and leadership development.

Purpose: "...helping member churches fulfill Christ's mission for His church in all communities God calls them to serve."

Year Founded in US: 1944
Income for Overseas Min: $8,572,110
Fully Supported US Personnel Overseas:
  Expecting to serve more than 4 years: 119
  Expecting to serve 1 to 4 years: 8
Other personnel:
  Short-term less than 1 year from US: 25
  Non-US serving in own/other country: 2
  Home ministry & office staff in US: 8

Countries: Argentina 8; Brazil 9; Bulgaria 1; Cameroon 7; Central Asia–General 4; Cote d'Ivoire 8; Estonia 2; Ethiopia 8; France 4; India 1; Japan 20; Mexico 10; Middle East 4; Philippines 24; Thailand 8; Uruguay 1; Vietnam

Baptist International Evangelistic Ministries

1337 North Eustis Dr.
Indianapolis, IN 46229 USA

Phone: (317) 899-9193
Fax: (317) 899-9194
E-mail: missions@baptistinternational.org
Web Site: www.baptistinternational.org

Dr. Sam Slobodian, President

A denominational sending agency of Baptist and Fundamental tradition engaged in church planting, Bible distribution, church construction, theological education, literature distribution and support of national workers.

Purpose: "...fulfilling the missionary mandate in Russia and Eastern Europe through the support, training and equipping of dedicated and prepared nationals."

Year Founded in US: 1981
Income for Overseas Min: $880,035
Gifts-in-Kind: $27,740
Fully Supported US Personnel Overseas:
  Expecting to serve more than 4 years: 3
  Nonresidential mission personnel: 2
Other personnel:
  Short-term less than 1 year from US: 102
  Non-US serving in own/other country: 93
  Home ministry & office staff in US: 4

Countries: Moldova; Romania; Russia 3; Ukraine

Baptist International Missions, Inc. (BIMI)

P.O. Box 9215
Chattanooga, TN 37412 USA

Phone: (423) 344-5050
Fax: (423) 344-4774

E-mail: info@bimi.org
Web Site: www.bimi.org

Dr. James Ray, President

An independent Baptist sending agency engaged in church planting, Bible distribution, broadcasting and evangelism. The mission services more than 8,000 independent Baptist churches in America and their missionaries serving in more than 90 countries. Financial statistics from 1998.

Year Founded in US: 1960
Income for Overseas Min: $26,400,000
Fully Supported US Personnel Overseas:
Expecting to serve more than 4 years: 1,040
Nonresidential mission personnel: 42

Other personnel:
Home ministry & office staff in US: 35
Countries: Unspecified Country 1,040

Baptist Intl. Outreach

P.O. Box 639
Maynardville, TN 37807 USA
Phone: (865) 992-0999
Fax: (865) 992-4999
E-mail: bio155@aol.com
Web Site: www.biomissions.org

Dr. William R. Vick, President/Director

A sending agency of independent Baptist and Fundamental tradition engaged in church planting, disability assistance programs, theological education, evangelism and providing medical supplies. Personnel information from 1998.

Year Founded in US: 1985
Income for Overseas Min: $1,800,000
Fully Supported US Personnel Overseas:
Expecting to serve more than 4 years: 31
Expecting to serve 1 to 4 years: 5

Other personnel:
Non-US serving in own/other country: 56
Home ministry & office staff in US: 6

Countries: Belarus 4; Botswana; Brazil 3; China 4; Costa Rica; Ethiopia; India; Kenya; Mexico; Nigeria; Peru 6; Philippines 2; South Africa 8; Uganda; Zambia 4

Baptist Medical & Dental Mission International

11 Plaza Dr.
Hattiesburg, MS 39402 USA

Phone: (601) 544-3586
Fax: (601) 544-6508
E-mail: info@bmdmi.org
Web Site: www.bmdmi.org

Mr. Dwight G. Carr, Exec. Director

A specialized agency of Baptist tradition engaged in medical work, childcare/orphanage programs, church construction, church planting, theological education and evangelism.

Purpose: "...to carry the message of salvation through the free grace of Jesus Christ."

Year Founded in US: 1974
Income for Overseas Min: $9,944,707
Gifts-in-Kind: $7,729,094

Fully Supported US Personnel Overseas:
Expecting to serve more than 4 years: 18
Other personnel:
Non-US serving in own/other country: 71
Home ministry & office staff in US: 7

Countries: Honduras 10; Latin America–General 4; Nicaragua 4

Baptist Mid-Missions

P.O. Box 308011
Cleveland, OH 44130 USA
Phone: (440) 826-3930
Fax: (440) 826-4457
E-mail: info@bmm.org
Web Site: www.bmm.org

Dr. Gary L. Anderson, President

A sending agency of independent Baptist and Fundamental tradition engaged in church planting, theological education, medical work, relief and/or rehabilitation, Bible translation and evangelism.

Year Founded in US: 1920
Income for Overseas Min: $19,000,000
Gifts-in-Kind: $200,000

Fully Supported US Personnel Overseas:
Expecting to serve more than 4 years: 495
Other personnel:
Short-term less than 1 year from US: 60
Non-US serving in own/other country: 17
Home ministry & office staff in US: 45
Bivocational/Tentmaker from US: 10

Countries: Argentina 3; Asia–General 7; Australia 18; Austria 4; Bangladesh; Belarus 2; Botswana 2; Brazil 149; Cambodia 4; Central African Republic 13; Chad 7; Chile 8; Cote d'Ivoire 21; Dominican Republic;

Ecuador 11; Ethiopia 5; Finland 2; France 24; Germany 19; Ghana 12; Guyana 2; Haiti 5; Honduras 8; India 8; Ireland 6; Italy 2; Jamaica; Japan 13; Liberia; Mexico 19; Micronesia, Federated States of 8; Netherlands 5; New Zealand 8; Peru 31; Puerto Rico 6; Romania 4; Russia 6; Saint Vincent and the Grenadines 4; Slovakia 4; Spain 6; Taiwan 2; Thailand 2; United Kingdom 18; Venezuela 11; Zambia 6

Baptist Missions to Forgotten Peoples

P.O. Box 37043
Jacksonville, FL 32236-7043 USA

Phone: (904) 783-4007
Fax: (904) 783-0402
E-mail: bmfp@compuserve.com
Web Site: www.bmfp.org

Dr. Gene Burge, President

A nondenominational sending agency of Baptist tradition engaged in church planting and evangelism.

Purpose: "...to serve the local church by providing a faith-missions ministry committed to strategic church planting...among the unevangelized people groups of the world."

Income for Overseas Min: NA

Fully Supported US Personnel Overseas:
   Expecting to serve more than 4 years: 125
Countries: Unspecified Country 125

Baptist World Mission

P.O. Box 2149
Decatur, AL 35602-2149 USA

Phone: (256) 353-2221
Fax: (256) 353-2266
E-mail: office@baptistworldmission.org
Web Site: www.baptistworldmission.org

Dr. Fred Moritz, Exec. Director

A sending agency of independent Baptist and fundamental tradition engaged in church planting and theological education.

Purpose: "...to furnish a channel for Bible-believing Baptist churches to carry out the Great Commission of our Lord through evangelism and the establishment of indigenous Baptist churches."

Year Founded in US: 1961
Income for Overseas Min: NR

Fully Supported US Personnel Overseas:
   Expecting to serve more than 4 years: 335
Other personnel:
   Home ministry & office staff in US: 15
Countries: Unspecified Country 335

Barnabas International

P.O. Box 11211
Rockford, IL 61126-1211 USA

Phone: (815) 395-1335
Fax: (815) 395-1385
E-mail: Barnabas@barnabas.org
Web Site: www.barnabas.org

Mr. Thomas L. Eckblad, Exec. Director

An interdenominational support agency of Evangelical tradition engaged in member care, leadership development, support of national churches, psychological counseling, services for other agencies and missionary training.

Purpose: "...to edify, enrich, encourage, and strengthen missionaries, pastors, national church leaders and their families... through personal, small group and conference ministries."

Year Founded in US: 1986

Income for Overseas Min: $860,860

Fully Supported US Personnel Overseas:
   Nonresidential mission personnel: 26
Other personnel:
   Home ministry & office staff in US: 1

BCM International

P.O. Box 249
Akron, PA 17501-0249 USA

Phone: (717) 859-6404
E-mail: info@bcmintl.org
Web Site: www.bcmintl.org

Dr. Robert T. Evans, President

A nondenominational sending agency of Evangelical tradition engaged in children's programs, camping programs, church planting, correspondence courses, evangelism and training. Income figure from 1998.

Purpose: "...dedicated to making disciples of all age groups for the Lord Jesus Christ through evangelism and diverse Bible Centered Ministries so that churches are established and the Church strengthened."

Year Founded in US: 1936

Income for Overseas Min: $4,900,000

Fully Supported US Personnel Overseas:
Expecting to serve more than 4 years: 39
Expecting to serve 1 to 4 years: 3

Other personnel:
Non-US serving in own/other country: 462
Home ministry & office staff in US: 55

Countries: Antigua; Austria 1; Belize 2; Bolivia; Brazil; Cuba 1; Dominican Republic; Egypt; Finland; France 2; Germany 3; Ghana; Greece; Guyana; Hungary; India; Ireland 5; Italy 6; Jamaica; Korea, South; Mexico; Myanmar/Burma; Nepal; Netherlands 1; Paraguay; Peru; Philippines; Poland 1; Portugal; Russia; Saint Vincent and the Grenadines; Spain 4; Sri Lanka; Suriname 2; Swaziland; Trinidad and Tobago; Ukraine 1; United Kingdom 9; Virgin Islands; Zimbabwe 1

Bethany Fellowship Missions

6820 Auto Club Rd., Suite D
Bloomington, MN 55438 USA

Phone: (952) 829-2492
Fax: (952) 829-2767
E-mail: bfm@bethfel.org
Web Site: www.bethfel.org

Mr. David Hicks, CEO

A nondenominational sending agency of Charismatic and Evangelical tradition engaged in missionary training, missionary education, theological education, evangelism and literature production.

Purpose: "...to witness, to train and send missionaries, to plant churches, to publish Christian literature, and to establish creative resource ventures for the expansion of Christ's Kingdom."

Year Founded in US: 1963

Income for Overseas Min: $1,981,292

Fully Supported US Personnel Overseas:
Expecting to serve more than 4 years: 82
Expecting to serve 1 to 4 years: 3

Other personnel:
Non-US serving in own/other country: 23
Home ministry & office staff in US: 15
Bivocational/Tentmaker from US: 2

Countries: Africa–General 1; Asia–General 11; Bolivia 4; Brazil 20; Cambodia 2; Central Asia–General 3; Croatia; Dominican Republic 2; France 7; Ghana 2; Hungary 2; Indonesia 3; Japan 2; Kenya 2; Kosovo 1; Mexico 12; Philippines 3; Slovenia 2; Spain 2; Thailand 1

Bethel Christian Ministries

1310 Mercer St., Ste. 100
Seattle, WA 98109-5576 USA

Phone: (206) 441-0444
Fax: (206) 441-5995
E-mail: bethelministry@w-link.net

Rev. Daniel W. Peterson, Senior Pastor

A nondenominational sending agency of Pentecostal and Charismatic tradition engaged in church planting, Bible distribution and evangelism. Statistical data from 1998.

Year Founded in US: 1914

Income for Overseas Min: $70,000

Fully Supported US Personnel Overseas:
Expecting to serve more than 4 years: 8
Expecting to serve 1 to 4 years: 2

Countries: Indonesia 2; Japan 4; Mexico 2

Bible League, The

P.O. Box 28000
Chicago, IL 60628 USA

Phone: (708) 367-8500
Fax: (708) 367-8600
E-mail: info@bibleleague.org
Web Site: www.bibleleague.org

Mr. Robert W. Cole, President

A nondenominational specialized agency of Evangelical tradition engaged in Bible distribution, church planting, evangelism, literacy work, support of national workers, Bible translation and training.

Purpose: "...provides Scriptures and training worldwide to bring people into fellowship with Christ and His Church."

Year Founded in US: 1938

Income for Overseas Min: $20,313,216

Gifts-in-Kind: $1,191,736

Personnel:
Non-US serving in own/other country: 588
Home ministry & office staff in US: 140

Countries: Albania; Armenia; Belarus; Bulgaria; Cambodia; Cameroon; Central Asia–General; Chad; China; Colombia; Dominican Republic; Ecuador; Ethiopia;

Ghana; Haiti; Hungary; India; Indonesia; Kenya; Macedonia; Malaysia; Mexico; Middle East; Moldova; Mozambique; Myanmar/Burma; Nepal; Nigeria; Philippines; Poland; Puerto Rico; Romania; Russia; Senegal; Serbia and Montenegro; South Africa; Sudan; Thailand; Uganda; Ukraine; Venezuela; Vietnam; Zimbabwe

Bible Literature Intl.

P.O. Box 477
Columbus, OH 43216-0477 USA

Phone: (614) 267-3116
Fax: (614) 267-7110
E-mail: bli@bli.org
Web Site: www.bli.org

Mr. James R. Falkenberg, Intl. President

An interdenominational specialized agency of Evangelical tradition engaged in literature distribution, Bible distribution, TEE and evangelism. Have assisted with literature in nearly every country in the world.

Purpose: "...to help individuals around the world find new life in Christ through God's Word..."

Year Founded in US: 1923

Income for Overseas Min: $2,666,847

Personnel:
   Home ministry & office staff in US: 23

Bible Missionary Church

P.O. Box 2030
Homedale, ID 83628 USA

Phone: (208) 337-3873
Fax: (208) 337-3860
E-mail: dbowman@bmcmail.com

Rev. Don Bowman, Gen. Foreign Msns. Secty.

A denominational sending agency of Wesleyan tradition engaged in church planting, theological education, furloughed missionary support, support of national churches and support of national workers. Personnel information from 1996.

Year Founded in US: 1956

Income for Overseas Min: $550,000

Fully Supported US Personnel Overseas:
   Expecting to serve more than 4 years: 32

Other personnel:
   Home ministry & office staff in US: 4

Countries: Germany 2; Ghana 2; Guyana 4; Japan 2; Mexico 2; Nigeria 2; Papua New Guinea 8; Peru 2; Philippines 2; Russia 4; Venezuela 2

Bible Training Centre for Pastors

2030 Tucker Industrial Rd.
Tucker, GA 30084 USA

Phone: (770) 938-6160
Fax: (770) 938-5884
E-mail: info@btcp.com
Web Site: www.bibletraining.com

Dr. Dennis Mock, President

Rev. Jeff Barber, Executive Director

A transdenominational training agency of Evangelical tradition engaged in training national pastors, church leaders, missionaries, evangelists and teachers in more than 25 languages.

Purpose: "To glorify God by providing a biblical concept and curriculum for equipping pastors and leaders for local church ministry who will not likely be trained otherwise. This curriculum is available in 75 countries."

Year Founded in US: 1990

Income for Overseas Min: $1,800,000.00

Fully Supported US Personnel Overseas:
   Expecting to serve more than 4 years: 6
   Nonresidential mission personnel: 8

Other personnel:
   Non-US serving in own/other country: 32
   Home ministry and office staff in US: 7

Bibles For The World, Inc.

P.O. Box 470
Colorado Springs, CO 80901 USA

Phone: (719) 630-7733
Fax: (719) 630-1449
Web Site: www.biblesfortheworld.org

Dr. Rochunga Pudaite, President

A nondenominational support agency of Evangelical tradition engaged in Bible distribution, Christian education, theological education, support of national churches and support of national workers.

Year Founded in US: 1972

Income for Overseas Min: $690,457

Gifts-in-Kind: $564,295

Personnel:
Short-term less than 1 year from US: 30
Non-US serving in own/other country: 400
Home ministry & office staff in US: 15
Countries: India

Biblical Literature Fellowship
(See Ad on page 97)
P.O. Box 629
Wheaton, IL 60189-0629 USA
Phone: (630) 858-0348
Fax: (630) 858-1946
E-mail: BLF@blfusa.org
Web Site: www.blfusa.org
Mr. Harry R. Enns, Exec. Director

A nondenominational specialized agency of Evangelical tradition engaged in literature production, Bible distribution, literature distribution and short-term programs.

Purpose: "...publishing and distributing quality Christian literature for evangelism, church planting and Christian growth."
Year Founded in US: 1958
Income for Overseas Min: $646,438
Fully Supported US Personnel Overseas:
Expecting to serve more than 4 years: 6
Non-residential mission personnel: 9
Other Personnel:
Home ministry and office staff in US: 6
Countries: Belgium 6

Biblical Ministries Worldwide
1595 Herrington Rd.
Lawrenceville, GA 30043-5616 USA
Phone: (770) 339-3500
Fax: (770) 513-1254
E-mail: bmwhq@biblicalministries.org
Web Site: www.biblicalministries.org
Rev. Paul G. Seger, Gen. Director

A nondenominational sending agency of Independent and Baptist tradition engaged in church planting, theological education, and evangelism. Personnel information from 1998.

Purpose: "...to evangelize and develop leaders who will reproduce themselves and the churches we serve."
Year Founded in US: 1948
Income for Overseas Min: $6,107,530
Gifts-in-Kind: $100,000

Fully Supported US Personnel Overseas:
Expecting to serve more than 4 years: 125
Nonresidential mission personnel: 4
Other personnel:
Short-term less than 1 year from US: 22
Bivocational/tentmaker from US: 8
Non-US serving in own/other country: 26
Home ministry & office staff in US: 20

Countries: Argentina 3; Australia 2; Austria 2; Cyprus 4; Fiji 4; France 2; Germany 7; Guam 4; Honduras 4; Hong Kong 5; Ireland 5; Italy 8; Japan 2; Luxembourg 2; Mexico 11; Netherlands 2; New Zealand 11; Puerto Rico 2; South Africa 9; Spain 5; Suriname; United Kingdom 19; Uruguay 12

BILD International
P.O. Box 1507
Ames, IA 50014-1507 USA
Phone: (515) 292-7012
Fax: (515) 292-1933
E-mail: bild@bild.org
Web Site: www.bild.org
Mr. Jeff Reed, CEO

A transdenominational support agency of Evangelical tradition engaged in church planting, leadership development, literature production, support of national workers and training. Statistical data from 1998.
Year Founded in US: 1986
Income for Overseas Min: $1,450,000
Personnel:
Non-US serving in own/other country: 5
Home ministry & office staff in US: 4
Countries: Guatemala; India; Nigeria

Billy Graham Center, The
500 College Ave.
Wheaton, IL 60187 USA
Phone: (630) 752-5157
Fax: (630) 752-5916
E-mail: BGCadm@wheaton.edu
Web Site: www.billygrahamcenter.org
Dr. Lon Allison, Director

Stimulating global evangelism, a transdenominational service agency of Evangelical tradition engaged in training, evangelism, missions information service, leadership development and mission-related research.

*R*eaching the *F*rench world for *C*hrist

Purpose: "...to develop strategies and skills for evangelism through leadership training, research, networking, strategic planning and communicating the gospel."

Year Founded in US: 1975

Income for Overseas Min: NA

Personnel:
   Home ministry & office staff in US: 30

Blessings International
5881 S. Garnett St.
Tulsa, OK 74146 USA

Phone: (918) 250-8101
Fax: (918) 250-1281
E-mail: info@blessing.org
Web Site: www.blessing.org

Dr. Harold C. Harder, President

Partnering with local churches, Blessings International serves as a resource of pharmaceuticals, vitamins and medical supplies for short-term medical mission teams and disaster relief outreaches.

Year Founded in US: 1981

Income for Overseas Min: $16,443,449

Gifts-in-Kind: $15,541,795

Personnel:
   Home ministry & office staff in US: 4

Brazil Gospel Fellowship Mission
125 W. Ash St.
Springfield, IL 62704 USA

Phone: (217) 523-7176
Fax: (217) 523-7186
E-mail: bgfm@earthlink.net

Rev. Larry Lipka, Exec. Director

A sending agency of Fundamental and Independent tradition engaged in church planting, broadcasting, camping programs, Christian education, theological education and evangelism.

Year Founded in US: 1939

Income for Overseas Min: $900,000

Fully Supported US Personnel Overseas:
   Expecting to serve more than 4 years: 51

Other personnel:
   Home ministry & office staff in US: 4

Countries: Brazil 51

Bread for the World
50 F St. NW #500
Washington, DC 20001-1530 USA

Phone: (202) 639-9400
Fax: (202) 639-9401
E-mail: bread@bread.org
Web Site: www.bread.org

Rev. David Beckmann, President

An interdenominational Christian citizens movement of many traditions helping citizens be active in public-policy issues important to the reduction of hunger.

Purpose: "...seeking justice for the world's hungry people by lobbying our nation's decision makers."

Year Founded in US: 1974

Income for Overseas Min: NA

Personnel:
   Home ministry & office staff in US: 58

Brethren Assemblies
(No central office)

The Brethren Assemblies are also known as "Christian Brethren" or "Plymouth Brethren." Missionaries are sent from each local assembly (church) and not through a central agency. Personnel totals are from the Christian Mission in Many Lands service agency. Statistical data from 1998.

Income for Overseas Min: NA

Fully Supported US Personnel Overseas:
   Expecting to serve more than 4 years: 346
   Expecting to serve 1 to 4 years: 24
   Nonresidential mission personnel: 7

Other personnel:
   Bivocational/Tentmaker from US: 2

Countries: Albania 6; Argentina 8; Austria 6; Bolivia 17; Brazil 7; Burundi 4; Caribbean–General 3; Chad; Chile 1; Colombia 19; Congo, Democratic Republic of the 8; Dominican Republic 2; Ecuador 14; El Salvador 6; France 15; French Guiana 2; Germany 3; Greece 3; Guatemala 4; Honduras 10; Hong Kong 2; Hungary 1; India 7; Indonesia 3; Ireland 9; Italy 5; Japan 7; Kenya 1; Korea, South 1; Mexico 36; Mozambique; Netherlands 2; Nigeria 6; Papua New Guinea 5; Paraguay 12; Peru 16; Philippines 12; Poland; Portugal 4; Puerto Rico 1; Romania 5; Russia 7; Senegal 3; South Africa 9; Spain 9; Taiwan 2; Tanzania 2; Uganda 2; Unspecified Country 17; Uruguay 1; Venezuela 1; Zambia 19; Zimbabwe 1

Brethren Church Missionary Board

524 College Ave.
Ashland, OH 44805 USA
Phone: (419) 289-1708
Fax: (419) 281-0450
E-mail: Brethren@brethrenchurch.org
Web Site: www.brethrenchurch.org
Kenneth Hunn, Exec. Director

A denominational sending agency of Brethren tradition engaged in evangelism, childcare/orphanage programs, church planting, leadership development, medical work and support of national workers. Overseas personnel data from 1996.

Year Founded in US: 1892

Income for Overseas Min: $636,752

Fully Supported US Personnel Overseas:
  Expecting to serve more than 4 years: 3
Other personnel:
  Home ministry & office staff in US: 4
Countries: Argentina 1; Mexico 2

Brethren in Christ World Missions

P.O. Box 390
Grantham, PA 17027-0390 USA
Phone: (717) 697-2634
Fax: (717) 691-6053
E-mail: bicwm@messiah.edu
Web Site: www.bic-church.org/wm
Rev. John A. Brubaker, Exec. Director

A denominational sending agency of Wesleyan and Mennonite tradition engaged in church planting, TEE, evangelism, leadership development and support of national churches.

Purpose: "A church for every people... the Gospel to every person... Jesus worshipped in the nations."

Year Founded in US: 1895

Income for Overseas Min: $1,117,069

Fully Supported US Personnel Overseas:
  Expecting to serve more than 4 years: 22
  Expecting to serve 1 to 4 years: 14
Other personnel:

Non-US serving in own/other country: 93
Home ministry & office staff in US: 9
Countries: Colombia 4; Honduras 2; India; Malawi 3; Mexico 2; Nepal; Nicaragua; South Africa; Spain 2; United Kingdom 2; Venezuela; Zambia 3; Zimbabwe 4

Bridge Builders International

P.O. Box 625
Philomath, OR 97370 USA
Phone: (541) 929-5627
Fax: (541) 929-5628
E-mail: kelleybbi@aol.com
Web Site: www.bridgebuildersint.com
Mr. Charles D. Kelley, President

A transdenominational mobilization agency of Evangelical tradition specializing in facilitating international partnerships for ministry and mission training.

Purpose: "...builds partnerships for effective ministry, mission, development and assistance [and] cultivates relationships that lead to strategic partnerships..."

Year Founded in US: 1994

Income for Overseas Min: $405,900

Fully Supported US Personnel Overseas:
  Expecting to serve more than 4 years: 7
  Expecting to serve 1 to 4 years: 1
  Nonresidential mission personnel: 2
Other personnel:
  Short-term less than 1 year from US: 75
  Non-US serving in own/other country: 10
  Home ministry & office staff in US: 7
Countries: Latvia 7

Bright Hope International

2060 Stonington Ave.
Hoffman Estates, IL 60195 USA
Phone: (847) 519-0012
Fax: (847) 519-0024
E-mail: info@brighthope.org
Web Site: www.brighthope.org
Mr. Craig H. Dyer, President

A nondenominational service agency of Evangelical tradition engaged in relief and/or rehabilitation, church planting and development.

Year Founded in US: 1968

Income for Overseas Min: $1,020,209

Personnel:
   Non-US serving in own/other country: 187
   Home ministry & office staff in US: 7

Countries: Cuba; India; Kenya; Mozambique; Peru; Zambia

Cadence International

P.O. Box 1268
Englewood, CO 80150 USA

Phone: (303) 762-1400
Fax: (303) 788-0661
E-mail: hdqtrs@cadence.org
Web Site: www.cadence.org

Mr. David Schroeder, Gen. Director

A nondenominational service agency of Evangelical tradition engaged in evangelism and youth programs to U.S. and foreign military communities.

Year Founded in US: 1954

Income for Overseas Min: $2,627,634

Gifts-in-Kind: $4,245

Fully Supported US Personnel Overseas:
   Expecting to serve 1 to 4 years: 91

Other personnel:
   Non-US serving in own/other country: 91
   Home ministry & office staff in US: 26

Countries: Germany; Italy; Japan; Korea, South; Philippines; Russia; Spain; United Kingdom

Caleb Project

#10 W. Dry Creek Circle
Littleton, CO 80120-4413 USA

Phone: (303) 730-4170
Fax: (303) 730-4177
E-mail: info@cproject.com
Web Site: www.calebproject.org

Mr. Gregory E. Fritz, President

An interdenominational service agency of Evangelical tradition engaged in mobilization for mission, Christian education, mission-related research, services for other agencies, short-term programs and missionary training.

Purpose: "...serves churches, mission agencies and campus ministries throughout the United States by educating, assisting and challenging them to complete their part in the goal of evangelizing the people groups of the world."

Year Founded in US: 1980

Income for Overseas Min: $200,000

Fully Supported US Personnel Overseas:
   Expecting to serve more than 4 years: 10
   Expecting to serve 1 to 4 years: 3

Other personnel:
   Short-term less than 1 year from US: 20
   Home ministry & office staff in US: 40

Countries: Asia–General 6; Europe–General 4

Calvary Commission, Inc.

P.O. Box 100
Lindale, TX 75771 USA

Phone: (903) 882-5501
Fax: (903) 882-7282
E-mail: missions@calvarycommission.org
Web Site: www.calvarycommission.org

Rev. Joe L. Fauss, Intl. Director

A transdenominational sending agency of Charismatic and Evangelical tradition engaged in missionary training, childcare/orphanage programs, missionary education, evangelism, support of national workers and short-term programs.

Year Founded in US: 1977

Income for Overseas Min: $150,000

Gifts-in-Kind: $125,000

Fully Supported US Personnel Overseas:
   Expecting to serve more than 4 years: 18
   Expecting to serve 1 to 4 years: 7

Other personnel:
   Short-term less than 1 year from US: 25
   Home ministry & office staff in US: 45
   Bivocational/Tentmaker from US: 3

Countries: Belize 6; Mexico 10; Romania 2

Calvary Evangelistic Mission, Inc.

P.O. Box 367000
San Juan, PR 00936-7000 USA

Phone: (787) 724-2727
Fax: (787) 723-9633
E-mail: admin@cem-wbmj.org

Mrs. Ruth Luttrell, Co-Founder/President

An interdenominational specialized agency of Evangelical tradition engaged in broadcasting, Bible distribution, correspondence courses, evangelism, literature distribution and services for other agencies.

Purpose: "...serves primarily in the West Indies, winning, challenging, training and motivating people to work for Jesus..."

Year Founded in US: 1953

Income for Overseas Min: $1,084,588

Gifts-in-Kind: $95,569

Fully Supported US Personnel Overseas:
Expecting to serve more than 4 years: 6
Expecting to serve 1 to 4 years: 8

Other personnel:
Non-US serving in own/other country: 1

Countries: Caribbean–General 6

Calvary International

P.O. Box 10305
Jacksonville, FL 32247-0305 USA

Phone: (904) 398-6559
Fax: (904) 398-6840
E-mail: calvary@gotonations.com
Web Site: www.gotonations.com

Mr. Jerry L. Williamson, President

An interdenominational sending agency of Charismatic tradition engaged in missionary training, church planting, evangelism, leadership development, medical work and mobilization for mission.

Purpose: "...to strategically reach the unreached peoples of the world through an international missionary force to help bring closure to the Great Commission."

Year Founded in US: 1981

Income for Overseas Min: $2,783,634

Fully Supported US Personnel Overseas:
Expecting to serve more than 4 years: 66
Nonresidential mission personnel: 22

Other personnel:
Non-US serving in own/other country: 68
Home ministry & office staff in US: 14
Bivocational/Tentmaker from US: 33

Countries: Africa–General 4; Asia–General 1; China 2; Colombia 1; Costa Rica 4; Guatemala 11; Italy 1; Jamaica 1; Japan 1; Jordan 1; Latin America–General 4; Latvia 2; Mexico 4; Nepal 1; Peru 1; Philippines 10; Russia 5; South Africa 1; Switzerland 1; Ukraine 1; United Kingdom 2; Unspecified Country 5; Venezuela 1; Vietnam 1

CAM International

8625 La Prada Dr.
Dallas, TX 75228 USA

Phone: (214) 327-8206
Fax: (214) 327-8201
E-mail: CAM@caminternational.org
Web Site: www.caminternational.org

Mr. Daniel Wicher, President

A nondenominational sending agency of Evangelical tradition engaged in church planting, broadcasting, camping programs, theological education, evangelism, leadership development, mobilization for mission, short-term programs and Bible translation.

Purpose: "...to produce and empower committed followers of Jesus Christ in Spanish speaking areas to reach the world."

Year Founded in US: 1890

Income for Overseas Min: $6,260,000

Fully Supported US Personnel Overseas:
Expecting to serve more than 4 years: 191
Expecting to serve 1 to 4 years: 19

Other personnel:
Short-term less than 1 year from US: 35
Non-US serving in own/other country: 187
Home ministry & office staff in US: 18

Countries: Albania 2; Costa Rica 13; El Salvador 8; Guatemala 68; Honduras 16; Mexico 60; Nicaragua 6; Panama 8; Spain 10

Campus Crusade for Christ, International

100 Lake Hart Drive
Orlando, FL 32832-0100 USA

Phone: (407) 826-2000
Fax: (407) 826-2851
E-mail: postmaster@ccci.org
Web Site: www.ccci.org

Dr. Steven Douglass, President

An interdenominational sending agency of Evangelical tradition engaged in evangelism, Christian education, support of national workers and training. As of December 31, 2001, CCI had 24,823 staff members and 553,700 trained volunteers ministering in 191 countries and protectorates.

Year Founded in US: 1951

Income for Overseas Min:$123,279,000

Fully Supported US Personnel Overseas:
Expecting to serve more than 4 years: 608

Expecting to serve 1 to 4 years: 488
Other personnel:
Short-term less than 1 year from US: 4,004
Non-US serving in own/other country:
14,134
Home ministry & office staff in US: 6,738
Countries: Africa–General 16; Albania 10;
Angola; Argentina 4; Asia–General 131;
Australia 4; Austria 1; Bangladesh; Belarus
7; Benin; Bolivia; Botswana; Brazil 5; Bul-
garia 11; Burkina Faso 2; Burundi; Cambo-
dia; Cameroon; Central African Republic;
Chad; Chile; Colombia; Congo, Democratic
Republic of the; Congo, Republic of the;
Costa Rica; Cote d'Ivoire; Croatia 10; Czech
Republic 12; Dominican Republic; Ecuador;
Egypt 3; El Salvador; Estonia 4; Ethiopia;
Europe–General; Fiji; France 32; Gabon;
Germany 23; Ghana; Greece 5; Guatemala
2; Guinea; Guyana; Haiti; Honduras; Hong
Kong; Hungary 58; India 2; Indonesia 2;
Italy 3; Jamaica; Japan 15; Kenya 21; Korea,
South; Latvia 7; Lebanon; Lesotho 2;
Liberia; Lithuania 11; Macau; Macedonia;
Madagascar; Malawi 2; Malaysia 2; Mali;
Mexico 5; Micronesia, Federated States of;
Moldova; Mozambique; Myanmar/Burma;
Nepal; Netherlands; New Zealand 6; Nica-
ragua; Niger; Nigeria 5; Pakistan; Panama
2; Papua New Guinea; Paraguay; Peru; Phil-
ippines 19; Poland 3; Portugal; Romania
15; Russia 45; Rwanda; Senegal 1; Sierra
Leone; Singapore 18; Slovakia 10; Slovenia
4; Solomon Islands; South Africa 4; Spain
10; Sri Lanka; Suriname; Swaziland; Taiwan;
Tanzania; Thailand 6; Togo; Tonga; Trinidad
and Tobago; Uganda; Ukraine 14; United
Kingdom 20; Uruguay; Venezuela; Yugoslavia; Zambia; Zimbabwe 14

Caring Partners Intl. Inc.

P.O. Box 44707
Middletown, OH 45044-0707 USA
Phone: (513) 727-1400
Fax: (513) 727-1401
E-mail: Roy@caringpartners.com
Web Site: www.caringpartners.com
Mr. Roy W. Cline, President & CEO

A transdenominational specialized agency
of Evangelical tradition engaged in short-
term programs, evangelism, providing
medical supplies, medical work, support of

national churches.
Purpose: "...to open the minds & hearts of
people around the world to the Gospel of
Jesus Christ while serving their health needs
with treatment, training and materials."
Year Founded in US: 1975
Income for Overseas Min: $276,000
Gifts-in-Kind: $100,000
Personnel:
Short-term less than 1 year from US: 35
Home ministry & office staff in US: 6
Countries: China; Cuba; Ecuador; Guate-
mala; India; Kenya; Nicaragua

Carpenter's Tools Intl.

P.O. Box 100
Willmar, MN 56201-0100 USA
Phone: (320) 235-0155
Fax: (320) 235-0185
E-mail: ctiinfo@ctimusic.org
Web Site: www.ctimusic.org
Mr. David Lien, President

An interdenominational support agency of
Evangelical and Ecumenical tradition en-
gaged in evangelism, leadership develop-
ment, youth programs, audio recording/
distribution in developing and other coun-
tries. An associate ministry of Youth for
Christ International.
Year Founded in US: 1988
Income for Overseas Min: $590,215
Personnel:
Home ministry & office staff in US: 10

Carver Intl. Missions, Inc.

Morris Brown Sta., Box 92091
Atlanta, GA 30314 USA
Phone: (770) 484-0610
Fax: (770) 484-0615
E-mail: carverfm@aol.com
Rev. Glenn Mason, Director

A nondenominational missionary agency of
Baptist and Evangelical tradition specializing in training and deploying national disciples to biblically analyze, attack and
resolve issues in their homes, communities,
churches and workplaces. Statistical data
from 1998.
Year Founded in US: 1955

Income for Overseas Min: $150,000

Fully Supported US Personnel Overseas:
Nonresidential mission personnel: 4

Other personnel:
Home ministry & office staff in US: 2

CBInternational

Other Name: Conservative Baptist Foreign
Mission Society (CBFMS)

1501 W. Mineral Ave.
Littleton, CO 80120-5612 USA

Phone: (720) 283-2000
Fax: (720) 283-9383
E-mail: cbi@cbi.org
Web Site: www.cbi.org

Dr. Hans Finzel, Exec. Director

A denominational sending agency of Baptist tradition engaged in church planting, development, TEE, theological education, evangelism, leadership development, literature distribution and medical work.

Purpose: "In vital partnership with churches at home and abroad… [to] be a pioneering force in fulfilling Christ's commission."

Year Founded in US: 1943

Income for Overseas Min: $19,155,068

Fully Supported US Personnel Overseas:
Expecting to serve more than 4 years: 490
Expecting to serve 1 to 4 years: 68
Nonresidential mission personnel: 2

Other personnel:
Short-term less than 1 year from US: 52
Home ministry & office staff in US: 76
Bivocational/Tentmaker from US: 4

Countries: Africa–General 20; Albania 2; Argentina 15; Asia–General 22; Austria 22; Belgium 6; Brazil 22; Central African Republic; Central Asia–General 6; Congo, Democratic Republic of the 2; Cote d'Ivoire 47; Czech Republic 3; Europe–General 2; France 14; Germany 2; Guinea 4; Hong Kong 6; Hungary 6; India 7; Indonesia 8; Ireland 4; Italy 10; Japan 22; Jordan 6; Kenya 11; Korea, South 2; Latin America–General 2; Lebanon 2; Lithuania 2; Macau 9; Madagascar 6; Mali 2; Mongolia 1; Mozambique 2; Netherlands 2; Pakistan 9; Philippines 34; Poland 13; Portugal 4; Romania 8; Russia 10; Rwanda 4; Senegal 12; Singapore 4; Slovenia 4; Spain 10; Sudan;

Taiwan 16; Uganda 19; Ukraine 11; United Kingdom 6; Unspecified Country 16; Uruguay 2; Venezuela 9; Zambia

Cedar Lane Missionary Homes

103 Cedar Lane
Laurel Springs, NJ 08021 USA

Phone: (856) 783-6525
Fax: (856) 783-8538
E-mail: Cedarlane@juno.com
Web Site: www.furloughhomes.org

Rev. James Callahan, Director

A nondenominational support agency of Evangelical tradition engaged in support of missionaries on home assignment.

Purpose: "…providing restful homes and otherwise assisting missionaries on furlough."

Year Founded in US: 1949

Income for Overseas Min: NA

Personnel:
Home ministry & office staff in US: 3

CEIFA Ministries International

729 Albers Lane
Bethalto, IL 62010-1120 USA

Phone: (618) 377-0579
E-mail: CEIFA@aol.com

Rev. David W. Runyan, President

An interdenominational service agency of Evangelical tradition engaged in literature distribution, childcare/orphanage programs, TEE, evangelism, leadership development and literature production. Statistical data from 1998.

Purpose: "To proclaim and demonstrate, through word and deed, the gospel of Jesus Christ in neglected world areas in cooperation with the Church."

Year Founded in US: 1991

Income for Overseas Min: $120,000

Gifts-in-Kind: $50,000

Fully Supported US Personnel Overseas:
Nonresidential mission personnel: 3

Other personnel:
Home ministry & office staff in US: 3
Bivocational/Tentmaker from US: 3

Celebrant Singers
P.O. Box 1416
Visalia, CA 93279 USA
Phone: (559) 740-4000
Fax: (559) 740-4040
E-mail: celebrants@celebrants.org
Web Site: www.celebrantsingers.org
Mr. Jon F. Stemkoski, President

An interdenominational service agency of Charismatic and Evangelical tradition engaged in music ministry evangelism, audio recording/distribution and broadcasting.

Purpose: "Teaching young adults by proclaiming His greatness and sharing His love with a hurting world through music, testimony, the preaching of the Word and our lives."

Year Founded in US: 1977
Income for Overseas Min: $1,200,000
Fully Supported US Personnel Overseas:
  Nonresidential mission personnel: 44

Other personnel:
  Short-term less than 1 year from US: 125
  Home ministry & office staff in US: 22

Centers for Apologetics Research (CFAR)
P.O. Box 1196
San Juan Capistrano, CA 92693 USA
Phone: (949) 496-2000
Fax: (949) 496-2244
E-mail: Thecenters@aol.com
Web Site: www.thecenters.org
Mr. Paul Carden, Exec. Director

A nondenominational service agency of Evangelical tradition engaged in countercult outreach, theological education, evangelism, literature production and mission-related research.

Year Founded in US: 1998
Income for Overseas Min: $69,486
Fully Supported US Personnel Overseas:
  Expecting to serve 1 to 4 years: 2

Other personnel:
  Non-US serving in own/other country: 11
  Home ministry & office staff in US: 2

Countries: Brazil; Hungary; Latin America–General; Russia; Ukraine

Central Missionary Fellowship
See: Seed International

Central Yearly Meeting of Friends Missions
P.O. Box 542
Westfield, IN 46074 USA
Phone: (317) 896-5082
Rev. Joseph A. Enyart, President

A denominational sending agency of Friends tradition engaged in church planting, Bible distribution and evangelism. Statistical data from 1996.

Year Founded in US: 1925
Income for Overseas Min: $28,899
Fully Supported US Personnel Overseas:
  Expecting to serve more than 4 years: 5
  Expecting to serve 1 to 4 years: 2
Countries: Bolivia 5

Child Evangelism Fellowship, Inc.
P.O. Box 348
Warrenton, MO 63383 USA
Phone: (636) 456-4321
Fax: (636) 456-4321
E-mail: webmaster@cefonline.com
Web Site: www.cefonline.com
Mr. Reese R. Kauffman, President

A nondenominational sending agency engaged in evangelism, correspondence courses, extension education, literature distribution, literature production and support of national workers.

Purpose: "...to evangelize boys and girls...and establish them in the Word of God and the local church..."

Year Founded in US: 1937
Income for Overseas Min: $4,460,518
Fully Supported US Personnel Overseas:
  Expecting to serve more than 4 years: 69
  Expecting to serve 1 to 4 years: 3
  Nonresidential mission personnel: 10

Other personnel:
  Non-US serving in own/other country: 196
  Home ministry & office staff in US: 450
  Bivocational/Tentmaker from US: 5

Countries: Albania 1; Angola; Argentina 1; Armenia 2; Australia 2; Austria 1; Belgium

2; Belize 2; Benin; Bolivia; Botswana 1; Brazil; Burkina Faso; Burundi; Cameroon; Chad; Chile; Colombia; Congo, Democratic Republic of; Cote d'Ivoire; Croatia 2; Cuba; Cyprus 7; Denmark 2; Ecuador; El Salvador; Estonia; Fiji 3; France 2; Gambia, The 2; Germany 4; Ghana; Greece 2; Guatemala; Guinea; Haiti 2; Hong Kong 1; Hungary 1; Israel 2; Japan; Jordan; Kenya 5; Liberia; Macau; Madagascar; Malawi; Mali; Mexico 1; Micronesia, Federated States of 2; Moldova 1; Mozambique; Namibia 3; Nepal; Netherlands Antilles 2; Niger; Nigeria; Pakistan; Peru; Philippines; Poland; Russia; Serbia and Montenegro 2; Singapore; Slovakia; Slovenia; South Africa 3; Suriname; Switzerland 6; Taiwan 2; Thailand; Togo; Uganda; Ukraine; Zambia; Zimbabwe

Childcare International
715 W. Orchard Dr., #7
Bellingham, WA 98225 USA
Phone: (360) 647-2283
Fax: (360) 647-2392
E-mail: gmlange@childcare-intl.org
Web Site: www.childcare-intl.org
Dr. G. Max Lange, President
A nondenominational service agency of Evangelical tradition engaged in childcare/orphanage programs, church planting, children's programs, medical work and relief and/or rehabilitation.
Year Founded in US: 1981
Income for Overseas Min: $12,333,763
Gifts-in-Kind: $10,657,870
Personnel:
Non-US serving in own/other country: 152
Home ministry & office staff in US: 13
Countries: Belarus; Haiti; India; Kenya; Mexico; Peru; Philippines; Sri Lanka; Thailand; Uganda

Children's Cross Connection USA
1328 Peachtree St. N.E.
Atlanta, GA 30309 USA
Phone: (404) 228-7770
Fax: (404) 228-7759
E-mail: REB@childspringintl.org
Web Site: www.childspringintl.org

Mrs. Rose Emily Bermudez, Exec. Director
An interdenominational support agency engaged in providing medical supplies and medical work.
Purpose: "...brings children to the United States for medical care not available in their own countries and returns them home with opportunities for a better life."
Year Founded in US: 2001
Income for Overseas Min: NA
Personnel:
Home ministry & office staff in US: 2
Bivocational/Tentmaker from US: 1

Children's Haven Intl.
400 E. Minnesota Rd.
Pharr, TX 78577 USA
Phone: (956) 787-7378
Fax: (956) 783-4637
E-mail: chii@prodigy.net
Mr. Fred Varner, Chairman
A nondenominational service agency of Mennonite tradition engaged in childcare/orphanage programs, services for other agencies and short-term programs.
Year Founded in US: 1972
Income for Overseas Min: NA
Fully Supported US Personnel Overseas:
Expecting to serve more than 4 years: 2
Nonresidential mission personnel: 12
Other personnel:
Short-term less than 1 year from US: 4
Countries: Mexico 2

Children's Medical Ministries
P.O. Box 3382
Crofton, MD 21114 USA
Phone: (301) 261-3211
Fax: (888) 410-4647
E-mail: childmed@olg.com
Web Site: www.childmed.org
Mr. Bill K. Collins, Co-Founder/CEO
An all volunteer nondenominational support agency engaged in medical and dental missions, child evangelism programs, literature distribution, relief aid, wheelchair and crutches distribution and exchanging of medical technology and information with foreign national and missionary counterparts in 30 countries.

Year Founded in US: 1988

Income for Overseas Min: $7,000,000

Gifts-in-Kind: $7,000,000

Personnel:
  Short-term less than 1 year from US: 300

China Connection

458 S. Pasadena Ave.
Pasadena, CA 91105 USA

Phone: (626) 793-3737
Fax: (626) 793-3362
E-mail: chinaconnection@juno.com
Web Site: www.chinaconnection.org

Ms. Kathy Call, Exec. Director

A nondenominational support agency of Evangelical tradition engaged in missions information service, agricultural programs, Bible distribution, church construction, childcare/orphanage programs and medical work.

Year Founded in US: 1989

Income for Overseas Min: $340,871

Gifts-in-Kind: $65,834

Personnel:
  Home ministry & office staff in US: 1

China Ministries International

P.O. Box 40489
Pasadena, CA 91104 USA

Phone: (626) 398-2343
Fax: (626) 398-2361
E-mail: cmius@compuserve.com
Web Site: www.cmi.org.tw

Dr. Jonathan Chao, Founder/President

A nondenominational support agency of Evangelical tradition engaged in theological education, extension education, Bible distribution, TEE, evangelism, mission-related research and missionary training.

Purpose: "...for the evangelization of China, the strengthening of the Chinese Church...by engaging in ministries of research, training of workers and sending them to the harvest field..."

Year Founded in US: 1987

Income for Overseas Min: $76,785

Personnel:
  Home ministry & office staff in US: 6

China Outreach Ministries

P.O. Box 310
Fairfax, VA 22030 USA

Phone: (703) 273-3500
Fax: (703) 273-3500
E-mail: chinaout@aol.com
Web Site: www.chinaoutreach.org

Rev. Glen Osborn, President

A nondenominational support agency of Presbyterian and Wesleyan tradition engaged in training, discipleship and literature distribution, primarily among Chinese intellectuals on U.S. university campuses.

Purpose: "...focuses on giving Christ to China's future leaders by...showing them the love of Christ...leading them to faith in Christ...discipling, training and mentoring them and equipping them to minister creatively to other Chinese people."

Year Founded in US: 1969

Income for Overseas Min: $125,546

Personnel:
  Home ministry & office staff in US: 39

ChinaSource

P.O. Box 4343
Fullerton, CA 92834-4343 USA

Phone: (714) 449-0611
Fax: (714) 449-0624
E-mail: info@chsource.org
Web Site: www.chsource.org

Dr. Brent Fulton, President

A specialized agency engaged in mission-related research, partnership development, and consulting/training. Founded as a cooperative effort of the EFMA, IFMA, WEF, Chinese Coordination Centre for World Evangelization, and the Billy Graham Center at Wheaton College.

Year Founded in US: 1995

Income for Overseas Min: NA

Personnel:
  Home ministry & office staff in US: 8

Chosen People Ministries
(See Ad on page 107)

241 E. 51st St.
New York, NY 10022 USA

Phone: (212) 223-2252
Fax: (212) 223-2576

You are the Light of the world

Inside of you is a light. Don't be ashamed of it. It is the power of God. Use it.

STEP & eXperience Israel
Internships, Summer Opportunities
www.**chosenpeople**.com
888-2-YESHUA

Chosen People Ministries...Reaching Jewish People for the Messiah

E-mail: cpm@chosenpeople.com
Web Site: www.chosenpeople.com
Dr. Mitch Glaser, President and CEO

A nondenominational service agency of Independent and Evangelical tradition engaged in evangelism, church planting, literature distribution and missionary training. Financial information from 1998.
Year Founded in US: 1894
Income for Overseas Min: $297,112
Personnel:
   Home ministry & office staff in US: 39
Countries: Argentina; Australia; France; Germany; Israel; Mexico; Ukraine; United Kingdom

Chosen, Inc.
3638 W. 26th St.
Erie, PA 16506 USA
Phone: (814) 833-3023
Fax: (814) 833-4091
E-mail: jay@chosenhands.org
Web Site: www.chosenhands.org
Rev. Jay W. Sterling, Exec. Director

A nondenominational specialized agency of Evangelical tradition engaged in supplying equipment, providing medical supplies and technical assistance.
Purpose: "...to promote health care programs in conjunction with missionaries and national Christian health care workers in a tangible effort to bring the love of Christ to those least able to help themselves."
Year Founded in US: 1969
Income for Overseas Min: $943,640
Gifts-in-Kind: $909,090
Personnel:
   Home ministry & office staff in US: 4

Christ Community Church
2500 Dowie Memorial Dr.
Zion, IL 60099 USA
Phone: (847) 746-1411
Fax: (847) 746-1452
E-mail: mike@ccczion.org
Web Site: www.ccczion.org
Ken Langley, Senior Pastor

A denominational sending agency of Evangelical tradition engaged in partnership development, camping programs, evangelism, theological education, support of national churches and support of national workers.
Year Founded in US: 1896
Income for Overseas Min: $234,000
Fully Supported US Personnel Overseas:
   Expecting to serve more than 4 years: 1
   Nonresidential mission personnel: 1
Other personnel:
   Short-term less than 1 year from US: 17
   Non-US serving in own/other country: 109
   Home ministry & office staff in US: 18
   Bivocational/Tentmaker from US: 2
Countries: Egypt 1; Guyana; Indonesia; Japan; Malawi; Palestine; Philippines; South Africa; Vietnam

Christ for India, Inc.
(See Ad on page 109)
P.O. Box 271086
Dallas, TX 75227 USA
Phone: (800) 934-0380
Fax: (972) 772-5919
E-mail: cfimin@christforindia.org
Web Site: www.christforindia.org
Mr. Jameson Titus, V.P. & Chief Dev. Officer

A nondenominational service agency of Charismatic and Evangelical tradition engaged in theological education, childcare/orphanage programs, church construction, church planting, medical work and training.
Purpose: "...to make ready a people, prepared for the coming of the Lord."
Year Founded in US: 1981
Income for Overseas Min: $253,156
Gifts-in-Kind: $1,147
Fully Supported US Personnel Overseas:
   Expecting to serve more than 4 years: 1
Other personnel:
   Short-term less than 1 year from US: 30
   Non-US serving in own/other country: 1
   Home ministry & office staff in US: 2
Countries: India 1

Christ for the City Intl.
P.O. Box 241827
Omaha, NE 68124-5827 USA
Phone: (402) 592-8332

Fax: (402) 592-8312
E-mail: info@cfci.org
Web Site: www.cfci.org
Dr. Duane "Chip" Anderson, President
An interdenominational support agency of
Evangelical tradition engaged in childcare/
orphanage programs, church planting, de-
velopment, leadership development, sup-
port of national churches and relief and/or
rehabilitation.
Purpose: " To multiply churches...which in
turn...send multinational teams into the
least evangelized cities of the world."
Year Founded in US: 1995
Income for Overseas Min: $794,179
Gifts-in-Kind: $11,391
Fully Supported US Personnel Overseas:
  Expecting to serve more than 4 years: 7
Other personnel:
  Non-US serving in own/other country: 10
  Home ministry & office staff in US: 10
Countries: Colombia; Costa Rica 5;
Mexico; Peru; Spain 2

Christ for the Lost World
P.O. Box 250
Brown Summit, NC 27214 USA
Phone: (336) 656-1393
Fax: (336) 656-1393
Clay Trainum, Chairman
An interdenominational support agency of
Evangelical tradition engaged in evange-
lism, literature distribution, supplying
equipment, support of national workers
and youth programs. Statistical data 1998.
Year Founded in US: 1983
Income for Overseas Min: $63,000
Personnel:
  Non-US serving in own/other country: 113
  Home ministry & office staff in US: 2
Countries: Indonesia; Russia

Christ for the Nations, Inc.
P.O. Box 769000
Dallas, TX 75376 USA
Phone: (214) 376-1711
Fax: (214) 302-6228
E-mail: Info@cfni.org
Web Site: www.cfni.org

Dr. Dennis Lindsay, President/CEO
A support agency of Charismatic tradition
engaged in literature distribution, short-
term programs, church construction, missionary education, agricultural programs,
theological education and youth programs.
Year Founded in US: 1948
Income for Overseas Min: NA

Christ to the Nations
(See Ad on page 111)
P.O. Box 1824
Cocoa, FL 32923-1824 USA
Phone: (321) 504-0778
Fax: (321) 504-0778
E-mail: harvesttoday@aol.com
Web Site: www.cttn.org
Dr. David L. Ralston, Director
A sending agency of Baptist and Indepen-
dent tradition engaged in church planting,
Bible distribution, children's programs, sup-
port of national churches, support of na-
tional workers and missionary training.
Personnel information from 1998.
Purpose: "...to help local churches and
God's people reach the unreached millions
with the Gospel of Jesus Christ..."
Year Founded in US: 1989
Income for Overseas Min: $100,000
Gifts-in-Kind: $3,000
Fully Supported US Personnel Overseas:
  Expecting to serve more than 4 years: 47
Other personnel:
  Non-US serving in own/other country: 47
  Home ministry & office staff in US: 6
Countries: Australia 2; Cuba 10; Ghana 2;
Hungary 2; Indonesia 2; Kenya 2; Lithuania
13; Philippines 10; Russia 4

Christar
(See Ad on page 112)
P.O. Box 14866
Reading, PA 19612-4866 USA
Phone: (610) 375-0300
Fax: (610) 375-6862
E-mail: info@christar.org
Web Site: www.christar.org
Dr. Patrick O. Cate, President
An interdenominational sending agency of

nya; Kyrgyzstan; Laos;
; Mongolia; Myanmar/
epal; Nigeria; Pakistan;
; Paraguay; Peru; Philip-
ania; Russia; Sierra
Lanka; Sudan;
; Thailand; Togo;
Uzbekistan; Vietnam

**d
Alliance**

CO 80935-3500 USA
-5999
393
alliance.org
cmalliance.org
President

sending agency of Evan-
ngaged in church plant-
, church construction,
ourses, development,
ation, evangelism and
pment.

develop missionary
tion movements among
esponsive peoples world-
nsion of the local church."

US: 1887

rseas Min: $24,743,649

US Personnel Overseas:
erve more than 4 years: 597
erve 1 to 4 years: 125

el:
than 1 year from US: 1,352
& office staff in US: 14
ntmaker from US: 57

a–General 4; Argentina 16;
and Herzegovina 10; Brazil
20; Cambodia 18; Chile
olombia 17; Congo, Repub-
ta Rica 1; Cote d'Ivoire 42;
ublic 13; Ecuador 32; Eu-
; France 21; Gabon 22; Ger-
; Guinea-Bissau 15;
srael 10; Japan 10; Jordan 3;
; Laos; Lebanon 2;
Malaysia; Mali 26; Mexico
; Panama; Paraguay 2; Peru
28; Poland 2; Russia 24;
an 17; Thailand 25; United

Kingdom 7; Uruguay 2; Venezuela 18; Vietnam 2

Christian Associates Intl.

1534 N. Moorpark Rd. #356
Thousand Oaks, CA 91360 USA

Phone: (818) 865-1816
Fax: (818) 865-0317
E-mail: usoffice@christianassociates.org
Web Site: www.christianassociates.org
Dr. Linus J. Morris, President

A transdenominational sending agency of Evangelical tradition engaged in church planting and support of national churches. Personnel information from 1998.

Purpose: "...to reach the unchurched through the multiplication of high-impact leaders and high-impact churches."

Year Founded in US: 1968

Income for Overseas Min: $2,330,050

Fully Supported US Personnel Overseas:
Expecting to serve more than 4 years: 30
Expecting to serve 1 to 4 years: 4

Other personnel:
Non-US serving in own/other country: 6
Home ministry & office staff in US: 12

Countries: Germany 4; Latvia; Netherlands 15; Portugal 4; Russia 1; Spain 6

Christian Blind Mission Intl.

P.O. Box 19000
Greenville, SC 29602 USA

Phone: (864) 239-0065
Fax: (864) 239-0069
E-mail: info@cbmi-usa.org
Web Site: www.cbmi-usa.org
Mr. Alan Harkey, U.S. President

An interdenominational service agency of Ecumenical tradition engaged in disability assistance programs, agricultural programs, providing medical supplies, relief and/or rehabilitation and missionary training. Personnel information from 1998.

Purpose: "Worldwide Christian service in eye care and projects for people with disabilities."

Year Founded in US: 1976
Income for Overseas Min: $20,482,603
Gifts-in-Kind: $19,226,433
Fully Supported US Personnel Overseas:

"Someone is counting on you."

- Church planting
- Bible and literature distribution
- Children's programs
- Supporting national churches
- Supporting national workers
- Missionary training

Christ to the Nations Missions supports both national and American missionaries, and is engaged in church planting, missionary training, and Bible distribution.

Bless the Children Program, a ministry of Christ to the Nations Missions, is helping to meet the needs of children in Eastern Europe, Africa, and Asia.

Christ to the Nations World Missions and Bless the Children Program

Christ to the Nations first began ministering to nations suffering under communist rule. Since 1989, we've grown to include other countries. We have sent God's word to thousands in Ukraine, India, Poland, Cuba, Lithuania, Russia, Kazakstan, and the Philippines. We continue to focus on establishing local New Testament Churches and reaching and teaching national peoples.

Founder and Director:
David Ralston and family
P.O. Box 1824, Cocoa, FL 32923
Phone/Fax: 321-504-0778
E-mail: DLRCTTN@aol.com
Website: www.CTTN.org

**Triple your church's mission giving!
Ask us how!**

Ralston Family

Evangelical tradition engaged in church planting, agricultural programs, childcare/orphanage programs, theological education, evangelism, leadership development and medical work.

Purpose: "To...proclaim the Gospel...and establish local indigenous churches, primarily among unreached Asian communities worldwide."

Year Founded in US: 1930

Income for Overseas Min: $6,429,331

Fully Supported US Personnel Overseas:
Expecting to serve more than 4 years: 186
Expecting to serve 1 to 4 years: 81
Nonresidential mission personnel: 385

Other personnel:
Short-term less than 1 year from US: 68
Home ministry & office staff in US: 39
Bivocational/Tentmaker from US: 120

Countries: Albania 6; Asia–General 13; China 17; Egypt 4; France 10; India 18; Japan 12; Jordan 12; Kazakhstan 6; Kenya 2; Mongolia 6; Morocco; Pakistan 11; Philippines 29; Tajikistan 6; Turkey 30; United Kingdom 4

Christian Advance Intl.

P.O. Box 741427
Houston, TX 77274-1427 USA

Phone: (713) 981-9033
E-mail: CAIHOU@aol.com

Rev. Chris G. Jones, President

An interdenominational sending agency of Pentecostal tradition engaged in medical work, short-term programs, youth programs, evangelism and children's programs. Financial data from 1996.

Year Founded in US: 1984

Income for Overseas Min: $617,000

Personnel:
Non-US serving in own/other country: 7
Home ministry & office staff in US: 6

Countries: Belize; Brazil; Mexico

Christian Aid Ministries

P.O. Box 360
Berlin, OH 44610 USA

Phone: (330) 893-2428
Fax: (330) 893-2305

Mr. David N. Troyer, Gen. Director

donesia; Jordan; K
Macedonia; Mexic
Burma; Namibia;
Papua New Guine
pines; Poland; Ron
Leone; Slovenia; S
Tajikistan; Tanzan
Ukraine; Uruguay

Christian an Missionary

P.O. Box 35000
Colorado Springs

Phone: (719) 59
Fax: (719) 262-5
E-mail: Info@cm
Web Site: www

Dr. Peter Nanfelt,

A denomination
gelical tradition
ing, broadcastin
correspondence
theological educ
leadership deve

Purpose: "...to
church-multipli
unreached and
wide, as an exte

Year Founded
Income for Ov
Fully Supporte
Expecting to
Expecting to

Other person
Short-term le
Home minist
Bivocational/

Countries: Afr
Bolivia 6; Bosr
30; Burkina Fa
16; China 20;
lic of the 4; C
Dominican Re
rope–General
many 13; Gu
Indonesia 40;
Korea, South
Macedonia 8
10; Mongolia
15; Philippin
Spain 10; Tai

Expecting to serve more than 4 years: 1
Expecting to serve 1 to 4 years: 18
Other personnel:
Home ministry & office staff in US: 8

Countries: Cameroon; Congo, Republic of the; Dominican Republic; Ecuador; Jordan; Kenya; Madagascar; Nigeria; Pakistan; Papua New Guinea; Philippines; Tanzania 1; Thailand; Togo; Uganda

Christian Broadcasting Network, The
977 Centerville Turnpk.
Virginia Beach, VA 23463 USA
Phone: (757) 579-7000
Fax: (757) 226-2017
Web Site: www.cbn.com
Mr. Pat Robertson, Chairman & CEO

The Christian Broadcasting Network (CBN) is one of the largest Christian television ministries in the world. A multifaceted non-profit organization, CBN provides programming by cable, broadcast and satellite to 180 countries produced in 71 languages. CBN's humanitarian arm, Operation Blessing Intl., includes The Hunger Strike Force and event-driven outreaches designed to provide relief and ministry to those in need.

Year Founded in US: 1960
Income for Overseas Min: $47,646,521
Gifts-in-Kind: $16,868,993

Christian Businessmen's Committee of USA
See: Connecting Businessmen to Christ

Christian Church (Disciples of Christ)
P. O. Box 1986
Indianapolis, IN 46206 USA
Phone: (317) 635-3100
Fax: (317) 635-4323
E-mail: DOM@disciples.org
Web Site: www.globalministries.org
Julia Brown Karimu, Mission Exec.

A denominational sending agency of Christian (Restoration Movement) tradition engaged in support of missionaries and national churches through a combined Global Ministries partnership with the Wider Church Ministries of the United Church of Christ.

Year Founded in US: 1849
Income for Overseas Min: NR
Personnel:
Home ministry & office staff in US: 21

Christian Church of North America
1294 Rutledge Rd.
Transfer, PA 16154 USA
Phone: (724) 962-3501
Fax: (724) 962-1766
E-mail: ccna@nauticom.net
Web Site: www.ccna.org
Rev. John Del Turco, Director Frgn. Missions

A denominational sending agency of Pentecostal and Charismatic tradition engaged in evangelism, childcare/orphanage programs, church construction, church planting, support of national workers and relief and/or rehabilitation. Personnel figures from 1998.

Year Founded in US: 1907
Income for Overseas Min: $408,000
Fully Supported US Personnel Overseas:
Expecting to serve more than 4 years: 12
Expecting to serve 1 to 4 years: 2
Other personnel:
Home ministry & office staff in US: 3
Countries: Colombia 1; Europe–General 2; India 4; Italy 1; Kenya; South Africa 4

Christian Churches/ Churches of Christ
(No central office)

A body of autonomous congregations and agencies of Christian (Restoration Movement) tradition (using instrumental music in worship) which sends and supports missionaries directly from local congregations. Data provided by Mission Services Association (all information based upon best estimates for an independent brotherhood of churches).

Income for Overseas Min: $52,000,000
Fully Supported US Personnel Overseas:
Expecting to serve more than 4 years: 915
Expecting to serve 1 to 4 years: 100

Nonresidential mission personnel: 50
Other personnel:
   Short-term less than 1 year from US: 2,000
   Non-US serving in own/other country: 422
Countries: Africa–General 4; Argentina 4; Asia–General 6; Australia 20; Austria 6; Bahamas, The 2; Bangladesh; Barbados 6; Belgium 1; Bosnia and Herzegovina 2; Brazil 28; Cayman Islands 2; Chile 32; Cote d'Ivoire 6; Czech Republic 2; Dominica 5; Dominican Republic 12; Ecuador 4; Equatorial Guinea 2; Ethiopia 8; France 5; Germany 8; Ghana 13; Grenada 2; Guatemala 2; Guinea 15; Guyana; Haiti 4; Honduras 19; Hong Kong 10; India 17; Indonesia 15; Ireland 6; Israel 2; Italy 14; Jamaica 12; Japan 30; Kenya 35; Korea, South 4; Kosovo 2; Liberia 2; Mali 2; Mexico 50; Mozambique 6; Myanmar/Burma; New Zealand 8; Nigeria 2; Pakistan; Panama 2; Papua New Guinea 30; Philippines 40; Poland 2; Portugal 4; Puerto Rico 5; Russia 16; Singapore 4; South Africa 32; Spain 1; Taiwan 21; Tanzania 21; Thailand 41; Ukraine 30; United Kingdom 20; Unspecified Country 160; Venezuela 15; Zimbabwe 34

Christian Dental Society
Box 296
Sumner, IA 50674 USA
Phone: (563) 578-8887
Fax: (563) 578-8887
E-mail: cdssent@iowatelecom.net
Web Site: www.christiandental.org
Dr. Robert F. Liebler, Exec. Director
An interdenominational specialized agency of Ecumenical tradition engaged in dental work, training local dentists in new techniques in 22 countries.
Purpose: "To carry out the Great Commission given by Christ in Matthew 28:19 & 20 through dentists and dentistry."
Year Founded in US: 1962
Income for Overseas Min: $257,628
Personnel:
   Short-term less than 1 year from US: 27
   Home ministry & office staff in US: 1

Christian Discipleship Ministries, Inc.
P.O. Box 1084

Eagle Point, OR 97524 USA
Phone: (541) 830-8161
Fax: (541) 830-1565
E-mail: cdmin@charter.net
Mr. Richard E. Cook, Exec. Dir.
A nondenominational sending agency of Baptist tradition engaged in funds transmission, Bible distribution, church planting, literature distribution and training.
Purpose: "...to support and strengthen mission work and the ministry of the local church in India."
Year Founded in US: 1994
Income for Overseas Min: $93,751
Fully Supported US Personnel Overseas:
   Expecting to serve more than 4 years: 1
Other personnel:
   Short-term less than 1 year from US: 1
   Non-US serving in own/other country: 7
Countries: India 1

Christian Fellowship Union
P.O. Box 909
McAllen, TX 78502 USA
Phone: (956) 686-5886
Fax: (956) 686-6427
E-mail: cfunion@juno.com
Rev. Steven P. Johnson, Gen. Director
An interdenominational support agency of Charismatic and Fundamental tradition engaged in church planting, theological education, leadership development and support of national churches.
Year Founded in US: 1945
Income for Overseas Min: $27,000
Personnel:
   Home ministry & office staff in US: 4

Christian Information Service, Inc.
P.O. Box 6511
Charlottesville, VA 22906 USA
Phone: (434) 817-1356
Fax: (434) 817-1357
E-mail: bbray@wcf-intl.org
Mr. Ray Miles, President
A transdenominational support agency engaged in providing growth services to indigenous missions, helping more than

30,000 workers serving with 500 native mission boards on every continent.

Year Founded in US: 1972

Income for Overseas Min: NA

Fully Supported US Personnel Overseas:
  Nonresidential mission personnel: 2

Other personnel:
  Home ministry & office staff in US: 2

Christian Laymen's Missionary Evangelism

826 Ford St.
Prosser, WA 99350 USA

Phone: (509) 786-3178
Fax: (509) 786-9977
E-mail: ltaylor@iopener.net

Mr. Larry Taylor, President

A nondenominational support agency of Charismatic tradition engaged in evangelism and literature distribution.

Purpose: "To raise up laymen for world evangelism."

Year Founded in US: 1977

Income for Overseas Min: NA

Christian Leadership Development, Inc.

P.O. Box 025240
Miami, FL 33102-5240 USA

Phone: (270) 821-0699
Fax: (506) 011-241-1001
E-mail: apuntes@racsa.co.cr
Web Site: www.desarrollocristiano.com

Mr. Randall Wittig, Gen. Director

An interdenominational service agency of Evangelical tradition engaged in leadership development, TEE, literature distribution and literature production.

Purpose: "...to assist pastors and church leaders in primarily Latin American countries by providing teaching, counseling and encouragement through personal contact, small groups, training courses and conferences, seminars and literature."

Year Founded in US: 1978

Income for Overseas Min: $315,147

Fully Supported US Personnel Overseas:
  Expecting to serve more than 4 years: 2
  Nonresidential mission personnel: 1

Other personnel:
  Non-US serving in own/other country: 2

Countries: Costa Rica 2

Christian Literacy Associates

541 Perry Highway
Pittsburgh, PA 15229-1851 USA

Phone: (412) 364-3777
E-mail: drliteracy@aol.com
Web Site: www.christianliteracy.org

Dr. William E. Kofmehl Jr., President

An interdenominational specialized agency of Ecumenical tradition engaged in literacy work. The "Christian Literacy Series" has been used in 54 countries.

Purpose: "...committed to reaching functionally illiterate adults and children throughout the world by helping them develop reading skills."

Year Founded in US: 1975

Income for Overseas Min: NA

Personnel:
  Home ministry & office staff in US: 4

Christian Literature Crusade
See: CLC Ministries Intl.

Christian Literature Intl.
(See Ad on page 118)
P.O. Box 777
Canby, OR 97013 USA

Phone: (503) 266-9734
Fax: (503) 266-1143
E-mail: newlife@spiritone.com
Web Site: www.newlifebible.org

Mr. Gleason H. Ledyard, President

A nondenominational support agency of Evangelical tradition engaged in Bible translation, Bible distribution, literacy work and literature distribution.

Year Founded in US: 1967

Income for Overseas Min: $68,000

Countries: Australia; United Kingdom

Christian Medical & Dental Society

P.O. Box 7500
Bristol, TN 37621 USA

Phone: (423) 844-1000
Fax: (423) 844-1017
E-mail: main@cmdahome.org
Web Site: www.cmdahome.org
Dr. David L. Stevens, Exec. Director

A nondenominational service agency engaged in short-term programs, agricultural programs, literature distribution, literature production and mobilization for mission. Sends short-term mission teams to more than 15 countries.

Purpose: "...to motivate, educate and equip Christian physicians and dentists to glorify God."

Year Founded in US: 1931
Income for Overseas Min: $1,895,800
Gifts-in-Kind: $1,018,725

Christian Ministries International (C.M.I.)
P.O. Box 18687-0687
Fairfield, OH 45018 USA
Phone: (513) 895-3959
Fax: (513) 895-0074
E-mail: cmi@hotmail.com
Dr. L. Lynn Hood, President

A transdenominational sending agency of Charismatic and Evangelical tradition engaged in leadership development, evangelism, literature distribution, management consulting/training, mobilization for mission and training. Personnel information from 1998.

Purpose: "...preparing national indigenous leaders of the local church to be empowered by New Testament principles of leadership to assist them in world evangelization and church planting in their generations."

Year Founded in US: 1984
Income for Overseas Min: $300,000
Gifts-in-Kind: $60,000
Fully Supported US Personnel Overseas:
   Expecting to serve more than 4 years: 4
   Expecting to serve 1 to 4 years: 14
Other personnel:
   Home ministry & office staff in US: 5
   Bivocational/Tentmaker from US: 10
Countries: Brazil 2; China; Russia; Ukraine 2

Christian Mission for the Deaf
P.O. Box 28005
Detroit, MI 48228-0005 USA
Phone: (313) 933-1424
Fax: (313) 933-1424
E-mail: cmd@cmdeaf.org
Web Site: www.cmdeaf.org
Mrs. Berta Foster, Administrator

A denominational support agency of Christian/Plymouth Brethren tradition engaged in literacy work, evangelism, Christian education, children's programs and church planting.

Year Founded in US: 1956
Income for Overseas Min: $76,724
Personnel:
   Non-US serving in own/other country: 6
   Home ministry & office staff in US: 2
Countries: Chad; Congo, Democratic Republic of the; Nigeria

Christian Missions in Many Lands
P.O. Box 13
Spring Lake, NJ 07762-0013 USA
Phone: (732) 449-8880
Fax: (732) 974-0888
Mr. Samuel E. Robinson, President

A nondenominational service agency of Christian/Plymouth Brethren tradition assisting missionaries through funds transmission and missions information service. Overseas personnel included under Brethren Assemblies. Statistical data from 1998.

Purpose: "...to provide necessary services which are difficult or impossible for the missionary or assembly to provide."

Year Founded in US: 1921
Income for Overseas Min: $12,800,000
Personnel:
   Home ministry & office staff in US: 7

Christian Missions Unlimited
P.O. Box 58
Hope Hull, AL 36043 USA
Phone: (334) 284-0878
Fax: (334) 284-1039
E-mail: cmu@mindspring.com

Web Site: www.christianmissions.org

Mr. Charles Conner, Jr., Exec. Director

A specialized agency of Baptist tradition engaged in church construction, Bible distribution, evangelism, support of national workers, mobilization for mission and short-term programs.

Purpose: "Church construction is the main focus."

Year Founded in US: 1973

Income for Overseas Min: NA

Fully Supported US Personnel Overseas:
   Nonresidential mission personnel: 3

Other personnel:
   Short-term less than 1 year from US: 300
   Home ministry & office staff in US: 4

Countries: Brazil

Christian Outreach Intl.

P.O. Box 2823
Vero Beach, FL 32961-2823 USA

Phone: (772) 778-0575
Fax: (772) 778-6781
E-mail: missions@coiusa.com
Web Site: www.coiusa.com

Mr. Jack Isleib, Exec. Director

A nondenominational service agency of Evangelical tradition engaged in evangelism, leadership development, mobilization for mission, short-term programs and missionary training.

Purpose: "...reaching the lost, and the development and training of believers."

Year Founded in US: 1984

Income for Overseas Min: $2,190,659

Fully Supported US Personnel Overseas:
   Expecting to serve more than 4 years: 13

Other personnel:
   Short-term less than 1 year from US: 115
   Non-US serving in own/other country: 17
   Home ministry & office staff in US: 14

Countries: Czech Republic 7; France 1; Mexico 3; Romania; Ukraine 1; United Kingdom; Venezuela 1

Christian Pilots Association

P.O. Box 90452
Los Angeles, CA 90009-0452 USA

Mr. Howard Payne, President

An interdenominational specialized agency of Evangelical tradition engaged in aviation services and providing medical supplies.

Year Founded in US: 1972

Income for Overseas Min: $17,000

Gifts-in-Kind: $10,000

Christian Reformed World Missions

2850 Kalamazoo Ave. SE
Grand Rapids, MI 49508 USA

Phone: (616) 224-0700
Fax: (616) 224-0707
E-mail: crwm@crcna.org
Web Site: www.crwm.org

Dr. Gary J. Bekker, Exec. Director

A denominational sending agency of Reformed and Evangelical tradition engaged in church planting, Christian education, theological education, evangelism, leadership development and support of national churches.

Purpose: "...to bring salvation to the ends of the earth...to proclaim the Gospel and develop churches around the world."

Year Founded in US: 1888

Income for Overseas Min: $7,875,000

Fully Supported US Personnel Overseas:
   Expecting to serve more than 4 years: 119
   Expecting to serve 1 to 4 years: 53

Other personnel:
   Short-term less than 1 year from US: 150
   Non-US serving in own/other country: 1
   Home ministry & office staff in US: 20

Countries: Bangladesh; China 2; Costa Rica 3; Dominican Republic 8; El Salvador 1; France 2; Guam 2; Guinea 10; Haiti 6; Honduras 4; Hungary 6; Japan 10; Mali 7; Mexico 17; Nicaragua 2; Nigeria 24; Philippines 13; Russia; Sierra Leone 2; Taiwan

Christian Reformed World Relief Committee

2850 Kalamazoo Ave. SE
Grand Rapids, MI 49560 USA

Phone: (616) 241-1691
Fax: (616) 224-0806
E-mail: degraffb@crcna.org
Web Site: www.crwrc.org

Mr. Andy Ryskamp, U.S. Director

A denominational service agency of Reformed tradition engaged in community development, Christian education, relief aid, technical assistance and leadership development. Personnel data from 1998.

Purpose: "...showing God's love to people in need by working with them and their communities to create positive permanent change..."

Year Founded in US: 1962

Income for Overseas Min: $7,041,005

Fully Supported US Personnel Overseas:
Expecting to serve more than 4 years: 13
Expecting to serve 1 to 4 years: 16
Nonresidential mission personnel: 22

Other personnel:
Non-US serving in own/other country: 30

Countries: Bangladesh 1; Cambodia; Dominican Republic 1; Ecuador; El Salvador; Guatemala; Haiti 1; Honduras 1; Indonesia; Kenya 2; Malawi; Mali 1; Mexico; Nicaragua 1; Niger; Nigeria; Philippines; Romania 1; Rwanda; Senegal 1; Sierra Leone 1; South Africa 1; Tanzania; Uganda; Zambia 1

Christian Resources Intl.

P.O. Box 356
Fowlerville, MI 48836-0356 USA

Phone: (517) 223-3193
Fax: (517) 223-7668
E-mail: csmbooks@ismi.net
Web Site: www.cribooks.org

Mr. Mark J. Campo, Director

An interdenominational specialized agency of Evangelical tradition engaged in literature distribution worldwide by sending overseas surplus and reusable Christian literature and Bibles.

Year Founded in US: 1956

Income for Overseas Min: $313,799

Personnel:
Home ministry & office staff in US: 6

Christian Service Intl.

1714 W. Royale Dr.
Muncie, IN 47304-2240 USA

Phone: (765) 286-0711
Fax: (765) 286-5773
E-mail: csimail@juno.com
Web Site: www.csiministries.com

Mr. Lenville Gross, President

An interdenominational service agency of Evangelical tradition engaged in medical work, evangelism and short-term programs.

Purpose: "...promotes world missions by taking people to see firsthand what God is doing to get His Word to a lost world."

Year Founded in US: 1963

Income for Overseas Min: $1,607,855

Fully Supported US Personnel Overseas:
Expecting to serve more than 4 years: 10

Other personnel:
Short-term less than 1 year from US: 975
Non-US serving in own/other country: 22
Home ministry & office staff in US: 10

Countries: Haiti 5; Jamaica 5

Christian Union Churches of North America

21621 County Rd. P
Fayette, OH 43521 USA

Phone: (419) 237-2015
E-mail: JoeRoseRedmond@juno.com

Mr. Joseph B. Redmond, Mission Director

A denominational sending agency of Independent tradition engaged in evangelism, church construction, literature distribution, literature production and youth programs. Financial statistics from 1998.

Year Founded in US: 1864

Income for Overseas Min: $95,450

Personnel:
Home ministry & office staff in US: 1

Christian World Publishers

101 Gregory Lane #42
Pleasant Hill, CA 94523 USA

Phone: (510) 689-9944
E-mail: cwpublishers@aol.com

Mr. Peter Cunliffe, President

A nondenominational specialized agency of Evangelical tradition engaged in training overseas publishers and management consulting/training. Statistical information from 1998.

Year Founded in US: 1974

Income for Overseas Min: $223,000

Personnel:
Home ministry & office staff in US: 1

Christians In Action, Inc.

P.O. Box 728
Woodlake, CA 93286-0728 USA

Phone: (559) 564-3762
Fax: (559) 564-1231
E-mail: cinamissions@christiansinaction.org
Web Site: www.christiansinaction.org

Mr. David W. Konold, Jr., Exec. Director

A transdenominational sending agency of Evangelical tradition engaged in evangelism, childcare/orphanage programs, churchm planting, support of national churches, relief and/or rehabilitation and missionary training.

Year Founded in US: 1957

Income for Overseas Min: $827,083

Fully Supported US Personnel Overseas:
　Expecting to serve more than 4 years: 26
　Nonresidential mission personnel: 2

Other personnel:
　Non-US serving in own/other country: 48
　Home ministry & office staff in US: 11

Countries: Brazil 2; Colombia 3; Ecuador 2; Germany 3; Ghana 4; Guatemala 2; India; Japan 2; Macau 2; Mexico 1; Philippines; Sierra Leone; United Kingdom 5

Church Ministries Intl.

500 Turtle Cove Blvd. #101
Rockwall, TX 75087-5300 USA

Phone: (972) 772-3406
Fax: (972) 722-0012
E-mail: cmioffice@churchministries.org
Web Site: www.churchministries.org

Mr. Jim Murray, Exec. Director

An interdenominational support agency of Evangelical tradition engaged in church construction, services for other agencies and church planting.

Purpose: "...to help urban churches evangelize their nation."

Year Founded in US: 1989

Income for Overseas Min: $285,731

Fully Supported US Personnel Overseas:
　Expecting to serve more than 4 years: 1
　Nonresidential mission personnel: 1

Other personnel:
　Non-US serving in own/other country: 3
　Home ministry & office staff in US: 3

Countries: Colombia 1; Ecuador

Church Missions Link

P.O. Box 14175
Spokane, WA 99206 USA

Phone: (509) 891-5595
Fax: (509) 891-5595
E-mail: CMLink@juno.com

Rev. Ken Parker, Director

A transdenominational support agency of Evangelical and Independent tradition engaged in missions information service, management consulting/training and missionary training. Statistical data from 1998.

Year Founded in US: 1997

Income for Overseas Min: $10,000

Personnel:
　Short-term less than 1 year from US: 25
　Home ministry & office staff in US: 2

Church of God (Anderson, Indiana), Global Missions

P.O. Box 2498
Anderson, IN 46018 USA

Phone: (765) 648-2140
Fax: (765) 642-4279
E-mail: bedwards@chog.org

Dr. Robert E. Edwards, Global Missions Coordinator

A nondenominational sending agency of Holiness tradition engaged in leadership development, church planting, TEE, support of national workers and short-term programs.

Year Founded in US: 1909

Income for Overseas Min: $5,000,000

Fully Supported US Personnel Overseas:
　Expecting to serve more than 4 years: 62

Other personnel:
　Home ministry & office staff in US: 8

Countries: Australia 4; Belize 2; Brazil 4; Costa Rica 2; Cote d'Ivoire 5; Ecuador 4; Guam 2; Hong Kong 2; Hungary 2; Japan 4; Kenya 8; Lebanon 3; Tanzania 5; Uganda 4; Unspecified Country 7; Venezuela 2; Zambia 2

Church of God (Cleveland, TN) World Missions

(See Ad on page 123)
P.O. Box 8016
Cleveland, TN 37320-8016 USA

Church of God World Missions

Feeding the hungry
Preaching the gospel
Housing the homeless
Planting the church
Training the ministry
... Since 1910

Church of God World Missions
P.O. Box 8016 • Cleveland, TN 37320-8016
(423) 478-7190 • (423) 478-7155 (fax) • 1-800-345-7492
MissionPhone: 1-800-624-7166
Website: www.cogwm.org
E-mail: info@cogwm.org

Phone: (423) 478-7190
Fax: (423) 478-7155
E-mail: Info@cogwm.org
Web Site: www.cogwm.org

Dr. Lovell R. Cary, Director

A denominational sending agency of Pentecostal tradition engaged in church planting, childcare/orphanage programs, theological education, TEE, evangelism and support of national workers.

Purpose: "...to help unchurched or nominal Christians become committed disciples of Christ and non-Christian people become Christians..."

Year Founded in US: 1910

Income for Overseas Min: $30,137,862

Fully Supported US Personnel Overseas:
   Expecting to serve more than 4 years: 154
   Expecting to serve 1 to 4 years: 2

Other personnel:
   Short-term less than 1 year from US: 8,131
   Non-US serving in own/other country: 79
   Home ministry & office staff in US: 62
   Bivocational/Tentmaker from US: 6

Countries: Albania; Aruba 2; Australia 2; Bahrain; Belgium 4; Botswana 2; Brazil 7; Bulgaria 2; Caribbean–General 2; Chile 3; China 4; Colombia 3; Cote d'Ivoire 2; Croatia 2; Dubai; Ecuador 6; Europe–General 2; France 1; Germany 9; Guatemala 4; Haiti 4; Honduras 10; Indonesia 2; Ireland 5; Israel 7; Italy 1; Kenya 13; Latin America–General 1; Liberia; Malawi; Malaysia 2; Mongolia 3; Morocco 2; Netherlands 1; New Zealand 2; Nicaragua 2; Nigeria 1; Panama; Paraguay 2; Peru 2; Philippines 15; Russia 5; Singapore; South Africa 1; Spain 1; Turkey 2; Ukraine 3; United Kingdom 2; Uruguay 2; Uzbekistan; Venezuela 3; Zambia 3

Church of God (Holiness) World Mission Board

P.O. Box 4711
Overland Park, KS 66204 USA

Phone: (913) 432-0303
Fax: (913) 722-0351
E-mail: WLHayton@aol.com

Rev. William L. Hayton, Exec. Secretary

A nondenominational sending agency of Independent tradition engaged in support of national churches, theological education, church planting, evangelism and support of national workers. Personnel statistics from 1996.

Year Founded in US: 1917

Income for Overseas Min: $274,373

Fully Supported US Personnel Overseas:
   Expecting to serve more than 4 years: 9
   Expecting to serve 1 to 4 years: 2

Other personnel:
   Non-US serving in own/other country: 11
   Home ministry & office staff in US: 2

Countries: Bolivia 3; Cayman Islands 4; Nigeria 2; Ukraine

Church of God (Seventh Day) General Conference

P.O. Box 33677
Denver, CO 80233 USA

Phone: (303) 452-7973
Fax: (303) 452-0657
E-mail: offices@cog7.org
Web Site: www.cog7.org

Mr. William C. Hicks, Dir. Missions

A denominational support agency of Evangelical tradition engaged in funds transmission, Bible and literature distribution, and support of national churches in 16 countries.

Year Founded in US: 1860

Income for Overseas Min: $109,950

Gifts-in-Kind: $30,000

Personnel:
   Home ministry & office staff in US: 14

Church of God in Christ, Mennonite General Mission Board

P.O. Box 230
Moundridge, KS 67107 USA

Phone: (620) 345-2532
Fax: (620) 345-2582

Dale Koehn, Information Contact

A denominational sending agency of Mennonite tradition engaged in evangelism, Bible distribution, support of national churches and relief and/or rehabilitation in 21 countries. Includes U.S. and Canadian totals.

Year Founded in US: 1933

Income for Overseas Min: $1,461,920

Fully Supported US Personnel Overseas:

Expecting to serve more than 4 years: 94
Countries: Unspecified Country 94

Church of God of Prophecy
P.O. Box 2910
Cleveland, TN 37320-2910 USA
Phone: (423) 559-5336
Fax: (423) 472-5037
E-mail: Global@cogop.org
Web Site: www.cogop.org
Mr. Randy Howard, Global Outreach

A denominational sending agency of Pentecostal tradition engaged in church planting, evangelism, leadership development, support of national churches and support of national workers.

Year Founded in US: 1903
Income for Overseas Min: $2,000,000
Fully Supported US Personnel Overseas:
Expecting to serve more than 4 years: 15
Non-residential mission personnel: 8
Other personnel:
Short-term less than 1 year from US: 50
Non-US serving in own/other country: 352
Bivocational/Tentmaker from US: 1
Countries: Angola; Argentina; Australia 2; Azerbaijan; Barbados; Belarus; Belgium; Belize; Benin; Bermuda; Bolivia; Botswana; Brazil; Bulgaria; Burkina Faso; Cameroon; Caribbean–General; Central African Republic; Chad; Chile; China 2; Colombia; Congo, Democratic Republic of the; Costa Rica; Cote d'Ivoire; Cuba; Cyprus; Ecuador; Egypt; El Salvador; Ethiopia; Fiji; Finland; France; French Guiana; Gabon; Gambia, The; Germany 4; Greece; Guyana; Haiti; Hungary; India; Indonesia; Israel; Japan 2; Kazakhstan; Kenya; Korea, South; Liberia; Malawi; Malaysia; Malta; Mozambique; Namibia; Netherlands Antilles; New Zealand; Pakistan; Panama; Paraguay; Peru; Philippines; Portugal; Romania; Russia; Rwanda; Samoa 2; Senegal; Sierra Leone; South Africa; Spain; Sri Lanka; Sudan; Suriname; Swaziland; Tanzania; Thailand; Togo; Trinidad and Tobago; Uganda; Ukraine 3; Uruguay; Venezuela; Virgin Islands; Zambia; Zimbabwe

Church of the Brethren
1451 Dundee Ave.
Elgin, IL 60120-1694 USA
Phone: (847) 742-5100
Fax: (847) 742-6103
E-mail: mission_gb@brethren.org
Web Site: www.brethren.org
Mr. Mervin Keeney,Dir. Global Msn. Partner

A denominational sending agency of Brethren tradition engaged in support of national churches, development and relief and/or rehabilitation.

Year Founded in US: 1884
Income for Overseas Min: $2,260,000
Personnel:
Home ministry & office staff in US: 3

Church of the Nazarene, World Mission Divison
6401 The Paseo
Kansas City, MO 64131 USA
Phone: (816) 333-7000
Fax: (816) 363-3100
Web Site: www.nazareneworldmission.org
Dr. Louie E. Bustle, Director

A denominational sending agency of Holiness and Wesleyan tradition engaged in church planting, TEE, evangelism, missions information service, missionary education, aviation services, providing medical supplies, medical work, relief and/or rehabilitation and missionary training.

Purpose: "...to respond to the Great Commission of Christ to 'go and make disciples of all nations'...to advance God's Kingdom by the preservation and propagation of Christian Holiness..."
Year Founded in US: 1895
Income for Overseas Min: $48,766,310
Fully Supported US Personnel Overseas:
Expecting to serve more than 4 years: 258
Expecting to serve 1 to 4 years: 66
Other personnel:
Short-term less than 1 year from US: 9,423
Non-US serving in own/other country: 85
Home ministry & office staff in US: 39
Bivocational/Tentmaker from US: 23
Countries: Albania 2; American Samoa 2; Angola 2; Antigua; Argentina 8; Armenia; Aruba; Australia 2; Azores; Bahamas, The; Bangladesh; Barbados; Belau; Belize; Benin 2; Bermuda; Bolivia 2; Botswana; Brazil 4;

Bulgaria 2; Burkina Faso; Burundi; Cambodia 2; Cameroon; Cape Verde; Chile 2; China 9; Colombia; Congo, Democratic Republic of; Congo, Republic of the; Costa Rica 6; Cote d'Ivoire 10; Croatia; Cuba; Cyprus; Denmark; Dominica; Dominican Republic; East Timor; Ecuador 4; Egypt; El Salvador; Equatorial Guinea; Eritrea; Ethiopia 2; Fiji 4; France 3; French Guiana; Gabon; Germany 6; Ghana; Greece; Grenada; Guadeloupe; Guam 2; Guatemala 7; Guyana; Haiti 4; Honduras; Hong Kong; Hungary; India 2; Indonesia 4; Ireland; Israel 3; Italy 2; Jamaica; Japan 2; Jordan; Kazakhstan; Kenya 14; Korea, South 6; Lebanon 2; Lesotho 2; Liberia; Macedonia; Madagascar 4; Malawi 2; Martinique; Mexico 6; Micronesia, Federated States of; Mozambique 9; N. Mariana Isls; Namibia 2; Nepal; Netherlands; New Zealand; Nicaragua; Nigeria 1; Pakistan; Panama; Papua New Guinea 25; Paraguay; Peru 7; Philippines 16; Poland; Portugal; Puerto Rico; Romania 1; Russia 7; Rwanda 3; Saint Kitts and Nevis; Saint Lucia; Saint Martin; Saint Vincent and the Grenadines; Samoa; Sao Tome and Principe 2; Senegal 2; Slovenia 1; Solomon Islands 2; South Africa 13; Spain; Sri Lanka; Suriname; Swaziland 7; Switzerland 6; Syria; Taiwan; Tanzania; Thailand 5; Togo; Tonga; Trinidad and Tobago 1; Turkey; Uganda 2; Ukraine 6; United Kingdom; Uruguay; Vanuatu; Venezuela 4; Virgin Islands; Zambia; Zimbabwe

Church of the United Brethren in Christ, Global Ministries

302 Lake St.
Huntington, IN 46750 USA
Phone: (260) 356-2312
Fax: (260) 356-4730
E-mail: missions@ub.org
Web Site: www.ub.org

Rev. Gary Dilley, Director

A denominational support agency of Evangelical tradition engaged in support of national workers, church planting, evangelism, funds transmission, support of national churches and mobilization for mission.

Purpose: "...to grow and multiply churches through worship, evangelism, discipleship and social concern by actively

seeking and winning the lost..."
Year Founded in US: 1853
Income for Overseas Min: $357,046
Fully Supported US Personnel Overseas:
  Expecting to serve more than 4 years: 5
Other personnel:
  Short-term less than 1 year from US: 100
  Home ministry & office staff in US: 5
Countries: India 2; Macau 3

Church Planting Intl.

P.O. Box 836
Gainesville, GA 30503 USA
Phone: (770) 535-7008
Fax: (770) 534-1025
E-mail: cpimission@juno.com

Rev. George P. Hutchinson, Exec. Director

A transdenominational support agency of Evangelical and Presbyterian tradition engaged in support of indigenous church planting movements in developing countries.

Purpose: "Assisting indigenous church planting ministries in developing countries."
Year Founded in US: 1983
Income for Overseas Min: $100,000
Personnel:
  Short-term less than 1 year from US: 9
  Non-US serving in own/other country: 1
  Home ministry & office staff in US: 1
  Bivocational/Tentmaker from US: 1
Countries: Myanmar/Burma; Portugal; Uganda

Church Resource Ministries

1240 N. Lakeview Ave., Ste.120
Anaheim, CA 92807 USA
Phone: (714) 779-0370
Fax: (714) 779-0189
E-mail: CRM@crmnet.org
Web Site: www.crmnet.org

Dr. Samuel F. Metcalf, President

A transdenominational sending agency of Evangelical tradition engaged in leadership development, church planting and development.

Purpose: "...to develop leaders to strengthen and start churches worldwide."
Year Founded in US: 1980
Income for Overseas Min: $3,079,961

Gifts-in-Kind: $21,233

Fully Supported US Personnel Overseas:
Expecting to serve more than 4 years: 60
Expecting to serve 1 to 4 years: 1
Nonresidential mission personnel: 2

Other personnel:
Short-term less than 1 year from US: 45
Non-US serving in own/other country: 1
Home ministry & office staff in US: 13

Countries: Asia–General 2; Cambodia 7; France 4; Hungary 10; Japan 4; Poland 4; Romania 6; Russia 11; Singapore 4; Venezuela 8

Church World Service & Witness, Unit of the Natl. Council of the Churches of Christ in the US.
P.O. Box 968
Elkhart, IN 46515 USA
Phone: (800) 297-1516
Fax: (574) 262-0966
E-mail: cws@ncccusa.org
Web Site: www.churchworldservice.org
John L. McCullough, Exec. Director

An interdenominational service agency of Ecumenical tradition engaged in relief and/ or rehabilitation, agricultural programs and development. Personnel and GIK data from 1998.

Purpose: "...meets basic needs of people in peril, works for justice and dignity with the poor and vulnerable, promotes peace and understanding among people of different faiths, races, and nations and affirms and preserves the diversity and integrity of God's creation."

Year Founded in US: 1946
Income for Overseas Min: $57,998,444
Gifts-in-Kind: $8,200,000
Fully Supported US Personnel Overseas:
Expecting to serve more than 4 years: 8
Expecting to serve 1 to 4 years: 204
Nonresidential mission personnel: 10

Other personnel:
Non-US serving in own/other country: 92
Home ministry & office staff in US: 35

Countries: Africa–General 5; Asia–General; Cambodia 1; Europe–General 1; Indonesia; Laos 1; Latin America–General; Pakistan; Thailand; Vietnam

Churches of Christ
(No Central Office) USA

A body of autonomous congregations and agencies of the Christian "Restoration Movement" (not using instrumental music in worship) which sends and supports missionaries directly from local congregations. Data furnished by Missions Resource Network.

Income for Overseas Min: NA
Fully Supported US Personnel Overseas:
Expecting to serve more than 4 years: 799
Expecting to serve 1 to 4 years: 17

Other personnel:
Short-term less than 1 year from US: 7,765
Non-US serving in own/other country: 364
Home ministry & office staff in US: 43

Countries: Albania 25; American Samoa 2; Antigua 2; Argentina 13; Australia; Austria 14; Bahamas, The 4; Bangladesh 1; Barbados 1; Belarus 2; Belgium 12; Belize 8; Benin 6; Bosnia and Herzegovina 2; Botswana; Brazil 79; Bulgaria 3; Burkina Faso 6; Cameroon; Central African Republic; Chile 19; China 6; Colombia; Costa Rica 4; Cote d'Ivoire 3; Croatia 2; Czech Republic 4; Denmark; Dominican Republic 5; Ecuador 12; Egypt 2; El Salvador; Estonia 10; Ethiopia; Finland 1; France 18; Germany 34; Ghana 8; Greece 2; Guatemala 4; Guyana 8; Haiti 2; Honduras 8; Hungary 11; India 9; Indonesia 5; Israel; Italy 28; Jamaica 1; Japan 11; Kazakhstan 2; Kenya 29; Korea, South 1; Latvia 1; Lithuania 9; Malawi 5; Malaysia; Mexico 47; Mozambique 2; Nepal 1; Netherlands 5; New Zealand 5; Nicaragua 3; Nigeria 14; Norway; Panama 1; Papua New Guinea 7; Paraguay 8; Peru 4; Philippines 22; Poland 1; Portugal 2; Romania 17; Russia 30; South Africa 14; Spain 2; Swaziland 3; Switzerland 4; Taiwan 2; Tanzania 5; Thailand 22; Togo 20; Trinidad and Tobago 1; Uganda 30; Ukraine 25; United Kingdom 51; Uruguay 2; Venezuela 2; Yugoslavia 2; Zambia; Zimbabwe 1

Churches of God, General Conference
P.O. Box 926
Findlay, OH 45839 USA
Phone: (419) 424-1961
Fax: (419) 424-3433
E-mail: Missions@cggc.org
Web Site: www.cggc.org

Rev. Wayne W. Boyer, Exec. Director

A denominational support agency of evangelical and Church of God tradition engaged in leadership development, church planting, Christian education, medical work, support of national churches and support of national workers.

Purpose: "...to evangelize, disciple and equip a community of Christians for effective witness and meaningful service within their own culture."

Year Founded in US: 1825

Income for Overseas Min: $1,009,300

Fully Supported US Personnel Overseas:
  Expecting to serve more than 4 years: 7
  Expecting to serve 1 to 4 years: 2

Other personnel:
  Short-term less than 1 year from US: 3
  Non-US serving in own/other country: 510
  Home ministry & office staff in US: 6

Countries: Bangladesh; Brazil 3; Haiti 4; India

Cities for Christ Worldwide

3644 Wild Horse Ct.
Loveland, CO 80538-5312 USA

Phone: (970) 663-0477
E-mail: Monsmatd1@aol.com

Dr. Timothy Monsma, Exec. Director

An interdenominational support agency of Presbyterian and Reformed tradition focused on developing-world cities and orphan care in Africa.

Year Founded in US: 1985

Income for Overseas Min: $47,590

Personnel:
  Short-term less than 1 year from US: 3
  Home ministry & office staff in US: 1

Citireach International

P.O. Box 63120
5801 N. Union. Blvd., #101
Colorado Springs, CO 80962-3120 USA

Phone: (719) 528-5770
Fax: (719) 548-9619
E-mail: citireach@cs.com
Web Site: www.citireach.org

Dr. Jack Dennison, President

A service agency of evangelical tradition engaged in evangelism, leadership develop-

ment and missions information service.

Purpose: "To serve the whole church, taking the whole gospel to the whole city, transforming society."

Year Founded in US: 1998

CityTeam Ministries

2304 Zanker Rd.
San Jose, CA 95131 USA

Phone: (408) 232-5600
Fax: (408) 428-9505
E-mail: info@cityteam.org
Web Site: www.cityteam.org

Patrick J. Robertson, President

A transdenominational support agency of Evangelical tradition engaged in evangelism, camping programs, leadership development, missionary training and youth programs in 6 U.S. cities and partnerships in more than 7 other countries. Personnel data from 1996.

Purpose: "...serving people in need, proclaiming the gospel, and establishing disciples among the disadvantaged people of cities."

Year Founded in US: 1957

Income for Overseas Min: NA

Personnel:
  Short-term less than 1 year from US: 4
  Home ministry & office staff in US: 102

Clark Theological College (India) Tribal Ministries, USA

555 Memory Lane, #d206
Santa Ana, CA 92706 USA

Phone: (714) 972-9048

Mr. Jon Washburn, Chairman

A support agency of Evangelical tradition engaged in missionary training, theological education, leadership development and support of national workers.

Purpose: "...to provide prayer and financial support to enable Clark Theological College to fulfill its ministry of training Christian leadership to serve the church in India and beyond its borders, to reach the unsaved for Christ."

Year Founded in US: 1993

Income for Overseas Min: $10,255

Personnel:
Short-term less than 1 year from US: 2

Countries: India

CLC Ministries International

701 Pennsylvania Ave.
Ft. Washington, PA 19034 USA

Phone: (215) 542-1244
Fax: (215) 542-7580
E-mail: almackclcusa@cs.com
Web Site: clcusa.org

Mr. William M. Almack, President

An interdenominational support agency of Evangelical tradition engaged in literature distribution, Bible distribution, correspondence courses, literacy work and missionary training.

Year Founded in US: 1957

Income for Overseas Min: NA

Fully Supported US Personnel Overseas:
Expecting to serve more than 4 years: 8
Expecting to serve 1 to 4 years: 5

Other personnel:
Home ministry & office staff in US: 24

Countries: Asia–General; Colombia 2; Hong Kong 2; Italy 2; Portugal; United Kingdom 2

CMF International

P.O. Box 501020
Indianapolis, IN 46250-6020 USA

Phone: (317) 578-2700
Fax: (317) 578-2827
E-mail: 76534.244@compuserve.com
Web Site: www.cmfi.org

Dr. Doug Priest, Gen. Director

A nondenominational sending agency of Christian (Restoration Movement) and Evangelical tradition engaged in church planting, development, evangelism, leadership development, medical work and missionary training.

Purpose: "...mobilizes Christians to draw people from all nations into relationship with Christ and His church."

Year Founded in US: 1949

Income for Overseas Min: $6,962,719

Fully Supported US Personnel Overseas:
Expecting to serve more than 4 years: 59

Expecting to serve 1 to 4 years: 50
Nonresidential mission personnel: 1

Other personnel:
Short-term less than 1 year from US: 50
Non-US serving in own/other country: 7
Home ministry & office staff in US: 25
Bivocational/Tentmaker from US: 13

Countries: Brazil 4; Chile 2; China; Cote d'Ivoire; Eritrea 1; Ethiopia 4; Indonesia 3; Kenya 23; Mexico 6; Singapore 2; Tanzania; Thailand; Ukraine 2; United Kingdom 12; Vietnam

CMTS Ministries, Inc.

321 Focht Rd.
Bernville, PA 19506-9118 USA

Phone: (610) 488-6975
Fax: (610) 488-6111
E-mail: CMTSmin@aol.com
Web Site: www.cmtsministries.org

Mr. Andrew Merrick, Sr., Exec.

An interdenominational service agency of Evangelical tradition engaged in technical assistance, furloughed missionary support, short-term programs, supplying equipment, training and video/film production/distribution.

Purpose: "...providing technical assistance, materials and equipment for use by Bible-believing missionaries and Christian organizations."

Year Founded in US: 1982

Income for Overseas Min: $43,731

Personnel:
Home ministry & office staff in US: 11

ComCare International

202 N. Lafayette St.
Macomb, IL 61455-2206 USA

Phone: (309) 833-3727
Fax: (309) 833-3727
E-mail: cci@comcareinternational.org
Web Site: www.comcareinternational.org

Julia Roskamp, Exec. Director

An interdenominational specialized agency of Evangelical tradition engaged in medical work, technical assistance, and training, including solar powered hearing aids for unreached people.

Year Founded in US: 1989

Income for Overseas Min: $24,000
Fully Supported US Personnel Overseas:
  Expecting to serve more than 4 years: 2
Other personnel:
  Non-US serving in own/other country: 2
Countries: Mexico 2

Commission to Every Nation
(See Ad on page 131)
P.O. Box 291307
Kerrville, TX 78029-1307 USA
Phone: (830) 896-8326
Fax: (830) 896-5262
E-mail: info@cten.org
Web Site: www.cten.org
Mr. Richard Malm, President

An interdenominational sending agency of Evangelical and Independent tradition engaged in member care, broadcasting, childcare/orphanage programs, development, Christian education and linguistics.

Purpose: "...partnering with churches to help Christians become personally involved in fulfilling the Great Commission to every nation."
Year Founded in US: 1994
Income for Overseas Min: NR
  Fully Supported US Personnel Overseas:
  Expecting to serve more than 4 years: 48
  Expecting to serve 1 to 4 years: 24
Other personnel:
  Short-term less than 1 year from US: 3
  Non-US serving in own/other country: 8
  Home ministry & office staff in US: 5
Countries: Bolivia 1; Cameroon; Costa Rica 2; Guatemala 16; India; Israel 2; Mexico 8; Mongolia 5; Namibia; Philippines 11; Romania 2; South Africa 1

Compassion Intl., Inc.
P.O. Box 65000
Colorado Springs, CO 80962-5000 USA
Phone: (719) 487-7000
Fax: (719) 487-6246
E-mail: ciinfo@us.ci.org
Web Site: www.compassion.com
Dr. Wesley K. Stafford, President/CEO

A nondenominational support agency engaged in youth programs, development, Christian education, evangelism, leadership development.

Purpose: "...an advocate for children to release them from their spiritual, economic, social and physical poverty and enable them to become responsible and fulfilled Christian adults."
Year Founded in US: 1952
Income for Overseas Min: $90,329,583
Gifts-in-Kind: $106,830
Fully Supported US Personnel Overseas:
  Expecting to serve more than 4 years: 2
Other personnel:
  Non-US serving in own/other country: 563
  Home ministry & office staff in US: 394
Countries: Bolivia; Brazil; Colombia; Congo, Democratic Republic of the; Dominican Republic; Ecuador; El Salvador; Ethiopia; Guatemala; Haiti; Honduras; India; Indonesia; Kenya 1; Malaysia 1 Mexico; Nicaragua; Peru; Philippines; Rwanda; Tanzania; Thailand; Uganda

Concordia Gospel Outreach
P.O. Box 201
St. Louis, MO 63166-0201 USA
Phone: (314) 268-1363
Fax: (314) 268-1202
E-mail: outreach@cph.org
Web Site: www.cgo-online.org
Annette Frank, Manager

A specialized agency of Lutheran tradition engaged in literature distribution.
Purpose: "...distributes Gospel materials and supports the expansion of the Gospel worldwide."
Year Founded in US: 1992
Income for Overseas Min: NR
Personnel:
  Home ministry & office staff in US: 1

Congregational Christian Churches, National Assoc.
8473 S. Howell Ave.
Milwaukee, WI 53154 USA
Phone: (414) 764-1620
Fax: (414) 764-0319
E-mail: naccc@naccc.org
Web Site: www.naccc.org
Ruth Mahnke, Exec. Assistant

We'll help you get there.

Photo by a CTEN missionary in Africa.

Most mission agencies invite you to join to accomplish their mission. That is wonderful but what if God has called you to do something unique that does not fit the mold?

CTEN serves these individuals by providing services and oversight to help them fulfill God's special call.

Training and internship options available.

Commission
TO EVERY NATION

P.O. Box 291307
Kerrville, TX 78029

www.cten.org
800.872.5404

Dear Pastor:
We specialize in partnering with churches to help you get your people onto the field as an extension of your church and ministry. Call us for details.

Effective ministry takes passion, dedication and a strong foundation.

Columbia Biblical Seminary

Equipping Great Commission Christians
to minister in multicultural communities.

www.ciu.edu/seminary • 800-777-2227

A Ministry of Columbia International University

An association of churches of Congregational tradition engaged in relief and/or rehabilitation, agricultural programs, church construction, development, funds transmission and missions information service.

Purpose: "To encourage and assist local churches in their development of vibrant and effective witnesses to Christ in Congregational ways."

Year Founded in US: 1953

Income for Overseas Min: $450,000

Personnel:
Short-term less than 1 year from US: 125
Non-US serving in own/other country: 22
Home ministry & office staff in US: 2
Bivocational/Tentmaker from US: 18

Congregational Holiness Church World

3888 Fayetteville Hwy.
Griffin, GA 30223 USA

Phone: (770) 228-4833

Fax: (770) 228-1177

Web Site: www.chchurch.com

Rev. Ronald Wilson, Supt. World Missions

A denominational support agency of Holiness and Pentecostal tradition engaged in support of national workers, church construction, Christian education and providing medical supplies in 17 countries.

Year Founded in US: 1921

Income for Overseas Min: NR

Personnel:
Home ministry & office staff in US: 4

Congregational Methodist Church, Division of Mission Ministries

P.O. Box 9
Florence, MS 39073 USA

Phone: (601) 845-8787

Fax: (601) 845-8788

E-mail: dmmissions@aol.com

Rev. Jerry M. Jones, Director

A denominational sending agency of Wesleyan tradition engaged in evangelism, Bible distribution, church planting, correspondence courses, TEE and theological education.

Year Founded in US: 1945

Income for Overseas Min: $87,042

Gifts-in-Kind: NA

Fully Supported US Personnel Overseas:
Expecting to serve more than 4 years: 15
Expecting to serve 1 to 4 years: 2

Other personnel:
Non-US serving in own/other country: 2
Home ministry & office staff in US: 3

Countries: Bolivia 1; Mexico 14; Uganda

Connecting Businessmen to Christ

6650 E. Brainard Rd., Ste. 100
Chattanooga, TN 37421 USA

Phone: (423) 698-4444

Fax: (423) 629-4434

E-mail: info@cbmc.com

Web Site: www.cbmc.com

Mr. Fritz Klumpp, Exec. Director

An interdenominational support agency of Evangelical tradition engaged in evangelism.

Purpose: "...saturating the business and professional community with the Gospel...by establishing, equipping and mobilizing teams where we work and live that yield spiritual reproducers."

Year Founded in US: 1950

Income for Overseas Min: NA

Conservative Baptist Foreign Mission Society (CBFMS) See: CBInternational

Conservative Baptist Home Mission Society (CBHMS) See: Mission to the Americas

Conservative Congregational Christian Conference

7582 Currell Blvd. #108
St. Paul, MN 55125 USA

Phone: (651) 739-1474

Fax: (651) 739-0750

E-mail: dmjohnson@ccccusa.org

Web Site: www.ccccusa.org

Rev. Clifford R. Christensen, Conf. Minister

A denominational support agency of Congregational and Evangelical tradition engaged in support of national churches and short-term programs. Financial information from 1996.

Year Founded in US: 1948

Income for Overseas Min: $107,805

Fully Supported US Personnel Overseas:
   Expecting to serve more than 4 years: 2

Other personnel:
   Short-term less than 1 year from US: 20
   Non-US serving in own/other country: 3
   Home ministry & office staff in US: 5

Countries: Federated States of Micronesia 2

Cook Communications Ministries

4050 Lee Vance View
Colorado Springs, CO 80918 USA

Phone: (719) 536-0100
Fax: (719) 536-3266
E-mail: ccmintl@ccmi.org
Web Site: www.cookministries.com

Mr. David Mehlis, President

An interdenominational ministry of evangelical tradition engaged in making Christian literature available from translations of their English language product and through training Christian publishers to provide Christian literature in their own language and country.

Purpose: "To encourage the acceptance of Jesus Christ as personal Savior and to aid, promote and contribute to the teaching and putting into practice of His two great commands..."

Year Founded in US: 1944

Income for Overseas Min: $2,176,000

Gifts-in-Kind: $96,753

Personnel:
   Home ministry & office staff in US: 11

Cornerstone International

P.O. Box 192
Wilmore, KY 40390 USA

Phone: (859) 858-4578
Fax: (859) 858-0981
E-mail: cornerstone407@juno.com
Web Site:
www.cornerstoneinternational.org
Mr. E. Duane Jones, Director

A nondenominational sending agency of Wesleyan and Charismatic tradition engaged in church planting, mobilization for mission, children's programs, TEE, evangelism and short-term programs.

Purpose: "...to evangelize and disciple...[in] partnership with local churches in the launching of short-term and career missionaries."

Year Founded in US: 1972

Income for Overseas Min: $565,226

Personnel:
   Home ministry & office staff in US: 4

Correll Missionary Ministries
(See Ad on page 135)

8116 S. Tryon St., Suite B3 #233
Charlotte, NC 28273

Phone: (803) 547-2475
Fax: (803) 547-2474
E-mail: office@correll.org
Web Site: www.correll.org

Rev. Jorge Parrott, President

An interdenominational service agency of Evangelical and Charismatic tradition engaged in support of national workers, broadcasting, church construction, church planting, Christian education and medical work.

Year Founded in US: 1978

Income for Overseas Min: $290,000

Gifts-in-Kind: $10,000

Fully Supported US Personnel Overseas:
   Expecting to serve more than 4 years: 8
   Expecting to serve 1 to 4 years: 6
   Nonresidential mission personnel: 2

Other personnel:
   Short-term less than 1 year from US: 50
   Non-US serving in own/other country: 145
   Home ministry & office staff in US: 5

Countries: Bolivia; Cuba; Dominican Republic; El Salvador; Ghana 1; Guatemala 5; India; Philippines; Spain; Thailand; Unspecified Country 2

Covenant Celebration Church Global Outreach

1819 E. 72nd St.
Tacoma, WA 98404 USA

Phone: (253) 475-6454

Fax: (253) 473-7515
E-mail: info@championscentre.com
Web Site: www.covenantcelebration.org
Kevin Gerald, Senior Pastor

A nondenominational support agency of Charismatic tradition engaged in church planting, leadership development, support of national workers and evangelism. Statistical data from 1998.

Purpose: "...[to] pursue the Great Commission both mono-culturally and cross-culturally through aggressive action in...evangelism and missions."

Year Founded in US: 1981

Income for Overseas Min: $50,000

Personnel:
    Home ministry & office staff in US: 1
    Bivocational/Tentmaker from US: 2

Countries: Burundi; Philippines; United Kingdom

Crisis Consulting Intl.
(See Ad on page 136)
9452 Telephone Rd., #223
Ventura, CA 93004 USA
Phone: (805) 642-2549
Fax: (805) 642-1748
E-mail: info@cricon.org
Web Site: www.cricon.org
Mr. Robert Klamser, Exec. Director

A nondenominational service agency of Evangelical tradition engaged in security/crisis management consulting/training and services for other agencies.

Purpose: "...providing security-related training and consultation services to... mission organizations with specific needs such as event security, protection of personnel and investigation of hostile acts..."

Year Founded in US: 1985

Income for Overseas Min: NA

Crossover Communications International
P.O. Box 211755
Columbia, SC 29221 USA
Phone: (803) 691-0688
Fax: (803) 691-9355
E-mail: info@crossoverusa.org
Web Site: www.crossoverusa.org

Dr. William H. Jones, President

A nondenominational service agency of Evangelical tradition engaged in church planting, Christian education, theological education, leadership development, medical work and short-term programs.

Purpose: "In the power of the Spirit...to communicate the message of Christ...to the peoples of the world."

Year Founded in US: 1989

Income for Overseas Min: $313,153

Fully Supported US Personnel Overseas:
    Expecting to serve more than 4 years: 5
    Expecting to serve 1 to 4 years: 2

Other personnel:
    Short-term less than 1 year from US: 444
    Non-US serving in own/other country: 3
    Home ministry & office staff in US: 22

Countries: Brazil 1; Moldova 2; Turkey 2

Cumberland Presbyterian Church Board of Missions
1978 Union Ave.
Memphis, TN 38104 USA
Phone: (901) 276-9988
Fax: (901) 276-4578
E-mail: missions@cumberland.org
Web Site: www.cumberland.org/bom
Rev. Michael Sharpe, Exec. Director

A denominational sending agency of Presbyterian tradition engaged in church planting, Christian education, furloughed missionary support, missions information service, support of national churches and relief and/or rehabilitation.

Year Founded in US: 1810

Income for Overseas Min: $383,594

Fully Supported US Personnel Overseas:
    Expecting to serve more than 4 years: 3
    Expecting to serve 1 to 4 years: 5

Other personnel:
    Short-term less than 1 year from US: 3
    Home ministry & office staff in US: 12
    Bivocational/Tentmaker from US: 6

Countries: Brazil; Colombia 3; Guatemala; Hong Kong; Zimbabwe

D & D Missionary Homes, Inc.
4020 58th Avenue North
St. Petersburg, FL 33714-1133 USA

Phone: (727) 522-0522
Fax: (727) 522-0524
E-mail: d_d.missionary.homes@juno.com
Web Site: www.ddmissionaryhomes.org
Mr. Philip R. Fogle, President

A service agency of Evangelical and Independent tradition engaged in furloughed missionary support, childrens programs and missions information service.

Purpose: "...ministry of hospitality for missionaries who may not otherwise have a place to call home for furloughs, medical leaves, sabbaticals and so on."

Year Founded in US: 1949

Income for Overseas Min: NA

Personnel:
   Home ministry & office staff in US: 18

David Livingstone KURE Foundation

P.O. Box 232
Tulsa. OK 74102 USA

Phone: (918) 742-9902
Fax: (918) 496-2873
E-mail: DLMFKURE@aol.com
Web Site: www.dlmfkure.org
Mr. H. Dwain Griffin, Chairman/CEO

A nondenominational service agency of Independent tradition engaged in support of national workers. Statistical data from 1998.

Year Founded in US: 1969

Income for Overseas Min: $1,500,000

Personnel:
   Non-US serving in own/other country: 113
   Home ministry & office staff in US: 9

Countries: Korea, South; Mexico; Philippines; Thailand; Ukraine

Dawn Ministries

5775 N. Union Blvd.
Colorado Springs, CO 80918 USA

Phone: (719) 548-7460
Fax: (719) 548-7475
E-mail:
DAWNinformation@dawnministries.org
Web Site: www.dawnministries.org
Dr. James H. Montgomery, Chairman

A transdenominational service agency of Evangelical tradition engaged in mobilizing

the whole body of Christ in 155 nations. Staff figure from 1996.

Purpose: "...to see saturation church planting become the generally accepted and fervently practiced strategy for completing the task of making disciples of all peoples in our generation."

Year Founded in US: 1985

Income for Overseas Min: NA

Personnel:
   Home ministry & office staff in US: 15

Dayspring Enterprises Intl.

1062 Laskin Rd., Suite 21A
Virginia Beach, VA 23451 USA

Phone: (757) 428-1092
Fax: (757) 428-0257
E-mail: daysprgint@aol.com
Web Site: www.dayspringinternational.org
Rev. John E. Gilman, President

A nondenominational support agency of Evangelical tradition engaged in evangelism, broadcasting, support of national workers, relief and/or rehabilitation and supplying equipment.

Purpose: "...to be an enabling servant to the indigenous church by providing innovative, creative and culturally relevant multimedia tools to aid in evangelizing and discipling of unreached people groups."

Year Founded in US: 1979

Income for Overseas Min: $411,617

Personnel:
   Home ministry & office staff in US: 11

Countries: India

Daystar U.S.

5701 Normandale Rd. #343
Edina, MN 55424 USA

Phone: (952) 928-2550
Fax: (952) 928-2551
E-mail: DAYSTARUS@compuserve.com
Web Site: www.daystarus.org
Dr. Dennis Morrow, Exec. Director

A nondenominational sending agency of Evangelical tradition engaged in providing support for Daystar Univ. in Nairobi, in theological education, management consulting/training, missionary training, extension education and mission-related research.

Purpose: "To expand God's Kingdom in Africa by equipping Christian servant leaders through B.A./M.A. programs, short courses and research services."

Year Founded in US: 1963

Income for Overseas Min: $1,232,618

Gifts-in-Kind: $66,334

Fully Supported US Personnel Overseas:
   Expecting to serve more than 4 years: 7

Other personnel:
   Home ministry & office staff in US: 7

Countries: Kenya 7

Deaf Missions International

P.O. Box 8514
Clearwater, FL 33758 USA

Phone: (727) 530-3020
E-mail: deafmissions@netzero.net

M. Eldeny Hale, Director

A transdenominational specialized agency of Evangelical tradition engaged in ministry to those with hearing disabilities through mission projects including missionary orientation and training.

Year Founded in US: 1967

Income for Overseas Min: NA

Personnel:
   Home ministry & office staff in US: 1

Derek Prince Ministries, Intl.

P.O. Box 19501
Charlotte, NC 28219 USA

Phone: (704) 357-3556
Fax: (704) 357-1413
E-mail: ContactUs@dpmusa.org
Web Site: www.dpmusa.org

Mr. David Selby, Exec. Director

A nondenominational support agency engaged in audio/video recording, production and distribution, broadcasting in 13 languages, and literature translation, production and distribution in up to 50 languages.

Purpose: "...seeking to reach the unreached, teach the untaught and touch the untouched with the pure truths of God's Word in all nations through the distribution of teaching material by Derek Prince..."

Year Founded in US: 1963

Income for Overseas Min: $286,358

Personnel:
   Home ministry & office staff in US: 27

Development Associates International (DAI)

P.O. Box 49278
Colorado Springs, CO 80949 USA

Phone: (719) 598-7970
Fax: (425) 988-8126
E-mail: info@daintl.org
Web Site: www.daintl.org

Mrs. Jane Overstreet, President/CEO

A transdenominational support agency of Evangelical and Ecumenical tradition engaged in leadership development, extension education and management consulting/training.

Purpose: "Development Associates International is committed to develop the integrity and effectiveness of Christian leaders worldwide so that the church can fulfill its role in extending the Kingdom of God."

Year Founded in US: 1996

Income for Overseas Min: $143,575

Fully Supported US Personnel Overseas:
   Nonresidential mission personnel: 2

Other personnel:
   Non-US serving in own/other country: 5

Countries: Belgium; Cote d'Ivoire; Egypt; Ghana; Haiti; India; Kazakhstan; Nigeria; Russia; South Africa; Switzerland; Uganda

Disciples International

P.O. Box 466
Wallingford, PA 19086 USA

Phone: (610) 872-8742
Fax: (610) 872-8762
E-mail: david.komarnicki@verizon.net
Web Site: www.disciplesinternational.org

Mr. David Komarnicki, President/CEO

A specialized agency of Evangelical tradition engaged in evangelism, literature distribution, literature production, services for other agencies and Bible memorization.

Purpose: "...to obtain translations of and distribute copies of the Apostles' Creed and certain Bible verses into the 100 most widely spoken languages."

Year Founded in US: 2002

Income for Overseas Min: $700

Donetsk Christian University

P.O. Box 52114
Tulsa, OK 74152-1144 USA
Phone: (918) 249-2011
E-mail: pr@dcu.donetsk.ua
Web Site: www.dcu.donbass.com

A nondenominational specialized agency of Evangelical and Baptist tradition engaged in theological education, missionary education and leadership development. Statistical data from 1998.

Purpose: "...to train national pastors, missionaries and teachers for the former Soviet Union."

Year Founded in US: 1991

Income for Overseas Min: $161,565

Fully Supported US Personnel Overseas:
  Expecting to serve more than 4 years: 6
Other personnel:
  Short-term less than 1 year from US: 22
  Non-US serving in own/other country: 20
  Home ministry & office staff in US: 1
Countries: Ukraine 6

DualReach

P.O. Box 427
Dana Point, CA 92629 USA
Phone: (949) 248-1236
E-mail: info@dualreach.org
Web Site: www.dualreach.org
Mr. Bruce Camp, President/CEO

A transdenominational service agency of Evangelical tradition engaged in missions mobilization of churches and assistance to the church-mobilization ministry mission of agencies via consulting, training and production of resources, to increase their global impact.

Purpose: "...to exponentially increase the number of churches effectively and strategically involved in world evangelization."

Year Founded in US: 2001

Income for Overseas Min: NA

Personnel:
  Home ministry & office staff in US: 2

East Gates Ministries Intl.

P.O. Box 2010
Sumner, WA 98390-0440 USA
Phone: (253) 770-2625

Fax: (253) 770-2817
E-mail: EGMI@eastgates.org
Web Site: www.eastgates.org
Rev. Nelson Graham, President

A specialized agency of Evangelical and Ecumenical tradition engaged in Bible distribution, audio recording/distribution, church construction, literature distribution, literature production and support of national workers.

Purpose: "...to have a positive impact on the Church history of China through diplomatic activity that helps Chinese leaders, at all levels, better understand and appreciate their Christian population."

Year Founded in US: 1990

Income for Overseas Min: $846,986

Personnel:
  Non-US serving in own/other country: 4
  Home ministry & office staff in US: 8
Countries: China; Hong Kong

East West Ministries

P.O. Box 270333
St. Paul, MN 55127 USA
Phone: (651) 765-2550
Fax: (651) 765-2523
E-mail: jonesewm@juno.com
Annette L. Jones, Director

A nondenominational support agency of Evangelical tradition engaged in support of national churches, leadership development, literature distribution and training.

Purpose: "...serving those who serve in the name of Jesus Christ and seeking to fulfill the two-fold mandate of evangelism; to share the gospel message and to care for people in obvious need."

Year Founded in US: 1993

Income for Overseas Min: $49,000

Personnel:
  Non-US serving in own/other country: 14
  Home ministry & office staff in US: 1
Countries: Ghana; Haiti; India; Myanmar

Eastern European Outreach, Inc.

(See Ad on page 143)
P.O. Box 685
Murrieta, CA 92564 USA

Phone: (909) 696-5244
Fax: (909) 696-5247
E-mail: info@eeo.org
Web Site: www.eeo.org
Mr. Jeff L. Thompson, Exec. Director
A nondenominational service agency of Evangelical tradition engaged in childcare/orphanage programs, camping programs, church planting, literature distribution, short-term programs and support of national workers.
Purpose: "...to promote the Gospel in the proper cultural context and make disciples of Jesus Christ in accordance with Matt. 28:18,19."
Year Founded in US: 1980
Income for Overseas Min: $1,200,000
Gifts-in-Kind: $25,000
Fully Supported US Personnel Overseas:
  Expecting to serve more than 4 years: 10
  Nonresidential mission personnel: 2
Other personnel:
  Short-term less than 1 year from US: 150
  Non-US serving in own/other country: 36
  Home ministry & office staff in US: 7
Countries: Kosovo 4; Romania 2; Russia; Ukraine 4

Eastern Mennonite Missions
P.O. Box 458
Salunga, PA 17538-0458 USA
Phone: (717) 898-2251
Fax: (717) 898-8092
Web Site: www.emm.org
Rev. Richard Showalter, President
A denominational sending agency of Mennonite tradition engaged in church planting, development, theological education, leadership development, relief and/or rehabilitation and youth programs.
Purpose: "To envision many people worldwide experiencing salvation in Jesus Christ, a new generation of leaders raised up and new Christ-centered congregations established from which more workers are sent."
Year Founded in US: 1914
Income for Overseas Min: $3,078,974
Fully Supported US Personnel Overseas:
  Expecting to serve more than 4 years: 91
  Expecting to serve 1 to 4 years: 49
Other personnel:

Non-US serving in own/other country: 2
Short-Term less than 1 year from US: 68
Countries: Africa–General 6; Albania 4; Asia–General 12; Australia; Belize; Brazil; Cambodia 3; Ethiopia 4; Europe–General; Germany 4; Guatemala 8; Honduras 2; Hong Kong 4; Hungary 3; Kazakhstan; Kenya 15; Lithuania 7; Macau 2; Mexico; Middle East; Peru 2; Singapore; Somalia 2; Tanzania 3; Thailand 10; Venezuela

East-West Ministries Intl.
4450 Sojourn Dr., Ste. 100
Addison, TX 75001-5043 USA
Phone: (214) 265-8300
Fax: (214) 373-8571
E-mail: info@eastwestministries.org
Web Site: www.eastwestministries.org
Mr. John Maisel, President
A nondenominational sending agency of Baptist and Evangelical tradition engaged in church planting, TEE, evangelism, leadership development, literature distribution and support of national workers. Income figure from 1998.
Purpose: "...to provide church planting training and coordination of evangelistic resources to help plant churches that are doctrinally sound, spiritually alive, grace oriented and multiplying..."
Year Founded in US: 1993
Income for Overseas Min: $1,288,822
Fully Supported US Personnel Overseas:
  Expecting to serve 1 to 4 years: 11
  Nonresidential mission personnel: 16
Other personnel:
  Short-term less than 1 year from US: 12
  Non-US serving in own/other country: 93
Countries: Albania; Bhutan; Burma; China; India; Kazakhstan; Kyrgyzstan; Nepal; Russia; Spain; Tajikistan; Turkmenistan; Uzbekistan

ECHO (Educational Concerns for Hunger Organization)
17391 Durance Rd.
N. Ft. Myers, FL 33917 USA
Phone: (239) 543-3246
Fax: (239) 543-5317
E-mail: echo@echonet.org

Web Site: www.echonet.org
Dr. Martin L. Price, Exec. Director

An interdenominational service agency of Evangelical tradition engaged in agricultural programs, services for other agencies, technical assistance and training.

Purpose: "...to strengthen the ministries of missionaries and national churches as they assist small-scale farmers or urban gardeners in the Third World."

Year Founded in US: 1973
Income for Overseas Min: $967,172
Personnel:
  Home ministry & office staff in US: 33

Edwin L. Hodges Ministries
P. O. Box 1921
Decatur, AL 35602 USA
Phone: (256) 355-3004
Fax: (256) 350-3502
E-mail: EHodges169@aol.com
Web Site: www.elhm.org
Edwin L. Hodges, President

A support agency engaged in literature production/distribution, audio recording/ distribution, and Bible distribution in 11 countries.

Year Founded in US:
Income for Overseas Min: $264,958
Gifts-in-Kind: $264,958
Personnel:
  Home ministry & office staff in US: 4

EFMA (Evangelical Fellowship of Mission Agencies)
(See Ad on page 147)
4201 N. Peachtree Rd. #300 USA
Atlanta, GA 30341-1207
Phone: (770) 457-6677
Fax: (770) 457-0037
E-mail: efma1@compuserve.com
Web Site: www.efmamissions.org
Dr. Paul E. McKaughan, Pres. & CEO

A confederation of mission agencies which serves for the exchange of ideas and building of supportive relationships.

Purpose: "...to aid agencies and boards to work more efficiently, tapping into the rich resource of all our members so that the gifts God gives can be used most effectively

in the task of world evangelization."
Year Founded in US: 1945
Income for Overseas Min: NA
Personnel:
  Home ministry & office staff in US: 4

Elim Fellowship, Intl. Dept.
1703 Dalton Rd.
Lima, NY 14485-0857 USA
Phone: (585) 582-2790
Fax: (585) 624-1229
E-mail: international@elimfellowship.org
Web Site: www.elimfellowship.org/id
Mr. Gary E. Ham, Director

A nondenominational sending agency of Charismatic tradition engaged in church planting, orphanages, missionary training, theological education and leadership development. See Teen World Outreach for short-term program.

Purpose: "...to provide spiritual covering, pastoral care, mutual accountability, ministry resources and fellowship for its credential holders, affiliated churches and ministries and to fellowship with all pastors, missionaries, leaders, churches and ministries who manifest the Spirit of Christ."

Year Founded in US: 1947
Income for Overseas Min: $2,212,271
Gifts-in-Kind: $6,106
Fully Supported US Personnel Overseas:
  Expecting to serve more than 4 years: 100
  Expecting to serve 1 to 4 years: 8
  Nonresidential mission personnel: 2
Other personnel:
  Non-US serving in own/other country: 108
  Home ministry & office staff in US: 4
Countries: Argentina 3; Asia–General 13; Australia 2; Austria 2; Bosnia and Herzegovina 3; Colombia 2; Cuba; Europe–General; France 2; Ghana; Guam 2; Haiti 2; Ireland; Jamaica 4; Kenya 19; Mexico 12; Middle East; New Zealand 2; Niger 8; Nigeria 2; Peru 3; Philippines 2; Poland 2; South Africa 2; Sweden 1; Tanzania 9; Uganda 1; United Kingdom 2

Emmanuel International Mission (U.S.)
3878 Concord Rd.

York, SC 29745 USA
Phone: (803) 831-1356
Fax: (803) 831-1369
E-mail: eim@mindspring.com
Web Site: www.e-i.org
Mr. Dave McCauley, Chairman

An interdenominational service agency of Evangelical tradition engaged in support of national churches, development, TEE, evangelism, leadership development and relief and/or rehabilitation.

Purpose: "...assists local churches worldwide to meet physical and spiritual needs of the poor."

Year Founded in US: 1978

Income for Overseas Min: $127,509

Fully Supported US Personnel Overseas:
  Expecting to serve more than 4 years: 2

Countries: Brazil; Ethiopia; Haiti; Malawi 1; Philippines 1; South Africa; Sudan; Tanzania; Uganda

Emmaus Road, Intl.

7150 Tanner Court
San Diego, CA 92111-4236 USA
Phone: (858) 292-7020
Fax: (858) 292-7020
E-mail: Emmaus_Road@eri.org
Web Site: www.eri.org
Mr. Neal Pirolo, Director

A transdenominational service agency engaged in mobilization and training through publications, audio and video recordings, prefield courses, short-term trips and seminars.

Purpose: "...to benefit churches, mission agencies, cross-cultural teams and national ministries as they take the 'next step' in cross-cultural outreach ministry."

Year Founded in US: 1983

Income for Overseas Min: $80,000

Gifts-in-Kind: $20,000

Personnel:
  Short-term less than 1 year from US: 9
  Home ministry & office staff in US: 3

Empowering Lives Intl.

P.O. Box 67
Upland, CA 91785 USA
Phone: (909) 476-6822

Fax: (909) 476-6618
E-mail: info@empoweringlives.org
Web Site: www.empoweringlives.org
Donald P. Rogers, Founder/Director

A nondenominational service agency of Evangelical tradition engaged in development, agricultural programs, children's programs, medical work, short-term programs and training.

Purpose: "To empower the poor and oppressed spiritually, physically and economically that they may be able to know, worship and serve God without hindrance and to motivate and involve others worldwide to invest their lives and gifts in this same mission."

Year Founded in US: 1994

Income for Overseas Min: $383,104

Personnel:
  Short-term less than 1 year from US: 49
  Home ministry & office staff in US: 2

Countries: Kenya

Engineering Ministries Intl.

110 S. Weber St., Suite 104
Colorado Springs, CO 80903 USA
Phone: (719) 633-2078
Fax: (719) 633-2970
E-mail: info@emiusa.org
Web Site: www.emiusa.org
Mr. Glen Woodruff, Exec. Director

A nondenominational specialized agency of Evangelical tradition engaged in technical assistance, development, evangelism and management consulting/training.

Purpose: "...to mobilize Christian design professionals to serve the poor in developing countries...by empowering people to transform their world through the design and development of hospitals, schools, orphanages, bridges, water supplies, wastewater facilities and more."

Year Founded in US: 1982

Income for Overseas Min: $1,100,000

Fully Supported US Personnel Overseas:
  Expecting to serve more than 4 years: 6
  Expecting to serve 1 to 4 years: 6

Other personnel:
  Short-term less than 1 year from US: 15
  Non-US serving in own/other country: 3

Standard
of
Excellence
for mission agencies

Evangelical Fellowship
of Mission Agencies
4201 North Peachtree Rd.
Suite 300
Atlanta, GA 30341
770/457-6677
Fax: 770/457-0037
efma1@compuserve.com

Home ministry & office staff in US: 2
Bivocational/Tentmaker from US: 13
Countries: Afghanistan; Guatemala 3; India 2; Panama 1

Enterprise Development Intl.
10395-B Democracy Lane
Fairfax, VA 22030 USA
Phone: (703) 277-3360
Fax: (703) 277-3348
E-mail: enterprise@endpoverty.org
Web Site: www.endpoverty.com
Mr. Juan A. Benitez, President & CEO

A transdenominational service agency engaged in management consulting, training and technical assistance for partner implementing agencies.
Purpose: "...enabling the poor to become productive, self supporting citizens."
Year Founded in US: 1985
Income for Overseas Min: NR
Gifts-in-Kind: $102,000
Personnel:
Home ministry & office staff in US: 9

Envoy International
2051 Warrington
Rochester Hills, MI 48307 USA
Phone: (248) 650-8974
Fax: (248) 650-8975
E-mail: dandersen@envoyinternational.org
Web Site: www.envoyinternational.org
Mr. David L. Andersen, President

A nondenominational service agency engaged in missions information service, leadership development, support of national churches, mission-related research, short-term programs and training.
Purpose: "...committed to helping the church overseas become personally and strategically involved in world missions."
Year Founded in US: 1995
Income for Overseas Min: $60,000
Fully Supported US Personnel Overseas:
Expecting to serve more than 4 years: 1
Nonresidential mission personnel: 2
Other personnel:
Non-US serving in own/other country: 4
Home ministry & office staff in US: 2

Bivocational/Tentmaker from US: 16
Countries: Bolivia; Bulgaria; Costa Rica 1; Croatia; Czech Republic; Lithuania; Poland; Romania; Slovakia

Episcopal Church Missionary Community
Box 278
Ambridge, PA 15003 USA
Phone: (724) 266-2810
Fax: (724) 266-6773
E-mail: ecmc@usaor.net
Web Site: www.episcopalian.org/ecmc
Sharon Stockdale, Director

A denominational support agency of Episcopal and Evangelical tradition engaged in missionary training, missions information service and mobilization for mission.
Purpose: "...to enable Episcopalians to be more knowledgeable, active and effective in world missions."
Year Founded in US: 1974
Income for Overseas Min: $30,000
Personnel:
Home ministry & office staff in US: 2

Episcopal Church, Domestic & Foreign Missionary Society
815 Second Ave.
New York, NY 10017 USA
Phone: (212) 716-6223
Fax: (212) 983-6377
E-mail: pmauney@episcopalchurch.org
Web Site: www.episcopalchurch.org
Most Rev. Frank T. Griswold, III, Presiding Bishop

A denominational sending agency of Episcopal tradition engaged in support of national churches, development, funds transmission, leadership development, services for other agencies and missionary training.
Purpose: "...to ensure, in the most comprehensive and coordinated manner possible, the full participation of Episcopalians in the worldwide mission of the church."
Year Founded in US: 1834
Income for Overseas Min: $11,915,649
Fully Supported US Personnel Overseas:

Expecting to serve more than 4 years: 100

Countries: Unspecified Country 100

EQUIP
(See Ad on page 151)
4725 River Green Pkwy.
Duluth, GA 30096 USA
Phone: (678) 225-3308
Fax: (678) 225-3349
E-mail: john.hull@iequip.org
Web Site: www.iequip.org
Dr. John D. Hull, President

A transdenominational support agency of Evangelical tradition engaged in leadership development.

Year Founded in US: 1996

Income for Overseas Min: $3,100,000

Gifts-in-Kind: $5,000

Fully Supported US Personnel Overseas:
   Nonresidential mission personnel: 1

Other personnel:
   Home ministry & office staff in US: 14

Equip, Inc.
P.O. Box 1126
Marion, NC 28752-1126 USA
Phone: (828) 738-7891
Fax: (828) 738-3946
Web Site: www.equipinternational.org
Rev. Barrie G. Flitcroft, Director

An interdenominational sending agency of Evangelical tradition engaged in technical assistance/training, agricultural programs, development, missionary education/training, medical work, and supplying equipment.

Purpose: "...to assist the church around the world to be responsive to the poor, sensitive to the Holy Spirit, focused on personal evangelism and practically engaged in strengthening the Body of Christ."

Year Founded in US: 1983

Income for Overseas Min: $662,516

Fully Supported US Personnel Overseas:
   Expecting to serve more than 4 years: 18
   Expecting to serve 1 to 4 years: 4

Other personnel:
   Non-US serving in own/other country: 17
   Home ministry & office staff in US: 10

Countries: Belize 2; Brazil 7; Ethiopia 2; Ja-

pan 1; Kenya; Liberia; Mexico 2; Nicaragua 2; Nigeria; Philippines 2; Uganda

Equipping the Saints
1254 Keezletown Road
Weyers Cave, VA 24486-2318 USA
Phone: (540) 234-6222
Fax: (540) 234-6262
E-mail: ETS@rica.net
Web Site: www.etsusa.org
Rev. Keith A. Jones, Exec. Director

A nondenominational service agency of Evangelical tradition engaged in supplying equipment. Statistical data from 1998.

Purpose: "...to enhance the outreach of indigenous evangelical ministries...by providing appropriate human, material and financial resources."

Year Founded in US: 1991

Income for Overseas Min: $370,176

Gifts-in-Kind: $88,363

Personnel:
   Home ministry & office staff in US: 4

European Christian Mission International
110 Juanita Drive
Zanesville, OH 43701 USA
Phone: (888) 368-3264
Fax: (740) 453-3418
E-mail: ECM.USA@ecmi.org
Web site: www.ecmi.org
Rev. Loren Anderson, Board President

A multinational interdenominational sending agency engaged in church planting, support of national churches and leadership development in 18 countries of Europe. ECMI has about 200 multinational staff and missionaries from 20 different countries.

Purpose: "...to be a nationwide network of passionate prayer and support for church planting in Europe."

Year founded in US: 1904

income for Overseas Min: NR

European Christian Mission NA, Inc.
P.O. Box 1006

Point Roberts, WA 98281 USA
Phone: (604) 943-0211
Fax: (604) 943-0212
E-mail: ecmnainc@cs.com
Rev. Vincent Price, International Director

An interdenominational sending agency of Evangelical tradition engaged in evangelism, broadcasting, literature distribution, support of national churches and support of national workers in E. Europe and the former USSR. Statistical information from 1998.

Year Founded in US: 1960
Income for Overseas Min: $723,800
Fully Supported US Personnel Overseas:
  Expecting to serve more than 4 years: 35
Other personnel:
  Home ministry & office staff in US: 3
Countries: Europe–General 15; Greece 7; Ireland 1; Italy 2; Spain 8; United Kingdom 2

European Evangelistic Society

P.O. Drawer 90150
East Point, GA 30364 USA
Phone: (404) 344-7458
E-mail: euroevansoc@juno.com
Mr. Bruce E. Shields, President

A nondenominational sending agency of Christian (Restoration Movement) tradition engaged in theological education, church planting, evangelism and mission-related research.

Year Founded in US: 1932
Income for Overseas Min: $205,817
Personnel:
  Home ministry & office staff in US: 2

Evangel Bible Translators

P.O. Box 669
Rockwall, TX 75087 USA
Phone: (972) 771-8886
Fax: (972) 722-1721
E-mail: info@evangelbible.org
Web Site: www.evangelbible.org
Rev. H. Syvelle Phillips, President

A nondenominational sending agency of Pentecostal tradition engaged in Bible translation, Bible distribution, church construction, linguistics, literacy work and support of national workers. Statistical data from 1998.

Year Founded in US: 1976
Income for Overseas Min: $534,007
Fully Supported US Personnel Overseas:
  Expecting to serve more than 4 years: 13
Other personnel:
  Non-US serving in own/other country: 15
  Home ministry & office staff in US: 6
Countries: Benin; France 2; Ghana 2; Guatemala 2; India 6; Liberia; Malaysia; Nigeria; Philippines 1; Uganda

Evangelical Baptist Missions

P.O. Box 2225
Kokomo, IN 46904-2225 USA
Phone: (765) 453-4488
Fax: (765) 455-0889
E-mail: ebm@ebm.org
Web Site: www.ebm.org
Dr. W. Paul Jackson, Gen. Director

A sending agency of Independent and Baptist tradition engaged in church planting, camping programs, childcare/orphanage programs, extension education, leadership development and video/film production/distribution.

Purpose: "...help churches reach the world."
Year Founded in US: 1928
Income for Overseas Min: $3,474,000
Gifts-in-Kind: $5,000
Fully Supported US Personnel Overseas:
  Expecting to serve more than 4 years: 104
  Expecting to serve 1 to 4 years: 9
  Nonresidential mission personnel: 12
Other personnel:
  Short-term less than 1 year from US: 35
  Home ministry & office staff in US: 57
Countries: Argentina 8; Benin 2; Brazil 4; Côte d'Ivoire 9; France 20; Germany 12; Haiti 2; Honduras; Italy 2; Japan 4; Mali 11; Mexico 6; Niger 2; Nigeria 2; Romania 4 Russia 1; South Africa 11; Sweden 2; United Kingdom 2

Evangelical Bible Mission

P.O. Drawer 189
Summerfield, FL 34492 USA
Phone: (352) 245-2560
Fax: (352) 245-9783
E-mail: EBMission@aol.com
Web Site: www.ebminternational.com

Rev. Gerald Bustin, President

An interdenominational sending agency of Holiness tradition engaged in church planting, Bible distribution, evangelism, literature distribution and supplying equipment.

Year Founded in US: 1939
Income for Overseas Min: NA
Personnel:
   Home ministry & office staff in US: 5

Evangelical Congregational Church, Global Ministries Commission

100 W Park Ave.
Myerstown, PA 17067-1235 USA
Phone: (800) 866-7584
Fax: (717) 866-7383
E-mail: ecdom@eccenter.com
Web Site: www.eccenter.com

Dr. John P. Ragsdale, Director Global Mins.

A denominational service agency of Wesleyan tradition engaged in support of national churches, childcare/orphanage programs, church planting, theological education and Bible translation. Additional missionaries sent under other mission agencies.

Year Founded in US: 1922
Income for Overseas Min: $826,955
Gifts-in-Kind: $10,000
Fully Supported US Personnel Overseas:
   Expecting to serve more than 4 years: 2
   Nonresidential mission personnel: 2
Other personnel:
   Non-US serving in own/other country: 2
   Home ministry & office staff in US: 3
   Bivocational/Tentmaker from US: 1
Countries: Japan; Malaysia 1; Mexico 1

Evangelical Covenant Church, Board of

5101 N. Francisco Ave.
Chicago, IL 60625 USA
Phone: (773) 784-3000
Fax: (773) 784-4366
E-mail: world.mission@covchurch.org
Web Site: www.covchurch.org

Rev. James W. Gustafson, Exec. Director

A denominational sending agency of Evangelical and Congregational tradition engaged in church planting, development, evangelism, medical work, support of national workers and training. Statistical data from 1999.

Year Founded in US: 1885
Income for Overseas Min: $5,200,000
Fully Supported US Personnel Overseas:
   Expecting to serve more than 4 years: 92
   Expecting to serve 1 to 4 years: 15
   Nonresidential mission personnel: 3
Other personnel:
   Short-term less than 1 year from US: 1,500
   Non-US serving in own/other country: 2
   Home ministry & office staff in US: 19
Countries: Africa–General 2; Argentina; Asia–General 2; Burkina Faso 2; Cameroon 2; Central African Republic 12; Colombia 9; Congo, Democratic Republic of the 2; Czech Republic 2; Ecuador 9; Equatorial Guinea 2; Europe–General 2; France 3; Germany 3; Japan 9; Laos 2; Mexico 13; Spain 4; Taiwan 2; Thailand 8; Latin America–General 2

Evangelical Fellowship of Mission Agencies—See: EFMA

Evangelical Free Church Mission

901 E. 78th St.
Bloomington, MN 55420 USA
Phone: (952) 854-1300
Fax: (952) 853-8474
E-mail: EFCM@efca.org
Web Site: www.efcm.org

Dr. Benjamin A. Sawatsky, Exec. Director

A denominational sending agency of Evangelical tradition engaged in church planting, theological education, evangelism and leadership development.

Purpose: "...making disciples of Jesus Christ and incorporating them into reproducing congregations with the goal of launching church planting movements internationally."

Year Founded in US: 1887
Income for Overseas Min: $16,847,282
Gifts-in-Kind: $273,000
Fully Supported US Personnel Overseas:

Expecting to serve more than 4 years: 330
Expecting to serve 1 to 4 years: 22
Other personnel:
  Short-term less than 1 year from US: 400
  Non-US serving in own/other country: 47
  Home ministry & office staff in US: 48
Countries: Austria 4; Belgium 15; Brazil 4;
Central African Republic 15; China 19;
Congo, Democratic Republic of the; Costa
Rica 4; Cote d'Ivoire 3; Czech Republic 13;
France 11; Germany 8; Hong Kong 6; Hungary 12; India 3; Japan 23; Kenya 9; Macau 3;
Malaysia 4; Mexico 12; Mongolia 9; Netherlands 2; Peru 10; Philippines 15; Poland 8;
Portugal 2; Romania 23; Russia 21; Singapore
2; Slovakia 4; Spain 8; Taiwan 2; Tanzania 10;
Thailand 4; Turkey 6; Ukraine 6; United Kingdom 3; Uzbekistan 4; Venezuela 23

Evangelical Friends Church Southwest

P.O. Box 1607
Whittier, CA 90609-1607 USA
Phone: (562) 947-2883
Fax: (562) 947-9385
E-mail: office@efcsw.org
Web Site: www.efcsw.org
Mr. Stan Leach, Superintendent
A denominational sending agency of Evangelical Friends tradition engaged in church
planting, TEE, evangelism, leadership development, mobilization for mission and missionary training.
Year Founded in US: 1895
Income for Overseas Min: $391,933
Fully Supported US Personnel Overseas:
  Expecting to serve more than 4 years: 6
  Expecting to serve 1 to 4 years: 6
Other personnel:
  Home ministry & office staff in US: 1
Countries: Cambodia 4; Guatemala 2;
Honduras; Indonesia

Evangelical Friends Mission

P.O. Box 525
Arvada, CO 80001 USA
Phone: (303) 421-8100
Fax: (303) 431-6455
E-mail: cmylander@yahoo.com
Web Site: www.friendsmission.org

Dr. Chuck Mylander, Exec. Director
A denominational sending agency of Evangelical and Friends tradition engaged in
church planting, theological education,
evangelism, missions information service
and leadership development.
Year Founded in US: 1978
Income for Overseas Min: $868,000
Fully Supported US Personnel Overseas:
  Expecting to serve more than 4 years: 17
Other personnel:
  Short-term less than 1 year from US: 5
  Non-US serving in own/other country: 4
  Home ministry & office staff in US: 12
Countries: India 2; Ireland 3; Mexico 2;
Nepal 4; Philippines; Rwanda 4; United
Kingdom 2

Evangelical Greenhouse Ministries International

P.O. Box 141
Wheaton, IL 60189 USA
Phone: (630) 682-0308
Fax: (630) 682-0308
E-mail: EGMI@aol.com
Mr. Stephen Darling, Director
An interdenominational sending agency of
Evangelical tradition engaged in evangelism,
church planting and theological education.
Purpose: "...ministering to the heart of
France."
Year Founded in US: 1996
Income for Overseas Min: $300,000
Fully Supported US Personnel Overseas:
  Expecting to serve more than 4 years: 3
Other personnel:
  Short-term less than 1 year from US: 4
  Non-US serving in own/other country: 4
  Home ministry & office staff in US: 2
Countries: France 3

Evangelical Lutheran Church in America, Division for Global Mission

8765 W. Higgins Road
Chicago, IL 60631 USA
Phone: (773) 380-2650
Fax: (773) 380-2410
Web Site: www.elca.org\dgm

Rev. Bonnie L. Jensen, Exec. Director

A denominational sending agency of Lutheran tradition engaged in development, theological education, funds transmission, medical work, support of national churches.

Year Founded in US: 1987

Income for Overseas Min: $29,172,306

Fully Supported US Personnel Overseas:
  Expecting to serve more than 4 years: 175
  Expecting to serve 1 to 4 years: 88
  Nonresidential mission personnel: 13

Other personnel:
  Short-term less than 1 year from US: 50
  Non-US serving in own/other country: 4
  Home ministry & office staff in US: 50

Countries: Argentina 1; Bangladesh 2; Brazil 4; Cameroon 18; Central African Republic 5; Chile 1; China 1; Costa Rica 2; Cyprus 3; Denmark 2; Egypt 6; El Salvador; Ethiopia 4; Germany 5; Guatemala 1; Guyana 2; Hong Kong 11; India 1; Indonesia 2; Israel 4; Jamaica 2; Japan 19; Kenya 2; Liberia 2; Lithuania 2; Madagascar 10; Mexico 3; Namibia 2; Nicaragua; Nigeria 1; Norway 2; Panama 2; Papua New Guinea 5; Puerto Rico 2; Russia 2; Senegal 9; Singapore 2; Slovakia 5; South Africa 2; Tanzania 22; Thailand 4; United Kingdom

Evangelical Mennonite Church Intl. Ministries

1420 Kerrway Court
Fort Wayne, IN 46805-5402 USA

Phone: (260) 423-3649
Fax: (260) 420-1905
E-mail: EMCmissions@aol.com
Web Site: www.emctoday.com

Rev. Earl I. Cecil, Director

A denominational sending agency of Anabaptist tradition engaged in church planting, association of missions, evangelism, support of national churches, partnership development and short-term programs.

Purpose: "...exists to facilitate local churches to spread the Gospel in worldwide cross-cultural ministry situations among unreached and unevangelized peoples with the goal of generating a reproducing church planting movement."

Year Founded in US: 1945

Income for Overseas Min: $1,088,062

Fully Supported US Personnel Overseas:
  Expecting to serve more than 4 years: 17
  Expecting to serve 1 to 4 years: 11

Other personnel:
  Short-term less than 1 year from US: 12
  Non-US serving in own/other country: 1
  Home ministry & office staff in US: 4

Countries: Albania 2; Asia–General 2; Botswana 2; Germany 1; Mexico; Middle East 2; Russia 2; United Kingdom 2; Venezuela 4

Evangelical Methodist Church, Board of Missions

P.O. Box 17070
Indianapolis, IN 46217 USA

Phone: (317) 780-8017
Fax: (317) 780-8078
E-mail: hq@emchurch.org
Web Site: www.emchurch.org

Rev. James Coulston, Gen. Conf. Sec./Treasurer

A denominational sending agency of Evangelical tradition engaged in evangelism, church planting, theological education and medical work. Statistical data from 1996.

Year Founded in US: 1946

Income for Overseas Min: $239,000

Fully Supported US Personnel Overseas:
  Expecting to serve more than 4 years: 6

Other personnel:
  Home ministry & office staff in US: 2

Countries: Bolivia 4; Mexico 2

Evangelical Presbyterian Church—World Outreach

29140 Buckingham Ave., Suite 5
Livonia, MI 48154 USA

Phone: (734) 261-2001
Fax: (734) 261-3282
E-mail: jeff.chadwick@epc.org
Web Site: www.epc.org/hmainwor.htm

Rev. Jeffrey Chadwick, Director

A denominational sending agency of Presbyterian and Evangelical tradition engaged in church planting, theological education, evangelism, support of national churches and support of national workers.

Purpose: "...to establish the church of

Jesus Christ in those cultures and people groups where opportunity and our ability to respond intersect."

Year Founded in US: 1981

Income for Overseas Min: $1,366,297

Fully Supported US Personnel Overseas:
Expecting to serve more than 4 years: 45
Expecting to serve 1 to 4 years: 2

Other personnel:
Non-US serving in own/other country: 4
Home ministry & office staff in US: 4

Countries: Afghanistan 2; Argentina 5; China 4; Egypt 2; France 2; India 2; Indonesia 2; Japan 2; Jordan 3; Kazakhstan 6; Lebanon 2; Malaysia 4; Russia 2; Uganda 2; United Kingdom 4; Yemen 1

Evangelism and Missions Information Service

P.O. Box 794
Wheaton, IL 60189 USA
Phone: (630) 752-7158
Fax: (630) 752-7155
E-mail: EMIS@wheaton.edu
Web Site: www.billygrahamcenter.org/emis

Dr. Kenneth D. Gill, Director

The publishing department of the Billy Graham Center, providing evangelism and missions information through publications such as *Evangelical Missions Quarterly, World Pulse, Mission Handbook* and other books about evangelism and missions.

Year Founded in US: 1964

Income for Overseas Min: NA

Personnel:
Home ministry & office staff in US: 8

Evangelism Explosion Intl.

P.O. Box 23820
Ft. Lauderdale, FL 33307 USA
Phone: (954) 491-6100
Fax: (954) 771-2256
E-mail: info@eeinternational.org
Web Site: www.eeinternational.org

Dr. D. James Kennedy, President

An interdenominational support agency of Evangelical tradition engaged in evangelism, leadership development, support of national workers, mobilization for mission and missionary training. Support mission

with contacts and representatives in more than 200 nations.

Year Founded in US: 1970

Income for Overseas Min: $1,000,000

Fully Supported US Personnel Overseas:
Expecting to serve more than 4 years: 2
Nonresidential mission personnel: 2

Other personnel:
Non-US serving in own/other country: 64
Home ministry & office staff in US: 40

Countries: Argentina; Armenia; Belgium; Ghana; Guatemala; India 2; Indonesia; Kazakhstan; Kyrgyzstan; Mexico; Moldova; Papua New Guinea; Russia; Turkmenistan; Ukraine; Uzbekistan

Evangelism Resources

425 Epworth Ave.
Wilmore, KY 40390 USA
Phone: (859) 858-0777
Fax: (859) 858-2907
E-mail: eroffice@qx.net
Web Site: www.erinfo.org

Dr. Willys K. Braun, President

An interdenominational sending agency of Evangelical tradition engaged in training and leadership development.

Purpose: "...equipping overseas churches for accelerated evangelism and church growth."

Year Founded in US: 1976

Income for Overseas Min: $650,000

Fully Supported US Personnel Overseas:
Expecting to serve 1 to 4 years: 2

Other personnel:
Non-US serving in own/other country: 29
Home ministry & office staff in US: 6

Countries: Angola; Bangladesh; Cameroon; Congo, Democratic Republic of the; Cote d'Ivoire; Ghana; India; Myanmar/Burma; Nepal; Nigeria

Evangelistic Faith Missions

P.O. Box 609
Bedford, IN 47421 USA
Phone: (812) 275-7531
Fax: (812) 275-7532
E-mail: efmjsm@juno.com

Rev. J. Steven Manley, President & Director

An interdenominational sending agency of Holiness and Wesleyan tradition engaged in evangelism, broadcasting, TEE, literature distribution and support of national workers.

Year Founded in US: 1905

Income for Overseas Min: $1,516,665

Fully Supported US Personnel Overseas:
Expecting to serve 1 to 4 years: 12

Other personnel:
Non-US serving in own/other country: 4
Home ministry & office staff in US: 7

Countries: Bolivia; Costa Rica; Dominican Republic; El Salvador; Guatemala; Honduras; Ukraine

Every Child Ministries, Inc.

P.O. Box 810
Hebron, IN 46341-0810 USA

Phone: (219) 996-4201

Fax: (219) 996-4203

E-mail: ecmafrica@netnitco.net

Web Site: www.kidsyes.org

John & Lorella Rouster, Intl. Directors

A nondenominational mission of Evangelical tradition engaged in children's programs, leadership development, childcare/orphanage programs, Christian education and youth programs for the forgotten children of Africa.

Purpose: "...encouraging and empowering African churches to reach the youth of their continent."

Year Founded in US: 1985

Income for Overseas Min: $240,204

Fully Supported US Personnel Overseas:
Nonresidential mission personnel: 2

Other personnel:
Short-term less than 1 year from US: 9
Non-US serving in own/other country: 26
Home ministry & office staff in US: 3

Countries: Angola; Congo, Democratic Republic of; Ghana

Every Home for Christ Intl.

P.O. Box 64000
Colorado Springs, CO 80962 USA

Phone: (719) 260-8888

Fax: (719) 260-7505

E-mail: info@ehc.org

Web Site: www.ehc.org

Dr. Dick Eastman, President

An interdenominational service agency of Evangelical tradition engaged in evangelism, church planting, correspondence courses, literature distribution and literature production.

Purpose: "...equipping and mobilizing believers everywhere to pray for and actively participate in the personal presentation of a printed or repeatable message of the Gospel of Jesus Christ, systematically, to every home in the whole world..."

Year Founded in US: 1946

Income for Overseas Min: $3,683,498

Gifts-in-Kind: $283,847

Personnel:
Non-US serving in own/other country: 765
Home ministry & office staff in US: 42

Countries: Albania; Argentina; Armenia; Austria; Bangladesh; Belgium; Benin; Bosnia and Herzegovina; Brazil; Burkina Faso; Cambodia; Cote d'Ivoire; Croatia; Czech Republic; Equatorial Guinea; Fiji; France; Georgia; Germany; Ghana; Guinea-Bissau; Honduras; India; Indonesia; Italy; Japan; Kazakhstan; Kenya; Lesotho; Liberia; Macedonia; Malawi; Malaysia; Mali; Mongolia; Mozambique; Namibia; New Zealand; Nicaragua; Niger; Nigeria; Philippines; Russia; Serbia and Montenegro; Sierra Leone; Slovakia; Slovenia; South Africa; Spain; Sri Lanka; Swaziland; Switzerland; Taiwan; Tanzania; Thailand; Togo; Uganda; Ukraine; United Kingdom; Unspecified Country; Zambia; Zimbabwe

Faith Christian Fellowship Intl.

P.O. Box 35443
Tulsa, OK 74153 USA

Phone: (918) 492-5800

Fax: (918) 492-6140

E-mail: homepage@fcf.org

Web Site: www.fcf.org

Mrs. Pat Harrison, President

A sending agency of Pentecostal tradition engaged in church planting, funds transmission, development, leadership development and training. Personnel data from 1998.

Year Founded in US: 1978

Income for Overseas Min: $413,000

Fully Supported US Personnel Overseas:

Expecting to serve more than 4 years: 22
Expecting to serve 1 to 4 years: 29
Nonresidential mission personnel: 12

Other personnel:
Non-US serving in own/other country: 7
Home ministry & office staff in US: 17
Bivocational/Tentmaker from US: 14

Countries: American Samoa; Andorra; Botswana 2; Czech Republic; Guatemala 6; Jamaica 2; Kenya; Mexico 6; Netherlands; Nigeria; Philippines 2; South Africa; Spain; Tonga; Uganda; United Kingdom 4; Vanuatu; Zimbabwe

Family Aid International, Inc.
1629 Pine Dr.
Grove, OK 74344 USA
E-mail: david@familyaidinternational.com
Web Site: www.familyaidinternational.com
Mr. David L. Tinney, President

A transdenominational support agency of Charismatic tradition engaged in childcare/orphanage programs, children's programs, leadership development, support of national churches, support of national workers and short-term programs.

Year Founded in US: 2001
Income for Overseas Min: $10,000
Fully Supported US Personnel Overseas:
Nonresidential mission personnel: 1
Other personnel:
Short-term less than 1 year from US: 17
Non-US serving in own/other country: 1
Countries: Ukraine

Far East Broadcasting Company, Inc.
P.O. Box 1
La Mirada, CA 90637-0001 USA
Phone: (562) 947-4651
Fax: (562) 943-0160
E-mail: febc@febc.org
Web Site: www.febc.org
Mr. Gregg Harris, President

An interdenominational sending agency of Evangelical tradition engaged in broadcasting, audio recording/distribution and evangelism.

Purpose: "...to develop radio program-

ming and deliver it to listeners in Asia in such a way that they move toward Jesus Christ and into His Kingdom..."

Year Founded in US: 1945
Income for Overseas Min: $3,665,166
Fully Supported US Personnel Overseas:
Expecting to serve more than 4 years: 31
Expecting to serve 1 to 4 years: 2
Other personnel:
Non-US serving in own/other country: 492
Countries: Cambodia; Finland 2; Indonesia; Korea, South 2; N. Mariana Isls 7; Philippines 18; Russia; United Kingdom 2

FARMS International, Inc.
P.O. Box 270
Knife River, MN 55609-0270 USA
Phone: (218) 834-2676
Fax: (218) 834-2676
E-mail: info@farmsinternational.com
Web Site: www.farmsinternational.com
Mr. Joseph E. Richter, Exec. Director

An interdenominational specialized agency of Evangelical tradition engaged in development, agricultural programs, evangelism and technical assistance.

Purpose: "...serving the church by equipping Christian families in poverty with the means for self-support...[to help]...families find a biblical path out of poverty."

Year Founded in US: 1961
Income for Overseas Min: $119,460
Personnel:
Home ministry & office staff in US: 4

Federation Missionaire Francaise International
P.O. Box 1117
Hanover, PA 17331 USA
Phone: (717) 892-3970
E-mail: aneedle@pa.net
Mr. Andrew Eldeen, President

An interdenominational service agency of evangelical tradition engaged in support of national workers, leadership development and funds transmission for outreach to the French world.

Purpose: "...an evangelical non-traditional mission assisting local churches in sending and providing funds transmission to those who would minister the Gospel of Jesus Christ to or from the French world."

Income for Overseas Min: NA

Personnel:
  Home ministry & office staff in US: 1

Fellowship Intl. Mission

555 S. 24th St.
Allentown, PA 18104-6666 USA
Phone: (610) 435-9099
Fax: (610) 435-2641
E-mail: Info@fimworldwide.org
Web Site: www.fimworldwide.org
Dr. Steve Wilt, Gen. Director

A nondenominational sending agency of Independent tradition engaged in church planting, childcare/orphanage programs, Christian education, evangelism and Bible translation.

Year Founded in US: 1950

Income for Overseas Min: $2,549,839

Fully Supported US Personnel Overseas:
  Expecting to serve more than 4 years: 84

Other personnel:
  Non-US serving in own/other country: 30
  Home ministry & office staff in US: 14

Countries: Australia 3; Belgium; Bolivia 2; Brazil 16; Colombia 2; Ecuador 2; Fiji; France; Germany; Guatemala 1; Japan 4; Mexico 17; Morocco 13; New Zealand 1; Niger 2; Nigeria 4; Poland 1; Suriname 4; Sweden 3; Uganda; Ukraine 2; United Kingdom 2; Venezuela 5

Fellowship of Associates of Medical Evangelism

P.O. Box 33548
Indianapolis, IN 46203-0548 USA
Phone: (317) 358-2480
Fax: (317) 358-2483
E-mail: medicalmissions@fameworld.org
Web Site: www.fameworld.org
Mr. Rick Wolford, Exec. Director

A nondenominational support agency of Christian (Restoration Movement) tradition engaged in church planting, providing medical supplies, medical work, support of national workers, mobilization for mission and short-term programs.

Year Founded in US: 1970

Income for Overseas Min: $1,132,576

Personnel:
  Non-US serving in own/other country: 41
  Home ministry & office staff in US: 8
  Bivocational/Tentmaker from US: 1

Countries: Ghana; Honduras; Panama; Zimbabwe

Final Frontiers Foundation, Inc.

1200 Peachtree St.
Louisville, GA 30434-1544 USA
Phone: (478) 625-9050
Fax: (478) 625-9996
E-mail: jnelms@finalfrontiers.org
Web Site: www.finalfrontiers.org
Rev. Jon Nelms, Chairman

A support agency of Baptist tradition engaged in support of national workers, Bible distribution, childcare/orphanage programs, church planting and evangelism.

Year Founded in US: 1987

Income for Overseas Min: $573,300

Personnel:
  Non-US serving in own/other country: 945
  Home ministry & office staff in US: 6
  Bivocational/Tentmaker from US: 7

Countries: Africa–General; Asia–General; Caribbean–General; Europe–General; India; Latin America–General; Oceania–General

Floresta USA, Inc.

4903 Morena Blvd. #1215
San Diego, CA   92117-7352 USA
Phone: (800) 633-5319
Fax: (808) 274-3728
E-mail: floresta@xc.org
Web Site: www.floresta.org
Mr. Scott C. Sabin, Exec. Director

An interdenominational support agency of Presbyterian tradition engaged in development, agricultural programs, evangelism, leadership development, literacy work and short-term programs.

Purpose: "...reversing deforestation and poverty by transforming the lives of the rural poor."

Year Founded in US: 1984

Income for Overseas Min: $635,395

Fully Supported US Personnel Overseas:
Nonresidential mission personnel: 3

Other personnel:
Short-term less than 1 year from US: 40
Non-US serving in own/other country: 28
Home ministry & office staff in US: 6

Countries: Dominican Republic; Haiti;
Mexico

Flying Doctors of America
1235 North Decatur Rd.
Atlanta, GA 30306 USA
Phone: (404) 815-7044
Fax: (404) 892-6672
E-mail: fdoamericaperu@mindspring.com
Web Site: www.fdoamerica.org
Mr. Allan M. Gathercoal, President

An interdenominational service agency of
Presbyterian tradition engaged in providing
medical and dental work, providing medical supplies and rehabilitation through
short-term medical missions in 14 countries. A division of Medical Mercy Missions,
Inc. Statistical data from 1998.

Purpose: "...helping people help
people...(by) ...creating a network of God's
love that reaches into the farthest corners
of the world and the human heart."

Year Founded in US: 1990
Income for Overseas Min: $134,000
Personnel:
Short-term less than 1 year from US: 162
Home ministry & office staff in US: 6

FOCAS (Foundation of Compassionate American Samaritans)
P.O. Box 428760
Cincinnati, OH 45242 USA
Phone: (513) 621-5300
Fax: (513) 621-5307
E-mail: rptaylor@focas-us.org
Web Site: www.focas-us.org
Mr. Richard P. Taylor, Exec. Director

A transdenominational service agency of
Pentecostal tradition engaged in medical
work, development, Christian education,
evangelism and short-term programs.

Purpose: "...to serve hurting poor people
(and) seek transformed lives by proclaiming

the gospel of Jesus Christ and assisting with
crucial physical and spiritual needs."

Year Founded in US: 1986
Income for Overseas Min: $656,993
Gifts-in-Kind: $99,016
Personnel:
Short-term less than 1 year from US: 3
Non-US serving in own/other country: 6
Home ministry & office staff in US: 8

Countries: Haiti

FOM (Fellowship of Missions)
140 Jacqueline Drive
Berea, OH 44017-2730 USA
Phone: (440) 243-0156
E-mail: office@fellowshipofmissions.org
Web Site: www.fellowshipofmissions.org
Mr. Leigh Adams, President

An inter-mission service agency of fundamental tradition engaged in research and
information service, acting as an accredit-
ing agency for its constituents and encouraging the formation of missionary and
church fellowships.

Year Founded in US: 1969
Income for Overseas Min: NA

Food for the Hungry, Inc.
(See Ad on page 162)
1224 East Washington Street
Phoenix, AZ 85034 USA
Phone: (480) 998-3100
Fax: (480) 998-9448
E-mail: go_now@fh.org
Web Site: www.fh.org
Mr. Benjamin Homan, President/CEO

A nondenominational service agency of
Evangelical tradition engaged in relief and/
or rehabilitation, agricultural programs,
children's programs, development, leadership development and missionary training.

Purpose: "...an organization of Christian
motivation committed to helping the poor
and needy throughout the world, by generating cash and in-kind gifts, and fostering
world hunger advocacy in the United States."

Year Founded in US: 1971
Income for Overseas Min: $69,896,261
Gifts-in-Kind: $43,357,894

God is calling.

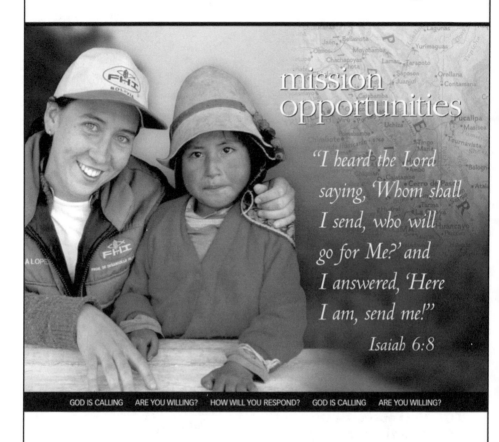

mission opportunities

"I heard the Lord saying, 'Whom shall I send, who will go for Me?' and I answered, 'Here I am, send me!'"

Isaiah 6:8

GOD IS CALLING   ARE YOU WILLING?   HOW WILL YOU RESPOND?   GOD IS CALLING   ARE YOU WILLING?

JOIN THE HUNGER CORPS!
- 3 to 4 years or longer
- short-term teams
  (1–2 weeks) available
- U.S. volunteer positions

WHERE YOU CAN SERVE:
- Africa   • Central/South Africa
- Asia   • U.S. inner city
- Europe   • Caribbean

FOR MORE INFORMATION:
toll-free: (877) 780-4261, x2508
email: go_now@fh.org
website: www.hungercorps.org

Food for the Hungry
Meeting physical and spiritual needs worldwide

Fully Supported US Personnel Overseas:
  Expecting to serve more than 4 years: 17
  Expecting to serve 1 to 4 years: 61
Other Personnel:
  Short-term less than 1 year from US: 12
  Home ministry & office staff in US: 60
Countries: Bangladesh; Bolivia 3; Brazil;
Cambodia 1; China 6; Dominican Republic;
Guatemala 2; India; Japan; Kenya; Laos;
Malaysia; Mongolia; Nicaragua 1; Nigeria;
Peru; Philippines; Romania 4

For Haiti with Love Inc.
P.O. Box 1017
Palm Harbor, FL 34682-1017 USA
Phone: (727) 938-3245
Fax: (727) 942-6945
E-mail: info@forhaitiwithlove.org
Web Site: www.forhaitiwithlove.org
Don DeHart, Founder/Pres.

A transdenominational service agency engaged in community development, emergency medical care, relief aid (at no charge)
and one-on-one evangelism. Statistical data
from 1998.
Year Founded in US: 1982
Income for Overseas Min: $263,000
Gifts-in-Kind: $60,000

Forward Edge International
15121-A NE 72nd Ave.
Vancouver, WA 98686-1928 USA
Phone: (360) 574-3343
Fax: (360) 574-2118
E-mail: fei@forwardedge.org
Web Site: www.forwardedge.org
Rev. Joseph Anfuso, Director

A transdenominational service agency of
Evangelical tradition engaged in evangelism, support of national churches, mobilization for mission, relief and/or rehabilitation and youth programs. Statistical data
from 1998.
Purpose: "...mobilizing ordinary Christians
to spread the gospel and serve the
poor...on U.S. Indian reservations and overseas."
Year Founded in US: 1983
Income for Overseas Min: $360,000
Gifts-in-Kind: $200,000

Fully Supported US Personnel Overseas:
  Nonresidential mission personnel: 3
Other personnel:
  Short-term less than 1 year from US: 320
  Home ministry & office staff in US: 7

Foundation For His Ministry
P.O. Box 74000
San Clemente, CA 92673-0134 USA
Phone: (949) 492-2200
Fax: (949) 492-0900
E-mail: info@ffhm.org
Web Site: www.ffhm.org
Charla Pereau, Exec. Director

A transdenominational service agency of
Charismatic and Evangelical tradition en-
gaged in childcare/orphanage programs,
church planting, Christian education, evan-
gelism, medical work and support of na-
tional workers.
Year Founded in US: 1967
Income for Overseas Min: $3,706,998
Gifts-in-Kind: $950,000
Personnel:
  Non-US serving in own/other country: 124
Countries: Mexico

Foursquare Missions Intl.
P.O. Box 26902
Los Angeles, CA 90026-0176 USA
Phone: (213) 989-4320
Fax: (213) 483-5863
E-mail: fmi@foursquare.org
Web Site: www.foursquare.org
Rev. Michael Larkin, Director

A denominational sending agency of Evan-
gelical tradition engaged in church plant-
ing, Christian education, TEE, evangelism,
leadership development and support of na-
tional churches.
Purpose: "...to glorify God and advance
His kingdom in obedience to Jesus Christ's
mandate to preach the gospel and make
disciples of all nations/peoples."
Year Founded in US: 1923
Income for Overseas Min: $6,818,285
Fully Supported US Personnel Overseas:
  Expecting to serve more than 4 years: 58
  Nonresidential mission personnel: 10

Other personnel:
Short-term less than 1 year from US: 2,041
Non-US serving in own/other country: 10
Home ministry & office staff in US: 23

Countries: Albania 2; Brazil 2; Cambodia 2; Chile 1; Costa Rica 2; Croatia 2; Dominican Republic 2; Ecuador 2; El Salvador 2; France 2; Germany 2; Israel 2; Italy 2; Japan 2; Malawi 2; Malaysia 2; Mexico 4; Norway; Panama 2; Papua New Guinea 2; Peru; Singapore 2; South Africa 4; Spain 2; Sri Lanka; Taiwan 2; Tajikistan 1; Thailand 2; Uganda 4; Ukraine 2

Free Gospel Church, Missions Department

P.O. Box 477
Export, PA 15632 USA

Phone: (724) 327-5454
Fax: (724) 327-3419
E-mail: fgmd@juno.com

Rev. Chester H. Heath, Gen. Superintendent

A denominational support agency of Pentecostal tradition engaged in evangelism, Bible distribution, church construction, church planting, theological education and support of national churches.

Year Founded in US: 1916

Income for Overseas Min: $100,000

Gifts-in-Kind: $20,000

Fully Supported US Personnel Overseas:
Expecting to serve 1 to 4 years: 3

Other personnel:
Short-term less than 1 year from US: 4
Non-US serving in own/other country: 45

Countries: Philippines; Sierra Leone

Free Methodist World Missions

P.O. Box 535002
Indianapolis, IN 46253 USA

Phone: (800) 342-5531
Fax: (317) 241-1248
E-mail: missions@fmcna.org
Web Site: www.fmcna.org/fmwm

Dr. Arthur Brown, Exec. Director

A denominational sending agency of Wesleyan and Evangelical tradition engaged in leadership development, childcare/orphanage programs, church planting, theological education and evangelism.

Purpose: "To help Free Methodists establish a mature church among the peoples of the world."

Year Founded in US: 1885

Income for Overseas Min: $5,667,742

Fully Supported US Personnel Overseas:
Expecting to serve more than 4 years: 65
Nonresidential mission personnel: 2

Other personnel:
Short-term less than 1 year from US: 1,323
Non-US serving in own/other country: 4
Home ministry & office staff in US: 23
Bivocational/Tentmaker from US: 4

Countries: Belgium 2; Brazil 2; Burundi 2; Cambodia 2; Chile 3; Dominican Republic 2; Ecuador 2; Greece 2; Haiti 7; Hong Kong 3; Hungary 7; Kenya 2; Korea, South 1; Malawi 2; Mexico 2; Middle East 2; Philippines 6; Rwanda 2; South Africa 2; Taiwan 6; Tanzania 2; Ukraine 1; Zimbabwe 2

Free Will Baptists, Inc., National Association Board of Foreign Mission

P.O. Box 5002
Antioch, TN 37011 USA

Phone: (615) 731-4950
Fax: (615) 731-5345
E-mail: James@nafwb.org
Web Site: www.nafwb.org

Rev. James Forlines, Gen. Director

A denominational sending agency of Baptist tradition engaged in church planting, development, theological education, evangelism, leadership development and mobilization for mission.

Year Founded in US: 1935

Income for Overseas Min: $4,813,801

Fully Supported US Personnel Overseas:
Expecting to serve more than 4 years: 75
Expecting to serve 1 to 4 years: 3

Other personnel:
Short-term less than 1 year from US: 60
Home ministry & office staff in US: 17

Countries: Brazil 16; Cote d'Ivoire 17; France 7; India 1; Japan 10; Korea, South 2; Panama 6; Russia 2; Spain 9; Uruguay 5

Friends of Israel Gospel Ministry

P.O. Box 908
Bellmawr, NJ 08099 USA
Phone: (609) 853-5590
Fax: (609) 853-9565
E-mail: FOI@foi.org
Web Site: www.foi.org
Mr. William E. Sutter, Exec. Director

A support agency of Evangelical tradition engaged in evangelism, broadcasting, theological education, literature distribution, literature production and video/film production/distribution.

Year Founded in US: 1938
Income for Overseas Min: $642,747

FRIENDS in Action, Intl.

802 N. Hwy. 5
Mansfield, MO 65704 USA
Phone: (417) 924-3220
Fax: (417) 924-3228
E-mail: FIA-USA@fiaintl.org
Web Site: www.fiaintl.org
Mr. Timothy Johnston, Exec. Director

An interdenominational service agency of Baptist and Independent tradition engaged in supplying equipment, development, furloughed missionary support, short-term programs and Bible translation.

Purpose: "...to accelerate the work of proclaiming the Gospel to isolated people groups around the world that have never had the opportunity to hear the Good News of Jesus Christ."

Year Founded in US: 1992
Income for Overseas Min: $359,209
Fully Supported US Personnel Overseas:
  Expecting to serve 1 to 4 years: 12
  Nonresidential mission personnel: 2
Other personnel:
  Short-term less than 1 year from US: 45
  Home ministry & Office Staff in US: 21
Countries: Cote d'Ivoire; Papua New Guinea; Vanuatu

Friends United Meeting, World Ministries

101 Quaker Hill Dr.

Richmond, IN 47374 USA
Phone: (765) 962-7573
Fax: (765) 966-1293
E-mail: missions@fum.org
Web Site: www.fum.org
Colin South, Director World Ministries

A denominational sending agency of Friends tradition engaged in development, Christian education, evangelism, leadership development and short-term programs. Financial data from 1998.

Purpose: "...to energize and equip Friends through the power of the Holy Spirit to gather people into fellowships where Jesus Christ is known..."

Year Founded in US: 1894
Income for Overseas Min: $1,500,000
Personnel:
  Short-term less than 1 year from US: 50
  Home ministry & office staff in US: 2

Friendship International

Box 50884
Colorado Springs, CO 80949-0884 USA
Phone: (719) 386-8808
Fax: (719) 594-4992
E-mail: FRINT@aol.com
Web Site: www.friendshipintl.org
Rev. Del Huff, Exec. Director

An interdenominational service agency of Evangelical tradition engaged in evangelism, audio recording/distribution, mobilization for mission, short-term programs and training. Statistical data from 1998.

Year Founded in US: 1990
Income for Overseas Min: $220,000
Personnel:
  Home ministry & office staff in US: 4

Frontier Mission Fellowship

1605 E. Elizabeth St.
Pasadena, CA 91104 USA
Phone: (626) 398-2234
Fax: (626) 398-2114
E-mail: personnel@uscwm.org
Web Site: www.uscwm.org
Rev. Greg Parsons, Gen. Director

An interdenominational sending agency engaged in missionary training, Christian education, extension education, missions information service, mobilization for mission and mission-related research.

Purpose: "To stimulate and encourage the growth of a movement for frontier missions throughout the US and the world..."

Year Founded in US: 1976

Income for Overseas Min: NA

Fully Supported US Personnel Overseas:
  Expecting to serve more than 4 years: 14
  Expecting to serve 1 to 4 years: 2

Other personnel:
  Home ministry & office staff in US: 95

Countries: India 2; Korea, South 1; Mexico 2; Philippines 5; United Kingdom 4

Frontiers

325 N. Stapley Dr.
Mesa, AZ 85203 USA
Phone: (480) 834-1500
Fax: (480) 834-1974
E-mail: info-us@frontiers.org
Web Site: www.frontiers.org
Rev. Robert A. Blincoe, US Director

An interdenominational sending agency engaged in church planting, evangelism, mobilization for mission, relief and/or rehabilitation and Bible translation.

Purpose: "...planting reproducing churches among unreached Muslim peoples."

Year Founded in US: 1982

Income for Overseas Min: $11,000,000

Fully Supported US Personnel Overseas:
  Expecting to serve more than 4 years: 356
Other personnel:
  Short-term less than 1 year from US: 6
  Home ministry & office staff in US: 65
  Bivocational/Tentmaker from US: 331

Countries: Unspecified Country 356

Full Gospel Evangelistic Association

1202 Three Forks Dr.
Katy, TX 77450 USA
Phone: (281) 693-3782
Fax: (281) 693-4082
E-mail: depruitt@juno.com
Rev. Earl Pruitt, President

An association of missions of Pentecostal and

Full Gospel tradition helping to support full-time missionaries and national churches engaged in evangelism, Bible distribution, church planting and church growth.

Year Founded in US: 1951

Income for Overseas Min: $117,285

Personnel:
  Home ministry & office staff in US: 5

Full Gospel Grace Fellowship

P.O. Box 4564
Tulsa, OK 74159 USA
Phone: (918) 224-7838
E-mail: FGGF@juno.com
Rev. F. W. Peck, Chairman

A nondenominational sending agency of Pentecostal and Independent tradition engaged in funds transmission and literature distribution.

Year Founded in US: 1945

Income for Overseas Min: $70,000

Personnel:
  Non-US serving in own/other country: 10

Countries: Argentina; Belarus; Belize; Mexico; Paraguay

Fundamental Baptist Mission of Trinidad & Tobago

P.O. Box 582011
Charleston, WV 25358 USA
Phone: (304) 345-9479
Pastor Bobby M. Sizemore, Board Chairman

A sending agency of Baptist and Fundamental tradition engaged in church planting, evangelism and support of national workers. Report covers both U.S. and Canadian Boards. Statistical data from 1998.

Year Founded in US: 1921

Income for Overseas Min: $139,000

Fully Supported US Personnel Overseas:
  Expecting to serve more than 4 years: 5
Other personnel:
  Non-US serving in own/other country: 6

Countries: Trinidad and Tobago 5

Galcom International (U.S.)

Box 270956
Tampa, FL 33688-0956 USA

Phone: (813) 933-8111
Fax: (813) 933-8886
E-mail: GalcomUSA@aol.com
Web Site: www.galcom.org
Mr. Gary Nelson, U.S. Administrator

A support agency of Independent and Baptist tradition engaged in supplying communications equipment, purchasing services, services for other agencies and technical assistance in nearly 100 countries.

Purpose: "To provide durable technical equipment for communicating the Gospel worldwide."

Year Founded in US: 1991

Income for Overseas Min: $300,000

Personnel:
   Short-term less than 1 year from US: 6
   Home ministry & office staff in US: 18

General Association of Regular Baptist Churches

1300 N. Meacham Rd.
Schaumburg, IL 60173 USA

Phone: (847) 843-1600
Fax: (847) 843-3757
E-mail: garbc@garbc.org
Web Site: www.garbc.org

Mr. John Greening, Natl. Representative

An association of Baptist tradition providing information for its associated local churches relative to cooperating mission agencies.

Year Founded in US: 1932

Income for Overseas Min: NA

General Baptists Intl.

100 Stinson Dr.
Poplar Bluff, MO 63901 USA

Phone: (573) 785-7746
Fax: (573) 785-0564
E-mail: imdir@generalbaptist.com
Web Site: www.generalbaptist.com

Rev. Jack Eberhardt, Director

A denominational sending agency of Baptist tradition engaged in church planting, childcare/orphanage programs, missions information service, literacy work, medical work and support of national workers.

Purpose: "...to assist [local associations and churches of General Baptists] in the

task of winning people to Christ at home and abroad..."

Year Founded in US: 1903

Income for Overseas Min: $304,320

Fully Supported US Personnel Overseas:
   Expecting to serve more than 4 years: 10
   Expecting to serve 1 to 4 years: 3
   Nonresidential mission personnel: 2

Other personnel:
   Short-term less than 1 year from US: 2
   Home ministry & office staff in US: 4

Countries: Honduras 5; India; Jamaica; N. Mariana Isls 2; Philippines 3

General Conf. Mennonite Church, Commission on Overseas Mission—See: Mennonite Mission Network

Gideons International, The

2900 Lebanon Road
Nashville, TN 37214 USA

Phone: (615) 883-8533
E-mail: tgi@gideons.org
Web Site: www.gideons.org

Mr. Jerry Burden, Exec. Director

An international Christian professional men's association engaged in Bible distribution and evangelism. Active in 172 countries with 58,500 overseas members.

Year Founded in US: 1899

Income for Overseas Min: $50,000,000

Personnel:
   Home ministry & office staff in US: 63

Global Action

7680 Goddard Street, Ste. 100
Colorado Springs, CO 80920 USA

Phone: (719) 528-8728
Fax: (719) 528-8718
E-mail: globalaction@global-act.org
Web Site: www.globalaction.nu

Dr. Lars B. Dunberg, President

A nondenominational sending agency engaged in evangelism, childrens programs, church planting, short-term programs, training and youth programs.

Purpose: "To proclaim the Kingdom of God in word and deed around the world and to serve the Church by empowering, training, motivating and mobilizing people to become fully devoted followers of Christ."

Year Founded in US: 1998
Income for Overseas Min: $966,077
Gifts-in-Kind: $222,333
Fully Supported US Personnel Overseas:
  Expecting to serve more than 4 years: 3
  Nonresidential mission personnel: 2
Other personnel:
  Short-term less than 1 year from US: 108
  Non-US serving in own/other country: 21
  Home ministry & office staff in US: 10
Countries: Asia–General; India; Latin America–General 2; Serbia and Montenegro; Ukraine 1

Global Advance

P.O. Box 742077
Dallas, TX 75374-2077 USA
Phone: (972) 771-9042
Fax: (972) 771-3315
E-mail: info@globaladvance.org
Web Site: www.globaladvance.org
Dr. David Shibley, President

An interdenominational service agency of Evangelical tradition engaged in training, leadership development, literature distribution and support of national churches.

Purpose: "...to help fulfill the Great Commission...by empowering national leaders to evangelize and disciple their own and surrounding nations..."
Year Founded in US: 1990
Income for Overseas Min: $753,199

Global Fellowship

P.O. Box 1
Meadow Vista, CA 95722 USA
Phone: (530) 888-9208
E-mail: don@globalfellowship.org
Web Site: www.globalfellowship.org
Mr. Don Oates, President

A nondenominational support agency of Evangelical tradition engaged in support of national workers, childcare/orphanage programs, church planting, evangelism, mission-related research and missionary education. Statistical data from 1998.

Year Founded in US: 1989

Income for Overseas Min: $110,000
Personnel:
  Non-US serving in own/other country: 603
Countries: Bangladesh; Bhutan; Cote d'Ivoire; Guatemala; India; Liberia; Mexico; Myanmar/Burma; Nepal; Philippines; Sri Lanka; Thailand; Uganda

Global Focus

P.O. Box 2428
Woodstock, GA 30188 USA
Phone: (770) 592-7011
Fax: (770) 592-7299
E-mail: globalfocus@aol.com
Web Site: www.globalfocus.info
Dr. Larry D. Reesor, President

An interdenominational service agency of Evangelical tradition engaged in serving, training and mobilizing pastors and church leaders to lead their churches to reach the world for Christ.

Purpose: "...to glorify God by serving pastors and church leaders, helping them to be more effective in leading their churches to reach the world for Christ."
Year Founded in US: 1995
Income for Overseas Min: NA
Personnel:
  Home ministry & office staff in US: 7

Global Harvest Ministries

P.O. Box 63060
Colorado Springs, CO 80962-3060 USA
Phone: (719) 262-9922
Fax: (818) 262-9920
E-mail: info@globalharvest.org
Web Site: www.globalharvestministries.org
Dr. C. Peter Wagner, President

A transdenominational support agency of Evangelical and Charismatic tradition engaged in leadership development and training.

Purpose: "...to strengthen global forces for evangelism; engage in apostolic ministries to train, encourage, network, and resource leaders; mobilize prayer for world evangelization; train leaders in prayer, spiritual warfare, practical ministry and deliverance."
Year Founded in US: 1991
Income for Overseas Min: NA

Personnel:
Home ministry & office staff in US: 33

Global Health Ministries
7831 Hickory St. NE
Minneapolis, MN 55432-2500 USA
Phone: (763) 586-9590
Fax: (763) 586-9591
E-mail: ghmoffice@cs.com
Web Site: www.ghm.org
Rev. Timon C. Iverson, Exec. Director

A denominational support agency of Lutheran tradition engaged in providing medical supplies, funds transmission, medical work and supplying equipment. Statistical data from 1998.

Purpose: "...providing financial support, shipping of urgently needed medical supplies, assisting in recruiting of medical personnel, funding for training of national health care givers."

Year Founded in US: 1987
Income for Overseas Min: $742,817
Gifts-in-Kind: $220,447
Personnel:
Home ministry & office staff in US: 3

Global Mapping Intl.
15435 Gleneagle Dr., Ste. 100
Colorado Springs, CO 80921 USA
Phone: (719) 531-3599
Fax: (719) 548-7459
E-mail: Info@gmi.org
Web Site: www.gmi.org
Mr. Michael O'Rear, President

An interdenominational support agency of Evangelical tradition engaged in missions information service, leadership development, mission-related research, services for other agencies, technical assistance and missionary training.

Purpose: "To enable ministry decision makers to acquire, manage, analyze, apply, communicate and share strategic information."

Year Founded in US: 1983
Income for Overseas Min: NA
Personnel:
Home ministry & office staff in US: 9

Global Opportunities
1600 Elizabeth St.
Pasadena, CA 91104-2720 USA
Phone: (626) 398-2393
Fax: (626) 398-2396
E-mail: info@globalopps.org
Web Site: www.globalopps.org
Mr. David E. English, Exec. Director

A nondenominational support agency of Evangelical tradition engaged in mobilization for mission, services for other agencies and training.

Purpose: "...mobilize and equip missions-committed lay Christians to serve abroad as effective tentmakers, especially in countries of greatest spiritual need."

Year Founded in US: 1984
Income for Overseas Min: NA
Personnel:
Home ministry & office staff in US: 3

Global Outreach Mission
(See Ad on page 171)
P.O. Box 2010
Buffalo, NY 14231-2010 USA
Phone: (716) 688-5048
Fax: (716) 688-5049
E-mail: glmiss1@adelphia.net
Web Site:
www.globaloutreachmission.com
Dr. James O. Blackwood, President

A transdenominational sending agency of Independent and Evangelical tradition engaged in evangelism, aviation services, broadcasting, church planting, theological education and medical work.

Purpose: "...sharing the Gospel of Jesus Christ around the world, planting and encouraging His church, helping the hurting physically and serving in every area of Christian development."

Year Founded in US: 1943
Income for Overseas Min: $2,623,317
Fully Supported US Personnel Overseas:
Expecting to serve more than 4 years: 117
Other personnel:
Short-term less than 1 year from US: 126
Non-US serving in own/other country: 99
Home ministry & office staff in US: 10
Countries: Australia 2; Austria 1; Bangla-

desh; Belgium 2; Belize 2; Bolivia 3; Brazil 2; Congo, Republic of the 5; France 33; Germany 7; Greece 2; Guatemala 3; Guyana 1; Honduras 2; India 2; Ireland 10; Jordan; Korea, South; Mexico 11; Micronesia, Federated States of 2; Myanmar/Burma; Netherlands; Netherlands Antilles 2; Paraguay 2; Peru; Portugal 2; Russia 4; Spain; Sweden; Ukraine 3; United Kingdom 14; Yugoslavia

Global Outreach, Ltd.

P.O. Box 1
Tupelo, MS 38802 USA
Phone: (225) 647-5609
E-mail: world@netbci.com
Web Site: www.globaloutreach.org

Dr. Sammy Simpson, Chief Operating Officer

An interdenominational sending agency of Evangelical tradition engaged in childcare/orphanage programs, children's programs, church planting, development and theological education. Financial information from 1998.

Year Founded in US: 1971
Income for Overseas Min: $2,933,610
Fully Supported US Personnel Overseas:
  Expecting to serve more than 4 years: 108
  Expecting to serve 1 to 4 years: 27
  Nonresidential mission personnel: 9

Other personnel:
  Short-term less than 1 year from US: 900
  Home ministry & office staff in US: 10

Countries: Argentina 2; Belize 9; Brazil 1; Cameroon 2; Chile 2; China 12; Costa Rica; Ecuador 9; Guatemala; Guyana 5; Haiti 8; Honduras 6; India 2; Israel 2; Kenya 2; Mexico; Mozambique 2; Myanmar/Burma 2; Paraguay 2; Philippines 2; Poland; Romania 10; Russia 2; Rwanda 1; Slovakia 2; Trinidad and Tobago; Uganda 21; Ukraine; United Kingdom 2

Global Strategy Mission Assoc.

P.O. Box 2069
Gonzales, LA 70707 USA
Phone: (225) 647-5609
Fax: (225) 647-5663
E-mail: usdept@gsma.org
Web Site: www.gsma.org

Mr. Jerry Claunch, Director

A nondenominational sending agency of

Charismatic tradition engaged in church planting, evangelism, funds transmission, mobilization for mission and missionary training. Personnel statistics from 1996.

Year Founded in US: 1986
Income for Overseas Min: $2,200,000
Fully Supported US Personnel Overseas:
  Expecting to serve more than 4 years: 10
  Expecting to serve 1 to 4 years: 40
  Nonresidential mission personnel: 1

Other personnel:
  Non-US serving in own/other country: 2
  Home ministry & office staff in US: 9
  Bivocational/Tentmaker from US: 4

Countries: China; Haiti 2; Japan; Mexico 4; Russia 2; Singapore 2

Global University

1211 S. Glenstone Ave.
Springfield, MO 65804 USA
Phone: (417) 862-9533
Fax: (417) 831-4918
E-mail: president@globaluniversity.edu
Web Site: www.globaluniversity.edu

Dr. Ronald A. Iwasko, President

A service agency of Pentecostal tradition engaged in TEE, correspondence courses, extension education, theological education, evangelism and leadership development.

Purpose: "...integrates education and service through a worldwide network for student support."

Year Founded in US: 1967
Income for Overseas Min: $2,137,000
Gifts-in-Kind: $1,957,000
Personnel:
  Home ministry & office staff in US: 81

Global Youth Ministry Network

283 Cline Ave, Ste. A
Mansfield, OH 44907 USA
Phone: (419) 756-4433
Fax: (419) 756-3041
E-mail: office@global-youth.com
Web Site: www.global-youth.com

Mr. Chris Davis, Exec. Director

A nondenominational specialized agency of Evangelical tradition engaged in leader-

OPPORTUNITIES

TO SERVE THE LORD IN A VARIETY OF MINISTRIES AROUND THE WORLD

Austria
Belgium
Brazil
Canada
Congo
France
Germany
Guatemala
Greece
Haiti
Honduras
Ireland
India
Mexico
Netherlands
Paraguay
Spain
Russia
South Africa
Sweden
Yugoslavia
Ukraine
United Kingdom

Write today for your information packet!

GLOBAL OUTREACH MISSION

USA: Box 2010, Buffalo, NY 14231-2010
Phone: 716-688-5048

CANADA: Box 1210, St. Catharines, ON L2R 7A7
Phone: 905-684-1401

www.globaloutreachmission.org
gom@globaloutreachmission.org

ship development, evangelism, support of national churches, support of national workers, training and youth programs.

Year Founded in US: 1997

Income for Overseas Min: $85,000

Gifts-in-Kind: $1,000

Fully Supported US Personnel Overseas:
Nonresidential mission personnel: 1

Other personnel:
Home ministry & office staff in US: 3

Globe Missionary Evangelism

P.O. Box 3040
Pensacola, FL 32516-3040 USA

Phone: (850) 453-3453
Fax: (850) 456-6001
E-mail: info@gme.org
Web Site: www.gme.org

Mr. J. Robert Bishop, President

A transdenominational sending agency of Charismatic tradition engaged in church planting, children's programs, theological education, evangelism, support of national churches and relief and/or rehabilitation. Financial data from 1998.

Year Founded in US: 1973

Income for Overseas Min: $2,209,831

Fully Supported US Personnel Overseas:
Expecting to serve more than 4 years: 50
Expecting to serve 1 to 4 years: 8

Other personnel:
Short-term less than 1 year from US: 6
Home ministry & office staff in US: 9
Bivocational/Tentmaker from US: 4

Countries: Africa–General 3; Albania 1; Asia –General 2; Germany; Guatemala 7; Haiti 2; Honduras 2; Hungary; India 5; Kenya 1; Malaysia 2; Mexico 9; Nicaragua 1; Philippines 4; Romania; Russia 1; Thailand 4; United Kingdom 6

GO InterNational

P.O. Box 123
Wilmore, KY 40390 USA

Phone: (859) 858-3171
Fax: (859) 858-4324
E-mail:
gointernational@gointernational.org
Web Site: www.gointernational.org

Rev. Larry G. Cochran, President

An interdenominational support agency of Wesleyan tradition providing assistance through ministry teams of believers from other countries engaged in development, children's programs, church planting, evangelism, leadership development and short-term programs. Statistical data from 1998.

Purpose: "...(to) collaborate with indigenous ministries (and) give Christians in the US the opportunity to become directly involved in the life and ministry of the church in the Two-Thirds World..."

Year Founded in US: 1968

Income for Overseas Min: $615,194

Fully Supported US Personnel Overseas:
Nonresidential mission personnel: 3

Other personnel:
Short-term less than 1 year from US: 250
Home ministry & office staff in US: 13

Go Ye Fellowship

P.O. Box 40039
Pasadena, CA 91114 USA

Phone: (626) 398-2305
Fax: (626) 797-5576
E-mail: GYFint@cs.com

Mr. William H. Gustafson, President

A nondenominational sending agency of Evangelical tradition providing administrative and spiritual support for missionaries.

Purpose: "...enabling missionaries to pursue their God-given call and vision by serving as the link between missionaries and those who send them."

Year Founded in US: 1944

Income for Overseas Min: $532,474

Fully Supported US Personnel Overseas:
Expecting to serve more than 4 years: 19
Expecting to serve 1 to 4 years: 7

Other personnel:
Non-US serving in own/other country: 4
Home ministry & office staff in US: 5

Countries: Brazil 4; Costa Rica 2; Egypt 1; India; Indonesia 1; Kazakhstan; Kenya 4; Korea, South 1; Latin America–General 2; Philippines 2; Romania 1; Taiwan 1; Turkey

Good News for India

P.O. Box 7576
LaVerne, CA 91750-7576 USA

Phone: (909) 593-7753
Fax: (909) 593-1155
E-mail: gnfi@goodnewsforindia.org
Web Site: www.goodnewsforindia.org
Mr. George Kuruvila Chavanikamannil,
President

An interdenominational support agency of Evangelical and Charismatic tradition engaged in theological education, church planting, Christian education, missionary education, leadership development and support of national workers. Statistical data from 1998.

Purpose: "To train, send out and support 'national missionaries' to plant churches in the unreached areas of India and neighboring countries."

Year Founded in US: 1986

Income for Overseas Min: $427,434

Personnel:
   Short-term less than 1 year from US: 10
   Non-US serving in own/other country: 57
   Home ministry & office staff in US: 2

Countries: Bhutan; India; Nepal

Good News Productions Intl.

P.O. Box 222
Joplin, MO 64802 USA
Phone: (417) 782-0060
Fax: (417) 782-3999
E-mail: gnpi@gnpi.org
Web Site: www.gnpi.com
Mr. Ziden L. Nutt, Exec. Director

A nondenominational specialized agency of Christian (Restoration Movement) tradition engaged in video/film production/distribution, broadcasting, evangelism, partnership development and mission-related research.

Purpose: "...works in partnership with Christians around the world to develop culturally-relevant strategies and resources which are used to effectively proclaim the gospel of Christ to the peoples of the world."

Year Founded in US: 1976

Income for Overseas Min: $800,000

Fully Supported US Personnel Overseas:
   Expecting to serve more than 4 years: 15
   Expecting to serve 1 to 4 years: 2
   Nonresidential mission personnel: 2

Other personnel:

   Non-US serving in own/other country: 34
   Home ministry & office staff in US: 18

Countries: Africa–General 2; India 2; Mexico 2; Myanmar/Burma; Philippines 1; Singapore 2; Thailand 4; Ukraine 2

Good Shepherd Ministries

P.O. Box 360963
Melbourne, FL 32936-1499 USA
Phone: (321) 752-0072
Mr. William S. Younger, Exec. Director

A support agency of Fundamental tradition engaged in Christian education. Statistical data from 1998.

Year Founded in US: 1974

Income for Overseas Min: $61,000

Personnel:
   Non-US serving in own/other country: 49
   Home ministry & office staff in US: 1

Countries: Haiti

Gospel Communications Intl.

P.O. Box 455
Muskegon, MI 49443 USA
Phone: (231) 773-3361
Fax: (231) 777-1847
E-mail: info@gospelcom.net
Web Site: www.gospelcom.net
Rev. William J. Zeoli, President

A nondenominational specialized agency of Evangelical tradition engaged in video/film production/distribution, technical assistance and Internet services.

Purpose: "...to proclaim the Gospel of Jesus Christ and empower the Body of Christ for ministry, worldwide, through the effective use of media resources and communication technologies."

Year Founded in US: 1950

Income for Overseas Min: NA

Personnel:
   Home ministry & office staff in US: 49

Gospel Fellowship Assn.

1809 Wade Hampton Blvd., #110
Greenville, SC 29609 USA
Phone: (864) 609-5500
Fax: (864) 609-5501
E-mail: GFA@gfamissions.org

Web Site: www.gfamissions.org

Dr. Mark Batory, Director Missions

A nondenominational sending agency of Fundamental tradition engaged in church planting, camping programs, correspondence courses, theological education, evangelism and medical work.

Year Founded in US: 1961

Income for Overseas Min: NR

Fully Supported US Personnel Overseas:
   Expecting to serve more than 4 years: 150
   Expecting to serve 1 to 4 years:13
   Nonresidential mission personnel: 3

Other personnel:
   Short-term less than 1 year from US: 4
   Home ministry & office staff in US: 23

Countries: Albania 2; Argentina 2; Australia 4; Austria 4; Azores 2; Botswana 2; Brazil 4; Cambodia 2; Cameroon 11; Chile 4; Costa Rica 2; Dominica 2; Equatorial Guinea 2; Germany 18; Italy 2; Japan 1; Kenya 2; Korea, South 6; Marshall Islands 4; Mexico 13; New Zealand 2; Panama 2; Papua New Guinea 6; Philippines 14; Puerto Rico 4; South Africa 6; Spain 6; Ukraine 2; United Kingdom 19

Gospel for Asia

1800 Golden Trail Ct.
Carrollton, TX 75010 USA

Phone: (972) 300-7777
Fax: (972) 300-7778
E-mail: info@gfa.org
Web Site: www.gfa.org

Rev. K. P. Yohannan, President

A nondenominational service agency of Evangelical tradition engaged in church planting, broadcasting, evangelism, leadership development, support of national workers and missionary training.

Year Founded in US: 1979

Income for Overseas Min: $17,297,000

Gifts-in-Kind: $428,400

Personnel:
   Short-term less than 1 yr. from US: 24
   Non-US serving in own/other country: 13,500
   Home ministry & office staff in US: 43

Countries: Bangladesh; Bhutan; China; India; Myanmar/Burma; Nepal; Pakistan; Sri Lanka; Unspecified Country

Gospel Furthering Fellowship

221 Hamilton Ave.
Myerstown, PA 17067 USA

Phone: (717) 866-1964
Fax: (717) 866-8527
E-mail: GFF@comcast.net
Web Site: www.gffministries.com

Rev. Bruce Busch, Gen. Director

A nondenominational sending agency of Baptist tradition engaged in church planting, theological education, evangelism and support of national churches. Statistical data from 1996.

Year Founded in US: 1935

Income for Overseas Min: $230,000

Fully Supported US Personnel Overseas:
   Expecting to serve more than 4 years: 7

Other personnel:
   Home ministry & office staff in US: 6

Countries: Kenya 3; Spain 2; Tanzania 2; Unspecified Country

Gospel Literature Intl., Inc.

2990 Inland Empire Blvd., #110
Ontario, CA 91764-4899 USA

Phone: (909) 481-5222
Fax: (909) 481-5216
E-mail: glintint@aol.com
Web Site: www.glint.org

Georgalyn B. Wilkinson, President

An interdenominational service agency of Evangelical and Independent tradition providing copyrighted English Christian education curriculum and literature for adaptation, translation and publication in more than 70 non-English languages.

Purpose: "...to provide resources for Christian publishers worldwide in producing effective Bible teaching curriculum, discipleship materials and other Christian literature in national languages, with the goal of making disciples, developing godly Christian leaders and building up God's church."

Year Founded in US: 1961

Income for Overseas Min: NA

Personnel:
   Home ministry & office staff in US: 5

Gospel Mission of South America

1401 SW 21st Ave.
Fort Lauderdale, FL 33312-3109 USA

Phone: (954) 587-2975
E-mail: gmsausa@email.msn.com
Web Site: www.gmsa.org

Rev. Terry Thompson, Gen. Director

A nondenominational sending agency of Baptist and Fundamental tradition engaged in church planting, broadcasting, theological education, literature distribution and literature production.

Purpose: "...to evangelize the people of Latin America by means of itinerant and localized work, with the object of establishing and developing indigenous churches."

Year Founded in US: 1923

Income for Overseas Min: $1,017,398

Fully Supported US Personnel Overseas:
Expecting to serve more than 4 years: 30
Nonresidential mission personnel: 2

Other personnel:
Short-term less than 1 year from US: 11
Home ministry & office staff in US: 5

Countries: Argentina 10; Chile 14; Uruguay 6

Gospel Missionary Union
See: Avant Ministries

Gospel Outreach Ministries International

P.O. Box 380
Hillsboro, MO 63050-0380 USA

Phone: (636) 948-9836
Fax: (636) 948-9835
E-mail: gomint@aol.com

Dr. Sam Paul Gokanakonda, President/CEO

A nondenominational support agency of Evangelical tradition engaged in evangelism, church planting, support of national workers, mission-related research, literacy work and development. Primary focus is the most unreached people groups of India.

Purpose: "...to fulfill the responsibility of the Great Commission to disciple the lost through a relationship with God and forming a community of local believers."

Year Founded in US: 1988

Income for Overseas Min: $93,534

Personnel:
Non-US serving in own/other country: 250
Home ministry & office staff in US: 2

Countries: India

Gospel Recordings (Global Recordings Network)

41823 Enterprise Circle North
Temecula, CA 92590 USA

Phone: (909) 719-1650
Fax: (909) 719-1651
E-mail: minfo@gospelrecordings.com
Web Site: www.gospelrecordings.com

Mr. Colin Stott, Exec. Director

An interdenominational specialized agency of Evangelical tradition engaged in audio recording/distribution, evangelism, national worker support, mission-related research, services for other agencies and technical assistance in more than 5,494 languages.

Purpose: "...helps spread the Gospel by recording and distributing evangelistic messages in the thousands of languages and dialects."

Year Founded in US: 1939

Income for Overseas Min: $500,000

Fully Supported US Personnel Overseas:
Nonresidential mission personnel: 3

Other personnel:
Short-term less than 1 year from US: 53
Home ministry & office staff in US: 32

Gospel Revival Ministries

314 W. Beltline Rd.
DeSoto, TX 75115 USA

Phone: (972) 230-4660
Fax: (972) 274-1318
E-mail: staff@gogoodnews.com
Web Site: www.gogoodnews.com

Mr. John Musser, President/Evangelist

A nondenominational support agency of Pentecostal tradition engaged in support of national workers, Bible distribution, evangelism, funds transmission, literature distribution and supplying equipment. Personnel figures and country data from 1998.

Year Founded in US: 1980

Income for Overseas Min: $86,000

Gifts-in-Kind: $25,000

Personnel:
 Non-US serving in own/other country: 235
 Home ministry & office staff in US: 3

Countries: Cameroon; Chad; Ghana; India; Malaysia; Niger; Nigeria; Sudan; Ukraine

Grace and Truth, Inc.
210 Chestnut St.
Danville, IL 61832 USA
Phone: (217) 442-1120
E-mail: gtpress@gtpress.org
Web Site: www.gtpress.org
Mr. Sam O. Hadley, Exec. Officer

A nondenominational support agency of Christian/Plymouth Brethren tradition engaged in literature production/distribution in 12 languages, and correspondence courses.

Year Founded in US: 1931

Income for Overseas Min: $300,000

Personnel:
 Home ministry & office staff in US: 10

Grace Baptist Missions Intl.
P.O. Box 9
Mehoopany, PA 18629-0009 USA
Phone: (570) 833-5403
E-mail: GBMI99@aol.com
Web Site: www.gracebaptistmissions.org
Dr. David A. Denny, Exec. Director

A denominational specialized agency of Baptist tradition engaged in mission-related research, church establishing, extension education, missions information service, leadership development, support of national workers and training. Personnel information from 1998.

Purpose: "...to provide education and research services to local Baptist churches sending missionaries directly to the field."

Year Founded in US: 1989

Income for Overseas Min: NA

Fully Supported US Personnel Overseas:
 Expecting to serve more than 4 years: 3
Other personnel:
 Non-US serving in own/other country: 3
Countries: Australia 2; Germany 1; Ghana; Saint Lucia

Grace Brethren Intl. Missions
P.O. Box 588
Winona Lake, IN 46590 USA
Phone: (574) 268-1888
Fax: (574) 267-5210
E-mail: gbim@gbim.org
Web Site: www.gbim.org
Rev. David Guiles, Exec. Director

A denominational sending agency of Brethren tradition engaged in church planting, Christian education, evangelism, support of national churches and mobilization for mission.

Purpose: "...to mobilize men and women to evangelize and disciple the nations through church multiplication movements."

Year Founded in US: 1900

Income for Overseas Min: $4,498,184

Gifts-in-Kind: $5,500

Fully Supported US Personnel Overseas:
 Expecting to serve more than 4 years: 92
 Expecting to serve 1 to 4 years: 14
 Nonresidential mission personnel: 1

Other personnel:
 Short-term less than 1 year from US: 189
 Non-US serving in own/other country: 40
 Home ministry & office staff in US: 19
 Bivocational/Tentmaker from US: 1

Countries: Argentina 7; Brazil 6; Cambodia 2; Central African Republic 12; Chad; Chile; Czech Republic 2; France 19; Germany 10; Ireland 2; Japan 4; Kyrgyzstan 2; Mexico 2; Paraguay; Philippines 5; Portugal 7; Spain 4; Turkey 2; United Kingdom 6

Grace Ministries Intl.
P.O. Box 9405
Grand Rapids, MI 49509 USA
Phone: (616) 241-5666
Fax: (616) 241-2542
E-mail: gmi@gracem.org
Web Site: www.gracem.org
Dr. Samuel R. Vinton, Jr., Exec. Director

A nondenominational sending agency of Evangelical tradition engaged in church planting, Christian education, extension education, TEE, leadership development and medical work.

Year Founded in US: 1939

Income for Overseas Min: $1,540,832

Fully Supported US Personnel Overseas:

Expecting to serve more than 4 years: 44
Expecting to serve 1 to 4 years: 1

Other personnel:
Short-term less than 1 year from US: 50
Non-US serving in own/other country: 16
Home ministry & office staff in US: 6

Countries: Australia 6; Bolivia 6; Congo,
Democratic Republic of the 5; Costa Rica 5
India; Puerto Rico 6; Tanzania 12; Zambia 4

Grand Old Gospel Fellowship

160 E. Main St.
Lansdale, PA 19446-2519 USA
Phone: (215) 361-8111
E-mail: gogf@comcast.net
Web Site: www.gogf.org
Mr. Tony Hart, President

A nondenominational support agency of
Evangelical tradition engaged in broadcasting, audio recording/distribution, church
planting and evangelism.

Year Founded in US: 1962

Income for Overseas Min: $50,000

Gifts-in-Kind: $10,000

Personnel:
Non-US serving in own/other country: 2
Countries: Bahamas; Jamaica

Great Commission Center Intl.

1101 San Antonio Rd., Ste. 400
Mountain View, CA 94043 USA
Phone: (650) 968-2985
Fax: (650) 968-4856
E-mail: info@gcciusa.org
Web Site: www.gcciusa.org
Dr. Thomas Wang, President

An interdenominational support agency of
Evangelical tradition engaged in mobilization for mission, literature distribution, literature production, short-term programs
and training.

Year Founded in US: 1989

Income for Overseas Min: $207,550

Personnel:
Non-US serving in own/other country: 1
Home ministry & office staff in US: 6
Countries: China; Middle East; Oceania–
General

Great Commission Ministries, Inc.

P.O. Box 7101
Winter Park, FL 32793 USA
Phone: (407) 671-9700
Fax: (407) 671-9776
E-mail: gcm@gcmweb.org
Web Site: www.gcmweb.org
Mr. Jeffrey Kern, Exec. Director

A nondenominational sending agency of
Evangelical tradition engaged in church
planting, evangelism, leadership development, management consulting/training
and youth programs.

Year Founded in US: 1990

Income for Overseas Min: $1,115,593

Fully Supported US Personnel Overseas:
Expecting to serve more than 4 years: 12
Expecting to serve 1 to 4 years: 16
Nonresidential mission personnel: 1

Other personnel:
Short-term less than 1 year from US: 78
Non-US serving in own/other country: 5
Home ministry & office staff in US: 216
Bivocational/Tentmaker from US: 14

Countries: Germany 2; Honduras; Italy;
Ukraine 10

Greater Europe Mission
(See Ad on page 179)
18950 Base Camp Rd.
Monument, CO 80132-8009 USA
Phone: (719) 488-8008
Fax: (719) 488-8018
E-mail: info@gemission.com
Web Site: www.gemission.org
Rev. Ted Noble, President/CEO
Dr. Jay Butler, U.S. Director

A nondenominational sending agency of
Evangelical tradition engaged in theological
education, camping programs, church
planting, evangelism and leadership development.

Year Founded in US: 1949

Income for Overseas Min: $11,997,671

Fully Supported US Personnel Overseas:
Expecting to serve more than 4 years: 235
Expecting to serve 1 to 4 years: 19
Nonresidential mission personnel: 1

Other personnel:

Short-term less than 1 year from US: 283
Home ministry & office staff in US: 65

Countries: Albania; Austria 11; Belgium 6; Bulgaria; Croatia 6; Czech Republic 6; Denmark; Finland; France 31; Germany 47; Greece 14; Hungary 7; Iceland 2; Ireland 13; Italy 8; Kosovo 4; Latvia 8; Luxembourg 2; Netherlands 10; Poland 4; Portugal 11; Romania 11; Russia 1; Slovakia 4; Slovenia; Spain 23; Sweden 2; Ukraine 2; United Kingdom 2

Greater Grace World Outreach

P.O. Box 18715
Baltimore, MD 21206 USA

Phone: (410) 483-3700
Fax: (410) 483-3708
E-mail: missions@ggwo.org
Web Site: www.ggwo.org

Mark A. Schollaert, Missions Director

A nondenominational support agency of Evangelical tradition engaged in church planting, missionary education, short-term programs, theological education, evangelism and missionary training. Personnel statistics from 1998.

Year Founded in US: 1986

Income for Overseas Min: NR

Fully Supported US Personnel Overseas:
Nonresidential mission personnel: 2

Other personnel:
Short-term less than 1 year from US: 80
Non-US serving in own/other country: 108
Home ministry & office staff in US: 45
Bivocational/Tentmaker from US: 150

Countries: Argentina; Asia–General; Azerbaijan; Belarus; Brazil; Czech Republic; El Salvador; Finland; France; Germany; Ghana; Greece; Hungary; India; Ireland; Kazakhstan; Kenya; Kyrgyzstan; Liberia; Lithuania; Nepal; Netherlands; Pakistan; Poland; Romania; Russia; Slovakia; Swaziland; Sweden; Thailand; Togo; Turkmenistan; Ukraine; United Kingdom

Habitat for Humanity Intl.

121 Habitat St.
Americus, GA 31709-3498 USA

Phone: (229) 924-6935
Fax: (229) 924-6541

E-mail: publicinfo@hfhi.org
Web Site: www.habitat.org

Dr. Millard D. Fuller, President

An interdenominational specialized service agency of Ecumenical tradition engaged in building low-income housing in partnership with/for people in need. Personnel data from 1996.

Purpose: "...works in partnership with God and people everywhere to develop communities with God's people in need by building and renovating houses...in which people can live and grow into all that God intended."

Year Founded in US: 1976

Income for Overseas Min: $17,081,351

Fully Supported US Personnel Overseas:
Expecting to serve more than 4 years: 10
Expecting to serve 1 to 4 years: 109

Other personnel:
Short-term less than 1 year from US: 1,200
Non-US serving in own/other country: 538
Home ministry & office staff in US: 463

Countries: Antigua; Bolivia; Botswana; Brazil; Central African Republic; Colombia; Congo, Democratic Republic of the; Costa Rica; Dominican Republic; Egypt; El Salvador; Ethiopia; Fiji; Ghana; Guatemala; Guyana; Haiti; Honduras; Hungary 2; India; Jamaica; Kenya; Korea, South 1; Kyrgyzstan 1; Malawi; Mexico; Netherlands 1; Nicaragua; Papua New Guinea; Paraguay; Peru; Philippines; Poland 1; Romania 1; Slovenia; South Africa; Sri Lanka; Tanzania; Trinidad and Tobago; Uganda; United Kingdom 3; Zambia; Zimbabwe

Haiti Lutheran Mission Society

P.O. Box 22544
Lincoln, NE 68542-2544 USA

Phone: (800) 247-0490
Fax: (402) 474-2596
E-mail: crnitz@aol.com
Web Site: www.haitilutheran.org

Rev./Dr. Charles A. Reimnitz, President

A denominational support agency of Lutheran tradition engaged in church planting, Christian education, theological education, medical work and relief and/or rehabilitation.

Purpose: "...to minister to the spiritual and physical needs of the Haitian people so that they might be won by the Holy Spirit to be disciples of Jesus Christ."

Year Founded in US: 1979

Income for Overseas Min: $120,000

Gifts-in-Kind: $20,000

Personnel:
Short-term less than 1 year from US: 30
Non-US serving in own/other country: 59

Countries: Haiti

Handclasp International, Inc.

P.O. Box 233
Crest Park, CA 92326 USA
Phone: (909) 337-1894
Fax: (909) 336-1674
E-mail: mediastrategy@readmail.biz
Web Site: www.comresource.com
Mr. Daniel J. Henrich, President

A transdenominational service agency of Baptist tradition engaged in video/film production/distribution, extension education, mission-related research and services for other agencies.

Year Founded in US: 1970

Income for Overseas Min: NA

Personnel:
Home ministry & office staff in US: 1

Hands for Christ

5720 Williamson Road NW, Office 111
Roanoke, VA 24012 USA
Phone: (540) 362-1214
Fax: (540) 563-8285
E-mail: hfc@rev.net
Web Site: www.handsforchrist.org
Mr. R. W. Bowers, President

An interdenominational specialized agency of Evangelical tradition engaged in literature distribution, literature production, audio recording/distribution and Bible distribution. Statistical data from 1998.

Purpose: "...providing Christian materials in the form of books, audio and video cassettes, tracts, bumper stickers and magazines which are educational, inspirational and biblically based."

Year Founded in US: 1929

Income for Overseas Min: $388,000

Gifts-in-Kind: $300,000

Personnel:
Home ministry & office staff in US: 10

Harvest

P.O. Box 2670
Phoenix, AZ 85002-2670 USA
Phone: (602) 258-1083
Web Site: www.harvestfoundation.org
Mr. Robert C. Moffitt, Exec. Director

A nondenominational service agency of Evangelical tradition engaged in wholistic ministry training for local church leaders, curriculum development, and training services and conferences.

Purpose: "...encourages and prepares the Christian church around the globe to carry out biblical wholistic ministry."

Year Founded in US: 1981

Income for Overseas Min: $280,130

Personnel:
Short-term less than 1 year from US: 25
Non-US serving in own/other country: 17
Home ministry & office staff in US: 20

Countries: Brazil; Dominican Republic; Ethiopia; Ghana; Haiti; Honduras; India; Philippines; Rwanda; Venezuela

Harvest Evangelism, Inc.

P.O. Box 20310
San Jose, CA 95160 USA
Phone: (408) 927-9052
Fax: (408) 927-9830
E-mail: mail@harvestevan.org
Web Site: www.harvestevan.org
Rev. Ed Silvoso, President

An interdenominational specialized agency of Evangelical tradition engaged in missionary training, evangelism, support of national churches, mobilization for mission and short-term programs. Statistical data from 1998.

Purpose: "...to help the Church of the city, comprised of its various congregations, implement a comprehensive strategy to effectively saturate the city with the Good News of the gospel..."

Year Founded in US: 1980

Income for Overseas Min: $200,000

Fully Supported US Personnel Overseas:
Nonresidential mission personnel: 4

Other personnel:
Short-term less than 1 year from US: 20
Home ministry & office staff in US: 20
Bivocational/Tentmaker from US: 5

Have Christ Will Travel Ministries

528 E. Church Lane
Philadelphia, PA 19144 USA
Phone: (215) 438-6308
Fax: (215) 438-6308

Dr. Joseph C. Jeter, Director/President

An interdenominational support agency of
Independent and Baptist tradition engaged
in evangelism, Christian education, support
of national churches and supplying equipment. Personnel data from 1998.

Year Founded in US: 1965

Income for Overseas Min: $226,000

Gifts-in-Kind: $55,000

Fully Supported US Personnel Overseas:
Nonresidential mission personnel: 5

Other personnel:
Non-US serving in own/other country: 38
Home ministry & office staff in US: 19

Countries: Haiti; India; Liberia

HBI Global Partners

P.O. Box 245
Union Mills, NC 28167 USA
Phone: (828) 286-8317
E-mail: gupta@blueridge.net
Web Site: www.globalpartners.org

Dr. Paul Gupta, President

A nondenominational sending agency of
Evangelical tradition engaged in church
planting, broadcasting, childcare/orphan-
age programs, theological education, evangelism and support of national workers.

Purpose: "...enabling the North American
Church to develop partnerships with national movements to reach the unreached
in India and beyond."

Year Founded in US: 1950

Income for Overseas Min: $695,270

Fully Supported US Personnel Overseas:
Expecting to serve more than 4 years: 1

Other personnel:
Short-term less than 1 year from US: 40
Non-US serving in own/other country: 177
Home ministry & office staff in US: 2

Countries: India

HCJB World Radio

P.O. Box 39800
Colorado Springs, CO 80949-9800 USA
Phone: (719) 590-9800
Fax: (719) 590-9801
E-mail: info@hcjb.org
Web Site: www.hcjb.org

Dr. David Johnson, President

A service agency of Evangelical tradition engaged in broadcasting, development,
medical work, supplying equipment, technical assistance and training.

Purpose: "To communicate the gospel of
Jesus Christ to all nations so that people are
transformed and become active, vital parts
of the Body of Christ."

Year Founded in US: 1931

Income for Overseas Min: $20,000,000

Gifts-in-Kind: $880,000

Fully Supported US Personnel Overseas:
Expecting to serve more than 4 years: 151

Other personnel:
Non-US serving in own/other country: 44
Home ministry & office staff in US: 80

Countries: Argentina; Cote d'Ivoire 2;
Czech Republic 2; Ecuador 139; Russia 2;
Spain 4; Ukraine 2

Health Emergent International Services

P.O. Box 1225
Issaquah, WA 98027 USA
Phone: (425) 837-0991
Fax: (425) 837-0992
E-mail: info@heis.org
Web Site: www.heis.org

Mr. Marvin G. Taylor, Medical Director

A service agency of Evangelical and Pentecostal tradition engaged in medical work,
development, management consulting/
training, providing medical supplies and relief and/or rehabilitation.

Purpose: "...strives to show love and compassion to international communities, continually delivering health care services, medical education and supporting indigenous medical communities."

Year Founded in US: 1999

Income for Overseas Min: $2,700,000

Gifts-in-Kind: $1,200,000

Fully Supported US Personnel Overseas:
Expecting to serve more than 4 years: 4
Expecting to serve 1 to 4 years: 12
Nonresidential mission personnel: 2

Other personnel:
Short-term less than 1 year from US: 53
Non-US serving in own/other country: 1

Countries: Afghanistan 2; Tajikistan 2

Health Teams International
7518 S. Evanston Ave.
Tulsa, OK 74136 USA
Phone: (918) 481-1115
Fax: (918) 523-2677
E-mail: HTIteams@cs.com
Dr. Richard E. Charlick, President

An interdenominational specialized agency of Christian (Restoration Movement) tradition engaged in medical work, church planting, evangelism, mobilization for mission, services for other agencies and short-term programs.

Year Founded in US: 1986

Income for Overseas Min: $73,218

Personnel:
Short-term less than 1 year from US: 100
Home ministry & office staff in US: 3

Heart of God Ministries
3720 S. Hiwassee Rd.
Choctaw, OK 73020 USA
Phone: (405) 737-9446
Fax: (405) 737-9448
E-mail: hgm@heartofgod.com
Web Site: www.heartofgod.com
Rev./Dr. James Lee West, Exec. Director

An interdenominational specialized agency of Evangelical and Holiness tradition engaged in missionary training, church planting and mobilization for mission.

Year Founded in US: 1995

Income for Overseas Min: $200,000

Personnel:
Short-term less than 1 year from US: 15
Non-US serving in own/other country: 15
Home ministry & office staff in US: 25

Countries: Asia–General

Heart to Heart Intl. Ministries
P.O. Box 1832
Ramona, CA 92065 USA
Phone: (760) 789-8798
Fax: (760) 789-8798
E-mail: info@heart2heartint.org
Web Site: www.heart2heartint.org
Mr. James Sorrels, President

A nondenominational support agency of Evangelical tradition engaged in childcare/orphanage programs, short-term programs, support of national workers and relief and/or rehabilitation.

Purpose: "...helping the orphans and poor in Romania, sharing God's love."

Year Founded in US: 1994

Income for Overseas Min: $420,363

Fully Supported US Personnel Overseas:
Expecting to serve more than 4 years: 1
Expecting to serve 1 to 4 years: 6
Nonresidential mission personnel: 3

Other personnel:
Short-term less than 1 year from US: 100
Non-US serving in own/other country: 5
Home ministry & office staff in US: 3

Countries: Romania 1

Heifer International
1015 Louisiana Street
Little Rock, AR 72202 USA
Phone: (501) 907-2600
Fax: (501) 907-2602
E-mail: info@heifer.org
Web Site: www.heifer.org
Jo Luck, President/CEO

A support agency engaged in environmental and sustainable agricultural development, extension education, and training. Eleven denominations have "covenant agency representatives" on the board.

Purpose: "...to work with communities to end hunger and poverty and care for the earth."

Year Founded in US: 1944

Income for Overseas Min: $26,880,000
Gifts-in-Kind: $300,000
Fully Supported US Personnel Overseas:
  Expecting to serve more than 4 years: 53
  Expecting to serve 1 to 4 years: 126
Other personnel:
  Short-term less than 1 year from US: 50
  Non-US serving in own/other country: 217
Countries: Asia–General 35; Europe–General 4; Latin America–General 14

Hellenic Ministries

P.O. Box 726
Wheaton, IL 60189 USA
Phone: (630) 462-7088
Fax: (630) 462-3740
E-mail: info@hmnet.org.gr
Web Site: www.hmnet.org.gr
Mr. Trevor Eby, Acting US Director

A nondenominational sending agency of Evangelical tradition engaged in evangelism, broadcasting, church planting, leadership development and youth programs.
Purpose: "Christ for Greece and the nations."
Year Founded in US: 1986
Income for Overseas Min: $185,520
Gifts-in-Kind: $8,648
Fully Supported US Personnel Overseas:
  Expecting to serve more than 4 years: 3
  Expecting to serve 1 to 4 years: 2
Other personnel:
  Short-term less than 1 year from US: 14
  Non-US serving in own/other country: 7
  Home ministry & office staff in US: 1
Countries: Greece 3

Help for Christian Nationals, Inc.

P.O. Box 381006
Duncanville, TX 75138 USA
Phone: (972) 780-5909
Dr. John Jauchen, President

A transdenominational sending agency of Evangelical tradition engaged in leadership development, theological education, literature distribution, support of national churches, support of national workers and training.

Purpose: "...serving Christian national workers through economic and educational assistance, equipping them to be more effective in reaching their own people for Jesus Christ."
Year Founded in US: 1982
Income for Overseas Min: $660,000
Fully Supported US Personnel Overseas:
  Expecting to serve more than 4 years: 6
  Nonresidential mission personnel: 1
Other personnel:
  Non-US serving in own/other country: 10
  Home ministry & office staff in US: 2
Countries: Guatemala 1; India 1; Philippines 2; Russia; Spain 2

Helps Intl. Ministries

573 Fairview Rd.
Asheville, NC 28803 USA
Phone: (828) 277-3812
Fax: (828) 274-7770
E-mail: HIM@helpsintl.com
Web Site: www.helpsintl.com
Rev. David A. Summey, CEO

A nondenominational specialized agency of Evangelical and Fundamental tradition engaged in services for other agencies and technical assistance. Statistical data from 1998.
Purpose: "...strengthening and equipping ministries serving God's kingdom by providing various 'helps'..."
Year Founded in US: 1976
Income for Overseas Min: $121,661
Fully Supported US Personnel Overseas:
  Expecting to serve more than 4 years: 4
  Nonresidential mission personnel: 4
Other personnel:
  Short-term less than 1 year from US: 12
  Home ministry & office staff in US: 19
Countries: United Kingdom 2; West Bank 2

Hermano Pablo Ministries

P.O. Box 100
Costa Mesa, CA 92628 USA
Phone: (949) 645-0676
Fax: (949) 645-0374
E-mail: hpm@box100.org
Web Site: www.box100.org
Rev. Paul Finkenbinder, Chairman

An interdenominational agency of Evangelical tradition whose four-minute "Message to the Conscience" is broadcast more than 3,200 times per day throughout the Spanish-speaking world. Income and home staff amounts from 1996.

Year Founded in US: 1964

Income for Overseas Min: $396,000

Personnel:
  Home ministry & office staff in US: 5

High Adventure Ministries/Voice of Hope Broadcasting Network

P.O. Box 197569
Louisville, KY 40259 USA

Phone: (800) 517-4673
Fax: (502) 968-7580
E-mail: mail@highadventure.net
Web Site: www.highadventure.org

Jackie Yockey, President/CEO

An interdenominational service agency of Evangelical tradition engaged in broadcasting, correspondence courses and evangelism.

Year Founded in US: 1972

Income for Overseas Min: $388,511

Fully Supported US Personnel Overseas:
  Expecting to serve more than 4 years: 2

Other personnel:
  Non-US serving in own/other country: 26
  Home ministry & office staff in US: 6

Countries: Belau 1; Israel 1

Holt International Children's Services, Inc.

P.O. Box 2880
Eugene, OR 97402 USA

Phone: (541) 687-2202
Fax: (541) 683-6175
E-mail: info@holtinternational.org
Web Site: www.holtinternational.org

Mr. David Cousineau, President/CEO

A nondenominational service agency of Evangelical tradition serving the needs of homeless children and families at risk through adoption, childcare, medical and camping programs. Non-USA staff figure from 1996.

Purpose: "...to carry out God's plan for ev-

ery child to have a permanent loving home through family preservation, in-country adoption or international adoption."

Year Founded in US: 1956

Income for Overseas Min: $9,015,685

Fully Supported US Personnel Overseas:
  Nonresidential mission personnel: 4

Other personnel:
  Non-US serving in own/other country: 552
  Home ministry & office staff in US: 90

Countries: Unspecified Country

Hope for the Hungry

P.O. Box 786
Belton, TX 76513 USA

Phone: (254) 939-0124
Fax: (254) 939-0882
E-mail: hhungry@stonemedia.com
Web Site: www.hopeforthehungry.org

Rebecca O'Banion, Exec. Director

An interdenominational sending agency of Evangelical tradition engaged in childcare/orphanage programs, children's programs, evangelism, support of national workers, short-term programs and missionary training.

Purpose: "To share Jesus Christ with those in the world who do not know Him and will suffer eternal death without Him."

Year Founded in US: 1982

Income for Overseas Min: $515,416

Fully Supported US Personnel Overseas:
  Expecting to serve more than 4 years: 20
  Expecting to serve 1 to 4 years: 3

Other personnel:
  Non-US serving in own/other country: 21
  Home ministry & office staff in US: 15

Countries: Africa–General 2; Belize 1; China 1; Colombia 1; Costa Rica 1; France 1; Guatemala 2; Haiti 3; India 1; Indonesia 1; Israel 1; Japan 1; Mexico 1; South Africa 1; Sri Lanka 2; Sudan; Uganda

Hope Missions Outreach Intl.

P.O. Box 73
Bethany, MO 64424 USA

Phone: (816) 425-2277

Bob & Sharon Johnson, Directors

An interdenominational service agency of Evangelical tradition engaged in short-term programs, church construction and mobilization for mission. Statistics from 1998.

Purpose: "...to serve the local evangelical church for the purpose of discipleship training through cross-cultural team ministries"

Year Founded in US: 1976

Income for Overseas Min: $450,000

Fully Supported US Personnel Overseas:
Expecting to serve more than 4 years: 3

Other personnel:
Short-term less than 1 year from US: 190
Home ministry & office staff in US: 5

Countries: Haiti 3

Hosanna/Faith Comes By Hearing
2421 Aztec Rd. NE
Albuquerque, NM 87107-4224 USA
Phone: (505) 881-3321
Fax: (505) 881-1681
E-mail: FCBH@hosanna.org
Web Site: www.fcbh.org
Mr. Jerry Jackson, President

A transdenominational service agency engaged in Bible distribution, audio recording/distribution, support of national workers, technical assistance and evangelism. Financial information from 1996.

Year Founded in US: 1972

Income for Overseas Min: $86,992

Fully Supported US Personnel Overseas:
Nonresidential mission personnel: 2

Other personnel:
Non-US serving in own/other country: 31
Home ministry & office staff in US: 106

Countries: Bolivia; Ghana; Guatemala; India; Indonesia; Peru; Suriname; Swaziland; Ukraine

Hundredfold Ministries Intl.
P.O. Box 625
Blue Jay, CA 92317 USA
Phone: (909) 336-9701
Fax: (909) 336-7367
E-mail: 102633.504@compuserve.com
Web Site: www.hundredfold.org
Mr. James O. Murphy, President

A service agency of Charismatic and Pentecostal tradition engaged in literature distri-

bution, theological education, leadership development, literature production, purchasing services and technical assistance.

Year Founded in US: 1988

Income for Overseas Min: $46,000

Personnel:
Home ministry & office staff in US: 2

Countries: Ghana; India; Nigeria; Philippines; Russia; Tanzania; Uganda; Zambia

IFMA (Interdenominational Foreign Mission Association)
(See Ad on page 187)
P.O. Box 398
Wheaton, IL 60189-0398 USA
Phone: (630) 682-9270
Fax: (630) 682-9278
E-mail: ifma@aol.com
Web Site: www.ifmamissions.org
Dr. John H. Orme, Exec. Director

An association of mission agencies without denominational affiliation organized for the purpose of strengthening the effectiveness and outreach of interdenominational missions.

Year Founded in US: 1917

Income for Overseas Min: NA

Personnel:
Home ministry & office staff in US: 3

Impact International
P.O. Box 160
Boca Raton, FL 33429-0160 USA
Phone: (561) 338-7000
Fax: (561) 338-7516
E-mail: BDM4@msn.com
Web Site: www.impactinternational.org
Rev. Bruce Woodman, Exec. Director

An interdenominational sending agency of Evangelical tradition engaged in broadcasting, church planting and evangelism. Statistical data from 1998.

Year Founded in US: 1959

Income for Overseas Min: $320,000

Fully Supported US Personnel Overseas:
Expecting to serve more than 4 years: 7
Nonresidential mission personnel: 4

Other personnel:
Short-term less than 1 year from US: 15

The symbol makes all the difference.

With the IFMA symbol you can trust its member missions' stewardship of the Gospel, Finances, Relationships, and Morals.

The Interdenominational Foreign Mission Association of North America plays a vital role in the missions community providing encouragement and essential resources.

But most importantly, since 1917 the IFMA has helped ensure the integrity of its member organizations. When Christians and churches see the IFMA symbol they know their mission agency deploys its people and resources under the accountability of highly stringent membership standards.

Because the IFMA has never deviated from these standards, its members can be trusted to be true to the Lord Jesus Christ and therefore, true to the gospel, and true to the high moral and ethical demands of Scripture through annual affirmations.

Look for the IFMA symbol of integrity.

www.ifmamissions.org

PREPARE FOR
CROSS-CULTURAL MISSIONS

Pre-field training in
how to learn another language

Teaching English to
speakers of other languages (TESOL)

Intercultural communication

Children's programs

Credit or non-credit courses
Three weeks each June

Institute for Cross-Cultural Training
Billy Graham Center, Wheaton College
Wheaton, IL 60187-5593
Phone: 630/752-7950   Fax: 630/752-7125
E-mail: Lonna.J.Dickerson@wheaton.edu
Website: www.wheaton.edu/bgc/icct

Wheaton College
For Christ and His Kingdom

Non-US serving in own/other country: 18
Home ministry & office staff in US: 4

Countries: Argentina; Colombia 2; Costa
Rica 1; Guatemala 2; Honduras 2; Mexico;
Peru; Venezuela

In Touch Mission Intl.

P.O. Box 7575
Tempe, AZ 85281-0020 USA
Phone: (480) 968-4100
Fax: (480) 968-5462
E-mail: itmi@intouchmission.org
Web Site: www.intouchmission.org

Mr. Steve Evers, Director

A nondenominational service agency of
Baptist and Evangelical tradition engaged
in support of national churches, Bible distribution, leadership development, support of
national workers, short-term programs and
video/film production/distribution.

Year Founded in US: 1981

Income for Overseas Min: $647,000

Fully Supported US Personnel Overseas:
Expecting to serve more than 4 years: 2
Expecting to serve 1 to 4 years: 2
Nonresidential mission personnel: 2

Other personnel:
Non-US serving in own/other country: 9
Home ministry & office staff in US: 4
Bivocational/Tentmaker from US: 2

Countries: Poland; Romania; South Africa
2; Sudan; Zambia

Independent Faith Mission

P.O. Box 7791
Greensboro, NC 27417 USA
Phone: (336) 292-1255
Fax: (336) 292-9348
E-mail: robertkurtz@ifmnews.com
Web Site: www.ifmnews.com

Rev. Robert F. Kurtz, Exec. Director

A nondenominational service agency of
Baptist tradition providing various services
to local churches sending missionaries engaged in church planting and evangelism.
Personnel data from 1998.

Year Founded in US: 1950

Income for Overseas Min: $2,580,000

Fully Supported US Personnel Overseas:
Expecting to serve more than 4 years: 101

Countries: Antigua 2; Congo, Democratic
Republic of the 8; Italy 5; Kenya 8; Korea,
South 2; Mexico 2; Micronesia, Federated
States of 2; Philippines 2; South Africa 9;
Suriname 17; United Kingdom 2; Unspeci-
fied Country 26; Zambia 12; Zimbabwe 4

Independent Gospel Missions: A Baptist Mission Agency

1135 Calkins Rd.
Rochester, NY 14623 USA
Phone: (585) 334-9048
Fax: (585) 334-9418
E-mail: igm@igmonline.org
Web Site: www.igmonline.org

Rev. Gary E. Newhart, Exec. Director

An agency of Baptist and Independent tradition engaged in church planting,
childcare/orphanage programs, leadership
development, national worker support,
short-term programs and training. IGM is a
total faith missionary agency, operating
solely on the support of individuals and
churches. Financial figure from 1998.

Purpose: "...serving the church, missionary, and national pastor to produce a con-
certed effort in the areas of accountability,
responsibility, need, and the harvest of
souls for the glory and kingdom of God."

Year Founded in US: 1968

Income for Overseas Min: $900,000

Personnel:
Home ministry & office staff in US: 1

India Evangelical Mission, Inc.

P.O. Box 163
Lakewood, CA 90716-0633 USA
Phone: (562) 484-0881
Fax: (562) 484-0889
E-mail: iemusa@jps.net
Web Site: www.indiaevangelical.org

Dr. G. V. Mathai, President

A nondenominational service agency of
Brethren tradition engaged in missionary
education, childcare/orphanage programs,
church planting, evangelism and support of
national workers. Non-USA statistic from
1998.

Purpose: "...winning the lost, building and
equipping the saints and then sending

them forth to fulfill the Great Commission of our Lord."

Year Founded in US: 1966

Income for Overseas Min: $350,000

Fully Supported US Personnel Overseas:
  Nonresidential mission personnel: 3

Other personnel:
  Non-US serving in own/other country: 525
  Home ministry & office staff in US: 5

Countries: India

India Gospel League Inc., North America

P.O. Box 317770
Cincinnati, OH 45231-7770 USA

Phone: (513) 522-4451
E-mail: igl@iglworld.org

Mr. Ron Whitener, Director

An interdenominational support agency of Evangelical tradition engaged in partnership development, funds transmission, management consulting/training, mobilization for mission, short-term programs and training.

Purpose: "...to promote and establish the Kingdom of God through the ministry of the India Gospel League, India."

Year Founded in US: 1994

Income for Overseas Min: $1,143,237

Personnel:
  Short-term less than 1 year from US: 60
  Home ministry & office staff in US: 5

India Gospel Outreach

P.O. Box 550
Rancho Cucamonga, CA 91729-0550 USA

Phone: (909) 948-2404
Fax: (909) 948-2406
E-mail: IGO@indiago.org
Web Site: www.indiago.org

Rev. T. Valson Abraham, Founder/Director

A transdenominational service agency of Evangelical tradition engaged in church planting, broadcasting, theological education, evangelism, leadership development, support of national churches and support of national workers.

Purpose: "...planting dynamic churches in all 3,000 castes and tribes...and establish-

ing Bible training centers in all states of India...by the year 2000."

Year Founded in US: 1984

Income for Overseas Min: $549,659

Personnel:
  Home ministry & office staff in US: 7

India National Inland Mission

P.O. Box 652
Verdugo City, CA 91046 USA

Phone: (818) 241-4010
E-mail: paulpil@vsnl.net

Mr. Paul Pillai, Director

A nondenominational support agency of Fundamental and Independent tradition engaged in support of national workers, Bible distribution, childcare/orphanage programs, church planting, theological education, Bible college and seminary and missionary training. Personnel statistics from 1998.

Year Founded in US: 1964

Income for Overseas Min: $1,177,621

Personnel:
  Non-US serving in own/other country: 330

Countries: India

India Partners

P.O. Box 5470
Eugene, OR 97405 USA

Phone: (541) 683-0696
Fax: (541) 683-2773
E-mail: info@indiapartners.org
Web Site: www.indiapartners.org

Mr. Brent Hample, Exec. Director

A nondenominational service agency engaged in partnership development, childcare/orphanage programs, church construction, Christian education, medical work and short-term programs.

Purpose: "...supporting self-help ministry projects in India."

Year Founded in US: 1994

Income for Overseas Min: $368,697

Gifts-in-Kind: $147,630

Personnel:
  Short-term less than 1 year from US: 26
  Non-US serving in own/other country: 1
  Home ministry & office staff in US: 3

Countries: Africa–General; India

India Rural Evangelical Fellowship

P.O. Box 1332
Park Ridge, IL 60068-7332 USA
Phone: (847) 604-3776
Fax: (847) 680-4270
E-mail: Info@irefusa.org
Web Site: www.irefusa.org
Mr. Emmanuel Rebba, President

An interdenominational service agency of Evangelical tradition engaged in evangelism, Bible distribution, childcare/orphanage programs, church planting, Christian education and theological education. Statistical data from 1998.

Purpose: "...to promote the gospel within the state of Andhra Pradesh; print and publish Christian literature... establish and maintain individual churches...Christian schools...homes for orphans and destitute children; provide financial assistance in supporting medical services for the rural poor; and encourage human development..."

Year Founded in US: 1985
Income for Overseas Min: $476,258
Personnel:
  Short-term less than 1 year from US: 48
  Non-US serving in own/other country: 127
  Home ministry & office staff in US: 1
Countries: India

Institute for International Christian Communication

6012 SE Yamhill St.
Portland, OR 97215 USA
Phone: (503) 234-1639
Fax: (503) 234-1639
E-mail: worldviewcenter@juno.com
Web Site: www.worldviewcenter
Dr. Donald K. & Mrs. Faye Smith, Dirs.

A transdenominational service agency of Evangelical tradition supporting the leadership of Third World churches by forging meaningful collaborations that result in sharing resources of research, education, personnel, and materials. Sponsors of WorldView Center, a residential and training center for international students and missionary candidates.

Year Founded in US: 1967

Income for Overseas Min: $70,000
Fully Supported US Personnel Overseas:
  Nonresidential mission personnel: 5
Other personnel:
  Short-term less than 1 year from US: 3
  Home ministry & office staff in US: 5

Institute of Theological Studies

3140 Three Mile Rd. NE
Grand Rapids, MI 49525 USA
Phone: (888) 487-5376
Fax: (616) 363-7880
E-mail: info@ITScourses.org
Web Site: www.ITScourses.org
Mr. Mark A. Sigmon, Exec. Director

A nondenominational theological education agency of Evangelical tradition engaged in independent study course development and training resources for students, pastors and laity worldwide.

Year Founded in US: 1971
Income for Overseas Min: $75,000
Personnel:
  Home ministry & office staff in US: 6

INTENT

5840 W. Midway Park
Chicago, IL 60644-1803 USA
Phone: (773) 921-0457
E-mail: info@intent.org
Web Site: www.intent.org
Mr. Gary D. Ginter, Board Chairman

A nondenominational service agency of Evangelical tradition providing tentmaking-related services, literature production and distribution and missions-related research.

Year Founded in US: 1987
Income for Overseas Min: NA
Personnel:
  Home ministry & office staff in US: 3

InterAct Ministries

31000 SE Kelso Rd.
Boring, OR 97009 USA
Phone: (503) 668-5571
Fax: (503) 668-6814
E-mail: info@interactministries.org
Web Site: www.interactministries.org

Rev. Gary Brumbelow, Gen. Director

A nondenominational sending agency of Evangelical tradition engaged in church planting, camping programs, evangelism, leadership development and mission-related research.

Purpose: "...to see culturally relevant churches in every community in the North Pacific Crescent."

Year Founded in US: 1951

Income for Overseas Min: $227,560

Fully Supported US Personnel Overseas:
Expecting to serve more than 4 years: 9

Other personnel:
Short-term less than 1 year from US: 46
Home ministry & office staff in US: 74

Countries: Russia 9

Interaction Intl. Inc.

P.O. Box 158
Houghton, NY 14744 USA
Phone: (585) 567-8774
Fax: (585) 567-4598
E-mail: Interaction@compuserve.com
Web Site: www.tckinteract.net

Dr. David C. Pollock, Exec. Director

A service agency of Evangelical tradition engaged in member care, childrens programs, Christian education, services for other agencies, missionary training and youth programs.

Purpose: "...serving as a catalyst and resource for service to youth and family."

Year Founded in US: 1968

Income for Overseas Min: $290,000

Fully Supported US Personnel Overseas:
Nonresidential mission personnel: 4
Home ministry & office staff in US: 4

Interchurch Medical Assistance

P.O. Box 429
New Windsor, MD 21776 USA
Phone: (410) 635-8720
Fax: (410) 635-8726
E-mail: imainfo@interchurch.org
Web Site: www.interchurch.org

Mr. Paul Derstine, President

An interdenominational support agency of Ecumenical tradition distributing medical supplies to healthcare facilities in more than 50 countries affiliated with member and associate organizations.

Purpose: "...to provide essential products and services for emergency, health and development programs of interest to members, which serve people in need with preference given to the poorest of the poor..."

Year Founded in US: 1960

Income for Overseas Min: $46,050,979

Gifts-in-Kind: $39,714,110

Personnel:
Home ministry & office staff in US: 15

INTERCOMM

P.O. Box 618
Winona Lake, IN 46590 USA
Phone: (574) 267-5774
Fax: (574) 267-5876
E-mail: info@intercommedia.org
Web Site: www.intercommedia.org

Mr. Douglas Haines, CEO

A nondenominational support agency of Evangelical tradition engaged in video/film production/distribution, audio recording/ distribution and evangelism, equipping national workers in more than 100 countries in evangelism outreach. A ministry of Ken Anderson Films.

Purpose: "...to equip national Christian leaders with appropriate Christian media to help them evangelize their country."

Year Founded in US: 1990

Income for Overseas Min: $400,000

Fully Supported US Personnel Overseas:
Nonresidential mission personnel: 2

Other personnel:
Home ministry & office staff in US: 5

Intercristo

19303 Fremont Ave., N.
Seattle, WA 98133 USA
Phone: (800) 251-7740
Fax: (206) 546-7375
E-mail: jobhunter@intercristo.com
Web Site: www.intercristo.com

Mr. Ron Rutherford, Exec. Director

An interdenominational service agency of Evangelical and Independent tradition providing assistance and information to mission agencies in locating qualified personnel for positions at home and abroad. An affiliate of CRISTA Ministries.

Purpose: "...to match Christians with opportunities in Christian organizations so both may fulfill their Kingdom purpose."

Year Founded in US: 1967
Income for Overseas Min: NA
Personnel:
   Home ministry & office staff in US: 11

Interdenominational Foreign Mission Association See: IFMA

Interdev
P.O. Box 3883
Seattle, WA 98124 USA
Phone: (425) 775-8330
Fax: (425) 775-8326
E-mail: idev-us@interdev.org
Web Site: www.interdev.org
Dr. Gary Walsh, President/CEO

A nondenominational service agency of Evangelical tradition engaged in development and services for other agencies.

Purpose: "...to serve the Church in accelerating fulfillment of the Great Commission through the development, formation and long-term effective operation of international partnerships for evangelism among the world's unreached people."

Year Founded in US: 1974
Income for Overseas Min: $687,187
Gifts-in-Kind: $69,789
Personnel:
   Home ministry & office staff in US: 9

International Aid
17011 W. Hickory St.
Spring Lake, MI 49456 USA
Phone: (616) 846-7490
Fax: (616) 846-3842
E-mail: ia@internationalaid.org
Web Site: www.internationalaid.org
Rev. Myles D. Fish, President/CEO

A nondenominational specialized agency of Evangelical tradition engaged in services for other agencies, providing medical supplies, medical work, relief and/or rehabilitation,

supplying equipment and training.
Purpose: "...responding to biblical mandates by providing and supporting solutions in healthcare."
Year Founded in US: 1980
Income for Overseas Min: $67,125,062
Gifts-in-Kind: $61,368,861
Personnel:
   Home ministry & office staff in US: 65
Countries: Ghana; Honduras; Kosovo; Philippines

International Bible Institute
12110 Slauson Ave., Suite 1
Santa Fe Sprgs., CA 90670 USA
Phone: (562) 907-5555
Fax: (562) 907-5552
E-mail: ibi@ibibible.org
Web Site: www.ibibible.org
Dr. Earle E. Williams, President

A nondenominational service agency of Evangelical tradition engaged in establishing extension Bible institutes in local churches using audiotapes, printed materials and other means. Financial figure from 1998.
Year Founded in US: 1971
Income for Overseas Min: $44,000
Personnel:
   Home ministry & office staff in US: 3

International Bible Society
1820 Jet Stream Drive
Colorado Springs, CO 80921 USA
Phone: (719) 488-9200
Fax: (719) 488-0912
E-mail: IBS@gospelcom.org
Web Site: www.ibs.org
Mr. Peter J. Bradley, President

A nondenominational service agency of Evangelical tradition engaged in Bible distribution, evangelism, literature distribution and Bible translation. Statistical data from 1998.
Purpose: "To serve the church in evangelism and discipleship by providing God's Word so that people around the world may come to faith and life in Jesus Christ."
Year Founded in US: 1809
Income for Overseas Min: $3,904,000
Personnel:

Non-US serving in own/other country: 314
Home ministry & office staff in US: 130

Countries: Africa–General; Asia–General; Europe–General; Latin America–General

International Board of Jewish Missions, Inc.

P.O. Box 1386
Hixson, TN 37343 USA

Phone: (423) 876-8150
Fax: (423) 876-8156
E-mail: amolam@ibjm.org
Web Site: www.ibjm.org

Dr. Orman L. Norwood, President

A sending agency of Baptist and Independent tradition engaged in evangelism, Bible distribution, broadcasting, church planting, literature distribution and video/film production/distribution.

Year Founded in US: 1949

Income for Overseas Min: $150,000

Personnel:
Home ministry & office staff in US: 17

International Cassette Bible Institute

4404 S. Florida Ave., Ste. 14
Lakeland, FL 33813-2124 USA

Phone: (863) 647-9290
Fax: (863) 648-1072
E-mail: ICBILKLN@earthlink.net

Rev. Sune K. Andersson, Founder & Intl. Dir.

An interdenominational sending agency of Evangelical and Pentecostal tradition engaged in leadership development, audio recording/distribution, correspondence courses, Christian education, TEE and theological education.

Year Founded in US: 1992

Income for Overseas Min: $100,000

Fully Supported US Personnel Overseas:
Expecting to serve more than 4 years: 8

Other personnel:
Non-US serving in own/other country: 71
Home ministry & office staff in US: 6

Countries: Argentina; Asia–General; Bolivia; Chile; Colombia 2; Ecuador; Finland; Latin America–General 6; Mexico; Russia; Sweden; Unspecified Country

International Child Care

P.O. Box 14485
Columbus, OH 43214 USA

Phone: (614) 447-9952
Fax: (614) 447-1123
E-mail: iccusa1@aol.com
Web Site: www.intlchildcare.org

Dr. John Yates, Exec. Director

An interdenominational service agency of Evangelical tradition engaged in development, disability assistance programs, providing medical supplies and technical assistance. Statistical data from 1996.

Year Founded in US: 1965

Income for Overseas Min: $354,456

Personnel:
Home ministry & office staff in US: 4

International Christian Leprosy Mission, Inc. (USA)

P.O. Box 596
Forest Grove, OR 97116 USA

Phone: (503) 285-9098
Fax: (503) 285-6035
E-mail: HealingHands8414@aol.com
Web Site: www.christian-relief.org

Dr. Daniel G. Pulliam, President

An interdenominational support agency of Evangelical tradition engaged in providing medical supplies and support of national medical ministries.

Year Founded in US: 1943

Income for Overseas Min: $70,000

Personnel:
Non-US serving in own/other country: 11
Home ministry & office staff in US: 3

Countries: Africa–General; Asia–General; Philippines

International Christian Ministries

P.O. Box 9071
Bakersfield, CA 93389 USA

Phone: (661) 832-9740
Fax: (661) 832-9741
E-mail: info@icm-intl.org
Web Site: www.icm-international.org

Mr. Phillip R. Walker, President

A transdenominational sending agency of

Evangelical tradition engaged in discipleship, TEE, extension education, theological education, leadership development and training.

Year Founded in US: 1990

Income for Overseas Min: $1,300,000

Fully Supported US Personnel Overseas:
Expecting to serve more than 4 years: 3
Nonresidential mission personnel: 2

Other personnel:
Short-term less than 1 year from US: 45
Non-US serving in own/other country: 39
Home ministry & office staff in US: 8

Countries: Egypt; Germany 2; Ghana; Kenya 1; Nigeria; Sierra Leone; Tanzania; Uganda

International Cooperating Ministries

606 Aberdeen Rd.
Hampton, VA 23661 USA
Phone: (757) 827-6704
Fax: (757) 838-6486
E-mail: icm@icmmbc.org
Web Site: www.icmmbc.org
Mr. Dois I. Rosser, Jr., Founder & Chairman

International Cooperating Ministries (ICM) is a ministry committed to transforming nations through Jesus Christ by building churches and broadcasting God's Word. Through God's grace and the partnership of donors and indigenous church organizations, ICM has 1,175 churches either built or under construction in 18 countries.

Purpose: "...to nurture believers and to assist the growth of the Church worldwide in accordance with Christ's Great Commission."

Year Founded in US: 1987

Income for Overseas Min: $1,545,490

Personnel:
Home ministry & office staff in US: 19

International Family Missions

P.O. Box 309
Lafayette, CO 80026-0309 USA
Phone: (303) 665-7635
Fax: (303) 661-0732
E-mail: ifm@internationalfamilymissions.org
Web Site:
www.internationalfamilymissions.org
Rev. Joseph Hart, President, Minister/Director

A transdenominational support agency of Evangelical tradition engaged in short-term programs, Bible distribution, children's programs, evangelism and missionary training. Financial figures from 1998.

Year Founded in US: 1987

Income for Overseas Min: $150,000

Fully Supported US Personnel Overseas:
Expecting to serve more than 4 years: 10
Nonresidential mission personnel: 4

Other personnel:
Short-term less than 1 year from US: 500
Non-US serving in own/other country: 6
Home ministry & office staff in US: 5
Bivocational/Tentmaker from US: 5

Countries: Mexico 10

International Foundation for EWHA Woman's University, Inc.

475 Riverside Dr. Rm. 1359
New York, NY 10115 USA
Phone: (212) 864-5759
Fax: (212) 864-2552
E-mail: Ewhafdn@aol.com
Web Site: www.ewhafoundation.org
Ji-yei Park, Exec. Director

An interdenominational support agency of Ecumenical tradition providing financial and other support to EWHA University in South Korea.

Year Founded in US: 1969

Income for Overseas Min: NA

International Gospel Outreach

P.O. Drawer 1008
Semmes, AL 36575 USA
Phone: (251) 645-2117
Fax: (251) 645-2118
E-mail: info@igominministries.org
Web Site: www.igoministries.org
Mr. Bertist Rouse, President

An interdenominational sending agency of Evangelical and Wesleyan tradition engaged in mobilization for mission, TEE, evangelism, funds transmission, management consulting/training and missionary training.

Year Founded in US: 1973

Income for Overseas Min: $475,000
Fully Supported US Personnel Overseas:
Expecting to serve more than 4 years: 17
Expecting to serve 1 to 4 years: 11
Other personnel:
Short-term less than 1 year from US: 8
Non-US serving in own/other country: 29
Home ministry & office staff in US: 22
Countries: Bangladesh 2; Chile; Cuba;
Guatemala 2; Honduras 6; India; Indonesia
2; Kenya 2; Korea, South; Mexico; Nicaragua; Philippines; Russia 2; Rwanda; Sudan;
Taiwan; Tanzania 1

International Health Services

P.O. Box 265
Southeastern, PA 19399-0265 USA
Phone: (610) 240-9502
Fax: (610) 296-8952
E-mail: IHSUSA@ihserve.org

Dr. Robert Snyder, President

An interdenominational service agency of
Evangelical tradition engaged in leadership
development, evangelism and medical work.

Year Founded in US: 1995
Income for Overseas Min: $490,122
Gifts-in-Kind: $5,600
Personnel:
Home ministry & office staff in US: 2

International Institute for Christian Studies

P.O. Box 12147
Overland Park, KS 66282-2147 USA
Phone: (913) 962-4422
Fax: (913) 962-1912
E-mail: iics@iics.com
Web Site: www.iics.com

Dr. Daryl McCarthy, CEO

A nondenominational sending agency of
Evangelical tradition engaged in theological
education, evangelism and leadership development.

Purpose: "To develop leaders who think and
live Christianly, by establishing Departments
of Christian Studies in secular universities and
by providing evangelical academicians, business leaders and professional teaching with a
Christian worldview overseas."

Year Founded in US: 1986

Income for Overseas Min: $1,012,417
Gifts-in-Kind: $26,344
Fully Supported US Personnel Overseas:
Expecting to serve more than 4 years: 15
Expecting to serve 1 to 4 years: 5
Other personnel:
Short-term less than 1 year from US: 6
Non-US serving in own/other country: 8
Home ministry & office staff in US: 8
Bivocational/Tentmaker from US:10
Countries: Asia–General; Czech Republic
10; Nigeria 5; Russia

International Justice Mission

P.O. Box 58147
Washington, DC 20037 USA
Phone: (703) 465-5495
Fax: (703) 465-5499
E-mail: contact@ijm.org
Web Site: www.ijm.org

Mr. Gary A. Haugen, Exec. Director

A service agency of Protestant tradition
engaged primarily in international justice
ministry.

Year Founded in US: 1996
Income for Overseas Min: NA
Fully Supported US Personnel Overseas:
Expecting to serve 1 to 4 years: 8
Nonresidential mission personnel: 7
Other personnel:
Short-term less than 1 year from US: 44
Non-US serving in own/other country: 22
Home ministry & office staff in US: 26
Countries: Bolivia; Brazil; Burundi; Cambodia; Cote d'Ivoire; El Salvador; Guatemala;
Haiti; Honduras; India; Indonesia; Kenya;
Mexico; Peru; Philippines; Thailand; Zambia

International Leadership Seminars

P.O. Box 56A
Lima, NY 14485 USA
Phone: (585) 624-9660
Fax: (585) 624-9129
E-mail: ils@familyvoice.com
Web Site: www.trainleaders.com

Mr. Salim C. Deir, Exec. Director

A nondenominational specialized agency of
Charismatic tradition engaged in leadership

development through seminars and publications.

Purpose: "...to reach, edify, mature and train the leadership in the Christian church worldwide to effectively reach the world with the gospel message of Jesus Christ."

Year Founded in US: 1973
Income for Overseas Min: $10,000

International Lutheran Laymen's League/Lutheran Hour Mins.

660 Mason Ridge Center Dr.
St. Louis, MO 63141-8557 USA
Phone: (314) 317-4100
Fax: (314) 317-4295
Web Site: www.lhmint.org
Mr. Rodger Hebermehl, Exec. Director

A denominational specialized agency of Lutheran tradition engaged in evangelism through broadcasting in 47 countries through 297 national staff. Personnel data from 1998.

Year Founded in US: 1917
Income for Overseas Min: NR
Fully Supported US Personnel Overseas:
  Nonresidential mission personnel: 5
Other personnel:
  Short-term less than 1 year from US: 50
  Home ministry & office staff in US: 130

International Messengers

P.O. Box R
Clearlake, IA 50428 USA
Phone: (641) 357-6700
Fax: (641) 357-6791
E-mail: office@internationalmessengers.org
Web Site:
www.internationalmessengers.org
Mr. Robert P. Rasmusson, President

A nondenominational sending agency of Evangelical tradition engaged in evangelism, camping programs, childcare/orphanage programs, children's programs, church construction, short-term programs and missionary training.

Purpose: "...partnering with local churches to renew, train and mobilize believers for active involvement in reaching the world for Christ."

Year Founded in US: 1984
Income for Overseas Min: NR
Fully Supported US Personnel Overseas:
  Expecting to serve more than 4 years: 24
  Expecting to serve 1 to 4 years: 4
Other personnel:
  Short-term less than 1 year from US: 300
  Non-US serving in own/other country: 47
  Home ministry & office staff in US: 33
  Bivocational/Tentmaker from US: 14
Countries: Czech Republic; Germany; Hungary 2; Poland 12; Romania 7; Slovakia 3; Ukraine

International Missionary Center

8863 E. 91st Street
Tulsa, OK 74133 USA
Phone: (918) 459-0431
Fax: (918) 294-9147
E-mail: imc@lwmcentral.com
Web Site: www.missionary.net
Mr. Russ Tatro, CEO

An interdenominational sending agency engaged in support of national workers, theological education, funds transmission, furloughed missionary support, missions information service and leadership development.

Year Founded in US: 1992
Income for Overseas Min: $963,034
Fully Supported US Personnel Overseas:
  Expecting to serve more than 4 years: 50
  Nonresidential mission personnel: 1
Other personnel:
  Short-term less than 1 year from US: 12
  Non-US serving in own/other country: 78
  Home ministry & office staff in US: 11
  Bivocational/Tentmaker from US: 2
Countries: Benin; Bolivia 4; Cameroon 1; Central African Republic; Chad; Colombia 2; Cote d'Ivoire 2; Egypt 3; Gambia, The; Germany 3; Ghana; Guatemala 2; Guinea; Guinea-Bissau; India 2; Liberia; Malaysia 2; Mali; Mexico 5; Netherlands 2; Nicaragua 2; Nigeria; Panama 2; Philippines; Poland 4; Senegal 3; Sierra Leone; Spain 3; Thailand 2; Togo; Turkey 4; Uruguay 2; Venezuela

International Needs—USA

P.O. Box 977
Lynden, WA 98264 USA
Phone: (360) 354-1991
Fax: (360) 354-1991
E-mail: inusa@inter-nationalneeds.com
Web Site: www.inter-nationalneeds.com
Mr. Rody Rodeheaver, Exec. Director

A transdenominational service agency of Evangelical tradition engaged in support of national workers.

Year Founded in US: 1974
Income for Overseas Min: $836,531
Personnel:
  Short-term less than 1 year from US: 40
  Non-US serving in own/other country: 804
  Home ministry & office staff in US: 7

Countries: Bangladesh; Colombia; Czech Republic; Egypt; Eritrea; Ethiopia; Ghana; India; Morocco; Nepal; Philippines; Romania; Slovakia; Sri Lanka; Tanzania; Uganda; Vietnam; Zambia

International Outreach Ministries

P.O. Box 2130
Daphne, AL 26526 USA
Phone: (251) 626-1777
Fax: (251) 626-8725
E-mail: IOM@pobox.com
Web Site: www.IOMsend.com
Rev. Gary Henley, President/Director

A nondenominational sending agency of Reformed Charismatic tradition engaged in church planting, childcare/orphanage programs, development, theological education, medical work and short-term programs.

Purpose: "...evangelize throughout the world with a focus on significantly unreached people groups and strategic areas of need, planting churches, training indigenous leaders, and utilizing Internet media to reach those beyond traditional missionary endeavors."

Year Founded in US: 1986
Income for Overseas Min: $900,000
Fully Supported US Personnel Overseas:
  Expecting to serve more than 4 years: 33
  Expecting to serve 1 to 4 years: 6

Nonresidential mission personnel: 5
Other personnel:
  Short-term less than 1 year from US: 40
  Non-US serving in own/other country: 5
  Home ministry & office staff in US: 4
  Bivocational/Tentmaker from US: 2

Countries: Belgium 6; China; Colombia 2; Congo, Democratic Republic of the 6; Costa Rica 6; France 4; Indonesia 1; Kenya 2; Mexico; Morocco 2; Uzbekistan 4

International Partnership Ministries, Inc.

P.O. Box 41
Hanover, PA 17331-0041 USA
Phone: (717) 637-7388
Fax: (717) 637-1618
E-mail: ipm@ipmworld.org
Web Site: www.ipmworld.org
Dr. Timothy B. Shorb, President

A nondenominational sending agency of Baptist and Fundamental tradition supporting, in partnership with Two-Thirds World mission agencies, national workers involved in church planting, evangelism and leadership development.

Year Founded in US: 1982
Income for Overseas Min: $1,332,660
Fully Supported US Personnel Overseas:
  Expecting to serve more than 4 years: 4
Other personnel:
  Non-US serving in own/other country: 254
  Home ministry & office staff in US: 17

Countries: Bhutan; Bolivia; Chile; Cote d'Ivoire; Cuba; Dominican Republic; Ghana 2; Haiti; India; Lebanon; Liberia; Mexico; Myanmar/Burma; Nepal; Paraguay; Peru; Philippines; Puerto Rico; Spain 2; Togo; Uruguay; Zambia

International Pentecostal Church of Christ Global Missions Dept.

P.O. Box 439
London, OH 43140 USA
Phone: (740) 852-0448
Fax: (740) 852-0348
E-mail: hqipcc@aol.com
Web Site: www.ipcc.cc
Bishop Clyde M. Hughes, General Overseer

A denominational sending agency of Pentecostal and Charismatic tradition engaged in support of national churches, childcare/orphanage programs, Christian education, theological education, leadership development and literature distribution.

Year Founded in US: 1917

Income for Overseas Min: $135,906

Fully Supported US Personnel Overseas:
  Expecting to serve more than 4 years: 5

Other personnel:
  Home ministry & office staff in US: 6

Countries: India 1; Kenya 3; Mexico 1

International Pentecostal Holiness Church World Missions Ministries

P.O. Box 12609
Oklahoma City, OK 73157 USA

Phone: (405) 787-7110
Fax: (405) 787-7729
E-mail: Ray@iphc.org
Web Site: www.iphc.org

Rev. M. Donald Duncan, Exec. Director

A denominational sending agency of Pentecostal and Holiness tradition engaged in church planting, theological education, furloughed missionary support, leadership development, support of national churches and mobilization for mission.

Year Founded in US: 1904

Income for Overseas Min: $6,742,948

Fully Supported US Personnel Overseas:
  Expecting to serve more than 4 years: 143
  Expecting to serve 1 to 4 years: 17

Other personnel:
  Non-US serving in own/other country: 13
  Home ministry & office staff in US: 19
  Bivocational/Tentmaker from US: 10

Countries: Africa–General 6; Asia–General; Australia 4; Belgium; Belize 1; Botswana 2; Cambodia; China 4; Colombia 1; Costa Rica 2; Cote d'Ivoire 2; Dominican Republic 2; Ecuador 2; France 1; Germany 2; Ghana 4; Guatemala 4; Haiti 2; Honduras 2; Hungary 2; India 2; Japan 4; Kenya 6; Malawi 4; Mexico 11; Mozambique 2; Nicaragua 3; Norway 3; Panama 4; Peru; Philippines 6; Portugal; Romania 2; Singapore 4; South Africa 17; Spain 4; Tanzania 5; Thailand 4; Trinidad and Tobago 2; Turkey; United Kingdom 8; Venezuela 2; Zambia 3; Zimbabwe 4

International Street Kids Outreach Ministries

P.O. Box 8551
Clearwater, FL 33758-8551 USA

Phone: (800) 265-1970
E-mail: iskom@tampabay.rr.com

Rev. John M. Schmidt, President

A nondenominational support agency of Evangelical tradition engaged in childcare/orphanage programs, camping programs and training.

Year Founded in US: 1995

Income for Overseas Min: $59,000

Fully Supported US Personnel Overseas:
  Expecting to serve more than 4 years: 2

Other personnel:
  Short-term less than 1 year from US: 180
  Non-US serving in own/other country: 36
  Home ministry & office staff in US: 1

Countries: Brazil; Botswana; Cambodia; Russia; Ukraine; Vietnam

International Students, Inc

P.O. Box C
Colorado Springs, CO 80901 USA

Phone: (719) 576-2700
Fax: (719) 576-5363
E-mail: isiteam@isionline.org
Web Site: www.isionline.org

Dr. Douglas Shaw, President

A transdenominational support agency of Evangelical and Ecumenical tradition engaged in international student friendship, evangelism and discipleship in the USA with students from other countries. Statistical data from 1998.

Year Founded in US: 1953

Income for Overseas Min: NA

Fully Supported US Personnel Overseas:
  Expecting to serve more than 4 years: 3

Other personnel:
  Home ministry & office staff in US: 180
  Bivocational/Tentmaker from US: 1

Countries: Israel 1; Singapore 1;Taiwan 1

International Teams, U.S.A.

411 W. River Rd.
Elgin, IL 60123 USA
Phone: (847) 429-0900
Fax: (847) 429-0800
E-mail: stephen.freed@iteams.org
Web Site: www.iteams.org
Mr. Stephen Freed, President

An interdenominational sending agency of Evangelical tradition engaged in church planting, development, support of national churches, relief and/or rehabilitation, missionary training and youth programs.

Year Founded in US: 1960
Income for Overseas Min: $8,110,000
Gifts-in-Kind: $420,000
Fully Supported US Personnel Overseas:
  Expecting to serve more than 4 years: 199
  Expecting to serve 1 to 4 years: 37
  Nonresidential mission personnel: 12
Other personnel:
  Short-term less than 1 year from US: 422
  Non-US serving in own/other country: 236
  Home ministry & office staff in US: 56
  Bivocational/Tentmaker from US: 15
Countries: Afghanistan; Albania 4; Australia 1; Austria 30; Bolivia 1; Bosnia and Herzegovina 3; Bulgaria 4; Cambodia 3; China; Colombia 3; Costa Rica 5; Czech Republic 12; Ecuador 12; Estonia 2; France 23; Greece 7; Honduras; Hungary 1; Indonesia; Ireland; Israel; Italy 4; Japan; Jordan 2; Kazakhstan; Kenya; Kosovo 2; Laos; Malaysia; Mexico 11; Nepal; Netherlands; New Zealand; Pakistan; Philippines; Poland 5; Romania 6; Russia 3; Singapore; Slovakia 7; Slovenia 4; Spain 10; Thailand; Turkey; Ukraine 15; United Arab Emirates; United Kingdom 13; Uzbekistan; Vietnam 6

International Urban Associates

1013 8th Ave., #405
Seattle, WA 98104-1222 USA
Phone: (206) 381-8893
E-mail: SeattleIUA@earthlink.net
Dr. Ray Bakke, CEO

A transdenominational information and service agency of Evangelical tradition engaged in leadership development through church consultations and theological education and training.

Purpose: "...to empower God's people in the largest cities of the world by means of leadership consultations that generate vision, partnerships, motivations and resources, so that the 'whole church can take the whole gospel to the whole city'."
Year Founded in US: 1989
Income for Overseas Min: $160,000
Gifts-in-Kind: $130,000
Personnel:
  Home ministry & office staff in US: 3

InterServe/USA

(See Ad on page 201)
P.O. Box 418
Upper Darby, PA 19082-0418 USA
Phone: (610) 352-0581
Fax: (610) 352-4394
E-mail: InterServeUSA@xc.org
Web Site: www.interserve.org
Rev. Douglas Van Bronkhorst, Exec. Director

An international interdenominational sending agency of Evangelical tradition whose personnel/partners are engaged in medical work, support of national churches, church planting, development and Christian education.

Year Founded in US: 1964
Income for Overseas Min: $3,311,272
Gifts-in-Kind: NA
Fully Supported US Personnel Overseas:
  Expecting to serve more than 4 years: 91
  Nonresidential mission personnel: 2
Other personnel:
  Short-term less than 1 year from US: 22
  Non-US serving in own/other country: 2
  Home ministry & office staff in US: 24
  Bivocational/Tentmaker from US: 68
Countries: Afghanistan 12; Asia–General 3; Bangladesh 7; China 7; Cyprus 2; India 7; Kazakhstan 2; Kyrgyzstan 18; Lebanon 1; Nepal 3; Pakistan 11; Tajikistan 3; Turkey 13; United Kingdom 2

InterVarsity Christian Fellowship/USA

P.O. Box 7895
Madison, WI 53707-7895 USA
Phone: (608) 274-9001
Fax: (608) 274-7882
E-mail: Link@ivcs.org

MULTI-LANGUAGE
COUNTER-CULT RESOURCES
That Respond Thoughtfully and Respectfully
to Mormonism and the Jehovah's Witnesses

"The Institute for Religious Research is leading the way in providing outstanding resources that respond effectively to these seductive heresies, yet reflect genuine compassion for the lost."

Ruth A. Tucker, Ph.D., Calvin Theological Seminary

Tracts & Videos in:

**ALBANIAN • ARMENIAN • BULGARIAN • CHINESE
DUTCH • ENGLISH • ESTONIAN • FILIPINO • FINNISH
FRENCH • GERMAN • GREEK • HUNGARIAN • KOREAN
LATVIAN • MALAGASY • PORTUGUESE • QUECHUA
ROMANIAN • RUSSIAN • SPANISH • UKRAINIAN**

View tracts and videos online at
www.irr.org/resources.html

Free samples available on request.

INSTITUTE FOR RELIGIOUS RESEARCH
1340 Monroe Ave. NW • Grand Rapids, MI 49505
Telephone: (616) 451-4562 • Toll Free: (877) 888-4477
Email: info@irr.org • Internet: www.irr.org

Web Site: www.ivlink.org

Rebecca D. Stephen, Dir. InterVarsity Link

A nondenominational sending agency of Evangelical tradition engaged in student evangelism, leadership development, discipleship training, and literature production. As a member movement of the International Fellowship of Evangelical Students, IVCF/USA supports work with student ministries in 141 countries.

Income for Overseas Min: $4,802,000

Fully Supported US Personnel Overseas:
   Expecting to serve more than 4 years: 44
   Expecting to serve 1 to 4 years: 25
   Nonresidential mission personnel: 70

Other personnel:
   Short-term less than 1 year from US: 500
   Home ministry & office staff in US: 9
   Bivocational/Tentmaker from US: 3

Countries: Azerbaijan; Belarus 2; Bosnia and Herzegovina 1; Gabon 2; Greece; Guatemala; Italy 3; Kazakhstan 2; Kenya 2; Kyrgyzstan 6; Mongolia 2; Poland; Portugal 1; Romania 2; Russia 6; South Africa; Turkey 1; Ukraine 3; United Arab Emirates 6; United Kingdom 4; Uzbekistan 1; Zimbabwe

Iranian Christians Intl.

P.O. Box 25607
Colorado Springs, CO 80936 USA
Phone: (719) 596-0010
Fax: (719) 574-1141
E-mail: ici@myprimus.com
Web Site: www.iranchristians.org

Mr. Ebrahim (Abe) Ghaffari, Exec. Director

A transdenominational support agency of Evangelical tradition engaged in support of national churches, Bible distribution, church planting, evangelism, literature distribution and translation work, focused on Persian speaking peoples.

Year Founded in US: 1981

Income for Overseas Min: $50,000

Personnel:
   Home ministry & office staff in US: 3

Ireland Outreach Intl. Inc.

P.O. Box 1772
Waterloo, IA 50704-1772 USA
Phone: (319) 277-8883

E-mail: charleville@eircom.net
Web Site: www.irelandoutreach.org

Mr. James W. Gillett, President

A nondenominational faith mission of Christian/Plymouth Brethren tradition engaged in literature production and evangelism, Scripture distribution, church planting, correspondence courses and short-term missions exposure teams in Ireland. Additional ministries include training and equipping national believers in English speaking Africa. Gospel literature and correspondence courses are also sent from Ireland to 30 countries around the world.

Year Founded in US: 1981

Income for Overseas Min: NA

Fully Supported US Personnel Overseas:
   Expecting to serve more than 4 years: 4
   Expecting to serve 1 to 4 years: 2

Other personnel:
   Short-term less than 1 year from US: 150
   Non-US serving in own/other country: 18

Countries: Ghana; Ireland 4; Nigeria; Togo

Italy for Christ

1301 Shiloh Rd., #1720
Kennesaw, GA 30144 USA
Phone: (770) 274-2800
Fax: (770) 274-2833
E-mail: info@italyforchrist.com
Web Site: www.italyforchrist.it

Gaetano Sottile, President/Founder

A nondenominational sending agency of Evangelical tradition engaged in evangelism, Bible distribution, leadership development, literature production and youth programs.

Purpose: "To present the Gospel of Christ to every Italian in this generation and to encourage the planting of new local churches in Italy."

Year Founded in US: 1983

Income for Overseas Min: NA

Fully Supported US Personnel Overseas:
   Expecting to serve more than 4 years: 2
   Expecting to serve 1 to 4 years: 2

Other personnel:
   Non-US serving in own/other country: 4
   Home ministry & office staff in US: 1

Countries: Italy 2

JAARS, Inc.

P.O. Box 248
Waxhaw, NC 28173 USA
Phone: (704) 843-6000
Fax: (704) 843-6355
E-mail: info@jaars.org
Web Site: www.jaars.org

Mr. Jim Akovenko, President

An interdenominational service agency of Evangelical tradition serving Wycliffe Bible Translators with various technical support services including aviation and radio. Personnel serves more than 70 countries.

Purpose: "...providing construction, technology and transportation services for Wycliffe Bible Translators."

Year Founded in US: 1947
Income for Overseas Min: NA

Janz Team Ministries USA

P.O. Box 2010
Buffalo, NY 14231 USA
Phone: (716) 688-0276
Fax: (716) 688-5049
E-mail: jtm@janzteam.com
Web Site: www.janzteam.org

Mr. Jack Stenekes, N. Am. Director

An interdenominational sending agency of evangelical tradition engaged in evangelism, camping programs and Christian education. Ministries arranged through personnel located in Canada.

Purpose: "...to be obedient to the Great Commission of Jesus Christ through evangelism and Christian education, contributing to the establishment and growth of vibrant churches."

Japanese Evangelical Missionary Society

948 E. Second St.
Los Angeles, CA 90012 USA
Phone: (213) 613-0022
Fax: (213) 613-0211
E-mail: info@jems.org
Web Site: www.jems.org

Rev. Sam Tonomura, Exec. Director

An interdenominational service agency of Evangelical tradition engaged in support of national churches, evangelism, short-term

programs and missionary training. Statistical data from 1996.

Year Founded in US: 1950
Income for Overseas Min: $300,000
Fully Supported US Personnel Overseas:
  Expecting to serve more than 4 years: 1
  Expecting to serve 1 to 4 years: 2
  Nonresidential mission personnel: 7
Other personnel:
  Short-term less than 1 year from US: 24
  Non-US serving in own/other country: 6
  Home ministry & office staff in US: 8
Countries: Brazil 1; Japan

Japanese Evangelization Center

1605 Elizabeth St.
Pasadena, CA 91104 USA
Phone: (626) 398-2235
E-mail: johntmizuki@aol.com

Dr. John Mizuki, Exec. Director

A nondenominational specialized agency of Evangelical tradition engaged in mission-related research, church planting and missions information service.

Purpose: "...to provide information to churches, mission agencies, pastors, missionaries, missionary candidates, students and to serve as consultants to those interested in Japanese culture and evangelization."

Year Founded in US: 1981
Income for Overseas Min: NA

JARON Ministries Intl.

5150 North 6th St., Ste. 132
Fresno, CA 93710 USA
Phone: (559) 227-7997
Fax: (559) 227-9603
E-mail: info@jaron.org
Web Site: www.jaron.org

Dr. Lyndel J. Moe, Exec. Director

An interdenominational support agency of Baptist tradition engaged in leadership development, theological education and short-term programs.

Year Founded in US: 1992
Income for Overseas Min: $96,328
Fully Supported US Personnel Overseas:
  Nonresidential mission personnel: 5

Other personnel:
  Short-term less than 1 year from US: 68
  Non-US serving in own/other country: 1
  Home ministry & office staff in US: 6
Countries: Philippines

Jews for Jesus
(See Ad on page 206)
60 Haight St.
San Francisco, CA 94102 USA
Phone: (415) 864-2600
Fax: (415) 552-8325
E-mail: jfj@jewsforjesus.org
Web Site: www.jewsforjesus.org
Mr. David Brickner, Exec. Director

A nondenominational sending agency of
Evangelical tradition engaged in Jewish
evangelism, literature distribution, literature
production and missionary training.
Year Founded in US: 1973
Income for Overseas Min: $990,400
Fully Supported US Personnel Overseas:
  Expecting to serve more than 4 years: 6
Other personnel:
  Short-term less than 1 year from US: 6
  Non-US serving in own/other country: 71
  Home ministry & office staff in US: 136
Countries: Australia 1; Brazil 1; France 1; Is-
rael 1; South Africa 1; Russia; Ukraine;
United Kingdom 1; Unspecified Country

Joni and Friends
P.O. Box 3333
Agoura Hills, CA 91301 USA
Phone: (818) 707-5664
Fax: (818) 707-2391
E-mail: joniandfriends.org
Web Site: www.joniandfriends.org
Mrs. Joni Eareckson Tada, President

A nondenominational service agency of
Evangelical tradition engaged in disability
assistance programs, broadcasting, camping programs, evangelism, leadership development and training. Home ministry
staff figures from 1998.

Purpose: "...to communicate the Gospel
and equip Christ-honoring churches worldwide to evangelize and disciple people affected by disabilities."
Year Founded in US: 1979

Income for Overseas Min: NA
Gifts-in-Kind: $7,602,661
Personnel:
  Home ministry & office staff in US: 25

Josue Yrion World Evangelism and Missions, Inc.
P.O. Box 876018
Los Angeles, CA 90087-1118 USA
Phone: (562) 928-8892
Fax: (562) 947-2268
E-mail: josueyrion@josueyrion.org
Web Site: www.josueyrion.org
Rev. Josue Yrion, President

An interdenominational sending agency of
Evangelical and Pentecostal tradition engaged in evangelism, audio recording/dis-
tribution, leadership development,
literature production and video/film pro-
duction/distribution.

Purpose: "...to serve the Body of Christ, to
edify, teach and prepare an effective evan-
gelistic ministry that can change lives by
the power of God's Word."
Year Founded in US: 1986
Income for Overseas Min: $41,057
Fully Supported US Personnel Overseas:
  Expecting to serve more than 4 years: 1
  Nonresidential mission personnel: 2
Other personnel:
  Non-US serving in own/other country: 12
  Home ministry & office staff in US: 4
Countries: Bhutan; Brazil; Ghana; India;
Mexico; Peru; Sri Lanka 1; United Kingdom

Key Communications
P.O. Box 13620
Portland, OR 97213 USA
Phone: (503) 233-7680
Fax: (503) 236-0733
E-mail: lee@keycom.org
Mr. Bryan L. Turner, Director

A specialized agency of Christian (Restoration Movement) tradition engaged in
broadcasting, Bible distribution, evangelism, literature distribution, literature production and translation work.
Year Founded in US: 1977
Income for Overseas Min: $73,820

JEWS F✡R JESUS

**We exist to make the messiahship of Jesus
an unavoidable issue to our Jewish people worldwide.**

If you'd like to partner with us in any of the 20 cities we're working in,
we'd love to hear from you!

US BRANCH LOCATIONS

Boston, Chicago, Fort Lauderdale, Los Angeles, New York,
San Francisco, Washington D.C. (contact: jfj@jewsforjesus.org)

INTERNATIONAL LOCATIONS

Sydney, Australia
australia@jewsforjesus.org
www.jewsforjesus.com.au

Rio De Janeiro, Brazil
JudeusporJesus@aol.com

Toronto, Canada
jfjcda@jewsforjesus.ca
www.jewsforjesus.ca

London, England
uk@jewsforjesus.org
www.jewsforjesus.org.uk

Paris, France
france@jewsforjesus.org
www.jewsforjesus.org/france

Essen, Germany
JudenfuerJesus@aol.com

Tel Aviv, Israel
jfjisrael@jewsforjesus.co.il
www.jewsforjesus.co.il

Moscow, Russia
moscow@jewsforjesus.org
www.jewsforjesus.org/CIS

Johannesburg, South Africa
southafrica@jewsforjesus.org
www.jewsforjesus.org/sa

Ukraine
dnepr@jewsforjesus.org
kharkov@jewsforjesus.org
kiev@jewsforjesus.org
odessa@jewsforjesus.org

INTERNATIONAL HEADQUARTERS
60 Haight Street, San Francisco, CA 94102 USA
Phone: (415) 864-2600 Fax: (415) 552-8325
jfj@jewsforjesus.org • www.jewsforjesus.org

Personnel:
  Non-US serving in own/other country: 1
  Home ministry & office staff in US: 10
Countries: Pakistan

Kids Alive International
2507 Cumberland Dr.
Valparaiso, IN 46383 USA
Phone: (219) 464-9035
Fax: (219) 462-5611
E-mail: kidsalive@kidsalive.org
Web Site: www.kidsalive.org
Mr. Alfred Lackey, President

An interdenominational sending agency of Evangelical tradition engaged in childcare/orphanage programs, Christian education, evangelism, partnership development, relief and/or rehabilitation and short-term programs.
Purpose: "...rescuing hopeless children from crisis by providing quality, holistic care, introducing them to the transforming power of Jesus Christ and enabling them to be a blessing to others."
Year Founded in US: 1916
Income for Overseas Min: $2,112,777
Gifts-in-Kind: $57,546
Fully Supported US Personnel Overseas:
  Expecting to serve more than 4 years: 17
  Expecting to serve 1 to 4 years: 8
Other personnel:
  Short-term less than 1 year from US: 115
  Non-US serving in own/other country: 37
  Home ministry & office staff in US: 13
Countries: Dominican Republic 9; Guatemala; Honduras 2; Hong Kong; Kenya 2; Lebanon; Myanmar/Burma; Papua New Guinea 1; Peru; Romania 1; Taiwan 2; Zambia

Kids Around the World, Inc.
560 S. Perryville Rd.
Rockford, IL 61108 USA
Phone: (815) 229-8731
Fax: (815) 229-8931
E-mail: info@kidsaroundtheworld.com
Web Site: www.kidsaroundtheworld.com
Mr. Jim Rosene, President

A nondenominational service agency of Evangelical tradition engaged in children's programs, development, Christian educa-
tion, services for other agencies, supplying equipment and training.
Purpose: "...reaching children around the world with the gospel of Jesus Christ and helping those who work with children."
Year Founded in US: 1994
Income for Overseas Min: $414,000
Personnel:
  Short-term less than 1 year from US: 75
  Home ministry & office staff in US: 5

Kingdom Building Ministries
14485 E. Evans Ave.
Denver, CO 80014 USA
Phone: (303) 745-8191
Fax: (303) 745-4196
E-mail: laborers@kbm.org
Web Site: www.kbm.org
Mr. Dwight Robertson, President

An interdenominational support agency of Evangelical tradition engaged in mobilization for mission, evangelism, support of national churches, short-term programs and training.
Purpose: "...to raise up a new generation of laborers for Kingdom service worldwide."
Year Founded in US: 1986
Income for Overseas Min: NA
Personnel:
  Short-term less than 1 year from US: 100

Larry Jones Intl. Ministries (Feed the Children)
P.O. Box 36
Oklahoma City, OK 73101-0228 USA
Phone: (405) 942-0228
Fax: (405) 945-4177
E-mail: ftc@feedthechildren.org
Web Site: www.feedthechildren.org
Dr. Larry W. Jones, President/Founder

An interdenominational service agency of Evangelical tradition engaged in food aid, evangelism, and other assistance in more than 20 countries. Statistical data from 1998.
Purpose: "...providing food, clothing, educational supplies, medical equipment and other necessities to people who lack these essentials because of famine, drought, flood, war or other calamities."

Year Founded in US: 1964

Income for Overseas Min: $45,178,413

Gifts-in-Kind: $41,870,450

Fully Supported US Personnel Overseas:
Nonresidential mission personnel: 4

Other personnel:
Non-US serving in own/other country: 131
Home ministry & office staff in US: 125

Countries: Albania; Angola; El Salvador; Ethiopia; Guatemala; Haiti; Honduras; Kenya; Nicaragua; Philippines; Romania; Russia; Thailand; Uganda

Latin America Assistance, Inc.

P.O. Box 123
Solvang, CA 93464-0123 USA

Phone: (800) 925-6359

Fax: (800) 693-9222

E-mail: lamanorth@earthlink.net

Web Site: www.lamontana.org

Mr. Joseph B. Pent, Director

A service agency of Evangelical and Ecumenical tradition engaged in evangelism, camping programs, leadership development and relief and/or rehabilitation.

Purpose: "...to equip youth leaders for aggressive evangelism and radical discipleship."

Year Founded in US: 1976

Income for Overseas Min: $442,000

Gifts-in-Kind: $25,000

Personnel:
Non-US serving in own/other country: 3
Home ministry & office staff in US: 1

Countries: Costa Rica

Latin America Lutheran Mission

3519 Salinas Ave.
Laredo, TX 78041 USA

Phone: (956) 722-4047

Fax: (956) 722-4047

E-mail: vgolalm@aol.com

Mr. V. Gary Olson, Director

A denominational support agency of Lutheran tradition engaged in support of national churches, support of national workers, short-term programs and partnership development. Income from 1997.

Purpose: "...to encourage Bible study and

discipleship, and to train and equip the Mexican people to fulfill Christ's 'Great Commission'."

Year Founded in US: 1936

Income for Overseas Min: $258,405

Fully Supported US Personnel Overseas:
Expecting to serve 1 to 4 years: 1

Other personnel:
Home ministry & office staff in US: 1

Countries: Mexico

Latin America Mission
(See Ad on page 209)

P.O. Box 52-7900
Miami, FL 33152-7900 USA

Phone: (305) 884-8400

Fax: (305) 885-8649

E-mail: info@lam.org

Web Site: www.lam.org

Dr. David R. Befus, President

An interdenominational sending agency of Evangelical tradition engaged in evangelism, childcare/orphanage programs, development, theological education, leadership development and short-term programs.

Purpose: "...to encourage, assist and participate with the Latin church in the task of building the church of Jesus Christ in the Latin world and beyond."

Year Founded in US: 1921

Income for Overseas Min: $963,143

Fully Supported US Personnel Overseas:
Expecting to serve more than 4 years: 106
Expecting to serve 1 to 4 years: 30

Other personnel:
Short-term less than 1year from US: 17
Non-US serving in own/other country: 136
Home ministry & office staff in US: 30

Countries: Argentina 2; Bolivia 2; Brazil 4; Colombia 8; Costa Rica 55; Ecuador 4; El Salvador; Honduras 1; Mexico 17; Paraguay Peru 4; Spain 5; Venezuela 4

Latin American Indian Ministries

P.O. Box 2050
Orange, CA 92859 USA

Phone: (626) 398-2105

Fax: (626) 398-2491

E-mail: Dale.Kietzman@wcio.edu

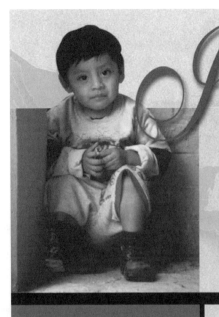

IS God calling
you to serve in
Latin America?

*LAM can help you
explore that calling.*

*Latin America
Mission offers
opportunities for
meaningful pro-
fessional service
with grass-roots
Latin ministries.
If the Lord is
calling you, count
the cost. Then call
Latin America
Mission.*

- *Summer* - *Limited-term*
- *YearOut* - *Career*

*Contact us today to
find out more!*

LAM **Latin America
Mission**

PO Box 52-7900 · Miami, FL 33152-7900
1-800-275-8410
mobilization@lam.org
www.lam.org

Web Site: www.laim.org

Mr. Dale W. Kietzman, President

A nondenominational service agency of Evangelical tradition engaged in support of national churches, church planting, development, TEE, evangelism and support of national workers.

Purpose: "...to encourage, strengthen and support the indigenous communities of Latin America in their efforts to evangelize and disciple their own people, as well as to help them improve living standards for their families..."

Year Founded in US: 1973

Income for Overseas Min: $45,000

Countries: Brazil; Mexico; Peru

Leadership Ministries Worldwide

Box 21310

Chattanooga, TN 37424 USA

Phone: (423) 855-2181

Fax: (423) 855-8616

E-mail: info@outlinebible.org

Web Site: www.outlinebible.org

Mr. Jack D. Walker, Exec. Director

A service agency of Evangelical tradition publishing and distributing the Preacher's OUTLINE and Sermon Bible and related OUTLINE Bible series.

Purpose: "...equipping God's servants worldwide in their understanding, preaching, and teaching of God's Word by publishing and distributing OUTLINE Bible materials, to reach and disciple people for Jesus."

Year Founded in US: 1992

Income for Overseas Min: $442,000

Personnel:
  Short-term less than 1 year from US: 9
  Non-US serving in own/other country: 1
  Home ministry & office staff in US: 11

Countries: Bolivia

Liberty Corner Mission

P.O. Box 204

Liberty Corner, NJ 07938 USA

Phone: (908) 647-1777

Fax: (908) 647-4117

Rev. E. E. Achenbach, President

An interdenominational sending agency of Evangelical tradition engaged in evangelism and support of national churches, working together with Marburg Mission of Germany.

Year Founded in US: 1933

Income for Overseas Min: NA

Fully Supported US Personnel Overseas:
  Expecting to serve more than 4 years: 3

Other personnel:
  Home ministry & office staff in US: 1

Countries: Japan 1; Taiwan 2

Liebenzell USA

P.O. Box 66

Schooley's Mtn., NJ 07870 USA

Phone: (908) 852-3044

Fax: (908) 852-4531

E-mail: missions@liebenzellusa.org

Web Site: www.liebenzellusa.org

Rev. George Hege, Director Global Missions

An interdenominational sending agency of Evangelical tradition engaged in evangelism, church planting, development, theological education and support of national churches.

Year Founded in US: 1941

Income for Overseas Min: $700,000

Fully Supported US Personnel Overseas:
  Expecting to serve more than 4 years: 29

Other personnel:
  Home ministry & office staff in US: 14

Countries: Central Asia–General 8; Ecuador 7; Micronesia, Federated States of 12; Spain 2

LIFE Ministries

P.O. Box 200

San Dimas, CA 91773 USA

Phone: (626) 914-8990

Fax: (626) 914-9572

E-mail: info@lifejapan.org

Web Site: www.lifejapan.org

Rev. S. Douglas Birdsall, President

An interdenominational sending agency of Evangelical tradition engaged in evangelism, church planting, leadership development, support of national churches and support of national workers.

Purpose: "...to strengthen and start Japanese churches in partnership with visionary pastors and congregations through innovation in evangelism and leadership training."

Year Founded in US: 1967

Income for Overseas Min: $2,589,402

Fully Supported US Personnel Overseas:
Expecting to serve more than 4 years: 21
Expecting to serve 1 to 4 years: 4

Other personnel:
Short-term less than 1 year from US: 100
Non-US serving in own/other country: 46
Home ministry & office staff in US: 18

Countries: Japan 21

Lifewater International
P.O. Box 3131
San Luis Obispo, CA 93403 USA
Phone: (805) 772-0600
Fax: (805) 772-0606
E-mail: Info@lifewater.org
Web Site: www.lifewater.org
Mr. Dan Stevens, Exec. Director

A nondenominational specialized agency engaged in development, technical assistance and services for other agencies.

Purpose: "...trains the rural poor to develop clean water supplies...works with mission agencies, local agencies and missionaries to train in shallow well drilling, pump repair, spring development, hygiene education and cottage industries."

Year Founded in US: 1979

Income for Overseas Min: $452,000

Gifts-in-Kind: $442,000

Personnel:
Short-term less than 1 year from US: 45
Non-US serving in own/other country: 3
Home ministry & office staff in US: 1

Countries: Kenya; Romania; Togo

LIGHT International, Inc.
P.O. Box 368
Etna, CA 96027 USA
Phone: (916) 467-5373
E-mail: bwaymire@sisqtel.net
Mr. Robert H. Waymire, President

A nondenominational specialized agency of Evangelical tradition engaged in church mobilization and mission-related research and training in 65 countries.

Year Founded in US: 1991

Income for Overseas Min: $30,000

Gifts-in-Kind: $30,000

Personnel:
Home ministry & office staff in US: 1

Link Care Foundation
(See Ad on page 213)
1734 W. Shaw Ave.
Fresno, CA 93711-3486 USA
Phone: (559) 439-5920
Fax: (559) 439-2214
E-mail: info@linkcare.org
Web Site: www.linkcare.org
Dr. Brent Lindquist, President

A nondenominational specialized agency of Evangelical tradition engaged in psychological counseling.

Year Founded in US: 1965

Income for Overseas Min: NA

Personnel:
Home ministry & office staff in US: 27

Literacy & Evangelism Intl.
1800 S. Jackson Ave.
Tulsa, OK 74107-1897 USA
Phone: (918) 585-3826
Fax: (918) 585-3225
E-mail: general@literacyevangelism.org
Web Site: www.literacyevangelism.org
Rev. John C. Taylor, Director

An interdenominational sending agency of Evangelical tradition engaged in literacy work, missionary education, evangelism, leadership development, management consulting/training, technical assistance and missionary training.

Purpose: "To encourage, equip and enable the Church worldwide to empower the functionally illiterate with God's Word, through literacy ministries."

Year Founded in US: 1967

Income for Overseas Min: $128,000

Fully Supported US Personnel Overseas:
Expecting to serve more than 4 years: 4

Other personnel:
Short-term less than 1 year from US: 9

Non-US serving in own/other country: 6
Home ministry & office staff in US: 7
Countries: Brazil; China; Dominican Republic; Ghana; India; Kenya; Paraguay; Peru 2; Philippines 2; Poland; Romania; Sierra Leone

Living Water Teaching Intl.
P.O. Box 1190
Caddo Mills, TX 75135 USA
Phone: (903) 527-4160
Fax: (903) 527-2134
E-mail: lwt@lwtusa.org
Web Site: www.lwtusa.org
Mr. Keith Spanberger, Assoc. Minister

A nondenominational sending agency of Charismatic and Pentecostal tradition engaged in theological education, aviation services, childcare/orphanage programs, evangelism, providing medical supplies and missionary training.
Year Founded in US: 1979
Income for Overseas Min: $665,278
Gifts-in-Kind: $22,318
Fully Supported US Personnel Overseas:
  Nonresidential mission personnel: 2
Other personnel:
  Short-term less than 1 year from US: 200
  Non-US serving in own/other country: 15
  Home ministry & office staff in US: 6
Countries: Costa Rica; Cuba; El Salvador; Guatemala; Honduras; Nicaragua; Panama; Paraguay

LOGOI, Inc./FLET
14540 SW 136th St., Suite 200
Miami, FL 33186 USA
Phone: (305) 232-5880
Fax: (305) 232-3592
E-mail: Logoi@logoi.org
Web Site: www.logoi.org
Rev. Leslie J. Thompson, President

A transdenominational service agency of Reformed and Evangelical tradition engaged in non-formal theological education and publishing print materials for use in 17 Spanish speaking countries.
Purpose: "...to build up the body of Christ and evangelize Latin American communities by education and equipping national Spanish pastors, teachers and leaders to effec-

tively teach and preach the Word of God."
Year Founded in US: 1968
Income for Overseas Min: $900,000
Fully Supported US Personnel Overseas:
  Nonresidential mission personnel: 7
Other Personnel:
  Home ministry & office staff in US: 19

Ludhiana Christian Medical College Board, USA, Inc.
900 S Arlington Ave., Ste. 111
Harrisburg, PA 17109 USA
Phone: (717) 651-0990
E-mail: Ludhianamc@aol.com
Web Site: www.cpcumc.org/ludhiana
Rev. Roberta K. Jones, Exec. Director

An interdenominational service agency of Ecumenical tradition engaged in medical work and providing medical supplies. Financial information from 1996.
Year Founded in US: 1894
Income for Overseas Min: $505,133
Gifts-in-Kind: $405,133
Personnel:
  Short-term less than 1 year from US: 15
  Home ministry & office staff in US: 2

Luis Palau Evangelistic Assoc.
P.O. Box 1173
Portland, OR 97207 USA
Phone: (503) 614-1500
Fax: (503) 614-1599
E-mail: Lpea@palau.org
Web Site: www.palau.org
Dr. Luis Palau, President

A nondenominational service agency of Evangelical tradition engaged in evangelism, leadership development, literature production and broadcasting.
Purpose: "...to win people...to Jesus Christ throughout the world, proclaiming His Good News by all available means...to stimulate, revive, train and mobilize the Church to continuous, effective evangelism, follow-up and church growth...raising up a new generation of godly leaders..."
Year Founded in US: 1978
Income for Overseas Min: $1,100,000
Fully Supported US Personnel Overseas:

Link Care Center

ENHANCING EFFECTIVENESS IN LIVING, WITNESSING, AND WORKING WITH MISSIONARIES AND PASTORS AROUND THE WORLD.

SINCE 1965, Link Care Center has been providing comprehensive counseling, pastoral care, and training resources across the wide human resources spectrum for mission agencies, denominations, and local churches.

IN FRESNO, our Restoration/Personal Growth Program combines intensive counseling and pastoral care in community for up to 25 individual and family units at a time. Each year, at least 60% to 70% of the people that come to us for help return to their arena of ministry, saving the entire Great Commission community substantial funds and heartache. Our licensed psychologists, marriage and family therapists and social workers qualify for many insurance plans, also reducing the out of pocket expenses.

AROUND THE WORLD we provide many services, including candidate assessment, training, consulting, crisis debriefing, intensive counseling and pastoral care.

IN PRINT and electronic media we provide books, newsletters, and other resources.

VISIT OUR WEBSITE for further details.

LINK CARE CENTER

1734 W. Shaw Ave.
Fresno, CA 93711
Phone 559-439-5920
Fax 559-439-2214
Website linkcare.org
E-mail info@linkcare.org

Nonresidential mission personnel: 4

Other personnel:
Non-US serving in own/other country: 9
Home ministry & office staff in US: 85

Countries: Argentina; Guatemala; United Kingdom

Luke Society, The

2204 S. Minnesota Ave.
Sioux Falls, SD 57105 USA

Phone: (605) 373-9686
Fax: (605) 373-9711
E-mail: office@lukesociety.org
Web Site: www.lukesociety.org

Dr. Wrede Vogel, Exec. Director

An interdenominational service agency of Evangelical tradition engaged in medical work, development, funds transmission and leadership development.

Year Founded in US: 1964

Income for Overseas Min: $802,000

Personnel:
Home ministry & office staff in US: 6

Lutheran Bible Translators

P.O. Box 2050
Aurora, IL 60507-2050 USA

Phone: (630) 897-0660
Fax: (630) 897-3567
E-mail: info@lbt.org
Web Site: www.lbt.org

Dr. Marshall R. Gillam, Exec. Director

A denominational sending agency of Lutheran tradition engaged in Bible translation, audio recording/distribution, leadership development, linguistics, literacy work and video/film production/distribution.

Purpose: "...to help bring people to faith in Jesus Christ by making the Word of God available to those who do not yet have it in the language of their hearts."

Year Founded in US: 1964

Income for Overseas Min: $1,052,490

Fully Supported US Personnel Overseas:
Expecting to serve more than 4 years: 28
Expecting to serve 1 to 4 years: 1
Nonresidential mission personnel: 1

Other personnel:
Non-US serving in own/other country: 70

Home ministry & office staff in US: 23

Countries: Botswana 6; Cameroon 4; Cote d'Ivoire 4; Ecuador; Guatemala 8; Liberia; Namibia 4; Papua New Guinea 2; Sierra Leone; Togo

Lutheran Brethren World Missions

P.O. Box 655
Fergus Falls, MN 56538-0655 USA

Phone: (218) 739-3336
Fax: (775) 522-1552
E-mail: lbwn@lbwn.org
Web Site: www.lbwm.org

Rev. Matthew Rogness, Exec. Director

A denominational sending agency of Evangelical and Lutheran tradition engaged in church planting, leadership development, literature production, support of national churches and Bible translation.

Purpose: "...serving the congregations of the Church of the Lutheran Brethren to facilitate their task of fulfilling the Great Commission..."

Year Founded in US: 1900

Income for Overseas Min: $975,000

Fully Supported US Personnel Overseas:
Expecting to serve more than 4 years: 20
Expecting to serve 1 to 4 years: 5

Other personnel:
Short-term less than 1 year from US: 6
Home ministry & office staff in US: 8
Bivocational/Tentmaker from US: 2

Countries: Asia–General 2; Chad 8; Japan 6; Taiwan 4

Lutheran Church— Missouri Synod, Board for Mission Services

1333 S. Kirkwood Rd.
St. Louis, MO 63122-7295 USA

Phone: (314) 965-9000
Fax: (314) 965-0959
E-mail: mission.info@lcms.org
Web Site: www.lcmsworldmission.org

Rev. Robert M. Roegner, Exec. Director

A denominational sending agency of Lutheran tradition engaged in church planting, theological education, evangelism, leadership development and partnership development.

Purpose: "Praying to the Lord of the harvest, LCMS World Mission in collaboration with its North American and worldwide partners will share the good news of Jesus with 100 million unreached people or uncommitted people by the 500th anniversary of the Reformation in 2017."

Year Founded in US: 1893

Income for Overseas Min: $15,882,554

Gifts-in-Kind: $6,124,915

Fully Supported US Personnel Overseas:
Expecting to serve more than 4 years: 121
Expecting to serve 1 to 4 years: 203

Other personnel:
Short-term less than 1 year from US: 89
Home ministry & office staff in US: 44

Countries: Argentina; Botswana 2; Brazil 1; China 15; Eritrea 2; Germany 4; Ghana 4; Guatemala 4; Guinea 3; Haiti; Hong Kong 19; Hungary; India 2; Indonesia 2; Jamaica 2; Japan 8; Kazakhstan 4; Kenya; Korea, South 2; Kyrgyzstan 4; Liberia 1; Macau; Mexico; Nigeria 7; Panama; Papua New Guinea 4; Philippines 2; Poland; Puerto Rico; Russia 6; Sierra Leone; Slovakia; South Africa; Taiwan 6; Thailand 6; Togo 1; Venezuela 8; Vietnam 2

Lutheran Literature Society for the Chinese

1827 Woodland Ave.
Duluth, MN 55803 USA
Phone: (218) 724-1068
E-mail: Revelness@aol.com
Rev. Jerome Elness, President

An interdenominational support agency of Lutheran tradition engaged in literature production, audio recording/distribution, Bible distribution and literature distribution.

Purpose: "...to promote evangelism among the Chinese...by supporting the production and distribution of Christian literature...and by using mass media."

Year Founded in US: 1942

Income for Overseas Min: $33,714

Lutheran World Relief

700 Light St.

Baltimore, MD 21230 USA
Phone: (410) 230-2700
Fax: (410) 230-2882
E-mail: LWR@lwr.org
Web Site: www.lwr.org
Dr. Kathryn F. Wolford, President

A denominational service agency of Lutheran tradition engaged in relief and/or rehabilitation, development, leadership development and agricultural programs. Statistical information from 1998.

Purpose: "...to alleviate suffering caused by natural disaster, conflict or poverty; through development efforts to enable marginalized people to realize more fully their God-given potential; and through education and advocacy efforts to promote a peaceful, just and sustainable global community."

Year Founded in US: 1945

Income for Overseas Min: $22,598,621

Gifts-in-Kind: $11,763,386

Personnel:
Home ministry & office staff in US: 38

M/E International, Inc. (Missionary Electronics)

655 Shadow Lake Dr.
Brea, CA 92821 USA
Phone: (714) 931-2712
Fax: (562) 691-5703
E-mail: JFORD767@aol.com
Web Site: www.me-intl.org
Mr. James R. Ford, President

An interdenominational support agency of Evangelical and Baptist tradition engaged in support of national workers, church planting, children's programs, evangelism, leadership development and training.

Purpose: "To enable nationals in developing countries to reach their own with the Gospel of the Lord Jesus Christ...using cassette discipleship programs...structured dialog messages with village evangelists."

Income for Overseas Min: $18,500

Personnel:
Non-US serving in own/other country: 95
Bivocational/Tentmaker from US: 65

Countries: Ghana; India

Macedonia World Baptist Missions, Inc.

P.O. Box 519
Braselton, GA 30517 USA
Phone: (706) 654-2818
Fax: (706) 654-2816
E-mail: mwbm@mwbm.org
Web Site: www.mwbm.org
Dr. Thurman Wade, Gen. Director

A denominational sending agency of Baptist and Independent tradition engaged in church planting, broadcasting, Christian education, literature distribution and literature production, with missionaries serving in 37 countries.

Year Founded in US: 1967
Income for Overseas Min: $5,040,000
Personnel:
   Short-term less than 1 year from US: 8
   Home ministry & Office staff in US: 8

Macedonian Missionary Service

P.O. Box 68
Polk City, FL 33868-0068 USA
Phone: (941) 984-4060
Fax: (941) 984-4505
E-mail: secretary@macedonianms.org
Web Site: www.macedonianms.org
Dr. Harold R. Williams, Chairman

A denominational support agency of Baptist tradition engaged in short-term programs, church construction, correspondence courses, broadcasting, Bible distribution, literature distribution, literature production and missionary training. Financial and personnel information from 1998.

Year Founded in US: 1973
Income for Overseas Min: $300,000
Personnel:
   Short-term less than 1 year from US: 12
   Home ministry & office staff in US: 10

Mahesh Chavda Ministries Intl.

P.O. Box 472009
Charlotte, NC 28247 USA
Phone: (704) 543-7272
Fax: (704) 541-5300

E-mail: Info@watchofthelord.com
Web Site: www.watchofthelord.com
Rev. Mahesh Chavda, Founder/President

A nondenominational support agency of Charismatic tradition engaged in evangelism, leadership development, literature production and support of national churches. Financial data from 1998.

Year Founded in US: 1985
Income for Overseas Min: $20,000
Gifts-in-Kind: NA
Personnel:
   Home ministry & office staff in US: 9

Mailbox Club International

404 Eager Rd.
Valdosta, GA 31602 USA
Phone: (912) 244-6812
E-mail: email@mailboxclub.org
Web Site: www.mailboxclub.org
Mr. John Mark Eager, Director

A nondenominational support agency of Independent tradition producing Bible correspondence courses for children in 20 languages.

Purpose: "...produces, facilitates translation and distribution of Mailbox Club lessons around the world for people of all ages, with particular emphasis on children and young people."

Year Founded in US: 1965
Income for Overseas Min: $388,105
Personnel:
   Home ministry & office staff in US: 16

MAP International

(See Ad on page 219)
P.O. Box 215000
Brunswick, GA 31521-5000 USA
Phone: (800) 225-8550
Fax: (912) 265-6170
E-mail: MAP@map.org
Web Site: www.map.org
Mr. Michael Nyenhuis, President/CEO

A nondenominational specialized agency of Ecumenical tradition engaged in medical work, development, literature production and relief and/or rehabilitation. Personnel data from 1998.

Purpose: "...promotes the total health of people living in the world's poorest communities by partnering in the provision of essential medicines, prevention and eradication of disease and the promotion of community health development."

Year Founded in US: 1954

Income for Overseas Min: $151,751,257

Gifts-in-Kind: $144,163,700

Personnel:
   Non-US serving in own/other country: 47
   Home ministry & office staff in US: 55

Countries: Bolivia; Cote d'Ivoire; Ecuador; Kenya

Marriage Ministries Intl.
See: University of the Family

MATS International, Inc.
4444 National Road E.
Richmond, IN 47374 USA
Phone: (765) 965-7777
Fax: (765) 962-9966
E-mail: car@mats.org
Web Site: www.mats.org
Mr. Tom Daugherty, Director

A nondenominational support agency of Fundamental tradition providing a purchasing service for vehicles used abroad and in the USA by mission agencies, churches and other ministries.

Year Founded in US: 1977

Income for Overseas Min: NA

Personnel:
   Home ministry & office staff in US: 1

MBMS International
4867 E. Townsend Ave.
Fresno, CA 93727 USA
Phone: (559) 456-4600
Fax: (559) 251-1432
E-mail: mbmsi@mbmsinternational.org
Web Site: www.mbmsinternational.org
Rev. Harold Ens, Gen. Director

A denominational sending agency of Mennonite tradition engaged in church planting, development, theological education, evangelism, support of national workers and youth programs. MBMS is a bi-national

organization and statistics cannot be separated into U.S. and Canadian. Canadian statistics are included in this U.S. listing.

Purpose: "...to participate in making disciples of all people groups, sharing the gospel of Jesus Christ cross-culturally and globally, in Spirit-empowered obedience to Christ's Commission and in partnership with local Mennonite Brethren churches."

Year Founded in US: 1878

Income for Overseas Min: $1,088,272

Fully Supported US Personnel Overseas:
   Expecting to serve 1 to 4 years: 53
   Nonresidential mission personnel: 2

Other personnel:
   Short-term less than 1 year from US: 849
   Non-US serving in own/other country: 104
   Home ministry & office staff in US: 33

Countries: Angola; Austria; Botswana; Brazil; Burkina Faso; Chile; China; CIS–General; Colombia; Congo, Democratic Republic of the; Costa Rica; Ethiopia; Germany; India; Japan; Lithuania; Mexico; Pakistan; Paraguay; Peru; Portugal; Thailand; Uruguay

Media Associates Intl.
P.O. Box 218
Bloomingdale, IL 60108-0218 USA
Phone: (630) 893-1977
Fax: (630) 893-1141
E-mail: MaiLittworld@cs.com
Web Site: www.littworld.org
Mr. John Maust, President

A nondenominational specialized agency of Evangelical tradition engaged in print media training, leadership development, management consulting/training, technical assistance, literature distribution and services for other agencies. Publishing and consulting for missions and national agencies in the Two-Thirds world.

Purpose: "...providing consultative and technical assistance to build competence in Christian communication, managerial, editorial, production and marketing skills."

Year Founded in US: 1985

Income for Overseas Min: NA

Gifts-in-Kind: $72,278

Personnel:
   Home ministry & office staff in US: 4

50 years
Sending
Health
and
Hope

Since 1954,
MAP has been a
trusted partner,
providing essential
**medicines and supplies
for short-term missions,**
disaster relief and
on-going health care
ministries. MAP's long-
term efforts promote
community health
development and
work to prevent and
eradicate disease
around the world.

MAP INTERNATIONAL
health & hope for a hurting world®

www.map.org
(800)225-8550

Medical Ambassadors Intl.

P.O. Box 576645
Modesto, CA 95357-6645 USA
Phone: (209) 524-0600
Fax: (209) 571-3538
E-mail: medamb@ix.netcom.com
Web Site: www.med-amb.org/index.html
Dr. Paul Calhoun, Exec. Director

An interdenominational support agency of Evangelical tradition engaged in medical work, agricultural programs, development, evangelism, management consulting/training and support of national workers.

Purpose: "...recruits, trains and supports national leaders among developing peoples...to reach their own people physically and spiritually..."

Year Founded in US: 1974
Income for Overseas Min: $3,297,400
Fully Supported US Personnel Overseas:
  Expecting to serve more than 4 years: 7
  Expecting to serve 1 to 4 years: 2
  Nonresidential mission personnel: 16

Other personnel:
  Short-term less than 1 year from US: 9
  Non-US serving in own/other country: 230
  Home ministry & office staff in US: 41

Countries: Afghanistan; Albania 2; Argentina; Bangladesh; Bolivia; Brazil; Cambodia; China; Congo, Democratic Republic of the; Costa Rica; Cuba; Dominican Republic; Egypt; El Salvador; Ethiopia; Gabon; Guatemala; Haiti; Honduras; India; Indonesia; Kazakhstan; Kenya; Korea, South; Kyrgyzstan; Laos; Mexico 1; Mongolia; Mozambique; Myanmar/Burma; Nepal; Nicaragua; Niger; Peru; Philippines; Romania 2; Sierra Leone; Tajikistan; Tanzania; Thailand; Trinidad and Tobago; Uganda 2; Ukraine; Uruguay; Uzbekistan; Venezuela; Vietnam; Yemen; Zambia

Medical Missions Philippines

P.O. Box 3656
Modesto, CA 95352 USA
Phone: (209) 531-3031
E-mail: rghagerty@aol.com
Mr. Richard G. Hagerty, President

A nondenominational support agency of Baptist tradition engaged in training, development, evangelism, providing medical supplies, medical work and support of national workers.

Year Founded in US: 1987
Income for Overseas Min: $34,000
Personnel:
  Non-US serving in own/other country: 50
Countries: Philippines

Men for Missions Intl.

941 Fry Road
Greenwood, IN 46142 USA
Phone: (317) 881-6752
Fax: (317) 865-1076
E-mail: whardig@omsinternational.org
Web Site: www.mfmi.org
Mr. Warren Hardig, Intl. Exec. Director

An interdenominational support agency of Evangelical tradition engaged in overseas missionary housing construction, literature production and providing other technical assistance as a short-term arm of OMS International.

Purpose: "Reaching the nations for Christ in this generation by doing whatever God asks us to do, going wherever God asks us to go and giving whatever God asks us to give."

Year Founded in US: 1954
Income for Overseas Min: NA
Fully Supported US Personnel Overseas:
  Expecting to serve more than 4 years: 2
  Expecting to serve 1 to 4 years: 2
  Nonresidential mission personnel: 2

Other personnel:
  Short-term less than 1 year from US: 434
Countries: South Africa; United Kingdom 2

Mennonite Board of Missions
See: Mennonite Mission Network

Mennonite Brethren Missions/Services
See: MBMS International

Mennonite Central Committee

P.O. Box 500
Akron, PA 17501-0500 USA

Phone: (717) 859-1151
Fax: (717) 859-2171
E-mail: MailBox@mcc.org
Web Site: www.mcc.org

Dr. Ronald J. R. Mathies, Exec. Director

A binational denominational service agency of Mennonite tradition engaged in development, agricultural programs, extension education, relief and/or rehabilitation, technical assistance, training and youth programs. Overseas personnel totals are for the U.S. and Canada.

Purpose: "...to demonstrate God's love by working among people suffering from poverty, conflict, oppression and natural disaster."

Year Founded in US: 1920
Income for Overseas Min: $41,560,475
Gifts-in-Kind: $5,531,368
Fully Supported US Personnel Overseas:
  Expecting to serve more than 4 years: 874
Other personnel:
  Home ministry & office staff in US: 318
Countries: Africa–General 187; Asia–General 451; Europe–General 29; Latin America–General 207

Mennonite Mission Network
500 S. Main
Elkhart, IN 46515-0370 USA
Phone: (866) 866-2872
Fax: (574) 294-8669
E-mail: info@MennoniteMission.net
Web Site: www.MennoniteMission.net

Mr. Stanley W. Green, Exec. Director

A denominational mobilizing, partnering and resource/equipping agency of Mennonite/Anabaptist tradition engaged in nurture and support of national churches, church planting/establishing, leadership development, community development, recruiting, medicine and short-term service.

Purpose: "With a vision for every congregation and all parts of the church to be fully engaged in God's mission, Mennonite Mission Network exists to lead, mobilize and equip the church for holistic witness to Jesus Christ in a broken world."

Year Founded in US: 1899
Income for Overseas Min: $5,686,027

Fully Supported US Personnel Overseas:
  Expecting to serve more than 4 years: 72
  Nonresidential mission personnel: 2
Other personnel:
  Short-term less than 1 year from US: 38
  Non-US serving in own/other country: 37
  Home ministry & office staff in US: 98
  Bivocational/Tentmaker from US: 1
Countries: Afghanistan 4; Argentina 4; Asia –General 2; Australia; Belgium; Benin 3; Bolivia 1; Botswana 2; Brazil; Burkina Faso; Chile; China 4; Colombia 2; Congo, Democratic Republic of; Cote d'Ivoire 2; Dominican Republic; Ecuador 2; Egypt 2; Finland; France 3; Germany; Ghana; Hong Kong 2; Hungary; India; Iran; Ireland 2; Israel 6; Japan 7; Korea, South; Lesotho; Liberia; Lithuania; Macau; Malaysia; Mexico 4; Mongolia 5; Nepal 2; Netherlands; Nigeria; Paraguay; Philippines; Russia 2; Senegal 7; South Africa; Spain 2; Sweden; Taiwan; Thailand; Togo; Ukraine; United Kingdom 2; Uruguay

Mercy Ships
P.O. Box 2020
Garden Valley, TX 75771-2020 USA
Phone: (903) 882-0887
Fax: (903) 882-0336
E-mail: info@mercyships.org
Web Site: www.mercyships.org

Mr. Donald K. Stephens, Founder/CEO

A service agency of Evangelical tradition engaged in medical work, agricultural programs, evangelism, support of national churches and relief and/or rehabilitation.

Purpose: "Mercy Ships, a global charity with land offices in 17 countries, is staffed by 1200+ staff coming from many Christian denominations and traditions with staff coming from over 40 nations. It runs the world's largest fleet of non-governmental hospital ships. Seeking to follow the example of Jesus, Mercy Ships brings hope and healing to the poor, mobilizing people and resources worldwide."

Year Founded in US: 1978
Income for Overseas Min: $19,682,881
Gifts-in-Kind: $13,501,582
Fully Supported US Personnel Overseas:
  Expecting to serve 1 to 4 years: 700

Other personnel:
Short-term less than 1 year from US: 1,100
Home ministry & office staff in US: 140
Countries: Unspecified Country 700

Mexican Medical Ministries
251 Landis Ave.
Chula Vista, CA 91910-2628 USA
Phone: (619) 420-9750
Fax: (619) 420-9570
E-mail: info@mexicanmedical.com
Web Site: www.mexicanmedical.com
Mr. Stephen M. Crews, President
A nondenominational service agency of
Evangelical tradition engaged in medical
work, evangelism, short-term programs,
missionary training and youth programs.
Personnel information from 1998.
Purpose: "...to bring the Gospel of Jesus
Christ to the various age groups of Mexican
people through a variety of ministries."
Year Founded in US: 1967
Income for Overseas Min: $2,162,018
Gifts-in-Kind: $1,445,692
Fully Supported US Personnel Overseas:
Expecting to serve more than 4 years: 12
Other personnel:
Short-term less than 1 year from US: 100
Home ministry & office staff in US: 6
Bivocational/Tentmaker from US: 2
Countries: Mexico 12

Middle East Christian Outreach
P.O. Box 531151
Indianapolis, IN 46253-1151 USA
Phone: (317) 271-4026
Fax: (317) 271-4026
E-mail: 75227.633@compuserve.com
Web Site: www.aboutmeco.org
Rev. James R. Smith, U.S. Director
An interdenominational sending agency of
Evangelical tradition engaged in support of
national churches, development, Christian
education, evangelism, literature distribu-
tion and video/film production/distribution.
Statistical data from 1998.
Year Founded in US: 1978
Income for Overseas Min: $60,922

Fully Supported US Personnel Overseas:
Expecting to serve more than 4 years: 4
Expecting to serve 1 to 4 years: 2
Other personnel:
Non-US serving in own/other country: 68
Home ministry & office staff in US: 2
Countries: Africa–General 1; Asia–General
3; Cyprus; Turkey

Middle East Media–USA
P.O. Box 2033
Westfield, NJ 07091-2033 USA
Phone: (425) 778-0752
Fax: (425) 778-0752
E-mail: ed@mem-usa.org
Web Site: www.middleeastmedia.org
Mr. Mark Marlowe, Interim CEO
An interdenominational support agency of
Ecumenical and Evangelical tradition en-
gaged in video/film production/distribu-
tion, audio recording/distribution,
evangelism, literature production and ser-
vices for other agencies.
Year Founded in US: 1976
Income for Overseas Min: $347,427
Personnel:
Short-term less than 1 year from US: 3
Non-US serving in own/other country: 75
Home ministry & office staff in US: 2
Countries: Middle East

Middle Eastern Outreach
P.O. Box 405
Duarte, CA 91009-0405 USA
Phone: (626) 359-5242
Fax: (626) 358-3331
E-mail: meo.e@usa.com
Dr./Rev. Elie Elbayadi, Founder/President
A support agency engaged in evangelism,
missions information service, missionary train-
ing, literature distribution, support of national
churches, and Muslim and jail ministry.
Year Founded in US: 1995
Income for Overseas Min: $22,000
Personnel:
Home ministry & office staff in US: 3

Ministries In Action
P.O. Box 571357

Miami, FL 33257-1357 USA

Phone: (305) 234-7855
Fax: (305) 234-7825
E-mail: info@mia.org
Web Site: www.mia.org

Rev. E. Walford Thompson, President

An interdenominational sending agency of Evangelical tradition engaged in support of national churches, development, extension education and relief aid. Statistical data from 1998.

Year Founded in US: 1961

Income for Overseas Min: $539,595

Fully Supported US Personnel Overseas:
  Expecting to serve more than 4 years: 2
  Expecting to serve 1 to 4 years: 1
  Nonresidential mission personnel: 2

Other personnel:
  Non-US serving in own/other country: 8
  Home ministry & office staff in US: 12

Countries: Dominican Republic; Grenada 1; Haiti 1; Jamaica; Saint Vincent and the Grenadines

Ministry to Eastern Europe

2520 Professional Rd., Suite C
Richmond, VA 23235 USA

Phone: (804) 320-6456
Fax: (804) 320-6456
E-mail: mtee@lts-isp.net
Web Site: www.gospelcom.net/mtee

Mr. Ernest R. Campe, President

A nondenominational sending agency of Charismatic and Evangelical tradition engaged in theological education, children's programs, Christian education, leadership development and Bible translation.

Year Founded in US: 1983

Income for Overseas Min: $258,500

Personnel:
  Short-term less than 1 year from US: 10
  Home ministry & office staff in US: 2

Mission Aviation Fellowship

P.O. Box 3202
Redlands, CA 92373 USA

Phone: (909) 794-1151
Fax: (909) 794-3016
E-mail: tmaxwell@maf.org
Web Site: www.maf.org

Mr. Gary L. Bishop, CEO/President

A nondenominational specialized agency of Evangelical tradition engaged in aviation services and missions information service.

Purpose: "...to multiply the effectiveness of the Church using aviation and other strategic technologies to reach the world for Christ."

Year Founded in US: 1945

Income for Overseas Min:$27,041,701

Fully Supported US Personnel Overseas:
  Expecting to serve more than 4 years: 185
  Expecting to serve 1 to 4 years: 21

Other personnel:
  Short-term less than 1 year from US: 21
  Non-US serving in own/other country: 6
  Home ministry & office staff in US: 133

Countries: Africa–General 10; Asia–General 4; Brazil 4; Central Asia–General 14; Congo, Democratic Republic of the 14; Ecuador 23; Haiti 7; Indonesia 57; Latin America–General 4; Lesotho 8; Mali 20; Mexico 6; Mozambique 2; Russia; Venezuela 10; Zimbabwe 2

Mission India

P.O. Box 141312
Grand Rapids, MI 49514 USA

Phone: (616) 453-8855
Fax: (616) 791-9926
E-mail: info@missionindia.org
Web Site: www.missionindia.org

Rev. John F. DeVries, President

An interdenominational support agency of Evangelical tradition engaged in church planting, children's programs, literacy work and leadership development. The entire staff in India are Indian nationals.

Purpose: "...assists national Indian Christians in the planting of 'Reproducing Churches' in a systematic and measurable pattern throughout India."

Year Founded in US: 1990

Income for Overseas Min: $4,262,396

Gifts-in-Kind: $24,000

Personnel:
  Home ministry & office staff in US: 16

Mission Ministries, Inc.

P.O. Box 10044
Costa Mesa, CA 92627 USA

Phone: (714) 722-1304
E-mail: missionmin@aol.com
Web Site: www.missionministries.org
Dr. John A. Lindvall, Director

An interdenominational sending agency of Evangelical tradition engaged in childrens programs, church planting, development, evangelism and support of national workers.

Year Founded in US: 1980
Income for Overseas Min: $221,431
Fully Supported US Personnel Overseas:
    Expecting to serve more than 4 years: 15
    Expecting to serve 1 to 4 years: 1
Other personnel:
    Short-term less than 1 year from US: 5
    Non-US serving in own/other country: 7
    Home ministry & office staff in US: 4
Countries: Asia–General 2; Belarus 2; Kenya 1; Mexico 2; Myanmar/Burma 2; Nigeria; Philippines 1; Uganda 2; Ukraine; Venezuela 3

Mission Nannys

P.O. Box 61805
Santa Barbara, CA 93160-1805 USA
Phone: (805) 683-7476
E-mail: bettysullins@juno.com
Web Site: www.missionnannys.org
Betty Sullins, CEO

A nondenominational service agency of Baptist tradition engaged in providing domestic services and home-schooling help for missionary families.

Year Founded in US: 1990
Income for Overseas Min: NA

Mission of Mercy

P.O. Box 62600
Colorado Springs, CO 80962 USA
Phone: (719) 481-0400
Fax: (719) 481-4649
E-mail: mominfo@mofm.org
Web Site: www.missionofmercy.org
Mr. Bob Houlihan, President

A nondenominational support agency of Evangelical tradition engaged in relief and/or rehabilitation, childcare/orphanage programs, children's programs and medical work in 13 countries. A division of Bethesda Ministries.

Purpose: "...helping to meet the physical and spiritual needs of hurting people in poverty stricken areas of the world through emergency and support roles."

Year Founded in US: 1977
Income for Overseas Min: $10,863,810
Fully Supported US Personnel Overseas:
    Expecting to serve more than 4 years: 1
    Expecting to serve 1 to 4 years: 1
Countries: India 1

Mission ONE, Inc.

P.O. Box 70
White House, TN 37188 USA
Phone: (615) 672-9504
Fax: (615) 672-9513
E-mail: staff@mission1.org
Web Site: www.mission1.org
Mr. Bob Schindler, Founder/Chairman

An interdenominational support agency of Baptist and Evangelical tradition engaged in training, church planting and evangelism through the support of national workers.

Purpose: "...to mobilize the Church for partnership with national missionaries, focusing on unreached people groups, and serving the poor and oppressed."

Year Founded in US: 1991
Income for Overseas Min: $204,723
Personnel:
    Home ministry & office staff in US: 5
Countries: Algeria; China; Ethiopia; India; Indonesia; Iraq; Jordan; Kazakhstan; Kenya; Laos; Lebanon; Myanmar/Burma; Nepal; Pakistan; Rwanda; Sudan; Tanzania; Thailand; Uganda; Vietnam

Mission Possible Foundation, Inc.

P.O. Box 2014
Denton, TX 76202-2014 USA
Phone: (940) 382-1508
Fax: (940) 566-1875
E-mail: contact@mp.org
Web Site: www.mp.org
Mr. Mark Krantz, President/CEO

A nondenominational support agency of Charismatic tradition engaged in TEE, childcare/orphanage programs, church planting, literature distribution, literature production and youth programs. Statistical data from 1998.

Purpose: "...to serve local national churches and enable them to evangelize unbelievers and disciple new believers..."

Year Founded in US: 1974

Income for Overseas Min: $360,051

Personnel:
Home ministry & office staff in US: 5

Countries: Albania; Bulgaria; China; Finland; Russia; Ukraine

Mission Possible, Inc.
P.O. Box 520
Fort Pierce, FL 34954 USA
Phone: (772) 465-0373
Fax: (772) 465-0639
E-mail: mpi@bellsouth.net
Web Site: www.mpint.org
Mr. Chris O'Donnell, President

A nondenominational support agency of Evangelical tradition engaged in evangelism, support of national workers, relief and/or rehabilitation and Christian education.

Year Founded in US: 1974

Income for Overseas Min: $624,411

Gifts-in-Kind: $90,866

Fully Supported US Personnel Overseas:
Expecting to serve 1 to 4 years: 4

Other personnel:
Non-US serving in own/other country: 153
Home ministry & office staff in US: 7

Countries: Dominican Republic; Haiti

Mission Safety International
328 E. Elk Ave. #1
Elizabethton, TN 37643-3210 USA
Phone: (423) 542-8892
Fax: (423) 542-5464
E-mail: info@msisafety.org
Web Site: www.msisafety.org
Mr. Joe Hopkins, President

A nondenominational specialized agency of Evangelical tradition engaged in aviation safety services for other agencies in 10 countries.

Purpose: "...to provide educational and consulting services to assist missions and related agencies in realizing their [aircraft op-

erations] objectives effectively and efficiently."

Year Founded in US: 1983

Income for Overseas Min: NA

Personnel:
Home ministry & office staff in US: 2

Mission Services Association
P.O. Box 13111
Knoxville, TN 37920-0111 USA
Phone: (800) 655-8524
Fax: (865) 573-5950
E-mail: msa@missionservices.org
Web Site: www.missionservices.org
Mr. W. Reggie Hundley, Exec. Director

A nondenominational support agency of Christian (Restoration Movement) tradition engaged in services for other agencies and missions information service. Income figure from 1998.

Year Founded in US: 1946

Income for Overseas Min: $300,000

Personnel:
Short-term less than 1 year from US: 2
Home ministry & office staff in US: 10

Mission Society for United Methodists
See: The Mission Society

Mission to the Americas
2530 Washington St.
Denver, CO 80205-3142 USA
Phone: (303) 308-1818
Fax: (303) 295-9090
E-mail: mta@mtta.org
Web Site: www.mtta.org
Rev. Rick Miller, Exec. Director

A sending agency of Baptist tradition engaged in church planting, urban ministry, campus ministry, evangelism, leadership development and support of national churches in North and Central America (including Canada, USA, Mexico and the Caribbean).

Purpose: "...to evangelize, disciple and congregationalize the unreached of the Americas, including disenfranchised and ethnically diverse people."

Year Founded in US: 1950

Income for Overseas Min: $1,500,000
Fully Supported US Personnel Overseas:
  Expecting to serve more than 4 years: 20
Other personnel:
  Non-US serving in own/other country: 46
  Home ministry & office staff in US: 15
Countries: Belize 2; Costa Rica 2; Dominican Republic; El Salvador; Guatemala 2; Haiti; Honduras 8; Mexico 6; Nicaragua; Panama

Mission to the World (PCA), Inc.
1600 N. Brown Rd.
Lawrenceville, GA 30043 USA
Phone: (678) 823-0004
Fax: (678) 823-0027
E-mail: info@mtw.org
Web Site: www.mtw.org
Dr. Paul D. Kooistra, Coordinator

A denominational sending agency of Presbyterian tradition engaged in church planting, TEE, evangelism, leadership development and support of national churches.
Purpose: "Mission sending agency of the PCA advancing Reformed and covenantal church planting movements through word and deed in strategic areas worldwide."
Year Founded in US: 1973
Income for Overseas Min: $34,149,834
Fully Supported US Personnel Overseas:
  Expecting to serve more than 4 years: 434
  Expecting to serve 1 to 4 years: 128
Other Personnel:
  Short-term less than 1 year from US: 28
  Home ministry & office staff in US: 95
Countries: Argentina 2; Asia–General 55; Australia 14; Austria 7; Belize 3; Brazil 4; Bulgaria 7; Chile 16; Colombia 5; Cote d'Ivoire 12; Czech Republic 4; Ecuador 18; Ethiopia 2; France 18; Germany 10; Guam 4; Hong Kong 2; Hungary; India 8; Indonesia 9; Ireland 4; Italy 2; Jamaica 5; Japan 28; Jordan 2; Kenya 9; Korea, South 2; Mexico 43; Micronesia, Federated States of; Niger 2; Nigeria 1; Papua New Guinea 4; Peru 30; Philippines 7; Portugal 8; Romania; Russia 1; Senegal 7; Slovakia 2; South Africa 26; Spain 5; Sweden 4; Taiwan 8; Tanzania 2; Thailand 2; Uganda 4; Ukraine 12; United Kingdom 12; Virgin Islands 2

Mission To Unreached Peoples
P.O. Box 30947
Seattle, WA 98103-0947 USA
Phone: (206) 781-3151
Fax: (206) 781-3182
E-mail: davidh@gafi.wa.com
Web Site: www.mup.org
Mr. David M. Hupp, U.S. Director

An interdenominational sending agency of Evangelical tradition engaged in church planting, agricultural programs, mobilization for mission, relief and/or rehabilitation, services for other agencies and youth programs.
Purpose: "...to obey the Great Commission of Jesus Christ by investing our lives, gifts, resources and vocational skills in God's work throughout Asia and Europe...to model Christ so that the peoples of the world will come to worship and glorify His name."
Year Founded in US: 1982
Income for Overseas Min: $2,308,273
Gifts-in-Kind: $2,633
Fully Supported US Personnel Overseas:
  Expecting to serve more than 4 years: 69
  Expecting to serve 1 to 4 years: 14
Other personnel:
  Short-term less than 1 year from US: 46
  Non-US serving in own/other country: 8
  Home ministry & office staff in US: 19
  Bivocational/Tentmaker from US: 104
Countries: Cambodia 10; China 15; Hungary 4; India 8; Japan 6; Kyrgyzstan 1; Malaysia 1; Nepal 2; Philippines 2; Poland 2; Russia 3; Thailand 13; Vietnam 2

Mission Training and Resource Center
3800 Canon Blvd.
Altadena, CA 91001 USA
Phone: (626) 797-7903
Fax: (626) 797-7906
E-mail: phil@paraclete.net
Web Site: www.paraclete.net/lami
Mr. Phillip Elkins, President

A transdenominational service agency of Evangelical tradition engaged in missionary training, mission-related research and missions information service.
Year Founded in US: 1979
Income for Overseas Min: NA

Personnel:
  Home ministry & office staff in US: 16

Mission Training International

P.O. Box 1220
Palmer Lake, CO 80133 USA
Phone: (719) 487-0111
Fax: (719) 487-9350
E-mail: info@mti.org
Web Site: www.mti.org
Dr. Stephen Sweatman, President/CEO

A specialized agency engaged in missionary training, children's programs and furloughed missionary support.

Purpose: "Working together with churches and mission agencies to train and nurture Christians for effective intercultural service."

Year Founded in US: 1954
Income for Overseas Min: NA
Personnel:
  Home ministry & office staff in US: 10

Mission: Moving Mountains, Inc.

P.O. Box 1168
Burnsville, MN 55337 USA
Phone: (952) 440-9100
Fax: (952) 440-9104
E-mail: mmm@movingmountains.org
Web Site: www.movingmountains.org
Dr. Gary T. Hipp, President/CEO

An interdenominational sending agency of Evangelical tradition engaged in development, leadership development, management consulting/training, support of national workers and mobilization for mission.

Purpose: "...to facilitate the physical and spiritual well-being of impoverished people in developing countries."

Year Founded in US: 1978
Income for Overseas Min: $825,616
Fully Supported US Personnel Overseas:
  Expecting to serve more than 4 years: 21
  Expecting to serve 1 to 4 years: 7
Other personnel:
  Non-US serving in own/other country: 8
  Home ministry & office staff in US: 9
Countries: Kenya 3; Senegal 2; Tanzania 16; Uganda

Missionaire International

P.O. Box 474
Kimball, NE 69145-0474 USA
Phone: (308) 235-4147
Fax: (308) 235-4147
E-mail: serve@missionaire.org
Web Site: www.missionaire.org
Mr. Jon O. Foote, Director Operations

An interdenominational service agency of Evangelical tradition engaged in services for other agencies, training and aviation maintenance and flight training.

Purpose: "...to supply other mission organizations with suitable aircraft for use in their ministry of spreading the gospel and to train people for a career in missionary aviation."

Year Founded in US: 1987
Income for Overseas Min: NA
Personnel:
  Home Ministry & Office staff in US: 8

Missionary Athletes Intl.

P.O. Box 1889
LaMirada, CA 90637 USA
Phone: (714) 739-5060
Fax: (714) 739-5078
E-mail: vickie@seahorsesoccer.com
Web Site: www.maisoccer.com
Mr. Pat Stewart, CEO

An interdenominational specialized agency of Evangelical and Fundamental tradition engaged in soccer evangelism, Bible distribution and short-term programs. Statistical data from 1998.

Year Founded in US: 1983
Income for Overseas Min: $620,000
Gifts-in-Kind: $61,000
Fully Supported US Personnel Overseas:
  Expecting to serve more than 4 years: 9
Other personnel:
  Short-term less than 1 year from US: 60
  Home ministry & office staff in US: 3
Countries: Czech Republic 2; United Kingdom 7

Missionary Flights Intl.

P.O. Box 15665
West Palm Beach, FL 33416 USA
Phone: (561) 686-2488

Fax: (561) 697-4882
E-mail: MFI@missionaryflights.org
Web Site: www.missionaryflights.org
Mr. Richard Snook, President

A nondenominational support agency of Baptist and Evangelical tradition engaged in aviation and mail services for 125 mission organizations.

Year Founded in US: 1964
Income for Overseas Min: $2,000,000
Gifts-in-Kind: $10,000
Personnel:
   Home ministry & office staff in US: 17

Missionary Gospel Fellowship
P.O. Box 1535
Turlock, CA 95381 USA
Phone: (209) 634-8575
Fax: (209) 634-8472
E-mail: mgfhq@mgfhq.org
Web Site: www.mgfhq.org
Mr. John L. Harvey, Gen. Director

An interdenominational sending agency of Evangelical tradition engaged in multi-ethnic ministries of church planting, broadcasting, camping programs, correspondence courses and TEE in the USA, Canada and Mexico.

Purpose: "...to share the Gospel and to disciple various ethnic or unreached groups of people in or near the USA."

Year Founded in US: 1939
Income for Overseas Min: NA
Gifts-in-Kind: $20,000
Fully Supported US Personnel Overseas:
   Expecting to serve more than 4 years: 14
   Nonresidential mission personnel: 6
Other personnel:
   Non-US serving in own/other country: 5
   Home ministry & office staff in US: 4
   Bivocational/Tentmaker from US: 2
Countries: Cambodia; India 1; Mexico 13

Missionary Retreat Fellowship Inc.
R.R. #4, Box 4590
Lake Ariel, PA 18436 USA
Phone: (717) 689-2984
Fax: (717) 689-2984

E-mail: MRF65@juno.com
Web Site: www.missionary-retreat.org
Mr. Donald E. Schuit, Exec. Director

An interdenominational support agency of Evangelical tradition engaged in furloughed missionary support and services for other agencies.

Purpose: "...to provide the furloughing missionary with fully furnished housing...at subsidized rates."

Year Founded in US: 1965
Income for Overseas Min: NA

Missionary Revival Crusade
101 Kenya St., Ste. 106
Cedar Hill, TX 75104 USA
Phone: (972) 293-8181
Fax: (972) 293-8184
Rev. Roger J. West, President

An interdenominational support agency of Charismatic and Evangelical tradition engaged in church planting, audio recording/distribution, broadcasting, correspondence courses, evangelism and leadership development. Personnel data from 1998.

Year Founded in US: 1959
Income for Overseas Min: NA
Fully Supported US Personnel Overseas:
   Expecting to serve more than 4 years: 38
   Nonresidential mission personnel: 10
Other personnel:
   Non-US serving in own/other country: 52
   Home ministry & office staff in US: 2
Countries: Argentina 3; Colombia 4; France 4; Germany 3; Mexico 24; Spain

Missionary TECH Team
225 FRJ Dr
Longview, TX 75602-4703 USA
Phone: (903) 757-4530
Fax: (903) 758-2799
E-mail: Administration@techteam.org
Web Site: www.techteam.org
Mr. Birne D. Wiley, President

A nondenominational service agency of Fundamental and Evangelical tradition engaged in services for other agencies, short-term programs, technical assistance and literature production. Countries served vary by requests for specific services.

Purpose: "...providing technical assistance, 'know-how' and support services to mission organizations around the world."

Year Founded in US: 1969

Income for Overseas Min: $82,808

Gifts-in-Kind: $30,002

Fully Supported US Personnel Overseas:
Expecting to serve 1 to 4 years: 2
Nonresidential mission personnel: 2

Other personnel:
Home ministry & office staff in US: 1

Countries: Uganda

Missionary Ventures Intl.

P.O. Box 593550
Orlando, FL 32859-3550 USA

Phone: (407) 859-7322
Fax: (407) 856-7934
E-mail: info@mvi.org
Web Site: www.mvi.org

Mr. Steven G. Beam, President

An interdenominational specialized agency of Evangelical tradition engaged in partnership development, church planting, leadership development, medical work, support of national churches and short-term programs.

Year Founded in US: 1982

Income for Overseas Min: $3,457,271

Fully Supported US Personnel Overseas:
Expecting to serve more than 4 years: 50
Nonresidential mission personnel: 2

Other personnel:
Short-term less than 1 year from US: 150
Home ministry & office staff in US: 8
Bivocational/Tentmaker from US: 3

Countries: Australia 4; Bolivia 1; Colombia 1; Costa Rica 2; Dominican Republic 1; Egypt 1; Guatemala 5; Haiti 1; Honduras 3; India 1; Indonesia 1; Ireland 2; Israel 1; Marshall Islands 1; Mexico 2; Nepal 2; Nicaragua 4; Nigeria 1; Pakistan 1; Paraguay 1; Peru 4; Philippines 1; Russia 1; Uganda 2; United Kingdom 4; Zambia 1; Zimbabwe 1

Missions Resource Center

9452 Winton Road
Cincinnati, OH 45231 USA

Phone: (513) 522-2847

Fax: (513) 522-2846
E-mail: MarvinGrooms@xc.org
Web Site: www.ccmrc.org

Mr. Marvin D. Grooms, Director

A nondenominational specialized agency of Christian (Restoration Movement) tradition engaged in missions information service and mission-related research.

Purpose: "...to collect, store and disseminate to the local church and its support agencies, data related to the worldwide fulfillment of the mission of God..."

Year Founded in US: 1991

Income for Overseas Min: NA

Personnel:
Home ministry & office staff in US: 2

Missions Resource Network

4001 Airport FWY-Suite 550
Bedford, TX 76021 USA

Phone: (817) 267-2727
Fax: (817) 267-2626
E-mail: missions@MRNet.org
Web Site: www.MRNet.org

Robert T. Waldron, Exec. Director

A nondenominational service agency of Christian (Restoration Movement) tradition engaged in mobilization for mission, church planting, missions information service, member care, mission-related research and missionary training.

Purpose: "...to develop church-planting teams, equip sending churches, nurture missionaries and their families and advance strategic thinking and cooperation."

Year Founded in US: 1998

Income for Overseas Min: $95,000

Personnel:
Home ministry & office staff in US: 9

Missions To Japan, Inc.

P.O. Box 1203
Campbell, CA 95009-1203 USA

Phone: (408) 998-1768

Rev. Joe Weigand, President

A nondenominational support agency of Evangelical tradition engaged in support of national churches, Christian education, and evangelism.

Purpose: "...to promote fellowship, cooperation, protection, recognition and the propagation of, the Christian Gospel at home and abroad..."

Year Founded in US: 1959

Income for Overseas Min: $16,590

Fully Supported US Personnel Overseas:
Expecting to serve more than 4 years: 5

Other personnel:
Home ministry & office staff in US: 3

Countries: China 3; India 1; Philippines 1

Missions to Military, Inc.

P. O. Box 6
Norfolk, VA 23321 USA

Phone: (757) 479-2288
Fax: (757) 479-3705
E-mail: hq@mtmi.org
Web Site: www.mtmi.org

Dr. Keith H. Davey, President

A sending agency of Independent Baptist tradition engaged in operating military Christian centers for active military personnel.

Year Founded in US: 1958

Income for Overseas Min: $190,000

Fully Supported US Personnel Overseas:
Expecting to serve more than 4 years: 7
Nonresidential mission personnel: 7

Other personnel:
Short-term less than 1 year from US: 2
Home ministry & office staff in US: 6

Countries: France 5; Ukraine 2

MMS Aviation

24320 County Road 202
Coshocton, OH 43812-9618 USA

Phone: (740) 622-6848
Fax: (740) 622-8277
E-mail: admin@mmsaviation.org
Web Site: www.mmsaviation.org

Mr. Dwight Jarboe, President & CEO

A nondenominational support agency of Evangelical tradition providing technical assistance and training in mission aviation for others.

Purpose: "Preparing people and planes for worldwide mission service."

Year Founded in US: 1975

Income for Overseas Min: NA

Personnel:
Home ministry & office staff in US: 22

Moravian Church in North America, Board of World Missions

P.O Box 1245
Bethlehem, PA 18018-1245 USA

Phone: (610) 868-1732
Fax: (610) 866-9223
E-mail: bwm@mcnp.org
Web Site: www.moravianmission.org

Rev. Hampton Morgan, Exec. Director

A denominational sending agency of Ecumenical and Evangelical tradition engaged in support of national churches, church planting, theological education, funds transmission, leadership development and medical work.

Year Founded in US: 1949

Income for Overseas Min: $900,000

Fully Supported US Personnel Overseas:
Expecting to serve more than 4 years: 5
Nonresidential mission personnel: 2

Other personnel:
Short-term less than 1 year from US: 45
Non-US serving in own/other country: 2
Home ministry & office staff in US: 7

Countries: Asia–General; 3 Mexico 2

Morelli Ministries Intl.

Box 700026
Tulsa, OK 74170 USA

Phone: (918) 664-2552
Fax: (918) 447-9131
E-mail: michael@morelliministries.org
Web Site: www.morelliministries.org

Rev. Michael Morelli, Founder-President

An interdenominational support agency of Evangelical tradition engaged in support of national churches, church planting, evangelism, leadership development, literature distribution and supplying equipment in 7 countries. Statistical data from 1998.

Year Founded in US: 1995

Income for Overseas Min: $32,000

Personnel:
Short-term less than 1 year from US: 2
Home ministry & office staff in US: 3

Muslim Hope

1000 Franklin Road
Lebanon, OH 45036 USA

Phone: (513) 932-8121
Fax: (513) 932-8121

Mr. Donald S. Tingle, Director of Ministries

A nondenominational service agency of Christian (Restoration Movement) tradition engaged in evangelism, Bible distribution, literature distribution and relief and/or rehabilitation. Statistical data from 1996.

Year Founded in US: 1996

Income for Overseas Min: $45,000

Fully Supported US Personnel Overseas:
Expecting to serve more than 4 years: 3

Other personnel:
Short-term less than 1 year from US: 6
Home ministry & office staff in US: 3
Bivocational/Tentmaker from US: 4

Countries: Asia–General 1; Ukraine 2

Mustard Seed, Inc., The

P.O. Box 20188
Charleston, SC 29413-0188 USA

Phone: (843) 388-9314
Fax: (843) 388-9315
E-mail: info@themustardseed.org
Web Site: www.themustardseed.org

Mr. William N. Deans, President

An interdenominational ministry partnering with churches engaged in Christian education, agricultural programs, church planting, childcare/orphanage programs, theological education and medical work. Statistics from 1998.

Purpose: "...committed to reaching people throughout Southeast Asia by partnering with indigenous churches."

Year Founded in US: 1948

Income for Overseas Min: $737,951

Fully Supported US Personnel Overseas:
Expecting to serve more than 4 years: 7
Expecting to serve 1 to 4 years: 1

Other personnel:
Non-US serving in own/other country: 298
Home ministry & office staff in US: 8

Countries: Fiji; India 2; Indonesia 2; Mongolia 1; Papua New Guinea 2; Taiwan

Mutual Faith Ministries Intl.

P.O. Box 951060
Mission Hills, CA 91395-1060 USA

Phone: (818) 837-3400
Fax: (818) 837-4686
E-mail: info@mutualfaith.org
Web Site: www.mutualfaith.org

Keith Hershey, President/Founder

A nondenominational support agency of Independent tradition engaged in short-term programs for evangelism teams in Central America, Africa, Asia, India and other nations. Statistical data from 1998.

Year Founded in US: 1984

Income for Overseas Min: $250,000

Gifts-in-Kind: $100,000

Fully Supported US Personnel Overseas:
Expecting to serve more than 4 years: 2
Nonresidential mission personnel: 1

Other personnel:
Short-term less than 1 year from US: 24
Home ministry & office staff in US: 7

Countries: Costa Rica 1; Guatemala 1

Narramore Christian Foundation

P.O. Box 661900
Arcadia, CA 91066-1900 USA

Phone: (626) 821-8400
Fax: (626) 821-8409
E-mail: ncf@ncfliving.org
Web Site: www.ncfliving.org

Dr. Clyde M. Narramore, Founder

A nondenominational specialized agency of Evangelical tradition providing crisis counseling and seminars for missionaries on location throughout the world and post high school children in the USA.

Year Founded in US: 1955

Income for Overseas Min: NA

Personnel:
Home ministry & office staff in US: 9

National Baptist Convention of America, Foreign Mission Board

P.O. Box 223665
Dallas, TX 75222 USA

Phone: (214) 942-3311

Experience
Nyack College

Nyack College
1 South Boulevard • Nyack, NY 10960-3698
1-800-33-NYACK • Fax: 845-358-3047
enroll@nyack.edu • www.nyackcollege.edu

Nyack College was founded in 1882 as the Missionary Training Institute, the first Bible college in North America. Nyack College's founder, Dr. A.B. Simpson, is widely recognized as one of the foremost figures in the American missionary movement. Today Nyack College, an accredited liberal arts college, continues to fulfill the vision of its founder. It is an educational institution rooted in the historic Christian faith, serving The Christian and Missionary Alliance, the church, the community and the world.

Nyack is unique in the multicultural mix of its students. Representing more than 30 countries and U.S. states and over 30 denominations, they come together in a common commitment to Jesus Christ. Students enjoy the flexibility of attending class in Manhattan or on the beautiful Rockland campus just a half hour north along the Hudson River.

Missiology can be taken as a major or minor and is one of more than 40 programs offered at *Nyack*. Missiology majors can specialize in Evangelism and Church Planting, Urban Ministries, Non-Christian Religions, Jewish Studies, or Teaching English to Speakers of Other Languages. Pastoral Ministry majors can choose from a number of concentrations including Evangelism and Church Planting and Urban Ministries.

A *Nyack* education is a life experience that urges spiritual growth, supplies opportunities for mission work, develops friendships for life and prepares students for a career and ministry.

More than 12 Nyack missions trips are planned for 2004!

Fax: (214) 943-4924

Rev. David A. Rooks, Interim Director

A denominational support agency of Baptist tradition engaged in evangelism, church construction, Christian education, funds transmission and support of national workers. Statistical data from 1998.

Purpose: "...operates as 'partner in ministry' with indigenous Christians and church bodies."

Year Founded in US: 1915

Income for Overseas Min: $222,071

Personnel:
  Short-term less than 1 year from US: 26
  Non-US serving in own/other country: 87
  Home ministry & office staff in US: 4

Countries: Ghana; Haiti; Jamaica; Panama; Virgin Islands

National Baptist Convention USA, Inc., Foreign Mission Bd.

P.O. Box 15783
Philadelphia, PA 19103 USA
Phone: (215) 735-7868
Fax: (215) 735-1721
E-mail: fmbnbc@comcast.net
Web Site: www.fmbusainc.org

Rev. Charles Walker, Exec. Secretary

A denominational sending agency of Baptist tradition engaged in evangelism, church construction, church planting, Christian education, furloughed missionary support and providing medical supplies.

Purpose: "...to accomplish the Great Commission by training ministers and mission workers and providing health services and occupational training and services at each mission station with the goal of self-sufficiency."

Year Founded in US: 1880

Income for Overseas Min: $793,787

Fully Supported US Personnel Overseas:
  Expecting to serve more than 4 years: 1
  Expecting to serve 1 to 4 years: 2

Other personnel:
  Non-US serving in own/other country: 7
  Home ministry & office staff in US: 6

Countries: Bahamas, The; Barbados; Guinea 1; Lesotho; Malawi; Nicaragua; Sierra Leone; South Africa; Swaziland; Zambia

National Religious Broadcasters

9510 Technology Dr.
Manassas, VA 20110 USA
Phone: (703) 330-7000
Fax: (703) 330-7100
E-mail: mglenn@nrb.org
Web Site: www.nrb.com

Mr. Michael T. Glenn, Exec. Vice Pres.

An interdenominational service agency of Evangelical tradition engaged in broadcasting, leadership development and training, including a Caribbean chapter and International Committee involving overseas associate members. Staff figure from 1998.

Year Founded in US: 1944

Income for Overseas Min: NA

Personnel:
  Home ministry & office staff in US: 17

Navigators, U.S. Intl. Missions Group

P.O. Box 6000
Colorado Springs, CO 80934 USA
Phone: (719) 594-2435
Fax: (719) 260-0405
E-mail: rod_beidler@compuserve.com
Web Site: www.navigators.org/usimg

Mr. Alan Andrews, U.S. Director

A nondenominational sending agency of Evangelical tradition engaged in missionary training, bible memorization, evangelism, leadership development, support of national churches, mobilization for mission and youth programs.

Purpose: "To reach, disciple and equip people to know Christ and to make Him known through successive generations."

Year Founded in US: 1933

Income for Overseas Min: $15,867,000

Fully Supported US Personnel Overseas:
  Expecting to serve more than 4 years: 207
  Expecting to serve 1 to 4 years: 52
  Nonresidential mission personnel: 29

Other personnel:
  Short-term less than 1 year from US: 280
  Non-US serving in own/other country: 84
  Home ministry & office staff in US: 85
  Bivocational/Tentmaker from US: 78

Countries: Argentina 6; Asia–General 4;

Australia 4; Austria 2; Brazil 10; Bulgaria 6; Cameroon 2; Chile 4; Congo, Democratic Republic of the 2; Costa Rica 2; Cote d'Ivoire 4; Estonia 4; France 2; Germany 1; Ghana 1; Hungary; Iceland 2; Indonesia 8; Italy 4; Japan 16; Kenya 4; Malawi 2; Malaysia 1; Mali 2; Mexico 10; Middle East 10; Mongolia 2; Morocco 4; Nepal 2; New Zealand; Norway 2; Philippines 7; Romania; Russia 40; Serbia and Montenegro 2; Slovenia 2; South Africa 2; Spain 8; Taiwan 8; Thailand 4; Ukraine 7; United Kingdom; Unspecified Country; Venezuela 2; Zambia 2

Nazarene Church World Mission—See: Church of the Nazarene World Mission Div.

Network of International Christian Schools

P.O. Box 1260
Southaven, MS 38671 USA
Phone: (662) 796-1830
Fax: (662) 796-1840
E-mail: info@nics.org
Web Site: www.nics.org
Dr. Joe Hale, Exec. Director

A nondenominational service agency of Evangelical tradition engaged in Christian education and evangelism.

Purpose: "...to establish a worldwide network of international Christian schools staffed by qualified Christian educators, instilling in each student a Biblical worldview in an environment of academic excellence and respect for people of all cultures and religions."

Year Founded in US: 1991

Income for Overseas Min: $767,346

Fully Supported US Personnel Overseas:
  Expecting to serve more than 4 years: 43
  Expecting to serve 1 to 4 years: 283

Other personnel:
  Home ministry & office staff in US: 11

Countries: Austria 8; Brazil; China; Ghana; Indonesia; Japan; Korea, South 21; Peru Singapore 4; Suriname; Thailand 10

New Directions Intl.

P.O. Box 2347
Burlington, NC 27216 USA

Phone: (336) 227-1273
Fax: (336) 570-1392
E-mail: ndi@newdirections.org
Web Site: www.newdirections.org
Dr. J. L. Williams, Founder & Director

A nondenominational support agency of Evangelical tradition engaged in partnership development, church construction, development, leadership development, support of national churches and support of national workers.

Purpose: "...encouraging, equipping and empowering indigenous national leaders to evangelize the unreached and edify the church in their respective countries."

Year Founded in US: 1968

Income for Overseas Min: $1,406,824

Gifts-in-Kind: $65,834

Personnel:
  Non-US serving in own/other country: 136
  Home ministry & office staff in US: 15

Countries: Bhutan; Ethiopia; Ghana; Haiti; India; Kenya; Nepal; Singapore; South Africa; Tanzania; Zimbabwe

New Hope International

P.O. Box 25490
Colorado Springs, CO 80936-5490 USA
Phone: (719) 577-4450
Fax: (719) 577-4453
E-mail: info@newhopeinternational.org
Web Site:
www.newhopeinternational.org
Mr. Hank Paulson, Founder/President

A nondenominational support agency of Evangelical tradition engaged in support of national workers, camping programs, evangelism, leadership development, training and youth programs.

Year Founded in US: 1972

Income for Overseas Min: $688,591

Fully Supported US Personnel Overseas:
  Nonresidential mission personnel: 2

Other personnel:
  Short-term less than 1 year from US: 100
  Home ministry & office staff in US: 9

New Life League International

P.O. Box 35857
Houston, TX 77235-5851 USA

Phone: (832) 242-7750
Fax: (832) 242-7751
E-mail: nlli@ix.netcom.com
Web Site: www.newlifeleague.org

Dr. David Depew, President

A nondenominational sending agency of Charismatic and Evangelical tradition engaged in Bible distribution, childcare/orphanage programs, church planting, development, evangelism, mobilization for mission and relief and/ rehabilitation.

Purpose: "...in partnership with local churches, to make disciples among the nations, to plant churches, to work for the relief of human suffering and to print the Word of God and distribute it to the nations of the world."

Year Founded in US: 1954
Income for Overseas Min: $728,595
Gifts-in-Kind: $8,000
Fully Supported US Personnel Overseas:
  Expecting to serve more than 4 years: 14
  Expecting to serve 1 to 4 years: 1
  Nonresidential mission personnel: 4
Other personnel:
  Short-term less than 1 year from US: 60
  Non-US serving in own/other country: 12
  Home ministry & office staff in US: 1
Countries: Bhutan; Brazil 1; China; Cuba; Guatemala 6; Haiti 2; India; Israel; Japan; Mexico 1; Nepal; Papua New Guinea; Philippines; Thailand 2; Turkey 2; Ukraine

New Tribes Mission

1000 E. First St.
Sanford, FL 32771-1487 USA
Phone: (407) 323-3430
Fax: (407) 330-0376
E-mail: NTM@ntm.org
Web Site: www.ntm.org

Mr. Oli Jacobsen, Chairman

A nondenominational sending agency of Evangelical and Independent tradition engaged in church planting, theological education, linguistics, literacy work, support of national churches, short-term programs, missionary training and Bible translation.

Purpose: "...to assist the ministry of the local church through mobilizing, equipping, and coordinating of missionaries to evangelize unreached people groups, translate

the Scriptures, and see indigenous New Testament churches established..."

Year Founded in US: 1942
Income for Overseas Min: $32,200,000
Gifts-in-Kind: $47,000
Fully Supported US Personnel Overseas:
  Expecting to serve more than 4 years: 1,417
  Expecting to serve 1 to 4 years: 79
Other personnel:
  Short-term less than 1 year from US: 135
  Non-US serving in own/other country: 148
  Home ministry & office staff in US: 480
Countries: Bolivia 97; Brazil 160; Colombia 55; Cote d'Ivoire 61; Germany 2; Greenland 1; Guinea 23; India 1; Indonesia 70; Korea, South 2; Malaysia 2; Mexico 84; Mongolia 7; Panama 80; Papua New Guinea 339; Paraguay 67; Philippines 104; Russia 18; Senegal 63; Singapore 4; Thailand 66; Venezuela 111

New Way Missions

14329 Western Riders Lane
Glen Allen, VA 23059 USA
Phone: (804) 798-6730
E-mail: mllaird@infi.net
Web Site: www.newwaymissions.org

Mary Lou Laird, President/Co-Founder

A transdenominational specialized agency of Evangelical tradition engaged in short-term programs, development, support of national churches, support of national workers, mobilization for mission and services for other agencies.

Year Founded in US: 2000
Income for Overseas Min: $8,000
Gifts-in-Kind: $1,500
Personnel:
  Home ministry & office staff in US: 2

No Greater Love Ministries, Inc.

P.O. Box 263
DuQuoin, IL 62832 USA
Phone: (618) 542-4503
Fax: (618) 542-4503
E-mail: NGL1FRED@midwest.net
Web Site: www.nogreaterlove.org

Rev. Fred L. Bishop, President

An interdenominational support agency of Evangelical tradition engaged in evangelism, leadership development and short-term programs. Statistics from 1998.

Year Founded in US: 1975

Income for Overseas Min: $10,000

Personnel:
Short-term less than 1 year from US: 2
Home ministry & office staff in US: 2
Bivocational/Tentmaker from US: 10

North American Baptist Conference Intl. Missions

1 S. 210 Summit Ave.
Oakbrook Terr., IL 60181 USA

Phone: (630) 495-2000
Fax: (630) 495-3301
E-mail: nabmissions@nabconf.org
Web Site: www.nabconference.org

Mr. Ronald D. Salzman, Intl. Missions Dir.

A denominational sending agency of Baptist tradition engaged in church planting, childcare/orphanage programs, church construction, theological education, medical work and mobilization for mission.

Purpose: "...to glorify God by making disciple-makers of Jesus Christ internationally on behalf of the churches of the North American Baptist Conference."

Year Founded in US: 1891

Income for Overseas Min: $3,858,000

Fully Supported US Personnel Overseas:
Expecting to serve more than 4 years: 36
Expecting to serve 1 to 4 years: 2

Other personnel:
Short-term less than 1 year from US: 56
Non-US serving in own/other country: 20
Home ministry & office staff in US: 9

Countries: Brazil 3; Cameroon 12; Japan 9; Mexico 6; Nigeria 2; Philippines 4

Northwest Medical Teams

P.O. Box 10
Portland, OR 97207-0010 USA

Phone: (503) 624-1000
Fax: (503) 624-1001
Web Site: www.nwmedicalteams.org

Bas Vanderzalm, President

A nondenominational specialized agency of Evangelical tradition engaged in medical work, children's programs, development, providing medical supplies and relief and/or rehabilitation.

Year Founded in US: 1979

Income for Overseas Min: $34,548,705

Gifts-in-Kind: $30,779,174

Fully Supported US Personnel Overseas:
Nonresidential mission personnel: 3

Other personnel:
Short-term less than 1 year from US: 546
Home ministry & office staff in US: 63

Countries: Afghanistan; Brazil; Burkina Faso; El Salvador; Honduras; Kosovo; Macedonia; Mexico; Moldova; Peru; Romania; Uzbekistan; Vietnam

OC International, Inc.

P.O. Box 36900
Colorado Springs, CO 80936-6900 USA

Phone: (719) 592-9292
Fax: (719) 592-0693
Web Site: www.oci.org

Dr. Greg Gripentrog, President

A nondenominational sending agency of Evangelical tradition engaged in leadership development, missions information service, mission-related research and missionary training.

Purpose: "...to assist the Body of Christ to make disciples of all peoples..."

Year Founded in US: 1950

Income for Overseas Min: $5,900,000

Gifts-in-Kind: $177,000

Fully Supported US Personnel Overseas:
Expecting to serve more than 4 years: 100
Expecting to serve 1 to 4 years: 54

Other personnel:
Short-term less than 1 year from US: 32
Non-US serving in own/other country: 56
Home ministry & office staff in US: 65
Bivocational/Tentmaker from US: 5

Countries: Argentina; Australia; Brazil 13; China; Germany 10; Greece; Guatemala 7; India; Indonesia 15; Japan 4; Kenya 4; Mexico 4; Nepal; Philippines 14; Romania 4; Singapore 4; South Africa 14; Spain 2; Taiwan 3; United Kingdom 2

Omega World Missions

P.O. Box 1423
Victorville, CA 92393 USA
Phone: (619) 241-2287
E-mail: fbrasel@aol.com
Rev. Frank Brasel, President

A transdenominational sending agency of Charismatic tradition engaged in support of national workers, church planting, leadership development and literacy work. Statistical data from 1996.

Year Founded in US: 1980
Income for Overseas Min: $166,000
Fully Supported US Personnel Overseas:
  Expecting to serve more than 4 years: 7
Other personnel:
  Non-US serving in own/other country: 15
Countries: Indonesia 2; Malaysia; Philippines 5; Unspecified Country

OMF International

10 W. Dry Creek Circle
Littleton, CO 80120-4413 USA
Phone: (303) 730-4160
Fax: (303) 730-4165
E-mail: OMFUS@omf.org
Web Site: www.omf.org
Dr. Neil O. Thompson, US National Director

An interdenominational sending agency of Evangelical tradition engaged in church planting, theological education, evangelism, leadership development and literature production.

Purpose: "...to see an indigenous biblical church movement in each people group of East Asia, evangelizing their own people and reaching out in mission to other peoples."

Year Founded in US: 1888
Income for Overseas Min: $5,000,000
Fully Supported US Personnel Overseas:
  Expecting to serve more than 4 years: 169
  Expecting to serve 1 to 4 years: 18
Other personnel:
  Short-term less than 1 year from US: 75
  Non-US serving in own/other country: 736
  Home ministry & office staff in US: 49
Countries: Asia–General 44; Cambodia 2; Hong Kong 3; Indonesia 15; Japan 20; Korea, South 4; Malaysia 1; Philippines 20; Taiwan 20; Thailand 40; Unspecified Country

OMS International, Inc.

P.O. Box A
Greenwood, IN 46142 USA
Phone: (317) 881-6751
Fax: (317) 888-5275
Web Site: www.omsinternational.org
Dr. J. B. Crouse, Jr., President

A nondenominational sending agency of Evangelical tradition engaged in church planting, broadcasting, TEE, evangelism, mobilization for mission and missionary training.

Purpose: "...to reach around the world with the good news of Jesus Christ...in cooperation with national churches..."

Year Founded in US: 1901
Income for Overseas Min: $15,311,000
Gifts-in-Kind: $891,244
Fully Supported US Personnel Overseas:
  Expecting to serve more than 4 years: 126
  Expecting to serve 1 to 4 years: 9
  Nonresidential mission personnel: 4
Other personnel:
  Short-term less than 1 year from US: 604
  Non-US serving in own/other country: 41
  Home ministry & office staff in US: 90
  Bivocational/Tentmaker from US: 28
Countries: Asia–General Brazil 7; Colombia 12; Ecuador 18; Haiti 6; Hong Kong 7; Hungary 1; India; Indonesia 6; Ireland 6; Japan 13; Korea, South 3; Mexico 14; Mozambique 8; Philippines 6; Russia 8; Spain 7; Taiwan 4

On The Go Ministries/ Keith Cook

P.O. Box 963
Springfield, TN 37172 USA
Phone: (615) 299-0222
Fax: (615) 299-0232
E-mail: keithcook@onthego.org
Web Site: www.onthego.org
Rev. Keith Cook, President

A transdenominational support agency of Evangelical tradition engaged in evangelism, leadership development, short-term programs, training and youth programs in 9 countries.

Year Founded in US: 1980
Income for Overseas Min: $200,000
Gifts-in-Kind: $100,000

Fully Supported US Personnel Overseas:
Nonresidential mission personnel: 12
Other personnel:
Short-term less than 1 year from US: 1,000
Home ministry & office staff in US: 12
Bivocational/Tentmaker from US: 4

Open Air Campaigners–
Overseas Ministries
P.O. Box 2542
Stuart, FL 34995 USA
Phone: (772) 692-4283
Fax: (772) 692-4712
E-mail: info@oaci.org
Web Site: www.oaci.org
Rev. David Wilson, International President

An interdenominational ministry of evangelism of Evangelical tradition engaged in
evangelism, short-term programs, training
and church planting. Each national branch
is autonomous, with national evangelists.

Purpose: "Committed to preaching the
gospel to the unreached through open air
and other outreaches in partnership with
the church."
Year Founded in US: 1956
Income for Overseas Min: $450,000
Fully Supported US Personnel Overseas:
Nonresidential mission personnel: 1
Other personnel:
Short-term less than 1 year from US: 45
Non-US serving in own/other country: 26
Home ministry & office staff in US: 1
Countries: Brazil; Ecuador; India; Jamaica;
Paraguay; Ukraine

Open Bible Standard
Churches, Intl. Ministries
2020 Bell Avenue
Des Moines, IA 50315-1096 USA
Phone: (515) 288-6761
Fax: (515) 288-2510
E-mail: missions@openbible.org
Web Site: www.openbible.org
Rev. Paul V. Canfield, Exec. Director

A denominational sending agency of Pentecostal and Charismatic tradition engaged in
church construction, church planting, TEE,
evangelism, leadership development and
support of national churches.

Purpose: "...exists to serve, equip and re-
source churches, missionaries and leaders
committed to global evangelism, disciple-
ship and church planting."
Year Founded in US: 1935
Income for Overseas Min: $1,089,009
Fully Supported US Personnel Overseas:
Expecting to serve more than 4 years: 14
Countries: Argentina 1; El Salvador 2; Hun-
gary 1; Mexico 2; Papua New Guinea 4;
Philippines 3; Romania 1

Open Door Baptist Missions
1115 Pelham Rd.
Greenville, SC 29615 USA
Phone: (864) 297-7890
Fax: (864) 297-5222
E-mail: info@odbm.org
Web Site: www.odbm.org
Rev. John Burnette, Director

A sending agency of Independent Baptist
and Fundamental tradition engaged in
church planting, Bible distribution, evangelism, leadership development, literature distribution and support of national churches.
Statistics from 1998.

Purpose: "...to promote the work of Christ
in regions that have been closed to the
gospel or that presently have little or no
fundamental gospel witness."
Year Founded in US: 1990
Income for Overseas Min: $265,500
Fully Supported US Personnel Overseas:
Expecting to serve more than 4 years: 17
Other personnel:
Non-US serving in own/other country: 2
Home ministry & office staff in US: 15
Countries: Haiti 4; India; Israel 2; Lithuania 4;
Puerto Rico 2; Senegal 2; Spain 2; Taiwan 1

Open Doors with
Brother Andrew USA
P.O. Box 27001
Santa Ana, CA 92799 USA
Phone: (949) 752-6600
Fax: (949) 752-6442
E-mail: usa@opendoors.org
Web Site: www.opendoorsusa.org
Mr. Terry Madison, President/CEO

A support agency of Evangelical tradition engaged in Bible distribution, Christian education, evangelism, leadership development, literature distribution and technical assistance.

Year Founded in US: 1973
Income for Overseas Min: $4,213,133
Personnel:
Home ministry & office staff in US: 40

Operation Blessing Intl.

977 Centerville Turnpike
Virginia Beach, VA 23463 USA
Phone: (757) 226-3440
Fax: (757) 226-6187
E-mail: operation.blessing@ob.org
Web Site: www.ob.org
Mr. William Horan, President

A nondenominational relief agency that has helped more than 164 million people in 96 countries, distributing more than $500 million in goods. Engaged in hunger relief, medical aid, disaster relief, children's programs and community development that will make a significant, long-term impact. Operating methodology focuses on capacity building and collaboration between indigenously-staffed field offices and local indigenous partners (including other NGOs, government agencies, community-based social service agencies, and grass-roots relief groups). An affiliate of the Christian Broadcasting Network. Short-term data from 1998.

Purpose: "...to demonstrate God's love by alleviating human need and suffering in the United States and around the world."
Year Founded in US: 1978
Income for Overseas Min: $9,932,410
Gifts-in-Kind: $8,690,228
Personnel:
Short-term less than 1 year from US: 540
Home ministry & office staff in US: 41

Operation Mobilization, Inc.

P.O. Box 444
Tyrone, GA 30290 USA
Phone: (770) 631-0432
Fax: (770) 631-0439
E-mail: info@usa.om.org
Web Site: www.usa.om.org
Dr. Rick Hicks, President

An interdenominational sending agency of Evangelical tradition engaged in missionary training, church planting, evangelism, literature distribution and mobilization for mission.

Purpose: "...to motivate, develop and equip people for world evangelization, and to strengthen and help plant churches, especially among the unreached in the Middle East, South and Central Asia and Europe."
Year Founded in US: 1957
Income for Overseas Min: $11,000,000
Fully Supported US Personnel Overseas:
Expecting to serve more than 4 years: 178
Expecting to serve 1 to 4 years: 162
Nonresidential mission personnel: 6
Other personnel:
Home ministry & office staff in US: 139
Bivocational/Tentmaker from US: 10
Countries: Africa–General 7; Albania 2; Asia–General 14; Australia 2; Bangladesh 2; Belgium 8; Caucasus; Czech Republic 2; Egypt 6; Europe–General 11; France 2; Germany 2; Hungary 4; India 5; Ireland 2; Israel 4; Italy 2; Latin America–General 4; Mexico 2; Middle East 23; Nepal 4; Papua New Guinea 2; Russia 2; South Africa 3; Spain; Sweden 2; Turkey 12; United Kingdom 29; Unspecified Country 20

Opportunity Intl. and the Women's Opportunity Fund

2122 York Rd., Ste, 340
Oak Brook, IL 60523 USA
Phone: (630) 645-4100
Fax: (630) 645-1458
E-mail: getinfo@opportunity.org
Web Site: www.opportunity.org
Mr. Christopher A. Crane, Chief Exec. Officer

A service agency engaged in microenterprise development in 27 countries. Personnel information from 1996.

Year Founded in US: 1971
Income for Overseas Min: $19,400,000
Fully Supported US Personnel Overseas:
Expecting to serve 1 to 4 years: 18
Other personnel:
Home ministry & office staff in US: 27
Countries: Africa–General; Asia–General; Europe–General; Latin America–General

Oriental Missionary Crusade

P.O. Box 6336
Laguna Niguel, CA 92607 USA
Phone: (949) 582-5041
Rev. Ernest A. Reb, President

An interdenominational sending agency of Charismatic tradition engaged in church construction, literature distribution and training. Statistics from 1996.

Year Founded in US: 1958

Income for Overseas Min: $93,361

Fully Supported US Personnel Overseas:
Expecting to serve more than 4 years: 2

Other personnel:
Home ministry & office staff in US: 3

Countries: Philippines 2

Orthodox Presbyterian Church, Committee on Foreign Missions

P.O. Box P
Willow Grove, PA 19090-0920 USA
Phone: (215) 830-0900
Fax: (215) 830-0350
E-mail: info@opc.org
Web Site: www.opc.org
Mr. Mark T. Bube, Gen. Secretary

A denominational sending agency committed to the establishment of indigenous churches in the Presbyterian and Reformed tradition, primarily through the ministry of the Word. Actively engaged in church planting, theological education, evangelism and literature production/distribution. Medical ministries of mercy supplement the gospel proclamation.

Year Founded in US: 1937

Income for Overseas Min: $1,600,000

Fully Supported US Personnel Overseas:
Expecting to serve more than 4 years: 26
Expecting to serve 1 to 4 years: 5

Other personnel:
Short-term less than 1 year from US: 23
Nonresidential mission personnel: 2
Home ministry & office staff in US: 3
Bivocational/Tentmaker from US: 8

Countries: Ethiopia 2; Japan 8; Kenya 2; Korea, South 2; Suriname 2; Uganda 10

Outreach Incorporated

3140 Three Mile Rd. NE
Grand Rapids, MI 49525 USA
Phone: (616) 363-7817
Fax: (616) 363-7880
E-mail: info@OutreachMission.org
Web Site: www.OutreachMission.org
Mr. Mark A. Sigmon, Exec. Director

A nondenominational support agency of Evangelical tradition engaged in theological and global leadership development, through the Institute of Theological Studies (independent study theology courses) , Project Partnership (leadership initiatives) and the Van Broekiyoven Resource Center (church mobilization resources).

Purpose: "...to assist in the theological education of individuals preparing for church leadership and cross-cultural ministry."

Year Founded in US: 1966

Income for Overseas Min: $200,000

Personnel:
Home ministry & office staff in US: 6

Outreach To Asia Nationals

P.O. Box 2440
Winchester, VA 22604 USA
Phone: (540) 665-6418
Fax: (540) 665-0793
E-mail: missions@direcway.com
Mr. Otis S. Goodwin, Director

A support agency engaged in support of national workers, Bible distribution, theological education, literature distribution, support of national churches and translation work.

Purpose: "...to serve, train, equip and empower national church workers in Asia to plant evangelistic, disciple-making and reproducing churches among the different people groups."

Year Founded in US: 1986

Income for Overseas Min: $850,000

Fully Supported US Personnel Overseas:
Expecting to serve more than 4 years: 4
Expecting to serve 1 to 4 years: 16
Nonresidential mission personnel: 12

Other personnel:
Short-term less than 1 year from US: 120
Non-US serving in own/other country: 161

Home ministry & office staff in US: 11
Bivocational/Tentmaker from US: 2

Countries: Bhutan 2; Burma; Cambodia 2; China; Nepal; Russia; Turkmenistan; Uzbekistan; Vietnam

Overseas Council Intl.

P.O. Box 17368
Indianapolis, IN 46217-0368 USA
Phone: (317) 788-7250
Fax: (317) 788-7257
E-mail: octeam@octeam.org
Web Site: www.octeam.org

Dr. L. David Lewis, President/CEO

A nondenominational support agency of Evangelical tradition engaged in establishing partnerships between Western Christians and non-Western students and evangelical theological schools. Affiliated organizations in Australia, Canada, Europe, New Zealand and UK.

Purpose: "...help develop biblical Christian leaders equipped as pastors, teachers, evangelists, missionaries and lay leaders in their own cultural context."

Year Founded in US: 1974
Income for Overseas Min: $11,237,016
Gifts-in-Kind: $1,010,401
Personnel:
Home ministry & office staff in US: 31

Overseas Ministries Study Center

(See Ad on page 244)
490 Prospect St.
New Haven, CT 06511-2196 USA
Phone: (203) 624-6672
Fax: (203) 865-2857
E-mail: mailbox@omsc.org
Web Site: www.omsc.org

Dr. Jonathan J. Bonk, Exec. Director

A nondenominational study center of Evangelical and Ecumenical tradition providing education and related activities. Publishes the *International Bulletin of Missionary Research* and the *Dictionary of African Christian Biography* (web only at www.dacb.org).

Purpose: "...to strengthen the Christian world mission by providing residential programs for the renewal of missionaries and

international church leaders, continuing education in cross-cultural Christian ministries and advancement of mission scholarship through research and publication."

Year Founded in US: 1922
Income for Overseas Min: NA
Fully Supported US Personnel Overseas:
Expecting to serve 1 to 4 years: 1
Other personnel:
Short-term less than 1 year from US: 2
Home ministry & office staff in US: 18
Countries: Zambia

Overseas Radio & Television, Inc.

130 S. First St.
Arcada, CA 91006 USA
Phone: (626) 462-0880
Fax: (626) 462-0008
E-mail: susan@ortv.com
Web Site: www.studioclassroom.com

Susan Cheng, N. America Director

A support agency of Evangelical tradition engaged in audio recording/distribution, broadcasting and video/film production/distribution. Financial figures from 1998.

Year Founded in US: 1952
Income for Overseas Min: $145,000
Fully Supported US Personnel Overseas:
Nonresidential mission personnel: 3
Other personnel:
Non-US serving in own/other country: 270
Home ministry & office staff in US: 6
Countries: Brazil; China; Singapore; Taiwan; United Kingdom

Pan American Missions

P.O. Box 710097
Santee, CA 92072-0097 USA
Phone: (619) 444-3077
Fax: (619) 440-8333
E-mail: fjappe@cwnet.com
Web Site:
www.panamericanmissions.com

Mr. Fred Jappe, President

An interdenominational support agency of Baptist and Wesleyan tradition engaged in music ministries, Bible distribution, church planting and childcare/orphanage programs.

Purpose: "...ministers in Mexico and other Spanish-speaking countries of Latin America for the establishing and building up of indigenous churches."

Year Founded in US: 1960

Income for Overseas Min: $33,000

Fully Supported US Personnel Overseas:
Expecting to serve more than 4 years: 4
Expecting to serve 1 to 4 years: 1

Other personnel:
Home ministry & office staff in US: 2
Bivocational/Tentmaker from US: 2

Countries: Mexico 4

Paraclete Inc.

P.O. Box 6507
Mesa, AZ 85216-6507 USA

Phone: (480) 854-4444
Fax: (480) 854-4741
E-mail: info@paraclete.net
Web Site: www.paraclete.net

Rev. Don Parrott, President/CEO

A nondenominational support agency of Evangelical tradition engaged in missionary training, leadership development, management consulting/training, mission-related research, services for other agencies and technical assistance.

Purpose: "...to serve mission agencies and churches in their efforts to effectively plant churches among unreached people groups."

Year Founded in US: 1988

Income for Overseas Min: $75,860

Fully Supported US Personnel Overseas:
Expecting to serve 1 to 4 years: 6
Nonresidential mission personnel: 3

Other personnel:
Short-term less than 1 year from US: 5
Home ministry & office staff in US: 14
Bivocational/Tentmaker from US: 1

Countries: Central Asia–General; India; Nepal; New Zealand

Partners in Asian Missions

P.O. Box 53101
Birmingham, AL 35253-1011 USA

Phone: (205) 854-8418
E-mail: jfsharpe@mindspring.com
Web Site: www.pam-ee.org

Rev. Jerry F. Sharpe, Intl. Director

A nondenominational support agency of Independent tradition engaged in leadership development, church planting, evangelism, support of national churches and support of national workers.

Purpose: "...establishes strategic-level alliances with key regional leaders in order to develop cooperative projects and share evangelism training materials."

Year Founded in US: 1972

Income for Overseas Min: $88,220

Fully Supported US Personnel Overseas:
Nonresidential mission personnel: 1

Other personnel:
Non-US serving in own/other country: 50

Countries: Asia–General

Partners in Christ Intl.

P.O. Box 237
Tempe, AZ 85280 USA

Phone: (480) 731-9170
Fax: (480) 731-9166
E-mail: partnersinchrist@qwest.net
Web Site: www.partnersinchrist-intl.org

Mr. Jeff Brosman, Dir. Operations

A nondenominational sending agency of Evangelical tradition engaged in short-term programs, Bible distribution, broadcasting, TEE, theological education and medical work.

Purpose: "Bringing people together across geographical and cultural boundaries for ministry together as we impact the world for Christ."

Year Founded in US: 1986

Income for Overseas Min: $300,000

Fully Supported US Personnel Overseas:
Expecting to serve more than 4 years: 1
Nonresidential mission personnel: 1

Other personnel:
Short-term less than 1 year from US: 1
Non-US serving in own/other country: 4
Home ministry & office staff in US: 1

Countries: Mexico 1

Partners International

(See Ad on page 247)
1313 N. Atlantic St., Ste 4000
Spokane, WA 99201 USA

Phone: (800) 966-5515
Fax: (509) 343-4015
E-mail: info@partnersintl.org
Web Site: www.partnersintl.org

Rev. Paul-Gordon Chandler, President/CEO

A nondenominational support agency of Evangelical tradition engaged in church planting, development, leadership development, management consulting/training, support of national workers and technical assistance. Income figure from 1998.

Purpose: "...to multiply the effectiveness of indigenous Christian ministries who are taking Christ to neglected peoples around the world."

Year Founded in US: 1943
Income for Overseas Min: $7,901,493
Gifts-in-Kind: $2,350,000
Fully Supported US Personnel Overseas:
 Nonresidential mission personnel: 17
Other personnel:
 Short-term less than 1 year from US: 14
 Non-US serving in own/other country: 4,700
 Home ministry & office staff in US: 38
Countries: Bangladesh; Bolivia; Cambodia; China; Cote d'Ivoire; Cuba; Egypt; Ghana; Guatemala; Hong Kong; India; Indonesia; Iran; Iraq; Jordan; Korea, South; Laos; Lebanon; Liberia; Macau; Macedonia; Malaysia; Mali; Malta; Myanmar/Burma; Nepal; Pakistan; Philippines; Senegal; Singapore; South Africa; Sudan; Syria; Taiwan; Tanzania; Thailand; Turkey; Unspecified Country; Vietnam

Pass the Torch Ministries

P.O. Box 7392
Bismarck, ND 58507 USA

Phone: (701) 223-6117
Fax: (701) 255-0541
E-mail: ptm@btinet.net

Mr. Greg S. Runyon, President

An interdenominational support agency of Charismatic tradition engaged in training, church planting, evangelism and short-term programs.

Year Founded in US: 1987
Income for Overseas Min: $7,735
Personnel:
 Short-term less than 1 year from US: 12
 Home ministry & office staff in US: 4

Pentecostal Church of God, World Missions Department

P.O. Box 2248
Joplin, MO 64803 USA

Phone: (417) 624-7050
Fax: (417) 624-7102
E-mail: wm@pcg.org
Web Site: www.pcg.org

Dr. Phil L. Redding, Gen. Superintendent

A denominational sending agency of Pentecostal tradition engaged in church planting, support of national churches, support of national workers, church construction, evangelism, and literature/Bible distribution. Statistical information from 1998.

Year Founded in US: 1919
Income for Overseas Min: $1,367,284
Fully Supported US Personnel Overseas:
 Expecting to serve more than 4 years: 32
Other personnel:
 Home ministry & office staff in US: 4
Countries: Africa–General 4; Belize 2; Bolivia 2; Haiti 2; Honduras 2; India 2; Mexico 6; Nicaragua 2; Philippines 6; Russia 2; Trinidad and Tobago 2

Pentecostal Free Will Baptist Church, World Witness Dept.

P.O. Box 1568
Dunn, NC 28335 USA

Phone: (910) 892-4161
Fax: (910) 892-6876
Web Site: www.pfwb.org

Rev. Dock Hobbs, Director

A denominational sending agency of Holiness tradition engaged in church planting, church construction, evangelism and support of national churches.

Year Founded in US: 1959
Income for Overseas Min: $131,840
Gifts-in-Kind: $52,000
Personnel:
 Home ministry & office staff in US: 4

Pentecostal Holiness Church See: Intl. Pentecostal Holiness Church World Missions

People International

P.O. Box 158
Vaughn, WA 98394 USA
Phone: (253) 884-1933
Fax: (253) 884-1934
E-mail: us@peopleintl.org
Web Site: www.peopleintl.org
Mr. Jim Roths, US Director

An interdenominational sending agency of Evangelical tradition engaged in church planting, development, evangelism, mobilization for mission, relief and/or rehabilitation and Bible translation. Financial figure from 1998.

Purpose: "...to see churches established that proclaim the Good News among the Muslim peoples of Central Asia and model true Christian living on the example of Jesus Christ."

Year Founded in US: 1992
Income for Overseas Min: $504,649
Fully Supported US Personnel Overseas:
  Expecting to serve more than 4 years: 27
  Expecting to serve 1 to 4 years: 5
Other personnel:
  Short-term less than 1 year from US: 6
  Home ministry & office staff in US: 5
Countries: Central Asia–General 27

Peoples Mission International

445C E. Cheyenne Mtn. Blvd.
Colorado Springs, CO 80906-4570 USA
Phone: (719) 531-9208
Fax: (650) 365-4194
E-mail: patelarryd@aol.com
Dr. Larry D. Pate, President

A transdenominational support agency of Evangelical tradition engaged in missionary training, management consulting and strategy development focusing on Christian missionaries sent from the non-Western world.

Year Founded in US: 1991
Income for Overseas Min: NR
Fully Supported US Personnel Overseas:
  Nonresidential mission personnel: 4
Other personnel:
  Non-US serving in own/other country: 4
  Home ministry & office staff in US: 1
Countries: Latin America–General; Unspecified Country

Perimeter Church, Global Outreach

9500 Medlock Bridge Pkwy.
Duluth, GA 30097 USA
Phone: (770) 582-6700
Fax: (770) 582-6709
E-mail: carlw@perimeter.org
Web Site: www.perimeter.org
Rev. Carl L. Wilhelm, Dir. Global Outreach

A denominational support agency of Presbyterian tradition engaged in church planting, theological education, evangelism and management consulting/training.

Purpose: "To facilitate movements of discipleship-based, saturation church planting in the United States and abroad by providing strategic, human and financial resources to Perimeter Ministries International and to nationals of other countries who share our vision for planting churches."

Year Founded in US: 1996
Income for Overseas Min: $799,817
Personnel:
  Short-term less than 1 year from US: 150
  Non-US serving in own/other country: 62
  Home ministry & office staff in US: 6
Countries: Albania; India; Russia

Peter Deyneka Russian Ministries

P.O. Box 496
Wheaton, IL 60189 USA
Phone: (630) 462-1739
Fax: (630) 690-2976
E-mail: mail@pdrm.org
Web Site: www.russian-ministries.org
Dr. Richard D. Scheuerman, President

An interdenominational support agency of Evangelical tradition engaged in literature distribution, camping programs, church planting, extension education, evangelism and support of national workers.

Purpose: "To promote indigenous evangelism, church planting and church growth in the former Soviet Union by developing creative and strategic ministries and facilitating partnerships between nationals and Western Christians."

Year Founded in US: 1991
Income for Overseas Min: $5,883,220

Gifts-in-Kind: $2,560,000

Fully Supported US Personnel Overseas:
  Expecting to serve more than 4 years: 3
  Nonresidential mission personnel: 2

Other personnel:
  Short-term less than 1 year from US: 8
  Non-US serving in own/other country: 404
  Home ministry & office staff in US: 13

Countries: Belarus; Latvia; Russia 3; Ukraine

Pilgrim Fellowship, Inc.

P.O. Box 557
Lebanon, PA 17042-0557 USA

Phone: (717) 867-1767
Fax: (717) 867-1767

Mr. William Martindale, Board President

A nondenominational support agency of
Fundamental tradition engaged in funds
transmission for mission workers involved in
audio recording/distribution and church
planting. Personnel information from 1998.

Year Founded in US: 1943

Income for Overseas Min: NR

Fully Supported US Personnel Overseas:
  Expecting to serve more than 4 years: 11

Other personnel:
  Non-US serving in own/other country: 3
  Home ministry & office staff in US: 11

Countries: Asia–General 1; Belgium 1; Brazil 5; Philippines 2; Spain 2

Pillar of Fire Missions Intl.

1302 Sherman St.
Denver, CO 80203 USA

Phone: (303) 839-1500
Fax: (303) 832-8560
E-mail: pillaroffiredenver@msn.com
Web Site: www.almatemple.org

Rev. Bernard Dawson, Director

A sending agency of Holiness tradition engaged in Christian education, church construction, theological education and
support of national workers.

Year Founded in US: 1960

Income for Overseas Min: $480,000

Personnel:
  Home ministry & office staff in US: 2

Pioneer Bible Translators

7500 W. Camp Wisdom Rd.
Dallas, TX 75137 USA

Phone: (972) 708-7460
Fax: (972) 708-7463
E-mail: PBT@pbtusa.org
Web Site: www.pbtusa.org

Dr. Rondal B. Smith, President

A nondenominational sending agency of
Christian (Restoration Movement) tradition
engaged in Bible translation, development,
evangelism, literacy work, support of national churches and mobilization for mission.

Purpose: "...discipling of the nations by:
Providing Scripture in the language of the
people. Developing mother-tongue literacy
programs. Establishing and strengthening
congregations. Training leadership among
nationals for partnership in reaching our
goals."

Year Founded in US: 1976

Income for Overseas Min: $2,245,982

Gifts-in-Kind: $29,954

Fully Supported US Personnel Overseas:
  Expecting to serve more than 4 years: 70
  Nonresidential mission personnel: 70

Other personnel:
  Short-term less than 1 year from US: 10
  Non-US serving in own/other country: 3
  Home ministry & office staff in US: 27

Countries: Guinea 27; Papua New Guinea
33; Tanzania 6; Ukraine 4

Pioneer Clubs

P.O. Box 788
Wheaton, IL 60189-0788 USA

Phone: (630) 293-1600
Fax: (630) 293-3053
E-mail: info@pioneerclubs.org
Web Site: www.pioneerclubs.org

Judy Bryson, President

A nondenominational service agency of
Evangelical tradition engaged in youth programs and camping programs.

Purpose: "...to serve God by assisting
churches and other ministries in helping
children and youth make Christ Lord in every aspect of life."

Year Founded in US: 1937

Income for Overseas Min: NA

Personnel:
Home ministry & office staff in US: 31

Pioneers

10123 William Carey Dr.
Orlando, FL 32827-6020 USA
Phone: (407) 382-6000
Fax: (407) 382-1008
E-mail: info@pioneers.org
Web Site: www.pioneers.org
Mr. Stephen L. Richardson, U.S. Director

An interdenominational sending agency of Evangelical tradition engaged in church planting, evangelism, leadership development and short-term programs. Statistical data from 1998.

Purpose: "...mobilizes teams to glorify God among unreached peoples by initiating church planting movements in partnership with local churches."

Year Founded in US: 1979

Income for Overseas Min: $8,506,522

Fully Supported US Personnel Overseas:
Expecting to serve more than 4 years: 317
Expecting to serve 1 to 4 years: 8

Other personnel:
Short-term less than 1 year from US: 155
Non-US serving in own/other country: 81
Home ministry & office staff in US: 38
Bivocational/Tentmaker from US: 10

Countries: Albania 3; Asia–General 172; Belize 3; Benin 2; Bolivia 8; Bosnia and Herzegovina 15; Central Asia–General 32; CIS–General 16; Croatia 2; Eastern Europe–General 9; Hungary 5; Japan 6; Lebanon 6; Mali; N. Mariana Isls 1; Papua New Guinea 14; Peru 8; Senegal 4; Thailand 11

PNMC Missions

19532 NE Glisan
Portland, OR 97230 USA
Phone: (503) 492-4216
E-mail: duncansmithpnmc@cs.com
Web Site: www.pnmc.org
Mr. Duncan Smith, Conference Minister

A denominational agency of Mennonite tradition engaged in support of regional churches for church planting, congregational outreach and overseas mission.

Year Founded in US: 1906

Income for Overseas Min: $12,000
Personnel:
Short-term less than 1 year from US: 2
Home ministry & office staff in US: 1

Pocket Testament League

P.O. Box 800
Lititz, PA 17543-7026 USA
Phone: (717) 626-1919
Fax: (717) 626-5553
E-mail: membercare@readcarryshare.org
Web Site: www.readcarryshare.org
Rev. John Kubinec, Assoc. Director

An interdenominational service agency of Evangelical tradition engaged in Bible distribution, correspondence courses, evangelism and literature distribution. Statistical data from 1998.

Purpose: "To assist and equip Christians worldwide in the effective proclamation of the Gospel of Jesus Christ through a coordinated program of Scripture distribution and evangelism."

Year Founded in US: 1908

Income for Overseas Min: $366,138

Fully Supported US Personnel Overseas:
Expecting to serve more than 4 years: 3

Other personnel:
Short-term less than 1 year from US: 60
Non-US serving in own/other country: 40
Home ministry & office staff in US: 21

Countries: Australia 1; Brazil; France; Germany 2; Indonesia; Mexico; Philippines; Poland; Portugal; Spain; Thailand; Yugoslavia

Prakash Association USA

43 Via Arroyo
Corralitos, CA 95076 USA
Phone: (831) 763-0189
E-mail: prakash4india@cs.com
Mr. Loren D. Eckhardt, Exec. Director

An interdenominational support agency of Baptist tradition engaged in training, agricultural programs, church planting, development and support of national churches.

Purpose: "...to support the training of nationals to become Christian businessmen and spiritual leaders...and carry out personal evangelism..."

Year Founded in US: 1973

Income for Overseas Min: $103,406
Gifts-in-Kind: NA
Fully Supported US Personnel Overseas:
Expecting to serve more than 4 years: 1
Other personnel:
Non-US serving in own/other country: 11
Home ministry & office staff in US: 2
Countries: India 1

Precept Ministries Intl.

P.O. Box 182218
Chattanooga, TN 37422 USA
Phone: (423) 892-6814
Fax: (423) 894-2449
E-mail: info@precept.org
Web Site: www.precept.org
Mr. Jack Arthur, President/CEO

A transdenominational sending agency of Evangelical and Independent tradition engaged in extension education, broadcasting, leadership development, literature distribution, literature production and training.
Year Founded in US: 1970
Income for Overseas Min: $1,503,140
Gifts-in-Kind: $63,000
Fully Supported US Personnel Overseas:
Expecting to serve more than 4 years: 2
Other personnel:
Non-US serving in own/other country: 90
Countries: Australia; Austria 1; Bahamas, The; Bolivia; Brazil; Bulgaria; Colombia; Costa Rica; El Salvador; Estonia; Germany; Guatemala; India; Korea, South; Mexico; Moldova; Nigeria; Peru; Philippines; Russia; Serbia and Montenegro; Slovakia; South Africa; Spain 1; Taiwan; Ukraine; United Kingdom; Uzbekistan; Venezuela

Precious Seed Ministries

Rte. 27, Box 5510
Mission, TX 78572 USA
Phone: (956) 585-9966
Fax: (956) 585-9966
E-mail: wyman1@msn.com
Wyman Pylant, President

A nondenominational support agency of Charismatic tradition engaged in childcare/orphanage programs, church planting, evangelism, support of national workers and short-term programs.
Year Founded in US: 1985
Income for Overseas Min: $30,000
Gifts-in-Kind: NA
Fully Supported US Personnel Overseas:
Expecting to serve more than 4 years: 5
Other personnel:
Non-US serving in own/other country: 3
Home ministry & office staff in US: 3
Countries: Mexico 5

Presbyterian Center for Mission Studies

1605 Elizabeth St.
Pasadena, CA 91104 USA
Phone: (626) 398-2468
Fax: (626) 398-2391
E-mail: pcms@pcusa.org
Web Site: www.pcms.ws
Mr. Larry Beckler, Exec. Director

A denominational support agency of Presbyterian tradition engaged in mobilization for mission and Christian education.
Purpose: "...to greatly multiply the mission efforts of individual, congregations, and the Presbyterian Church (USA) toward completing the task of world evangelization."
Year Founded in US: 1972
Income for Overseas Min: NA
Personnel:
Home ministry & office staff in US: 3

Presbyterian Church (USA) Worldwide Ministries

100 Witherspoon St.
Louisville, KY 40202 USA
Phone: (888) 728-7228
Fax: (502) 569-8039
E-mail: tchrappa@pcusa.org
Web Site: www.pcusa.org/pcusa/wmd
Dr. Marian McClure, Director

A denominational sending agency of Presbyterian tradition engaged in support of national churches, church planting, development, Christian education, evangelism, leadership development and medical work. Statistical data from 1996.
Purpose: "...to share the transforming power of the Gospel of Jesus Christ and to

carry out this mission by being committed to the whole church, the whole Gospel and the whole inhabited earth...assist the church in the quest for Christian unity and ecumenical commitment...nourish and strengthen the global perspective and mission effort of the General Assembly Council, the Divisions and the church-at-large."

Year Founded in US: 1837

Income for Overseas Min: $40,107,046

Fully Supported US Personnel Overseas:
Expecting to serve more than 4 years: 368
Expecting to serve 1 to 4 years: 404

Other personnel:
Short-term less than 1 year from US: 150
Home ministry & office staff in US: 100
Bivocational/Tentmaker from US: 60

Countries: Albania 7; Argentina 13; Australia 2; Bangladesh 6; Belgium 3; Brazil 14; Cameroon 4; Chile 7; China 4; Colombia 7; Congo, Democratic Republic of the 12; Costa Rica 4; Croatia 2; Dominican Republic 3; Egypt 13; Ethiopia 4; Fiji 2; France 2; Germany 2; Ghana 4; Guatemala 14; Haiti 6; Honduras 9; Hong Kong 9; India; Indonesia 14; Israel 4; Italy 2; Jamaica 5; Japan 4; Kazakhstan 4; Kenya 11; Korea, South 6; Kyrgyzstan 6; Lebanon 3; Lesotho 2; Lithuania 2; Madagascar 3; Malawi 9; Mauritius 2; Mexico 4; Mozambique 2; Nepal 10; New Zealand 4; Nicaragua 4; Pakistan 20; Papua New Guinea 3; Philippines 4; Poland 2; Portugal 2; Romania 5; Russia 7; Slovakia 4; South Africa 6; Spain 4; Sri Lanka 2; Sudan 10; Taiwan 9; Thailand 10; Turkey 2; United Kingdom 11; Uzbekistan; Venezuela 2; Vietnam 4; Zambia 5; Zimbabwe 2

Presbyterian Church in America—See: Mission to the World (PCA)

Presbyterian Evangelistic Fellowship

P.O. Box 1890
Decatur, GA 30031 USA

Phone: (404) 244-0740
Fax: (404) 244-0914
E-mail: admin@pefministry.org
Web Site: www.pefministry.org

Rev. Rick Light, Exec. Director

An interdenominational sending agency of Presbyterian and Reformed tradition engaged in evangelism, camping programs, literature distribution, support of national workers and youth programs. Overseas personnel data from 1998.

Purpose: "...to practice, train and equip God's people to do Biblical evangelism, anywhere, anytime, with anyone."

Year Founded in US: 1958

Income for Overseas Min: $1,000,000

Fully Supported US Personnel Overseas:
Expecting to serve more than 4 years: 47

Other personnel:
Non-US serving in own/other country: 24
Home ministry & office staff in US: 8
Bivocational/Tentmaker from US: 49

Countries: Bulgaria 2; Chile 1; Costa Rica 1; Europe–General 9; France 5; Greece 1; India; Japan 2; Kazakhstan 1; Kenya 2; Latin America–General 2; Liberia; Mexico 8; Nigeria 1; Peru 4; Russia 2; Uganda 2; United Kingdom 4

Presbyterian Missionary Union

1650 Love Rd
Grand Island, NY 14072-2311 USA

Phone: (727) 773-8003
E-mail: webmaster@bpc.org
Web Site: www.bpc.org

A denominational sending agency of Presbyterian tradition engaged in support of national churches, Bible distribution, funds transmission and literature distribution. Financial figure from 1996.

Purpose: "...to establish and strengthen indigenous Bible believing churches, related institutions and works agreeable to the (Westminster) doctrinal standards and principles of (Presbyterian) church government."

Year Founded in US: 1985

Income for Overseas Min: $50,400

Personnel:
Home ministry & office staff in US: 2

Presbyterian Order for World Evangelization

1469 Bresee Ave.
Pasadena, CA 91104 USA

Phone: (626) 794-5544
Fax: (626) 794-6655

Mr. Robert Blincoe, Gen. Director

A denominational support agency of Evangelical tradition engaged in mobilization for mission.

Purpose: "...attracting, coordinating, sponsoring, managing and establishing whatever project, activities, program or organizations that contribute strategically toward the fulfillment of the Great Commission."

Year Founded in US: 1974

Income for Overseas Min: $20,000

Primitive Methodist Church in the USA, International Mission Board

33 W. Barrows St.
Cumberland, RI 02864-7404 USA

Phone: (215) 675-2639
Fax: (215) 675-1576
E-mail: fjeffrey@juno.com
Web Site:
www.primitivemethodistchurch.org

Rev. Fred Jeffrey, Dir. Intl. Mission Board

A denominational sending agency of Wesleyan and Methodist tradition engaged in support of national churches, church planting, correspondence courses, theological education, TEE and medical work. Financial figure from 1998.

Year Founded in US: 1922

Income for Overseas Min: $455,000

Fully Supported US Personnel Overseas:
  Expecting to serve more than 4 years: 7
Countries: Dominican Republic 2; Guatemala 5

Priority One International

555 Republic Dr. #510
Plano, TX 75074 USA

Phone: (972) 423-3800
Fax: (972) 422-7535
E-mail: info@priorityonetv.com
Web Site: www.priorityonetv.com

Marty Mosley, President

A nondenominational service agency of Baptist tradition producing mission-related videos for mobilization and offering video production services to mission agencies.

Purpose: "...bringing awareness, focus and vision to the cause of world missions within the local church in order to mobilize Christian young people and adults for missionary service."

Year Founded in US: 1979

Income for Overseas Min: $340,000

Gifts-in-Kind: $340,000

Personnel:
  Home ministry & office staff in US: 50

Prison Mission Association

P.O. Box 2300
Port Orchard, WA 98366 USA

Phone: (360) 876-0918
E-mail: pma@pmabcf.org
Web Site: www.pmabcf.org

Dr. Donald Sommer, Director

A nondenominational support agency engaged in correspondence courses, Bible distribution, evangelism, literature distribution and literature production to prison inmates and others.

Year Founded in US: 1955

Income for Overseas Min: $4,000

Fully Supported US Personnel Overseas:
  Nonresidential mission personnel: 1

Other personnel:
  Non-US serving in own/other country: 1
  Home ministry & office staff in US: 1

Countries: Cameroon

Progressive National Baptist Convention USA

601 50th St., NE
Washington, DC 20019 USA

Phone: (202) 396-0558
Fax: (202) 398-4998
E-mail: info@pnbc.org
Web Site: www.pnbc.org

Dr. Major L. Jemison, President

A denominational support agency of Baptist tradition engaged in supplying equipment, Bible distribution, church construction and children's programs.

Year Founded in US: 1962

Income for Overseas Min: NR

Progressive Vision

P.O. Box 2008
Laguna Hills, CA 92654-2008 USA
Phone: (949) 582-8600
Fax: (949) 582-8608
E-mail: info@progressivevision.org
Web Site: www.progressivevision.org
Mr. Marcus Vegh, President

An international Christian digital publisher and distributor, committed to developing resources for discipling nations in strategic languages of the world.
Purpose: "...to develop and distribute effective, digitally based, Christian leadership training resources in strategic languages of the world."
Year Founded in US: 1995
Income for Overseas Min: $700,000
Personnel:
Home ministry & office staff in US: 4

Project AmaZon

P.O. Box 913
Morton, IL 61550 USA
Phone: (309) 263-2299
Fax: (309) 263-2299
E-mail: dove@dpc.net
Web Site: www.projectamazon.org
Jeffrey Hrubik, President

An interdenominational sending agency of Evangelical tradition engaged in church planting, Christian education, evangelism, leadership development and medical work.
Purpose: "...fulfilling the great commission by planting nationally-led churches, focusing on the Amazon Basin."
Year Founded in US: 1986
Income for Overseas Min: $1,382,898
Fully Supported US Personnel Overseas:
Expecting to serve more than 4 years: 29
Other personnel:
Stort-term less than 1 year from US: 4
Bivocational/Tentmaker from US: 2
Countries: Brazil 25; Japan 4

Project Care

2034 S. 308th St.
Federal Way, WA 98003 USA
Phone: (253) 529-2644
Fax: (253) 529-2642
E-mail: projectcare@xc.org
Mr. Chuck Schukar, Director

A nondenominational support agency of Reformed tradition engaged in support of national workers, church construction, development, TEE, leadership development and supplying equipment.
Purpose: "Making disciples and assisting disciple makers."
Year Founded in US: 1991
Income for Overseas Min: $42,000
Gifts-in-Kind: $27,000
Personnel:
Short-term less than 1 year from US: 18
Countries: Czech Republic; Hungary; Poland; Romania; Russia; Slovakia

Project Christ International

124-08 Linden Blvd.
So. Ozone Park, NY 11420 USA
Phone: (718) 845-6992
Fax: (718) 845-6992
E-mail: ssamraj@juno.com
Dr. S. Samraj, President

An independent support agency of Fundamental tradition engaged in missionary training, Bible distribution, childcare/orphanage programs, church planting, missionary education, medical work, short-term programs and support of national workers. Statistics from 1998.
Year Founded in US: 1984
Income for Overseas Min: $52,000
Fully Supported US Personnel Overseas:
Nonresidential mission personnel: 1
Other personnel:
Non-US serving in own/other country: 127
Countries: India; Nepal

Project Mercy, Inc.

7011 Ardmore Ave.
Fort Wayne, IN 46809 USA
Phone: (260) 747-2559
Fax: (260) 478-1361
E-mail: pminfo@projectmercy.org
Web Site: www.projectmercy.org
Marta Gabre-Tsadick, Exec. Director

An interdenominational agency engaged in

community development and evangelism in Ethiopia, Sudan and Djibouti.

Purpose: "...providing aid, comfort and support to those in need anywhere in Africa...also participates to alleviate human suffering anywhere in the world in the name of Jesus Christ."

Year Founded in US: 1977

Income for Overseas Min: $2,198,420

Fully Supported US Personnel Overseas:
Expecting to serve more than 4 years: 2
Nonresidential mission personnel: 2

Other personnel:
Non-US serving in own/other country: 51
Home ministry & office staff in US: 6

Countries: Djibouti; Ethiopia 2; Sudan

Project Partner with Christ

P.O. Box 610
Springboro, OH 45066-0610 USA
Phone: (513) 425-0938
E-mail: partner@projectpartner.com
Web Site: www.projectpartner.com
Mr. Robert L. Gregory, President

An evangelical training ministry dedicated to the development of national-led ministries around the world. Statistics from 1998.

Purpose: "...provides opportunities for national leaders and effective Christian leaders and laity in the United States to develop interdependent partnerships."

Year Founded in US: 1984

Income for Overseas Min: $770,268

Fully Supported US Personnel Overseas:
Nonresidential mission personnel: 2

Other personnel:
Short-Term less than 1 year from US: 27
Non-US serving in own/other country: 4
Home ministry & office staff in US: 4

Countries: China; Costa Rica; India; Mexico

Providence Mission Homes, Inc.

P.O. Box 40727
Pasadena, CA 91114 USA
Phone: (626) 398-2487
Fax: (626) 398-2488
E-mail: PMHomesI@juno.com
Dr. Marvin Eyler/Rev. Vic Springer, Co-Directors

A support agency of Evangelical tradition

engaged in furloughed missionary support.

Year Founded in US: 1973

Income for Overseas Min: NA

Personnel:
Home ministry & office staff in US: 2

Radio Voice of Christ, Inc.

P.O. Box 7145
Beaverton, OR 97007-7145 USA
Phone: (503) 259-9422
Fax: (503) 649-3717
E-mail: info@rvoc.org
Web Site: www.rvoc.org
Mr. Richard B. Papworth, President

A specialized agency of Evangelical tradition engaged in broadcasting, evangelism and training.

Purpose: "to teach the Word of God to Iranians and other Persian-speaking people through the production, distribution and broadcasting of Persian radio programs and ongoing follow-up."

Year Founded in US: 1984

Income for Overseas Min: $172,563

Fully Supported US Personnel Overseas:
Expecting to serve more than 4 years: 1
Expecting to serve 1 to 4 years: 1

Other personnel:
Home ministry & office staff in US: 7

Countries: Asia–General 1

Ramabai Mukti Mission

P.O. Box 4912
Clinton, NJ 08809-0912 USA
Phone: (908) 735-8770
E-mail: muktil@eclipse.net
Rev. David L. Scott, Exec. Director

An interdenominational support agency of Evangelical tradition engaged in childcare/orphanage programs, outreach, education, medical work and support of national workers.

Year Founded in US: 1929

Income for Overseas Min: $245,000

Personnel:
Short-term less than 1 year from US: 4
Non-US serving in own/other country: 100
Home ministry & office staff in US: 3

Countries: India

Ramesh Richard Evangelism and Church Helps Intl.

5500 W. Plano Parkway #100
Plano, TX 75093 USA
Phone: (972) 733-3402
Fax: (972) 733-3495
E-mail: info@rreach.org
Web Site: www.rreach.org
Dr. Ramesh P. Richard, President

A proclamation ministry of Evangelical tradition engaged in pastoral training, TV/radio broadcasting/Internet and evangelism.
Purpose: "A global proclamation ministry, RREACH International implements God's calling on Ramesh Richard to proclaim the message of the Lord Jesus Christ worldwide, with a strategic burden for strengthening pastoral leaders and evangelizing opinion leaders of weaker economies.

Year Founded in US: 1987
Income for Overseas Min: $664,792
Personnel:
  Home ministry & office staff in US: 7

Raul Zaldivar Evangelistic Ministry

P. O. Box 8601
Northfield, IL 60093 USA
Phone: (847) 441-6861
E-mail: Rzministerio@aol.com
Web Site: www.rzem.org
Dr. Raul Zaldivar, President

An interdenominational service agency engaged in evangelism, broadcasting, TEE, leadership development, short-term programs and missionary training.
Year Founded in US: 1998
Income for Overseas Min: $40,000
Personnel:
  Home ministry & office staff in US: 3

Ravi Zacharias International Ministries

4725 Peachtree Corners Circle
Norcross, GA 30092 USA
Phone: (770) 449-6766
Fax: (770) 729-1729
E-mail: rzim@rzim.com
Web Site: www.rzim.org

Mr. Ravi Zacharias, President

An interdenominational specialized agency of Evangelical tradition involved in apologetics training with professionals, theological education, evangelism and leadership development. Statistics from 1998.
Purpose: "...to support, expand and enhance the preaching and teaching ministry of Ravi Zacharias, distinctive in its strong evangelistic and apologetic foundation, intended to touch both the heart and the intellect of the thinkers and opinion-makers of society..."
Year Founded in US: 1984
Income for Overseas Min: $1,000,000
Gifts-in-Kind: $500,000
Fully Supported US Personnel Overseas:
  Expecting to serve more than 4 years: 4
  Nonresidential mission personnel: 2
Other personnel:
  Home ministry & office staff in US: 26
Countries: India 2; United Kingdom 2

RBC Ministries

3000 Kraft Ave. SE
Grand Rapids, MI 49512 USA
Phone: (616) 942-6770
Fax: (616) 957-5741
E-mail: rbc@rbc.net
Web Site: www.rbc.net
Mr. Luis Seoane, Director IMO

A nondenominational service agency of Evangelical tradition engaged in radio and TV broadcasting in Spanish and English, literature production/distribution in more than 20 languages, and audio webcasting available worldwide wherever the Internet can be accessed. Financial figure from 1998.
Year Founded in US: 1938
Income for Overseas Min: $267,000
Personnel:
  Home ministry & office staff in US: 300

Reach Ministries International

P.O. Box 842
La Habra, CA 90631 USA
Phone: (562) 690-4252
Fax: (562) 690-5612
E-mail: reachmin@cosmoslink.net

Mr. Gene Tabor, Board Chairman

A nondenominational sending agency of Evangelical tradition engaged in evangelism, leadership development, support of national workers, missionary training, disciplemaking and intercultural Bible studies.

Purpose: "...to propagate the gospel of the Lord Jesus Christ and to promote aid and develop contextualized, holistic disciplemaking ministries in the Philippines and India with expansion to other countries and cultures as the Lord leads."

Year Founded in US: 1976

Income for Overseas Min: $213,034

Fully Supported US Personnel Overseas:
Expecting to serve more than 4 years: 5
Nonresidential mission personnel: 1

Other personnel:
Non-US serving in own/other country: 7
Home ministry & office staff in US: 3

Countries: India; Philippines 5

Reciprocal Ministries Intl.
14540 SW 136th St., Suite # 208
Miami, FL 33186 USA
Phone: (305) 233-9903
Fax: (305) 233-9907
E-mail: info@rminet.org
Web Site: www.rminet.org

Rev. Herbert L. Shoemaker, President

An interdenominational sending agency of Evangelical tradition engaged in support of national churches, church construction, Christian education, funds transmission and training.

Year Founded in US: 1988

Income for Overseas Min: $500,000

Personnel:
Home ministry & office staff in US: 4

Red Sea Team International
(See Ad on page 259)
P.O. Box 2047
Lexington, SC 29071-2047 USA
Phone: (803) 358-2330
Fax: (803) 358-2330
E-mail: hpbrasher@aol.com
Web Site: www.rsmt.u-net.com

Rev. Herb Brasher, US Director

An interdenominational support agency of Evangelical tradition engaged in evangelism, agricultural programs, church planting, extension education, medical work and Bible translation.

Purpose: "...to glorify God through our lives and testimony in order to proclaim the Gospel of Christ's redeeming love to Muslims."

Year Founded in US: 1953

Income for Overseas Min: $1,200,000

Fully Supported US Personnel Overseas:
Expecting to serve more than 4 years: 5

Other personnel:
Home ministry & office staff in US: 2

Countries: Africa–General 3; Asia–General 2

Reformation Translation Fellowship
302 E. 1st St.
Bloomington, IN 47401 USA
Phone: (812) 339-1922
E-mail: Bill4RTF@aol.com
Web Site: www.rtfchina.org

Rev. William Roberts, American Representative

A nondenominational service agency of Reformed tradition engaged in translation work, literature production and literature distribution.

Year Founded in US: 1950

Income for Overseas Min: $60,000

Reformed Baptist Mission Services
P.O. Box 289
Carlisle, PA 17013 USA
Phone: (717) 249-7473
Fax: (717) 258-0614
E-mail: arbca@reformedbaptist.com
Web Site: www.reformedbaptist.com

Rev. Robert B. Selph, Coordinator

A mission service coordinating member churches to assist one another to send missionaries and plant churches worldwide. Financial information from 1996.

Purpose: "...to provide to churches that hold to the London Confession of 1689, those services that will assist them in promoting gospel missions."

Year Founded in US: 1985

...reaching out

Our Task:

To make the Good News of the Lord Jesus Christ known to unreached Muslims

- Tangible love – serving people in the Muslim world through medical work, language schools, literacy work, and development projects

- Personal involvement – sharing the Gospel through many different means, for example the Jesus Film, literature distribution, etc.

- Practical faith – discipling Muslim background believers and encouraging indigenous church growth

Contact us at:	Red Sea Team International P. O. Box 2047 Lexington, SC 29071-2047 Phone and Fax: (803) 358-2330 E-mail: hpbrasher@aol.com
Or in Canada:	Red Sea Mission Team 7719 – 138th Street Surrey, BC V3W 6A4 Phone: (604) 596 7937 Fax: (604) 596 7926 E-mail: RSMTC@cs.com

Or look us up on the Web at:
www.rsmt.u-net.com

RSTI

$AVING CHURCH/MISSION WORKERS SINCE 1947

RAPTIM
-AFRICA-

RAPTIM
-ASIA-

RAPTIM
-CENTRAL AMERICA-

RAPTIM
-EUROPE-

RAPTIM
-ORIENT-

RAPTIM
-RUSSIA-

RAPTIM
-SOUTH AMERICA-

RAPTIM
-ANYWHERE WORLDWIDE-

www.raptimusa.com

RAPTIM TRAVEL
ALL YOU NEED TO KNOW...

TOLL FREE 1-800-777-9232 · FAX 1-800-766-2881 · E-MAIL: raptim@raptimusa.com

LEWISTON · NEW YORK · 14092

Income for Overseas Min: $301,517
Fully Supported US Personnel Overseas:
  Expecting to serve more than 4 years: 16
Other personnel:
  Non-US serving in own/other country: 9
  Home ministry & office staff in US: 3
Countries: Argentina 2; Colombia 2;
France 2; Ireland; Israel 2; Jamaica 2; Kenya
2; Mauritius 2; United Kingdom 2

Reformed Church in America, Gen. Synod
4500 - 60th St, S.E.
Grand Rapids, MI 49301 USA
Phone: (616) 698-7071
Fax: (616) 698-6606
E-mail: bmenning@rca.org
Web Site: www.rca.org
Rev. Bruce Menning, Director Mission

A denominational sending agency of Reformed and Presbyterian tradition engaged in evangelism, theological education, leadership development, providing medical supplies, support of national churches and relief and/or rehabilitation.
Year Founded in US: 1857
Income for Overseas Min: $7,228,541
Fully Supported US Personnel Overseas:
  Expecting to serve more than 4 years: 59
  Expecting to serve 1 to 4 years: 7
Other personnel:
  Short-term less than 1 year from US: 40
  Non-US serving in own/other country: 21
  Home ministry & office staff in US: 18
  Bivocational/Tentmaker from US: 27
Countries: Albania 2; Bahrain 4; China;
Cyprus; Ecuador; Egypt 2; Estonia 2; Ethiopia 4; Gambia, The 4; Honduras; Hungary
2; India 4; Japan 5; Kenya 6; Malawi 2;
Mexico 9; Nicaragua; Niger 2; Oman 2;
Senegal; South Africa 2; Sudan 2; Taiwan 5

Reformed Episcopal Board of Foreign Missions
316 Hunters Rd.
Swedesboro, NJ 08085 USA
Phone: (856) 467-1641
E-mail: westbj@rcn.com
Web Site: www.recus.org/bfm/index.html

Dr. Barbara J. West, Pres. Bd. Foreign Missions
A denominational sending agency of Anglican tradition engaged in church planting, medical work and Bible translation. Statistical data from 1998.
Year Founded in US: 1892
Income for Overseas Min: $176,338
Fully Supported US Personnel Overseas:
  Expecting to serve more than 4 years: 9
Other personnel:
  Short-term less than 1 year from US: 50
  Non-US serving in own/other country: 7
  Home ministry & office staff in US: 3
Countries: Brazil 1; France 2; Germany 2;
Uganda 2; Unspecified Country 2

Rehoboth Ministries, Inc
333 Hilliard Dr.
Fayetteville, NC 28311-8751 USA
Phone: (910) 630-3730
Rev. Pritchard Adams, III, President
A transdenominational sending agency of Pentecostal tradition engaged in evangelism, Christian education, theological education and leadership development. Statistics from 1996.
Year Founded in US: 1985
Income for Overseas Min: $63,270
Fully Supported US Personnel Overseas:
  Expecting to serve more than 4 years: 2
Countries: Haiti 2

Rio Grande Bible Institute
4300 S. Business Hwy. #281
Edinburg, TX 78539 USA
Phone: (956) 380-8100
Fax: (956) 380-8256
E-mail: rgbimail@riogrande.edu
Web Site: www.riogrande.edu
Mr. Bob Kracht, Interim President
An interdenominational service agency of Evangelical tradition engaged in theological education, correspondence courses, missionary education, training and video/film production/distribution. Personnel totals from 1996.
Purpose: "...serving the Hispanic church through equipping leaders, edifying believers and evangelizing the lost."
Year Founded in US: 1946

Gifts-in-Kind: $152,000

Fully Supported US Personnel Overseas:
Expecting to serve more than 4 years: 51
Expecting to serve 1 to 4 years: 8

Other personnel:
Home ministry & office staff in US: 90
Bivocational/Tentmaker from US: 5

Countries: Mexico 51

Ripe for Harvest, Inc.

P.O. Box 182184
San Diego, CA 92178 USA
Phone: (619) 435-0432
E-mail: rfhphoenix@juno.com
Web Site: www.ripeforharvest.org

Dr. Tim Smith, Exec. Director

A nondenominational sending agency of
Evangelical tradition engaged in evangelism,
Bible distribution, church planting, funds
transmission and literature distribution.

Year Founded in US: 1979

Income for Overseas Min: $570,673

Fully Supported US Personnel Overseas:
Expecting to serve more than 4 years: 61
Expecting to serve 1 to 4 years: 15

Other personnel:
Non-US serving in own/other country: 1
Home ministry & office staff in US: 6
Bivocational/Tentmaker from US: 40

Countries: Bolivia 2; Brazil 1; China 2; Colombia 1; Costa Rica 1; Cyprus 3; Denmark
1; Finland 2; France 7; Germany 2; Greece
2; Guatemala 5; Honduras 2; Hungary 2; India 2; Japan 2; Malaysia 2; Malta 1; Mexico;
Middle East 2; Nigeria 1; Peru 1; Philippines
1; Poland 1; Puerto Rico 1; Romania 1; Russia 3; Taiwan 1; Thailand 3; Turkey 2; United
Kingdom 4

Rock the World Youth Mission Alliance

P.O. Box 43
Ambridge, PA 15003 USA
Phone: (724) 266-8876
Fax: (724) 266-5916
E-mail: info@rocktheworld.org
Web Site: www.rocktheworld.org

Mr. Whis Hays, Exec. Director

A nondenominational support agency
of Episcopal and Evangelical tradition
engaged in youth programs, theological
education, evangelism, leadership development, mobilization for mission and short-
term programs.

Purpose: "Mobilize young people to make
an impact for God."

Year Founded in US: 1989

Income for Overseas Min: $38,000

Fully Supported US Personnel Overseas:
Nonresidential mission personnel: 1

Other personnel:
Short-term less than 1 year from US: 13
Home ministry & office staff in US: 7

Countries: Belize; Honduras; Peru; Nepal

Romanian Missionary Society

P.O. Box 527
Wheaton, IL 60189-0527 USA
Phone: (630) 665-6503
Fax: (630) 665-6538
E-mail: info@rmsonline.org
Web Site: www.rmsonline.org

Dr. Darrel Anderson, Exec. Director

A nondenominational sending agency of
Baptist and Presbyterian tradition engaged
in theological education, broadcasting,
camping programs, literature production,
support of national workers and relief and/
or rehabilitation.

Purpose: "...to support Christian projects
and ministries in Romania."

Year Founded in US: 1968

Income for Overseas Min: $568,000

Personnel:
Non-US serving in own/other country: 2
Home ministry & office staff in US: 5

Countries: Romania

Rosedale Mennonite Missions

9920 Rosedale Milford Ctr. Rd.
Irwin, OH 43029-9537 USA
Phone: (740) 857-1366
Fax: (740) 857-1605
E-mail: info@rmmoffice.org
Web Site:
www.rosedalemennonitemissions.org

Mr. Joseph Showalter, President

A denominational sending agency of Mennonite tradition engaged in church planting,
support of national churches, relief and/or

rehabilitation, short-term programs, youth programs and leadership development.

Purpose: "...to stimulate and facilitate Biblical, Spirit-led missions vision and action with local congregations to launch believers into Christ-centered evangelism, service and discipleship both at home and abroad."

Year Founded in US: 1919

Income for Overseas Min: NA

Fully Supported US Personnel Overseas:
Expecting to serve more than 4 years: 19

Other personnel:
Short-term less than 1 year from US: 22
Non-US serving in own/other country: 4
Home ministry & office staff in US: 23
Bivocational/Tentmaker from US: 9

Countries: Costa Rica 2; Ecuador 7; Germany; Mexico; Middle East 8; Nicaragua 2

Russian Bible Society, Inc.
P.O. Box 6068
Asheville, NC 28816 USA
Phone: (828) 681-0370
Fax: (828) 681-0371
E-mail: russianbibles@juno.com
Dr. Robert Doom, Director

An interdenominational specialized agency of Baptist and Fundamental tradition engaged in Bible distribution, literature distribution, literature production, Bible translation and translation work.

Purpose: "...to continue providing the 'Synodal Translation' of the Russian Bible...and its translation into many of the minority languages [of Russia]."

Year Founded in US: 1944

Income for Overseas Min: $105,437

Personnel:
Short-term less than 1 year from US: 10
Home ministry & office staff in US: 1

Russian Christian Radio
P.O. Box 1667
Estes Park, CO 80517 USA
Phone: (970) 586-8638
Fax: (970) 586-8317
E-mail: radiorcr@earthlink.net
Web Site: www.rcr.ru
Mr. Robert Poysti, Director

A specialized agency of Evangelical tradition engaged in broadcasting, audio recording/distribution, literature distribution and literature production.

Year Founded in US: 1982

Income for Overseas Min: $428,478

Personnel:
Home ministry & office staff in US: 5

Russian Language Ministries
P.O. Box 213026
Columbia, SC 29221-3026 USA
Phone: (803) 333-9119
Fax: (803) 333-9117
E-mail: rlmoffice@juno.com
Web Site: www.russianlanguage.org
Mr. Marc T. Canner, Exec. Director

An interdenominational service agency of Evangelical tradition engaged in training, missionary education, linguistics, and mission-related research.

Purpose: "...committed to furthering the cause of Christ among Russian-speaking peoples."

Year Founded in US: 1992

Income for Overseas Min: $10,400

Gifts-in-Kind: $8,400

Personnel:
Short-term less than 1 year from US: 6
Non-US serving in own/other country: 2
Home ministry & office staff in US: 17

Countries: Kazakhstan

Salvation Army, U.S.A.
P.O. Box 269
Alexandria, VA 22313 USA
Phone: (703) 684-5500
Fax: (703) 684-3478
E-mail:
NHQInformation@USN.salvationarmy.org
Web Site: www.salvationarmyusa.org
Commissioner Todd Bassett, Natl. Commander

A denominational sending agency of Holiness tradition engaged in evangelism expressed through worship services and social services including medical services, children's programs, development, adult training and disaster services in 108 countries. Statistical information from 1998.

Year Founded in US: 1880

Income for Overseas Min: $20,000,000
Gifts-in-Kind: $500,000
Fully Supported US Personnel Overseas:
  Expecting to serve more than 4 years: 96
  Nonresidential mission personnel: 98
Countries: Antigua 1; Brazil 4; Chile 6; Costa Rica 7; Czech Republic 2; Finland 5; Georgia 6; Germany 2; India 2; Italy 1; Jamaica 7; Kenya 2; Malawi 2; Mexico 5; Moldova 3; Philippines 2; Portugal 1; Russia 8; South Africa 2; Spain 2; United Kingdom 17; Zambia 7; Zimbabwe 2

Samaritan's Purse

P.O. Box 3000
Boone, NC 28607 USA
Phone: (828) 262-1980
Fax: (828) 266-1052
E-mail: usa@samaritan.org
Web Site: www.samaritanspurse.org
Mr. Franklin Graham, President
A nondenominational specialized agency of Evangelical tradition engaged in relief and/ or rehabilitation, evangelism, providing medical supplies, medical work, support of national churches and children's programs.
Purpose: "...specializing in meeting the needs of victims of war, poverty, natural disasters and disease while sharing the Good News of Jesus Christ."
Year Founded in US: 1970
Income for Overseas Min: $111,797,883
Gifts-in-Kind: $76,699,277
Fully Supported US Personnel Overseas:
  Expecting to serve more than 4 years: 1
  Expecting to serve 1 to 4 years: 18
  Nonresidential mission personnel: 8
Other personnel:
  Short-term less than 1 year from US: 709
  Non-US serving in own/other country: 15
  Home ministry & office staff in US: 381
Countries: Afghanistan; Bosnia and Herzegovina; El Salvador; Honduras; Kenya 1; Kosovo; Mongolia; Mozambique; Nicaragua; Sudan; Uganda; Vietnam

SAND International

P.O. Box 3937
Bartlesville, OK 74006 USA
Phone: (918) 331-9319

Fax: (918) 331-9319
E-mail: sand32@juno.com
Web Site: www.sandinternational.org
Mr. Don Sobkoviak, President
An interdenominational support agency of Evangelical tradition engaged in missionary training, agricultural programs, development and short-term programs.
Purpose: "Helping needy people everywhere to know and receive the Two-Handed Gospel."
Year Founded in US: 1982
Income for Overseas Min: $14,000
Personnel:
  Short-term less than 1 year from US: 2
  Non-US serving in own/other country: 5
  Home ministry & office staff in US: 2
  Bivocational/Tentmaker from US: 2
Countries: Cuba; India; Pakistan; Poland

SAT-7 North America
(See Ad on page 265)
P.O. Box 2770
Easton, MD 21601 USA
Phone: (410) 770-9807
Fax: (410) 770-9804
Web Site: www.sat7.org
Mr. Ronald Ensminger, CEO/Exec.
An interdenominational specialized agency engaged in broadcasting.
Purpose: "...a satellite television service...to serve the churches...present relevant television programs...mobilize related spiritual, financial and human resources for the [Middle East and North Africa) ."
Year Founded in US: 1997
Income for Overseas Min: $3,200,000
Gifts-in-Kind: $5,500
Personnel:
  Home ministry & office staff in US: 12

Seed International

P.O. Box 69
Merrifield, VA 22116-0069 USA
Phone: (703) 689-3133
Fax: (703) 689-3180
E-mail: email@seedusa.org
Web Site: www.seedusa.org
Mr. John Park, Exec. Director

They want to sing His praises.

Help teach them the lyrics.

For one dollar per viewer, *per year*, SAT-7® Christian television is changing lives in the Middle East.

At this critical juncture, when our eyes are turned toward the Middle East, SAT-7 is emerging as a dynamic force in touching the lives and hearts of millions of people throughout the Middle East and North Africa.

While illiteracy rates in this region range between 60 and 80 percent, 95 percent of the people own television sets, and more than 115 million have access to a satellite dish.

SAT-7 is not a rebroadcast or repackaging of content produced in the West, but culturally and socially sensitive Christian programming created, written and produced by Arabic-speaking Christians within the region. In addition to working effectively with indigenous churches, SAT-7 partners with Campus Crusade for Christ, the Bible Societies, and 35 other widely respected Christian agencies.

As the region grows and changes, so too does SAT-7—from 2 hours a week in 1996 to the current schedule of 12 hours of broadcasting a day, seven days a week, reaching eleven million viewers. Plans are to expand to 24 hours a day. But the continued growth and success of SAT-7 in encouraging minority Christians in their life and witness needs your support, both in the form of your prayers and your financial contributions.

To learn more about SAT-7, and to find out how you can help, visit our Web Site at www.sat7.org, or call us, toll-free, at **1-866-286-4027**.

Seeing Is Believing

SAT-7® North America • P.O. Box 2770 • Easton, MD 21601
Phone: 410-770-9804 • Fax: 410-770-9807 • Email: usa@sat7.org • Website: www.sat7.org

www.send.org

HOW WILL THEY HEAR, unless...

SEND INTERNATIONAL

Starting churches

Evangelizing the unreched

Nurturing disciples

Developing leaders

Romans 10:14,15

An interdenominational sending agency of Presbyterian and Independent tradition engaged in church planting, development, theological education, evangelism and leadership development.

Year Founded in US: 1990

Income for Overseas Min: $694,163

Fully Supported US Personnel Overseas:
  Expecting to serve more than 4 years: 30
  Expecting to serve 1 to 4 years: 7

Other personnel:
  Non-US serving in own/other country: 2
  Home ministry & office staff in US: 5
  Bivocational/Tentmaker from US: 2

Countries: Asia–General 4; Chad 2; Costa Rica 2; Croatia 2; Israel 2; Jordan 2; Kenya; Mexico 6; Thailand 2; Uganda 2; Uzbekistan 6

Self-Help International

805 W. Bremer Ave.
Waverly, IA 50677-2027 USA

Phone: (319) 352-4040
Fax: (319) 352-4820
E-mail: selfhelp@netins.net
Web Site: www.selfhelpinternational.org

Merry Fredrick, Exec. Director

An interdenominational service agency of Ecumenical tradition engaged in agricultural programs, development, extension education, technical assistance and training.

Purpose: "To train small-scale farmers... improve and maintain their farming and transport methods; train people in developing countries...increase crop yields and improve nutrition...cooperate with others in the introduction of appropriate farming practices ...and help the people of the United States understand the problems of life in developing countries."

Year Founded in US: 1959

Income for Overseas Min: $180,000

Gifts-in-Kind: $40,000

Fully Supported US Personnel Overseas:
  Nonresidential mission personnel: 5

Other personnel:
  Short-term less than 1 year from US: 4
  Non-US serving in own/other country: 6
  Home ministry & office staff in US: 2

Countries: Ghana; Nicaragua

SEND International

(See Ad on page 266)
P.O. Box 513
Farmington, MI 48332 USA

Phone: (248) 477-4210
Fax: (248) 477-4232
E-mail: info@send.org
Web Site: www.send.org

Dr. Frank M. Severn, Gen. Director

An interdenominational sending agency of Evangelical tradition engaged in church planting, TEE, theological education, evangelism, leadership development and support of national churches.

Purpose: "...to make disciples through evangelism, nurturing new believers and developing leaders while planting the church where it does not exist and serving it where it does."

Year Founded in US: 1947

Income for Overseas Min: $11,458,957

Fully Supported US Personnel Overseas:
  Expecting to serve more than 4 years: 208
  Expecting to serve 1 to 4 years: 14
  Nonresidential mission personnel: 10

Other personnel:
  Short-term less than 1 year from US: 282
  Non-US serving in own/other country: 46
  Home ministry & office staff in US: 88

Countries: Albania 2; Bulgaria 6; Croatia 5; Czech Republic 4; Germany; Hong Kong 4; Hungary 6; Japan 48; Macedonia 9; Philippines 25; Poland 12; Romania 2; Russia 15; Slovenia; Spain 8; Taiwan 17; Ukraine 28; Unspecified Country 17

Sending Experienced Retired Volunteers

P.O. Box 284
Elverson, PA 19520 USA

Phone: (610) 286-1978
Fax: (610) 286-1978
E-mail: JB_SERVE@prodigy.net
Web Site: www.serve-intl.org

Mr. Jennings B. Bunch, Jr., Exec. Director

An interdenominational specialized agency of Evangelical and Presbyterian tradition engaged in sending volunteer short and long-term teams overseas to countries including Kenya, Zimbabwe, Mozambique,

South Korea, Malawi and Peru. All volunteers pay their own expenses.

Purpose: "...to enhance the missions vision of retirees primarily and assist the church in building kingdom communities for worship and the glory of God worldwide."

Year Founded in US: 1993

Income for Overseas Min: $1,557

Personnel:
Short-term less than 1 year from US: 45

Sentinel Group, The

P.O. Box 6334
Lynnwood, WA 98036 USA

Phone: (425) 672-2989
Fax: (425) 672-3028
E-mail: info@sentinelgroup.org
Web Site: www.sentinelgroup.org

George K. Otis, Jr., President & CEO

A transdenominational support agency engaged in mission-related research, training and video/film production/distribution.

Purpose: "...helping the Church mobilize prayer and ministry resources intelligently during the latter stages of world evangelization."

Year Founded in US: 1990

Income for Overseas Min: $209,000

Personnel:
Home ministry & office staff in US: 13

Servants in Faith & Technology (SIFAT)

2944 County Rd. 113
Lineville, AL 36266 USA

Phone: (256) 396-2015
Fax: (256) 396-2501
E-mail: corsont@sifat.org
Web Site: www.sifat.org

Mr. Thomas Corson, Exec. Director

An interdenominational service agency of Methodist tradition engaged in training, development and technical assistance. Personnel information from 1998.

Purpose: "...teaching appropriate technology as a means of promoting self-help...to people in need."

Year Founded in US: 1979

Income for Overseas Min: $444,953

Gifts-in-Kind: $63,950
Personnel:
Home ministry & office staff in US: 11
Bivocational/Tentmaker from US: 15

ServLife International

P.O. Box 79675
Houston, TX 77279 USA

Phone: (713) 464-8400
E-mail: info@servlife.org
Web Site: www.servlife.org

Mr. Joel Vestal, President

An interdenominational support agency of Evangelical tradition engaged in support of national workers, church planting, development, funds transmission and support of national churches.

Year Founded in US: 1996

Income for Overseas Min: NA

Seventh Day Baptist Missionary Society

119 Main St.
Westerly, RI 02891 USA

Phone: (401) 596-4326
Fax: (401) 348-9494
E-mail: sdbmissoc@mindspring.com
Web Site: www.seventhdaybaptist.org

Mr. G. Kirk Looper, Exec. Director

An associational agency of Baptist tradition engaged in church planting, TEE, extension education, missions information service, leadership development, literature distribution, support of national workers, purchasing services, relief and/or rehabilitation, short-term programs and missionary training.

Purpose: "...to coordinate and carry out...the message of salvation through faith in Christ to all who will hear, so they may accept Him as Savior."

Year Founded in US: 1842

Income for Overseas Min: $85,000

Seventh-day Adventists General Conference

12501 Old Columbia Pike
Silver Spring, MD 20904 USA

Phone: (301) 680-6000
Fax: (301) 680-6090

Web Site: www.gc.adventist.org

Dr. Jan Paulsen, President

A denominational sending agency of Adventist tradition engaged in evangelism, church planting, Christian education, theological education, literature production, medical work, mobilization for mission, relief and/or rehabilitation and missionary training.

Purpose: "...to proclaim to all peoples the everlasting gospel in the context of the three angels' messages of Revelation 14:6-12, leading them to accept Jesus as personal Savior and to unite with His church."

Year Founded in US: 1863

Income for Overseas Min: $62,973,862

Fully Supported US Personnel Overseas:
   Expecting to serve more than 4 years: 314
   Expecting to serve 1 to 4 years: 259

Other personnel:
   Short-term less than 1 year from US: 1,524
   Non-US serving in own/other country: 542

Countries: Albania; Antigua; Argentina 2; Australia 4; Azerbaijan; Bangladesh 2; Belau; Benin; Bolivia; Botswana; Brazil; Burkina Faso; Burundi; Cambodia 4; Cameroon 2; Chad; Chile 4; China 12; Colombia; Congo, Democratic Republic of; Costa Rica 4; Cote d'Ivoire; Cyprus; Czech Republic 1; Djibouti; Dominican Republic; Egypt; Equatorial Guinea; Ethiopia 4; Fiji; France 2; French Guiana; French Polynesia; Gambia, The; Georgia; Germany; Ghana; Greece; Guam 45; Guinea; Guinea-Bissau; Guyana; Haiti 2; Honduras 6; India 4; Indonesia 6; Israel; Italy 2; Jamaica 4; Japan 8; Kazakhstan; Kenya 16; Korea, South 10; Kyrgyzstan 2; Laos; Lebanon 2; Lesotho 3; Liberia 1; Macau 2; Madagascar 4; Malawi 4; Mali; Marshall Islands 2; Mexico 22; Mongolia; Mozambique; Myanmar/Burma; N. Mariana Isls 8; Nepal 2; New Caledonia 2; Nicaragua; Niger; Nigeria 6; Norway 2; Pakistan 2; Papua New Guinea 4; Paraguay; Peru 4; Philippines 29; Puerto Rico 6; Russia 5; Rwanda 2; Saint Kitts and Nevis 4; Saint Vincent and the Grenadines; Senegal; Sierra Leone; Singapore 4; Solomon Islands; South Africa 3; Sri Lanka 2; Sudan 2; Swaziland; Switzerland; Taiwan 8; Tajikistan; Tanzania 2; Thailand 10; Togo; Trinidad and Tobago; Tunisia; Uganda 2; United Kingdom 5; Venezuela 2; Vietnam 2; Zambia; Zimbabwe 10

Share International

207 N. Service Rd. East
Ruston, LA 71270 USA

Phone: (318) 513-2535
Fax: (318) 513-2535
E-mail: shareusa@bayou.com
Web Site: www.shareinternationalinc.com

Sammy Murimi, President

An interdenominational support agency of Evangelical tradition engaged in support of national workers, mobilization for mission and training.

Purpose: "...challenging, training, sending, and supporting missionaries in partnership with the Church, with an initial emphasis on African nationals."

Year Founded in US: 1989

Income for Overseas Min: $154,419

Personnel:
   Short-term less than 1 year from US: 5
   Non-US serving in own/other country: 9
   Home ministry & office staff in US: 1

Countries: Kenya

Shelter for Life International, Inc.

P.O. Box 1306
Oshkosh, WI 54902 USA

Phone: (920) 426-1207
Fax: (920) 426-4321
E-mail: info@shelter.org
Web Site: www.shelter.org

Mr. Norm Leatherwood, Exec. Director

A Christian relief and development agency committed to serving refugees and the poor all over the world, regardless of race, religion or country of origin. Personnel data from 1998.

Purpose: "...to respond quickly and with compassion to those who are homeless by equipping and deploying volunteers and indigenous workers to complete the task of building homes and providing immediate relief..."

Year Founded in US: 1979

Income for Overseas Min: $10,753,000

Gifts-in-Kind: $2,233,000

Fully Supported US Personnel Overseas:
   Expecting to serve 1 to 4 years: 13

Other personnel:
  Non-US serving in own/other country: 2
  Home ministry & office staff in US: 14

Countries: Afghanistan; Honduras; Sri Lanka; Tajikistan

Shield of Faith Ministries

P.O. Box 327
Texas City, TX 77590 USA

Phone: (888) 241-9185
Web Site: www.sofministries.com

Mr. Rocky J. Malloy, Director

A nondenominational support agency of Charismatic and Evangelical tradition engaged in evangelism, church planting, Christian education, leadership development and youth programs.

Year Founded in US: 1990

Income for Overseas Min: NA

Shield of Faith Mission Intl.

P.O. Box 144
Bend, OR 97709 USA

Phone: (541) 382-7081
Fax: (541) 382-4471
E-mail: sfmi@sfmiusa.org
Web Site: www.sfmiusa.org

Mr. Jim Lucas, President

A nondenominational sending agency of Evangelical tradition engaged in evangelism, church planting and missionary training.

Year Founded in US: 1953

Income for Overseas Min: NA

Personnel:
  Home ministry & office staff in US: 2

SIM USA

P.O. Box 7900
Charlotte, NC 28241-7900 USA

Phone: (704) 588-4300
Fax: (704) 587-1518
E-mail: info@sim.org
Web Site: www.sim.org

Dr. Steve Strauss, U.S. Director

An interdenominational sending agency of Evangelical tradition engaged in church planting, broadcasting, development, theological education, medical work and Bible translation.

Purpose: "...planting, strengthening and partnering with churches around the world as we evangelize the unreached, minister to human need, disciple believers into churches and equip churches to fulfill Christ's Commission."

Year Founded in US: 1893

Income for Overseas Min: $26,392,453

Gifts-in-Kind: $278,297

Fully Supported US Personnel Overseas:
  Expecting to serve more than 4 years: 522
  Expecting to serve 1 to 4 years: 35
  Nonresidential mission personnel: 2

Other personnel:
  Short-term less than 1 year from US: 107
  Home ministry & office staff in US: 228

Countries: Angola 5; Bangladesh 8; Benin 12; Bolivia 50; Botswana 9; Burkina Faso 11; Central African Republic 1; Chile 7; Cote d'Ivoire 13; Djibouti 3; Ecuador 8; Ethiopia 70; Ghana 10; Guatemala 2; Guinea 13; India 24; Italy 2; Kenya 16; Liberia 4; Malawi 12; Mongolia 1; Mozambique 8; Niger 57; Nigeria 65; Pakistan 1; Paraguay 15; Peru 11; Philippines 8; Portugal 3; Senegal 7; Singapore 2; South Africa 10; Sudan 4; Tanzania 2; Togo 2; Uruguay 6; Zambia 35; Zimbabwe 5

Slavic Gospel Association

6151 Commonwealth Dr.
Loves Park, IL 61111 USA

Phone: (815) 282-8900
Fax: (815) 282-8901
E-mail: sga@sga.org
Web Site: www.sga.org

Dr. Robert W. Provost, President

A nondenominational support agency of Evangelical and Independent tradition engaged in Bible distribution, theological education, leadership development, support of national churches, support of national workers and translation work.

Purpose: "To serve evangelical churches, helping make disciples of the people in the lands of Russia."

Year Founded in US: 1934

Income for Overseas Min: $6,972,710

Gifts-in-Kind: $2,693,536

Fully Supported US Personnel Overseas:

Nonresidential mission personnel: 6

Other Personnel:
Short-term less than 1 year from US: 100

Slavic Missionary Service

P.O. Box 307
South River, NJ 08882 USA
Phone: (732) 873-8981
Fax: (732) 873-1625
E-mail: smsusa@smsusa.org
Web Site: www.smsusa.org

Rev. Alex Leonovich, Exec. Director

An interdenominational support agency of Evangelical tradition engaged in church planting, support of national churches, literature distribution and broadcasting.

Year Founded in US: 1933

Income for Overseas Min: NR

Personnel:
Home ministry & office staff in US: 5

Society of St. Margaret

17 Highland Park St.
Boston, MA 02119-1436 USA
Phone: (617) 445-8961
Fax: (617) 445-7120
E-mail: ssmconvent@ssmbos.com
Web Site: www.ssmbos.com

Sister Carolyn Darr, Reverend Mother

A religious order of Episcopal tradition engaged in Christian education, children's programs, development, leadership development, literacy work and support of national churches.

Purpose: "...seeking to find Jesus present in the common life, and in ministries which concentrate on responding to the needs of the time."

Year Founded in US: 1873

Income for Overseas Min: NA

Fully Supported US Personnel Overseas:
Expecting to serve more than 4 years: 2

Other personnel:
Non-US serving in own/other country: 2

Countries: Haiti 2

Son Shine Ministries Intl.

P.O. Box 456
Azle, TX 76098-0456 USA

Phone: (817) 444-3777
Fax: (817) 270-0199
E-mail: SSMShaffer@cs.com
Web Site: www.ssmii.org

Mr. David A. Shaffer, Director

An interdenominational sending agency of Baptist and Methodist tradition engaged in evangelism, missionary training and correspondence courses.

Year Founded in US: 1977

Income for Overseas Min: NR

Personnel:
Home ministry & office staff in US: 6

Source of Light Ministries International, Inc.

1011 Mission Rd.
Madison, GA 30650 USA
Phone: (706) 342-0397
Fax: (706) 342-9072
E-mail: solm@sourcelight.org
Web Site: www.sourcelight.org

Rev. Thomas S. Weber, Gen. Director

An interdenominational sending agency of Baptist tradition engaged in correspondence courses, literature distribution, literature production and support of national workers.

Purpose: "...to strengthen and establish local churches by developing and distributing Bible lessons for evangelism and discipleship."

Year Founded in US: 1952

Income for Overseas Min: $437,958

Personnel:
Non-US serving in own/other country: 66
Home ministry & office staff in US: 46

Countries: Argentina; Bolivia; Brazil; Chile; Cote d'Ivoire; Ghana; Guyana; Haiti; India; Jamaica; Japan; Kenya; Korea, South; Liberia; Mexico; Peru; Philippines; Romania; Singapore; Togo; Uganda

South America Mission

5217 S. Military Trail
Lake Worth, FL 33463-6099 USA
Phone: (561) 965-1833
Fax: (561) 439-8950
E-mail: samusa@samlink.org
Web Site: www.samlink.org

Rev. William K. Ogden, Exec. Director

A nondenominational sending agency of Evangelical tradition engaged in leadership development, training, aviation services and church planting.

Purpose: "...to establish the church of Jesus Christ in South America by planting and nurturing churches, training church leaders, [and] developing church associations."

Year Founded in US: 1914

Income for Overseas Min: $3,277,763

Fully Supported US Personnel Overseas:
Expecting to serve more than 4 years: 86
Expecting to serve 1 to 4 years: 8

Other personnel:
Short-term less than 1 year from US: 7
Non-US serving in own/other country: 94
Home ministry & office staff in US: 12

Countries: Bolivia 36; Brazil 16; Colombia 8; Paraguay 2; Peru 24

South American Missionary Society

P.O. Box 399
Ambridge, PA 15003 USA
Phone: (724) 266-0669
Fax: (724) 266-5681
E-mail: nitaporto@sams-usa.org
Web Site: www.sams-usa.org

Mr. Stewart Wicker, Interim Director

A denominational sending agency of Episcopal and Evangelical tradition engaged in church planting, development, Christian education, evangelism, leadership development and support of national churches.

Purpose: "To be witnesses and make disciples for Jesus Christ in fellowship with the Episcopal/Anglican Church in Latin America."

Year Founded in US: 1976

Income for Overseas Min: $1,142,741

Fully Supported US Personnel Overseas:
Expecting to serve more than 4 years: 20
Expecting to serve 1 to 4 years: 5

Other personnel:
Short-term less than 1 year from US: 1
Non-US serving in own/other country: 7
Home ministry & office staff in US: 11

Countries: Bolivia 3; Chile 2; Costa Rica; Dominican Republic 3; Ecuador; Honduras 5; Paraguay 1; Peru 1; Spain 5

Southern Baptist Convention International Mission Board

3806 Monument Ave.
Richmond, VA 23230 USA
Phone: (804) 353-0151
Fax: (804) 254-8982
E-mail: IMBResourceCenter@imb.org
Web Site: www.imb.org

Dr. Jerry Rankin, President

A denominational sending agency of Baptist tradition engaged in church planting, theological education, leadership development and relief and/or rehabilitation.

Purpose: "...to lead Southern Baptists in international missions efforts to evangelize the lost, disciple believers, develop churches and minister to people in need..."

Year Founded in US: 1845

Income for Overseas Min: $197,866,000

Fully Supported US Personnel Overseas:
Expecting to serve more than 4 years: 3,898
Expecting to serve 1 to 4 years: 1,539

Other personnel:
Short-term less than 1 year from US: 33,963
Home ministry & office staff in US: 523

Countries: Africa–General; Asia–General; Caribbean–General; Europe–General; Latin America–General; Oceania–General; Unspecified 3,898

Southern Mexico Missions

P.O. Box 7956
Riverside, CA 92513-7956 USA
Phone: (323) 256-1111

Mr. William Pile, Director

A nondenominational support agency of Christian (Restoration Movement) tradition engaged in evangelism.

Year Founded in US: 1957

Income for Overseas Min: $126,000

Fully Supported US Personnel Overseas:
Expecting to serve more than 4 years: 8
Expecting to serve 1 to 4 years: 2

Other personnel:
Non-US serving in own/other country: 10

Countries: Mexico 8

Sowers International, The

26347 Governor Ave.
Harbor City, CA 90710-3617 USA

Phone: (310) 325-0950
Fax: (310) 325-9593
E-mail: gwynn@sower.org
Web Site: www.sower.org

Mr. Gwynn Lewis, Exec. Director

A transdenominational support agency of Evangelical tradition engaged in funds transmission for support of national and short-term workers engaged in evangelism, development and children's ministries.

Purpose: "...to sow the word by raising up, equipping and sending out workers into the harvest."

Year Founded in US: 1993

Income for Overseas Min: $479,971

Fully Supported US Personnel Overseas:
  Expecting to serve more than 4 years: 1
  Nonresidential mission personnel: 3

Other personnel:
  Short-term less than 1 year from US: 65
  Non-US serving in own/other country: 30
  Home ministry & office staff in US: 10

Countries: Brazil 1; China; Colombia; Philippines; Taiwan; Thailand

SP Ministries

250 Pennsylvania Ave., Ste 101
Glen Ellyn, IL 60137 USA

Phone: (630) 260-6440
Fax: (630) 871-1148
E-mail: spmin@enteract.com
Web Site: www.kidbuilders.org

V. Gilbert Beers, President

A nondenominational support agency of Evangelical tradition engaged in children's programs, Christian education, literature distribution, literature production, partnership development and training.

Purpose: "Building kids for Christ around the world by equipping their leaders."

Year Founded in US: 1933

Income for Overseas Min: $127,676

Personnel:
  Home ministry & office staff in US: 4

Spanish World Ministries

P.O. Box 542
Winona Lake, IN 46590 USA

Phone: (800) 419-3683
Fax: (574) 267-3524
E-mail: info@spanishworld.org
Web Site: www.spanishworld.org

Mr. Cornelius Rivera, Exec. Director

A nondenominational support agency of Evangelical and Fundamental tradition engaged in broadcasting, Bible distribution, correspondence courses, evangelism, literature distribution and support of national workers.

Purpose: "To assist local churches in the Spanish speaking world to carry out the ministry of communicating the Gospel of the Lord Jesus Christ and making disciples."

Year Founded in US: 1959

Income for Overseas Min: $323,000

Personnel:
  Home ministry & office staff in US: 6

Spiritual Growth Resources, Inc.

P.O. Box 2081
Gilroy, CA 95021 USA

Phone: (408) 848-5608
Fax: (408) 848-4198
E-mail: SGR@sgrresources.org

Rev. Royal L. Peck, President

An interdenominational support agency of Baptist and Presbyterian tradition engaged in support of national workers, evangelism, leadership development, literature distribution and literature production.

Year Founded in US: 1984

Income for Overseas Min: $85,000

Fully Supported US Personnel Overseas:
  Expecting to serve more than 4 years: 2

Other personnel:
  Non-US serving in own/other country: 9
  Home ministry & office staff in US: 2

Countries: Albania; Italy 2

Sports & Rec Plus

6911 Richmond Hwy., Ste. 299
Alexandria, VA 22306-1803 USA

Phone: (703) 768-1995
Fax: (703) 768-0641

E-mail: 104063.2435@compuserve.com
Web Site: www.sportsrecplus.org
Rev. Rick Mitchell, President

A specialized agency of Baptist and Evangelical tradition engaged in sports and recreation evangelism, church planting, development and training.

Purpose: "...helping churches and mission organizations use sports and all forms of recreation—camping, drama, trips, arts & crafts and social activities—for outreach, evangelism, church planting and church growth."

Year Founded in US: 1995
Income for Overseas Min: $5,000
Gifts-in-Kind: $3,000
Personnel:
  Short-term less than 1 year from US: 5
  Home ministry & office staff in US: 2

STEER, Inc.

P.O. Box 1236
Bismarck, ND 58502 USA

Phone: (701) 258-4911
Fax: (701) 258-7684
E-mail: steerinc@steerinc.com
Web Site: www.steerinc.com

Mr. Keith Kost, Exec. Director

A nondenominational support agency of Evangelical tradition engaged in a three-way partnership program to help raise funds, agricultural programs and services for other agencies.

Purpose: "...raising money to help existing missionary societies get the Gospel to the ends of the earth in the shortest possible time..."

Year Founded in US: 1957
Income for Overseas Min: $625,917
Personnel:
  Home ministry & office staff in US: 8

STEM (Short-Term Evangelical Missions) Intl.

P.O. Box 386001
Minneapolis, MN 55438-6001 USA

Phone: (952) 996-1385
Fax: (952) 996-1384
E-mail: office@stemmin.org
Web Site: www.stemmin.com

Rev. Roger P. Peterson, Exec. Director

A transdenominational support agency of Evangelical tradition engaged in short-term programs, church construction, evangelism, literature distribution, support of national churches and mobilization for mission.

Purpose: "Using mutually-beneficial short-term mission in Caribbean and Latin American nations, STEM mobilizes the North American church into lifetime strategies for world evangelization."

Year Founded in US: 1984
Income for Overseas Min: $420,647
Fully Supported US Personnel Overseas:
  Expecting to serve 1 to 4 years: 2
Other personnel:
  Short-term less than 1 year from US: 91
  Home ministry & office staff in US: 11

Countries: Belize; Dominican Republic; Haiti; Honduras; Jamaica; Trinidad and Tobago

Strategic Ventures Network

28556 Highway 67
Woodland Park, CO 80863 USA

Phone: (719) 687-5072
E-mail: gary@global-d.biz

Mr. Gary Taylor, President

A nondenominational business enablement network assisting nationals and expatriates in identifying and starting overseas mission-based businesses from microenterprise to corporate level commerce.

Year Founded in US: 1981
Income for Overseas Min: $4,000
Personnel:
  Short-term less than 1 year from US: 1
  Bivocational/Tentmaker from US: 1

Surfing the Nations— Targeting the 10/40 Window

3097 Kalihi Street
Honolulu, HI 96819 USA

Phone: (808) 843-2342
Fax: (808) 853-1184
E-mail: surfingnations@yahoo.com
Web Site: www.surfingthenations.com

Mr. Tom Bauer, Director

A specialized agency of Charismatic tradition engaged in evangelism, leadership development, short-term programs and youth programs.

Purpose: "...to use surfing as a creative method to preach the gospel in all the surfable nations of the world with a priority of targeting the 10/40 window; teaching evangelism as a life style; training leaders in short-term missions and church planting."

Year Founded in US: 1997

Income for Overseas Min: $51,000

Fully Supported US Personnel Overseas:
Expecting to serve more than 4 years: 8
Expecting to serve 1 to 4 years: 6
Nonresidential mission personnel: 6

Other personnel:
Short-term less than 1 year from US: 21
Non-US serving in own/other country: 6

Countries: Asia–General 4; South Pacific 4

TCM International

P.O. Box 24560
Indianapolis, IN 46224 USA
Phone: (317) 299-0333
Fax: (317) 290-8607
E-mail: tcm@tcmi.org
Web Site: www.tcmi.org

Dr. Tony Twist, President

A service agency of Christian (Restoration Movement) tradition engaged in theological education, benevolence and support of national churches in Eastern Europe.

Purpose: "...to assist, disciple, encourage and equip Eastern and Central European Christians to reach their own people for Christ."

Year Founded in US: 1957

Income for Overseas Min: $1,600,000

Gifts-in-Kind: $11,000

Personnel:
Home ministry & office staff in US: 6

TEAM (The Evangelical Alliance Mission)

P.O. Box 969
Wheaton, IL 60189-0969 USA
Phone: (630) 653-5300
Fax: (630) 653-1826
E-mail: team@teamworld.org
Web Site: www.teamworld.org

Dr. Charles Davis, Exec. Director

An interdenominational sending agency of Evangelical tradition engaged in establish-ing churches through evangelism, disciple-ship, leadership development, theological education, and medical work.

Purpose: "...to help churches send missionaries to establish reproducing churches among the nations."

Year Founded in US: 1890

Income for Overseas Min: $23,500,000

Gifts-in-Kind: $40,000

Fully Supported US Personnel Overseas:
Expecting to serve more than 4 years: 632
Expecting to serve 1 to 4 years: 43
Nonresidential mission personnel: 6

Other personnel:
Short-term less than 1 year from US: 255
Home ministry & office staff in US: 107
Bivocational/Tentmaker from US: 29

Countries: Africa–General 33; Asia–General; Austria 15; Brazil 6; Cambodia; Central Asia–General 104; Chad 19; Colombia 14; Croatia 2; Czech Republic 12; France 40; Germany 24; Honduras 8; Hong Kong 6; India 2; Ireland 11; Irian Jaya 16; Italy 19; Japan 101; Java 2; Mexico 14; Mozambique 2; Peru 8; Philippines 19; Poland 1; Portugal 8; Russia 8; Spain 35; Sri Lanka 2; Swaziland 2; Taiwan 19; Trinidad and Tobago 4; Turkey 2; Ukraine 1; United Kingdom 2; Venezuela 49; Zimbabwe 22

Team Expansion, Inc.

3700 Hopewell Road
Louisville, KY 40299 USA
Phone: (800) 447-0800
E-mail: info@teamexpansion.org
Web Site: www.teamexpansion.org

Mr. Doug Lucas, Coordinator Intl. Services

A nondenominational sending agency of Christian (Restoration Movement) tradition engaged in church planting, Christian education, short-term programs, support of national workers, mobilization for mission and translation work.

Purpose: "...partnering with local churches to send and sustain teams of interdependent missionaries to plant indigenous churches among unreached people groups worldwide."

Year Founded in US: 1978

Income for Overseas Min: NR

Fully Supported US Personnel Overseas:
Expecting to serve more than 4 years: 111
Expecting to serve 1 to 4 years: 12
Other personnel:
Short-term less than 1 year from US: 80
Non-US serving in own/other country: 9
Home ministry & office staff in US: 25
Countries: Africa–General 2; Argentina;
Asia–General 20; Colombia 3; Ecuador 6;
Europe–General 11; Ireland 7; Italy 9; Russia 2; Taiwan 18; Tanzania 4; Ukraine 13;
Venezuela 16

Tech Serve International

40335 Winchester Rd.,Ste E#156
Temecula, CA 92591 USA
Phone: (909) 304-0528
Fax: (909) 304-0529
E-mail: techserve@compuserve.com
Web Site: techserve.org
Mr. Wes Syverson, President

A specialized agency engaged in technical assistance.
Year Founded in US: 1989
Personnel:
Home ministry & office staff in US: 4

Teen Missions International

885 East Hall Rd.
Merritt Island, FL 32953 USA
Phone: (321) 453-0350
Fax: (321) 452-7988
E-mail: info@teenmissions.org
Web Site: www.teenmissions.org
Rev. Robert M. Bland, President/Director

An interdenominational sending agency of Evangelical tradition engaged in short-term programs, evangelism, leadership development, support of national workers, services for other agencies and missionary training.
Purpose: "...to challenge, train, and disciple young people, exposing them to worldwide missions."
Year Founded in US: 1970
Income for Overseas Min: $4,195,209
Fully Supported US Personnel Overseas:
Expecting to serve more than 4 years: 14
Other personnel:
Short-term less than 1 year from US: 1,000
Non-US serving in own/other country: 70

Home ministry & office staff in US: 72
Countries: Australia 3; Brazil; Cameroon;
Ecuador 2; Honduras 3; India; Madagascar;
Malawi 3; Mongolia; Mozambique; New
Zealand; Philippines; South Africa; Uganda
1; Ukraine; Zambia 2; Zimbabwe

Teen World Outreach

P.O. Box 57A
Lima, NY 14485 USA
Phone: (585) 582-2792
Fax: (585) 624-1229
E-mail: jkporter@compuserve.com
Web Site: www.t-w-o.org
Rev. James Porter, Director

A transdenominational service agency of Pentecostal tradition engaged in short-term programs, evangelism, medical work, support of national churches and youth programs. An affiliate of ELIM Fellowship.
Statistics from 1998.
Year Founded in US: 1981
Income for Overseas Min: $670,000
Personnel:
Short-term less than 1 year from US: 240
Home ministry & office staff in US: 3

Tentmakers International Exchange—T.I.E

P.O. Box 30947
Seattle, WA 98103 USA
Phone: (206) 781-3151
Fax: (206) 781-3182
E-mail: tie@gati.wa.com
Web Site: www.tieinfo.com
Dr. Danny Martin, Intl. Director

A nondenominational specialized agency of Evangelical tradition engaged in missionary training, missionary education, evangelism, missions information service, management consulting/training and services for other agencies with 70 representatives in more than 25 countries.
Year Founded in US: 1982
Income for Overseas Min: NA

The Church of God of the Apostolic Faith, Inc.

P.O. Box 691745

Tulsa, OK 74169-1745 USA
Phone: (918) 437-7652
Fax: (918) 438-5633
Rev. Joseph L. Edmonson, Gen. Superintendent

A denominational sending agency of Pentecostal tradition engaged in theological education, Bible distribution, church construction, church planting, evangelism, literature distribution, providing medical supplies, training, video/film production/distribution and youth programs.

Year Founded in US: 1914
Income for Overseas Min: NR
Fully Supported US Personnel Overseas:
  Expecting to serve more than 4 years: 5
  Nonresidential mission personnel: 2
Other personnel:
  Short-term less than 1 year from US: 3
  Home ministry & office staff in US: 5
Countries: Honduras 1; Mexico 4

The Master's Harvest

P.O. Box 955
Alamo, TX 78516 USA
Phone: (956) 782-0316
E-mail: harvestbdr@aol.com
Mr. Kenny Ingram, Director

A transdenominational sending agency of Baptist and Charismatic tradition engaged in short-term programs, evangelism, support of national churches and youth programs.

Year Founded in US: 1992
Income for Overseas Min: NA
Fully Supported US Personnel Overseas:
  Expecting to serve more than 4 years: 4
Countries: Mexico 4

The Master's Mission, Inc.

(See Ad on page 278)
P.O. Box 547
Robbinsville, NC 28771 USA
Phone: (828) 479-6873
Fax: (828) 479-2471
E-mail: feedback@mastersmission.org
Web Site: www.mastersmission.org
Rev. Paul Teasdale, Exec. Director

An interdenominational sending agency of Baptist tradition engaged in missionary training, church planting, theological edu-

cation, leadership development and services for other agencies.

Year Founded in US: 1980
Income for Overseas Min: $1,652,000
Gifts-in-Kind: $3,226
Fully Supported US Personnel Overseas:
  Expecting to serve more than 4 years: 13
  Expecting to serve 1 to 4 years: 7
Other personnel:
  Non-US serving in own/other country: 8
  Home ministry & office staff in US: 7
Countries: Congo, Democratic Republic of 1; India; Israel; Kazakhstan; Kenya 8; Mexico 2; Nigeria 1; Romania; Uganda 1

The Mission Society

6234 Crooked Creek Road
Norcross, GA 30092 USA
Phone: (770) 446-1381
Fax: (770) 446-3044
E-mail: phoebe@msim.org
Web Site: www.themissionsociety.org
Dr. Philip R. Granger, President & CFO

A sending agency of Methodist and Wesleyan tradition engaged in evangelism, childcare/orphanage programs, church planting, Christian education, medical work and support of national churches.

Purpose: "...reaching the unreached with the Gospel, and helping national churches finish the task of winning their own people for Christ."

Year Founded in US: 1984
Income for Overseas Min: $4,871,146
Gifts-in-Kind: $4,713
Fully Supported US Personnel Overseas:
  Expecting to serve more than 4 years: 81
  Expecting to serve 1 to 4 years: 9
Other personnel:
  Home ministry & office staff in US: 29
Countries: China 3; Colombia 2; Costa Rica 2; France 9; Ghana 8; Guatemala 2; Hungary 2; India 2; Japan 2; Kazakhstan 20; Mexico 4; Paraguay 10; Peru 8; Philippines 2; Russia 5

Things To Come Mission, Inc.

2200 English Ave.
Indianapolis, IN 46201 USA

Out here the auto club isn't going to be of much help.

Obstacles. Missionaries face them every day. But with the proper training they can be equipped to handle the toughest situations as well as the thickest mud. Jesus called us to be His witnesses to the ends of the earth. Not just to the end of the pavement.

The Master's Mission provides a unique and comprehensive year of training for missionary candidates. Doctrinally grounded and technically equipped, they are READY for ministry, SET for missionary life, and prepared to GO into all nations with the Gospel. To find out more about TMM , call **1-800-419-8618.**

THE MASTER'S MISSION
READY. SET. GO. ™

Phone: (317) 262-8806
Fax: (317) 262-8852
E-mail: tcmusa@compuserve.com
Web Site: www.tcmusa.org
Rev. Joseph W. Watkins, Exec. Director

A nondenominational sending agency of Fundamental tradition engaged in church planting, theological education, evangelism and training. Personnel information from 1998.

Purpose: "...preaching of the gospel of salvation through faith in the shed blood of Jesus Christ, training believers for ministry and leadership and establishing indigenous, local churches..."

Year Founded in US: 1955

Income for Overseas Min: $783,794

Fully Supported US Personnel Overseas:
  Expecting to serve more than 4 years: 12
  Expecting to serve 1 to 4 years: 3

Other personnel:
  Short-term less than 1 year from US: 10
  Non-US serving in own/other country: 39
  Home ministry & office staff in US: 4
  Bivocational/Tentmaker from US: 1

Countries: Australia 1; Brazil 4; Cameroon; Indonesia; Kenya 5; Philippines; Senegal; South Africa 2

Third World Baptist Missions

207 Manitou Road
Manitou Beach, MI 49253-9661 USA
Phone: (517) 547-5516
E-mail: Cturbeville@dmci.net
Web Site: www.3rdworld.org
Dr. Caroll D. Turbeville, Asst. Director

A sending agency of Fundamental and Independent Baptist tradition engaged in church planting, Bible distribution, camping programs, church construction, theological education and support of national workers. Statistics from 1998.

Year Founded in US: 1991

Income for Overseas Min: $700,000

Gifts-in-Kind: $600,000

Fully Supported US Personnel Overseas:
  Expecting to serve more than 4 years: 4
  Nonresidential mission personnel: 1

Other personnel:
  Non-US serving in own/other country: 88
  Home ministry & office staff in US: 2

Bivocational/Tentmaker from US: 20
Countries: India 2; Philippines 2

TITUS International

1515 McBrien Rd.
Chattanooga, TN 37412-3103 USA
Phone: (423) 867-7079
Fax: (423) 867-7263
E-mail: titusint@cs.com
Web Site: www.titusinternational.org
Mr. Lowell David Marcum, President

A service agency engaged in training nationals, camping programs, childcare/orphanage programs, children's programs, church construction, church planting and Christian education.

Year Founded in US: 1983

Income for Overseas Min: $400,000

Fully Supported US Personnel Overseas:
  Expecting to serve more than 4 years: 2

Other personnel:
  Short-term less than 1 year from US: 20
  Non-US serving in own/other country: 68
  Home ministry & office staff in US: 4
  Bivocational/Tentmaker from US: 6

Countries: Moldova; Romania 2; Ukraine

TMA Ministries

P.O. Box 38366
Memphis, TN 38183 USA
Phone: (901) 367-2677
Fax: (901) 367-2677
E-mail: 74241.332@compuserve.com
Dr. John L. Langston III, President

A nondenominational service agency of Evangelical tradition engaged in technical assistance, evangelism, support of national churches, services for other agencies and theological education.

Purpose: "A focus on architectural support services for the global missionary enterprise, worldwide evangelism among the architectural professional community, and preaching/teaching for theological education."

Year Founded in US: 1982

Income for Overseas Min: $45,200

Gifts-in-Kind: $4,520

Fully Supported US Personnel Overseas:
  Expecting to serve more than 4 years: 16

Nonresidential mission personnel: 2
Other personnel:
Short-term less than 1 year from US: 2
Non-US serving in own/other country: 6
Countries: Asia–General 2; Europe–General 4; Guyana 2; Latin America–General 2; Middle East 2; Trinidad and Tobago 2; United Kingdom 2

Touch the World Ministries
1 Maple Street
Allendale, NJ 07401 USA
Phone: (888) 281-4887
E-mail: info@touchtheworld.org
Web Site: www.touchtheworld.org
Rev. Jeff Boucher, President

A nondenominational sending agency of Evangelical and Baptist tradition engaged in short-term programs, evangelism, missionary training and youth programs.

Purpose: "...to introduce teenagers to Jesus Christ as their Savior and Lord and to disciple Christian students to share Christ."

Year Founded in US: 1944
Income for Overseas Min: $350,825
Fully Supported US Personnel Overseas:
Expecting to serve more than 4 years: 8
Other personnel:
Short-term less than 1 year from US: 100
Home ministry & office staff in US: 22
Bivocational/Tentmaker from US: 2
Countries: Cuba 1; Japan 5; Uganda 1; United Kingdom 1

Training Evangelistic Leadership
P.O. Drawer E
Denton, TX 76202 USA
Phone: (940) 321-3913
E-mail: roy.rob@verizon.net
Web Site: www.tel-china.com
Dr. Sean Collins, American Director

An interdenominational sending agency of Baptist tradition engaged in evangelism, leadership development, missionary training, and follow-up discipleship training.

Year Founded in US: 1976
Income for Overseas Min: $503,348
Fully Supported US Personnel Overseas:

Expecting to serve more than 4 years: 33
Expecting to serve 1 to 4 years: 4
Other personnel:
Short-term less than 1 year from US: 14
Non-US serving in own/other country: 55
Home ministry & office staff in US: 1
Countries: China 12; Hong Kong 9; India 2; Indonesia 4; Philippines 5; Vietnam 1

Trans World Missions
P.O. Box 10
Glendale, CA 91209 USA
Phone: (818) 830-3437
Fax: (818) 830-2787
E-mail: TWMLmejia@aol.com
Web Site: www.transworldmissions.com
Rev. Luis R. Mejia, President

An interdenominational support agency of Evangelical and Pentecostal tradition engaged in church planting, Bible distribution, childcare/orphanage programs, children's programs, evangelism and leadership development.

Purpose: "...ministering to the whole man spiritually, physically, emotionally and mentally..."

Year Founded in US: 1949
Income for Overseas Min: $323,009
Personnel:
Non-US serving in own/other country: 52
Home ministry & office staff in US: 4
Countries: Unspecified Country

Trans World Radio
P.O. Box 8700
Cary, NC 27512 USA
Phone: (919) 460-3700
Fax: (919) 460-3702
E-mail: info@twr.org
Web Site: www.twr.org
David G. Tucker, President

An interdenominational specialized agency of Evangelical tradition engaged in broadcasting, audio recording/distribution, church planting, correspondence courses, evangelism and technical assistance.

Purpose: "...to assist the Church to fulfill the command of Jesus Christ to make disciples of all peoples and to do so by using and making available mass media..."

Year Founded in US: 1952

Income for Overseas Min: $29,383,223

Fully Supported US Personnel Overseas:
Expecting to serve more than 4 years: 91
Expecting to serve 1 to 4 years: 4

Other personnel:
Non-US serving in own/other country: 15
Home ministry & office staff in US: 69

Countries: Australia; Austria 10; Cambodia 2; Germany; Guam 18; Monaco 9; Netherlands 6; Netherlands Antilles 8; Singapore 7; Slovakia 10; South Africa 11; Swaziland 10

Tribes and Nations Outreach

P.O. Box 1454
Baldwin Park, CA 91706 USA

Phone: (626) 856-8772
Fax: (626) 856-8772
E-mail: tnousa@aol.com

Arlene del Campo, Interim Base Director

A nondenominational support agency of Charismatic and Pentecostal tradition engaged in missionary training, agricultural programs, Bible distribution, church planting, medical work and short-term programs.

Purpose: "...to build the body of Christ in Asia through training of nationals and provision of Bibles and other encouragement like sending medical missions. It seeks to mobilize, equip and involve the body of Christ worldwide for missions in Asia."

Year Founded in US: 1986

Income for Overseas Min: $21,300

Turkish World Outreach

508 Fruitvale Court
Grand Junction, CO 81504 USA

Phone: (970) 434-1942
Fax: (970) 434-1461
E-mail: TWO@onlinecol.com
Web Site: www.missionsalive.org/two

Rev. Steven E. Hagerman, U.S. Director

A nondenominational support agency of Christian (Restoration Movement) tradition engaged in church planting, Bible distribution, broadcasting, evangelism, literature distribution, literature production, support of national churches and mobilization for mission.

Year Founded in US: 1969

Income for Overseas Min: $648,500

Fully Supported US Personnel Overseas:
Expecting to serve more than 4 years: 23

Other personnel:
Short-term less than 1 year from US: 2
Non-US serving in own/other country: 9
Home ministry & office staff in US: 14
Bivocational/Tentmaker from US: 7

Countries: Australia 2; Germany 2; Turkey 19

UFM International
(See Ad on page 282)
P.O. Box 306
Bala-Cynwyd, PA 19004 USA

Phone: (610) 667-7660
Fax: (610) 660-9068
E-mail: bala@ufm.org
Web Site: www.ufm.org

Rev. D. James O'Neill, Gen. Director

An interdenominational sending agency of Evangelical tradition engaged in church planting, Christian education, theological education, evangelism, leadership development and medical work.

Purpose: "...helps churches start new churches by evangelizing the unreached, discipling believers and training leaders."

Year Founded in US: 1931

Income for Overseas Min: NR

Fully Supported US Personnel Overseas:
Expecting to serve more than 4 years: 303
Expecting to serve 1 to 4 years: 9

Other personnel:
Short-term less than 1 year from US: 58
Non-US serving in own/other country: 35
Home ministry & office staff in US: 71

Countries: Asia–General 2; Austria 4; Bosnia and Herzegovina 4; Brazil 66; Cambodia 2; Congo, Democratic Republic of the 3; Dominican Republic 17; Ecuador 10; France 26; Germany 20; Guatemala 2; Guyana 18; Haiti 26; Indonesia 27; Ireland 5; Italy 20; Kenya 4; Mexico 11; Monaco 2; New Zealand; Philippines 9; Puerto Rico 3; Romania 2; Slovakia 3; South Africa 3; Spain 4; Sweden 2; Ukraine 6; United Kingdom 2

United Board for Christian Higher Education in Asia

475 Riverside Dr. Rm. 1221

still there -
still waiting -
still time!

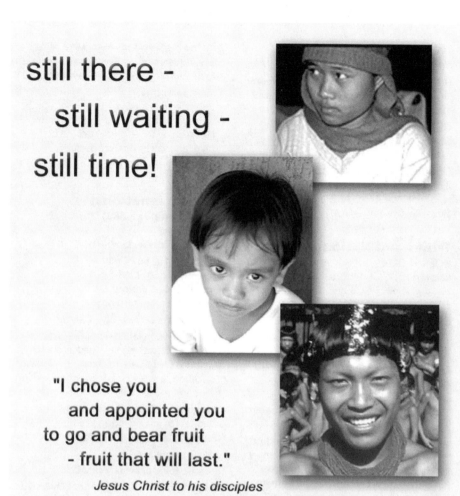

"I chose you
and appointed you
to go and bear fruit
- fruit that will last."

Jesus Christ to his disciples

opportunities
with ufm international

getinvolved@ufm.org

www.ufm.org

New York, NY 10115 USA
Phone: (212) 870-2609
Fax: (212) 870-2322
E-mail: staff@ubchea.org
Web Site: www.unitedboard.org
Dr. Richard J. Wood, President

An interdenominational service agency of Ecumenical tradition engaged in leadership development, technical assistance and training.

Purpose: "...to contribute to higher education and to the exchange of resources in and with Asia for the pursuit of truth and knowledge...and full human development understood from the perspective of Christian faith."

Year Founded in US: 1932
Income for Overseas Min: $5,425,196
Personnel:
    Home ministry & office staff in US: 11

United Church Board for World Ministries

700 Prospect Ave. E.
Cleveland, OH 44115 USA
Phone: (216) 736-3202
E-mail: bishopd@ucc.org
Web Site: www.ucc.org
Dr. Dale L. Bishop, Exec. Vice-President

A denominational sending agency of Reformed, Ecumenical and Congregational tradition engaged in development, Christian education, theological education, leadership development and medical work. Financial figure from 1998.

Year Founded in US: 1812
Income for Overseas Min: $13,379,044
Fully Supported US Personnel Overseas:
    Expecting to serve 1 to 4 years: 126
Other personnel:
    Home ministry & office staff in US: 48
Countries: Argentina; Asia–General; Australia; Botswana; Brazil; Chile; China; Dominican Republic; Ecuador; El Salvador; Fiji; Germany; Guatemala; Haiti; Honduras; Hong Kong; Hungary; India; Indonesia; Israel; Jamaica; Japan; Kenya; Korea, South; Lebanon; Lesotho; Marshall Islands; Mexico; Namibia; Nepal; Nicaragua; Paraguay; Philippines; South Africa; Sri Lanka;

Swaziland; Taiwan; Thailand; Turkey; Vietnam; Zimbabwe

United Evangelical Churches

P.O. Box 1000
S. Juan Batista, CA 95045-1000 USA
Phone: (800) 228-2289
Fax: (831) 635-0909
E-mail: uec@uecol.org
Web Site: www.uecol.org
Mr. Robert B. Fort, Chairman/CEO

A transdenominational service agency of Charismatic and Evangelical tradition engaged in credentialing ministers, evangelism, church planting, leadership development, member care and services for other agencies. Financial and personnel information from 1998.

Year Founded in US: 1964
Income for Overseas Min: $40,138
Fully Supported US Personnel Overseas:
    Expecting to serve more than 4 years: 4
Other personnel:
    Non-US serving in own/other country: 4
    Home ministry & office staff in US: 4
Countries: Bolivia 2; Philippines 2

United Methodist Church, Gen. Bd. of Global Ministries

475 Riverside Dr., Rm. 1400
New York, NY 10115 USA
Phone: (800) 862-4246
Fax: (212) 870-3748
E-mail: info@gbgm-umc.org
Web Site: www.gbgm-umc.org
Rev. Randy Day, Gen. Secretary

A denominational sending agency of Methodist tradition responding to program and personnel needs through relationships to partner churches and ecumenical organizations all over the world, including support of national churches, church construction, development, evangelism, advocacy, relief and/or rehabilitation and missionary training.

Year Founded in US: 1820
Income for Overseas Min: $70,000,000
Fully Supported US Personnel Overseas:
    Expecting to serve more than 4 years: 481
Other personnel:
    Short-term less than 1 year from US: 117,000

Non-US serving in own/other country: 330
Home ministry & office staff in US: 280
Countries: Unspecified Country 481

United Pentecostal Church Intl., Foreign Missions Div.
8855 Dunn Rd.
Hazelwood, MO 63042 USA
Phone: (314) 837-7300
Fax: (314) 837-2387
E-mail: fmd@upci.org
Web Site: www.upci.org
Rev. Bruce A. Howell, Gen. Director
A denominational sending agency of Pente-
costal tradition engaged in evangelism,
church planting, theological education,
leadership development, and literature dis-
tribution/production.
Year Founded in US: 1924
Income for Overseas Min: $19,352,247
Fully Supported US Personnel Overseas:
Expecting to serve more than 4 years: 267
Countries: Unspecified Country 267

U.S. Center for World Mission
See: Frontier Mission Fellowship

United World Mission
9401-B Southern Pines Blvd.
Charlotte, NC 28273-5596 USA
Phone: (704) 357-3355
Fax: (704) 357-6389
E-mail: info@uwm.org
Web Site: www.uwm.org
Rev. John Bernard, Executive Director
A nondenominational sending agency of
evangelical tradition engaged in church
planting, theological education, leadership
development, support of national churches
and missionary training.
Year Founded in US: 1946
Income for Overseas Min: NR

University of the Family
P.O. Box 1040
Littleton, CO 80160-1040 USA
Phone: (303) 933-7495

Fax: (303) 933-2153
E-mail: MMI@marriage.org
Web Site: www.marriage.org
Mike & Marilyn Phillipps, Co-Presidents
A specialized agency providing training ma-
terials in 90 countries and 30 languages for
strengthening married couples for evange-
lism and other ministries. More than
20,000 leaders lead marriage classes in
their homes around the world. Statistical
data for 1998.
Purpose: "To help couples establish their
homes as powerful lighthouses in their
neighborhoods, reaching out to those
around in the storms of life."
Year Founded in US: 1983
Income for Overseas Min: $70,000
Personnel:
Short-term less than 1 year from US: 6
Non-US serving in own/other country: 10
Home ministry & office staff in US: 20
Bivocational/Tentmaker from US: 10
Countries: Bahrain; Cuba; Egypt; Spain;
Zimbabwe

VELA Ministries International
P.O. Box 28840
San Jose, CA 95159 USA
Phone: (408) 995-5090
Fax: (408) 995-5092
E-mail: cecilia@velaministries.org
Web Site: www.velaministries.org
Mr. Dan Christensen, President
An interdenominational support agency of
Evangelical tradition engaged in leadership
development, church planting, evangelism,
mission-related research and training.
Year Founded in US: 1990
Income for Overseas Min: $102,235
Fully Supported US Personnel Overseas:
Expecting to serve 1 to 4 years: 1
Other personnel:
Non-US serving in own/other country: 1
Home ministry & office staff in US: 2
Countries: Latin America–General; Russia

Vellore Christian Medical College Board
475 Riverside Dr. Rm. 243

New York, NY 10115 USA

Phone: (212) 870-2640
Fax: (212) 870-2173
E-mail: usaboard@vellorecmc.org
Web Site: www.vellorecmc.org

Rev. Louis Knowles, President

An interdenominational specialized agency of Ecumenical tradition engaged in medical work, development, funds transmission, volunteer recruitment, providing medical supplies, supplying equipment and training.

Purpose: "...to provide a focus for excellence and integrity through the support of the wide range of programs of Vellore Christian Medical College and Hospital, Vellore, India."

Year Founded in US: 1948

Income for Overseas Min: $1,041,423

Gifts-in-Kind: $118,000

Personnel:
   Home ministry & office staff in US: 6

Venture International

P.O. Box 7396
Tempe, AZ 85281 USA

Phone: (800) 421-2159
Fax: (480) 730-2720
E-mail: info@VentureFTF.org
Web Site: www.ventureftf.org

Mr. Leonard Rodgers, President

An interdenominational service agency of Evangelical tradition engaged in support of nurturing families via local churches, development, children programs, disability assistance programs, medical work and relief aid.

Purpose: "...serves as a bridge between those in need and those who want to help God's people in the Middle East; empowering and enhancing their work through strategic partnerships, emergency relief, small business creation and people development."

Year Founded in US: 1986

Income for Overseas Min: $515,674

Personnel:
   Short-term less than 1 year from US: 2
   Non-US serving in own/other country: 5
   Home ministry & office staff in US: 4

Countries: Cyprus; Egypt; Israel; Jordan; Kyrgyzstan

Village Ministries Intl., Inc.

P.O. Box 7205
Edmond, OK 73083 USA

Phone: (405) 634-4373
Fax: (405) 634-4465
E-mail: usaoffice@villageministries.org
Web Site: www.villageministries.org

Rev. Dan R. Hawkins, Chief Executive

A nondenominational service agency of Independent and Evangelical tradition engaged in theological education, evangelism and short-term programs. Statistics from 1998.

Purpose: "...to take the Gospel and the teaching of God's Word to people...in villages and remote cities that ordinarily are not exposed to missionary activity or Bible teaching."

Year Founded in US: 1990

Income for Overseas Min: $172,000

Personnel:
   Non-US serving in own/other country: 40
   Home ministry & office staff in US: 4

Countries: Belarus; Ghana; Mexico; Nigeria; Sri Lanka

Vineyard Intl. Consortium

112 Harvard Ave., #265
Claremont, CA 91711 USA

Phone: (909) 626-0773
E-mail: info@vineyardinternational.org
Web Site: www.vineyardinternational.org

Mr. Mark Fields, Missions Coordinator

A consortium of 8 different associations of Charismatic and Evangelical tradition engaged in church planting, evangelism, leadership development and support of national churches. There are approximately 380 Vineyard Churches outside the US in 52 countries. The 8 associations oversee the work in different areas of the world.

Purpose: "...to equip the saints for the advancement of the Kingdom of God through evangelizing and church planting."

Year Founded in US: 1982

Income for Overseas Min: NA

Virginia Mennonite Board of Missions

901 Parkwood Dr.
Harrisonburg, VA 22801 USA

Phone: (540) 434-9727
Fax: (540) 434-7627
E-mail: info@vmbm.org
Web Site: www.vmbm.org
Mr. Loren E. Horst, President

A denominational sending agency of Mennonite tradition engaged in leadership development, church planting, theological education, evangelism, support of national churches and short-term programs.

Purpose: "...[to] meet human needs, extend an invitation to a relationship with Jesus Christ, promote communities of faith that continue God's work in the world..."

Year Founded in US: 1919

Income for Overseas Min: $561,400

Gifts-in-Kind: $550

Fully Supported US Personnel Overseas:
Expecting to serve more than 4 years: 6
Expecting to serve 1 to 4 years: 7

Other personnel:
Short-term less than 1 year from US: 89
Non-US serving in own/other country: 9
Home ministry & office staff in US: 14

Countries: Albania; Italy 2; Jamaica 2; Trinidad and Tobago 2

Voice of the Martyrs, The

P.O. Box 443
Bartlesville, OK 74005-0443 USA

Phone: (918) 337-8015
Fax: (918) 337-9287
E-mail: thevoice@vom-usa.org
Web Site: www.persecution.com
Mr. Tom White, USA Director

An interdenominational support agency of Evangelical tradition engaged in literature distribution, Bible distribution and evangelism.

Year Founded in US: 1967

Income for Overseas Min: $21,364,009

Gifts-in-Kind: $14,124,777

Personnel:
Home ministry & office staff in US: 85

Walk Thru The Bible Ministries

4201 N. Peachtree Rd.
Atlanta, GA 30338 USA

Phone: (770) 458-9300
Fax: (770) 454-9313

E-mail: tsparks@walkthru.org
Web Site: www.walkthru.org
Mr. Chip Ingram, CEO USA

An interdenominational service agency of Evangelical tradition engaged in Christian education, evangelism, leadership development, literature distribution, literature production, support of national workers and training.

Purpose: "...to contribute to the spiritual growth of Christians worldwide through Bible teaching, tools, and training."

Year Founded in US: 1976

Income for Overseas Min: $4,498,184

Fully Supported US Personnel Overseas:
Nonresidential mission personnel: 5

Other personnel:
Non-US serving in own/other country: 233
Home ministry & office staff in US: 85

Countries: Armenia; Australia; Austria; Bangladesh; Belarus; Bolivia; Botswana; Cambodia; Congo, Democratic Republic of the; Dominican Republic; Ecuador; Egypt; El Salvador; Estonia; Georgia; Ghana; Guatemala; Honduras; Hungary; India; Indonesia; Ireland; Japan; Jordan; Kenya; Korea, South; Latvia; Lesotho; Lithuania; Malaysia; Mexico; Moldova; Mongolia; Mozambique; Myanmar/Burma; Namibia; Nepal; Nigeria; Peru; Philippines; Romania; Russia; Serbia and Montenegro; Sierra Leone; Singapore; South Africa; Sri Lanka; Sudan; Swaziland; Syria; Tanzania; Thailand; Togo; Uganda; Ukraine; Vietnam; Zambia; Zimbabwe

Waymakers International

Box 203131
Austin, TX 78720-3131 USA

Phone: (512) 419-7729
Fax: (512) 219-1999
E-mail: Steve@waymakers.org
Web Site: www.waymakers.org
Mr. Steve Hawthorne, Director

A nondenominational service agency of Evangelical tradition engaged in prayer evangelism, literature distribution and literature production.

Purpose: "...to create local movements of united prayer evangelism that will reproduce where Christ is not known."

Year Founded in US: 1995

Income for Overseas Min: NA

Personnel:
Home ministry & office staff in US: 3

Waymarks International Radio Ministries

P.O. Box 2324
Macon, GA 31203 USA

Phone: (478) 750-1422
Fax: (478) 750-1422
E-mail: lorenwilson@juno.com
Web Site: www.waymarks.org

Rev. Loren H. Wilson, Director

A nondenominational specialized agency of Baptist tradition engaged in broadcasting, audio recording/distribution, Bible distribution, church planting and literature distribution. Shortwave broadcasts to 17 countries.

Year Founded in US: 1987

Income for Overseas Min: $15,000

Personnel:
Home ministry & office staff in US: 1

WEC International

P.O. Box 1707
Fort Washington, PA 19034 USA

Phone: (215) 646-2322
Fax: (215) 646-6202
E-mail: 105501.3520@compuserve.com
Web Site: www.wec-int.org

Rev. James Raymo, U.S.A. Director

An interdenominational sending agency of Evangelical tradition engaged in church planting, childcare/orphanage programs, Christian education, missionary education, TEE, theological education and literature production.

Purpose: "To bring the gospel... to the remaining unevangelized peoples with the utmost urgency, to demonstrate the compassion of Christ to a needy world... to inspire, mobilize and train for cross-cultural mission."

Year Founded in US: 1939

Income for Overseas Min: $3,044,824

Fully Supported US Personnel Overseas:
Expecting to serve more than 4 years: 128
Expecting to serve 1 to 4 years: 7

Other personnel:
Short-term less than 1 year from US: 11
Non-US serving in own/other country: 1,189
Home ministry & office staff in US: 42

Countries: Africa–General 2; Albania; Asia–General 27; Australia; Belgium; Brazil; Bulgaria; Burkina Faso; Cambodia 3; Chad 3; Colombia; Congo, Democratic Republic of the; Cote d'Ivoire 9; Equatorial Guinea; Fiji; Finland; France 2; Gambia, The 1; Germany 1; Ghana 2; Greece; Guinea 1; Guinea-Bissau 2; Hong Kong; Indonesia; Italy 4; Japan; Liberia; Mexico 14; Middle East 24; Nepal; Netherlands; New Zealand 2; Portugal; Senegal 1; Singapore; South Africa 2; Spain 11; Switzerland; Taiwan; Thailand 8; United Kingdom 7; Venezuela 2

Wesleyan World Missions

P.O. Box 50434
Indianapolis, IN 46250 USA

Phone: (317) 774-7907
Fax: (317) 774-7913
E-mail: WWM@wesleyan.org
Web Site: www.wesleyan.org/wwm/wmission.htm

Dr. Donald L. Bray, Gen. Director

A denominational sending agency of Wesleyan tradition engaged in evangelism, theological education, TEE, leadership development, support of national churches and mobilization for mission.

Purpose: "...calling Wesleyans to evangelism, church planting, leadership development, and ministries of compassion for the establishing of a flourishing international church."

Year Founded in US: 1889

Income for Overseas Min: $6,562,214

Fully Supported US Personnel Overseas:
Expecting to serve 1 to 4 years: 112

Other personnel:
Short-term less than 1 year from US: 1,110
Non-US serving in own/other country: 10
Home ministry & office staff in US: 23

Countries: Albania; Australia; Brazil; Cambodia; Colombia; Costa Rica; Croatia; Czech Republic; Guyana; Haiti; Honduras; Mexico; Mozambique; Nepal; Papua New Guinea; Peru; Puerto Rico; Russia; South Africa; Suriname; United Kingdom; Unspecified Country; Zambia

Westminister Biblical Missions

P.O. Box 602
Carbondale, PA 18407 USA
E-mail: wbminc@nccn.net
Web Site: www.nccn.net/~wbminc
Rev. Dennis E. Roe, Gen. Secretary

A transdenominational sending agency of Presbyterian tradition engaged in theological education, literature production and support of national churches. Financial figure from 1998.

Purpose: "...planting and multiplying Reformed churches on the foreign field."

Year Founded in US: 1974

Income for Overseas Min: $375,000

Fully Supported US Personnel Overseas:
  Expecting to serve more than 4 years: 3

Other personnel:
  Non-US serving in own/other country: 51
  Home ministry & office staff in US: 3

Countries: Hungary 1; Korea, South 1; Mexico; Pakistan 1

White Fields, Inc. (USA)

P.O. Box 226
Stillwater, MN 55082 USA
Phone: (651) 430-0090
Fax: (651) 430-0090
E-mail: usa@whitefields.org
Web Site: www.whitefields.org
Rev. Stephen Lonetti, General Director

A service agency of Evangelical tradition engaged in support of national churches, support of national workers and leadership development.

Purpose: "...assisting national church planters working with experienced missionaries in reaching their own people with the gospel of Christ."

Year Founded in US: 1955

Countries: Brazil; India; Japan; Myanmar; Philippines; South Africa; Zimbabwe

Wisconsin Evangelical Lutheran Synod, Board for World Missions

2929 N. Mayfair Road
Milwaukee, WI 53222 USA
Phone: (414) 256-3233
Fax: (414) 256-6480
E-mail: bwm@sab.wels.net
Web Site: www.wels.net
Rev. Daniel H. Koelpin, Administrator

A denominational sending agency of Lutheran tradition engaged in church planting, broadcasting, theological education, literature production, support of national churches and relief aid. Personnel data from 1998.

Purpose: "...to make disciples throughout the world...using the gospel to win the lost for Christ and to nurture believers for lives of Christian service..."

Year Founded in US: 1955

Income for Overseas Min: $8,220,079

Fully Supported US Personnel Overseas:
  Expecting to serve more than 4 years: 66
  Expecting to serve 1 to 4 years: 10

Other personnel:
  Home ministry & office staff in US: 7

Countries: Albania; Brazil 4; Bulgaria 6; Cameroon; Colombia 3; Cuba 1; Dominican Republic 2; Hong Kong 2; India 3; Indonesia 1; Japan 5; Malawi 10; Mexico 4; Puerto Rico 2; Russia 6; Sweden 2; Taiwan 3; Thailand 1; Zambia 11

Word of Life Fellowship

P.O. Box 600
Schroon Lake, NY 12870 USA
Phone: (518) 494-6000
Fax: (518) 494-6359
E-mail: im@wol.org
Web Site: www.wol.org
Mr. Donald H. Lough, Jr., VP Intl. Ministries

A nondenominational sending agency of Independent tradition engaged in evangelism, broadcasting, camping programs, extension education, short-term programs, youth programs, Bible clubs and Bible institutes.

Year Founded in US: 1940

Income for Overseas Min: $9,518,556

Gifts-in-Kind: $340,892

Fully Supported US Personnel Overseas:
  Expecting to serve more than 4 years: 132
  Expecting to serve 1 to 4 years: 1
  Nonresidential mission personnel: 13

Other personnel:

Prepare for intercultural service.

With a Masters in Missions & Intercultural Studies from Wheaton College Graduate School

Scholarship Committed to Servanthood

A re you called to global missions? Whether your area of service is church planting, leadership development, theological education, community health and development, or teaching English as a second language, the graduate school at Wheaton College can give you the foundational training and multifaceted skills needed in today's dynamically changing world.

You'll get all the benefits of a Wheaton College exper-ience, plus close proximity to local ministries and mission agencies helping you relate classroom experiences to relevant ministries.

Begin your Masters in Missions & Intercultural Studies at the Wheaton College Graduate School by contacting us today, toll-free at 800-888-0141 or www.wheatongrad.com.

FACULTY

Missions
Dr. Evvy Hay Campbell
Dr. Robert L. Gallagher
Dr. A. Scott Moreau

TESOL
Dr. Cheri Pierson
Dr. Alan Seaman

Graduate Admissions
Local: 630.752.5195
Toll-free: 800.888.0141
gradadm@wheaton.edu
www.wheatongrad.com

Wheaton College
Graduate School
For Christ and His Kingdom

Short-term less than 1 year from US: 768
Non-US serving in own/other country: 705
Home ministry & office staff in US: 413

Countries: Argentina 8; Australia 8; Austria 2; Bermuda; Bolivia; Brazil 50; Chile; Colombia; Costa Rica; Czech Republic 4; Dominican Republic; Ecuador 2; El Salvador 2; France 2; Germany 6; Guatemala; Honduras 2; Hungary 14; Italy; Japan; Kenya 2; Korea, South 4; Mexico; Netherlands; New Zealand; Nigeria 2; Panama 4; Papua New Guinea; Paraguay 2; Peru; Philippines; Poland 6; Portugal 2; Romania; South Africa 6; Spain 1; Ukraine; United Kingdom 3; Uruguay; Venezuela

Word To Russia

P.O. Box 1521
West Sacramento, CA 95691 USA

Phone: (916) 372-4610
Fax: (916) 375-6770
E-mail: wtrmlokteff@bigvalley.net
Web Site: www.wordtorussia.org

Mr. Michael D. Lokteff, President

A nondenominational support agency of Evangelical tradition engaged in audio recording/distribution, literature distribution, and radio outreach to Russian-speaking immigrants, with outreach in the former Soviet Union and Ukraine. Emphasis is on the children and youth.

Year Founded in US: 1972
Income for Overseas Min: NA
Personnel:
  Home ministry & office staff in US: 5

World Baptist Fellowship Mission Agency

P.O. Box 13459
Arlington, TX 76094 USA

Phone: (817) 274-7161
Fax: (817) 861-1992
E-mail: wbfraley@earthlink.net
Web Site: www.wbfi.net

Rev. Thomas M. Raley, Missions Director

A denominational sending agency of Baptist and Fundamental tradition engaged in church planting, evangelism, funds transmission and literature distribution. Country data from 1998.

Year Founded in US: 1928
Income for Overseas Min: $5,600,000
Fully Supported US Personnel Overseas:
  Expecting to serve more than 4 years: 102
  Expecting to serve 1 to 4 years: 28
Other personnel:
  Home ministry & office staff in US: 6

Countries: Australia; Belarus; Brazil 28; Cambodia; Caribbean–General 8; Colombia 4; Ecuador 12; France; Guatemala 2; Honduras 6; Indonesia 5; Ireland 2; Latvia; Mexico 24; New Zealand 4; Singapore 2; Spain 4; Thailand 1

World Bible Translation Center

P.O. Box 820648
Fort Worth, TX 76182 USA

Phone: (817) 595-1664
Fax: (817) 589-7013
E-mail: info@wbtc.com
Web Site: www.wbtc.com

Mr. Dale Randolph, President

A nondenominational specialized agency of Evangelical tradition engaged in Bible distribution, literacy work and Bible translation.

Purpose: "...to translate the Scriptures and make them accessible to the common people around the world in their everyday language."

Year Founded in US: 1973
Income for Overseas Min: NA
Gifts-in-Kind: $1,097,824
Personnel:
  Home ministry & office staff in US: 17

World Concern

19303 Fremont Ave. North
Seattle, WA 98133 USA

Phone: (206) 546-7201
Fax: (206) 546-7269
E-mail: worldconcern@worldconcern.org
Web Site: www.worldconcern.org

Mr. Paul Kennell, President

A nondenominational sending agency of Evangelical tradition engaged in development, agricultural programs, broadcasting, disability assistance programs, evangelism, leadership development, providing medical supplies and relief and/or rehabilitation.

Purpose: "To overcome human suffering through emergency relief, rehabilitation and long-term development programs so that families and individuals can be in right relationship with God, with one another and with creation."

Year Founded in US: 1973

Income for Overseas Min: $34,325,723

Gifts-in-Kind: $20,888,795

Fully Supported US Personnel Overseas:
Expecting to serve more than 4 years: 23
Expecting to serve 1 to 4 years: 31

Other personnel:
Short-term less than 1 year from US: 100
Non-US serving in own/other country: 622
Home ministry & office staff in US: 41

Countries: Bangladesh; Bolivia 1; Cambodia 1; Ethiopia 3; Georgia; Haiti 2; Honduras; Kenya 3; Laos; Mongolia 4; Myanmar/Burma; Nepal 4; Peru; Rwanda; Somalia; Thailand 5; Uganda; Ukraine; Vietnam

World Evangelization Research Center and Global Evangelization Movement

P.O. Box 6628
Richmond, VA 23230 USA

Web Site: www.gem-werc.org

Mr. Todd M. Johnson, Director

A multidenominational specialized agency initiating, promoting, publishing and disseminating research related to all varieties of global Christian evangelization and mission.

Purpose: "...to document world Christianity and its progress in completing the Great Commission, communicate this information to the global body of Christ and advocate the unevangelized as the leading priority of world mission."

Year Founded in US: 1965

Personnel:
Home ministry & office staff in US: 7

World Gospel Mission

P.O. Box 948
Marion, IN 46952 USA

Phone: (765) 664-7331
Fax: (765) 671-7230
E-mail: wgm@wgm.org

Web Site: www.wgm.org

Rev. Hubert P. Harriman, President

An interdenominational sending agency of Wesleyan and Holiness tradition engaged in evangelism, aviation services, TEE, theological education, leadership development, medical work and support of national churches.

Purpose: "...to proclaim the good news of salvation through faith in Jesus Christ by calling believers to scriptural holiness as a doctrine to be believed, an experience to be received, a message to be declared and a lifestyle to be demonstrated."

Year Founded in US: 1910

Income for Overseas Min: $11,322,529

Gifts-in-Kind: $796,292

Fully Supported US Personnel Overseas:
Expecting to serve more than 4 years: 197

Other personnel:
Short-term less than 1 year from US: 772
Non-US serving in own/other country: 10
Home ministry & office staff in US: 76

Countries: Argentina 10; Bolivia 39; Dominica 4; Haiti 2; Honduras 29; Hungary 4; India 2; Japan 4; Kenya 47; Mexico 15; Papua New Guinea 11; Paraguay 7; Taiwan 2; Tanzania 4; Uganda 11; Ukraine 6

World Harvest Mission

100 West Ave., Ste. W960
Jenkintown, PA 19046-2697 USA

Phone: (215) 885-1811
Fax: (215) 885-4762
E-mail: info@whm.org
Web Site: www.whm.org

Mr. Clyde Godwin, Exec. Director

A nondenominational sending agency of Evangelical tradition engaged in Christian education, church planting, missionary education, TEE, theological education, evangelism, furloughed missionary support and mobilization for mission.

Purpose: "...[to see] local churches revived, mobilized and...sending teams of trained men and women to plant churches overseas."

Year Founded in US: 1983

Income for Overseas Min: $3,879,850

Gifts-in-Kind: $1,137

Fully Supported US Personnel Overseas:

Expecting to serve more than 4 years: 55
Expecting to serve 1 to 4 years: 9

Other personnel:
  Short-term less than 1 year from US: 256
  Home ministry & office staff in US: 19

Countries: Chile 2; Germany 3; India 4; Ireland 5; Italy 2; Kenya 4; Netherlands 4; Russia; Spain 3; Uganda 15; Ukraine 2; United Kingdom 11

World Harvest Now, Inc.

P.O. Box 911
Denton, TX 76202 USA
Phone: (940) 891-4400
Fax: (940) 484-6097
E-mail: WHN@whn.org
Web Site: www.whn.org

Mr. Lamont Brown, President/Founder

A nondenominational sending agency of Evangelical tradition engaged in church planting, evangelism, leadership development, support of national churches and missionary training. Statistics from 1998.

Purpose: "...to facilitate the planting of cell group churches among the least evangelized people in or near the 10/40 Window."

Year Founded in US: 1992
Income for Overseas Min: $687,400
Gifts-in-Kind: $430,000
Fully Supported US Personnel Overseas:
  Expecting to serve more than 4 years: 2
  Expecting to serve 1 to 4 years: 7
  Nonresidential mission personnel: 1

Other personnel:
  Non-US serving in own/other country: 11
  Home ministry & office staff in US: 8
  Bivocational/Tentmaker from US: 3

Countries: Asia–General 2; Russia

World Help

(See Ad on page 295)
P.O. Box 501
Forest, VA 24551 USA
Phone: (434) 525-4657
Fax: (434) 525-4727
E-mail: info@worldhelp.net
Web Site: www.worldhelp.net

Dr. F. Vernon Brewer, President

An interdenominational support agency of Evangelical tradition engaged in Bible distribution, church construction, church planting, leadership development, providing medical supplies and support of national churches.

Purpose: "...to fulfill the Great Commission and the Great Commandment through partnering, training, helping and serving, especially in the unreached areas of the world."

Year Founded in US: 1992
Income for Overseas Min: $6,903,787
Gifts-in-Kind: $4,611,374
Personnel:
  Short-term less than 1 year from US: 78
  Non-US serving in own/other country: 164
  Home ministry & office staff in US: 55

Countries: China; Cuba; Honduras; India; Lithuania; Myanmar/Burma; Nepal; Philippines; Romania; Russia; Thailand; Ukraine

World Horizons

P.O. Box 17721
Richmond, VA 23226 USA
Phone: (804) 225-5517
Fax: (804) 225-5517
E-mail: worldhorizons@compuserve.com
Web Site: www.worldhorizons.org

Mr. Andrew Fuller, Operations Director

An interdenominational support agency of Charismatic and Evangelical tradition engaged in church planting, evangelism mobilization for mission, short-term programs and missionary training. The US arm of an international ministry with more than 400 field personnel drawn from more than 20 nations.

Purpose: "...to take the good news of Jesus Christ to the remotest places, to ensure that all who have yet to hear of the Lord, have an opportunity to respond to the gospel."

Year Founded in US: 1992
Income for Overseas Min: $175,000
Fully Supported US Personnel Overseas:
  Expecting to serve more than 4 years: 21
  Expecting to serve 1 to 4 years: 1

Other personnel:
  Short-term less than 1 year from US: 70
  Non-US serving in own/other country: 19
  Home ministry & office staff in US: 2

Countries: Africa–General 5; Asia–General

4; Brazil 2; Cambodia 2; France 4; Spain 2; Unspecified Country 2

World Indigenous Missions

P.O. Box 310627
New Braunfels, TX 78131 USA
Phone: (830) 629-0863
Fax: (830) 629-0357
E-mail: wim@worldim.com
Web Site: www.worldim.com
Mr. Charles E. Hall, President

A nondenominational sending agency of Charismatic tradition engaged in church planting, evangelism and short-term programs.

Year Founded in US: 1981

Income for Overseas Min: $1,192,406

Gifts-in-Kind: $32,200

Fully Supported US Personnel Overseas:
 Expecting to serve more than 4 years: 35
 Expecting to serve 1 to 4 years: 15
 Nonresidential mission personnel: 11

Other personnel:
 Short-term less than 1 year from US: 40
 Non-US serving in own/other country: 11
 Home ministry & office staff in US: 8

Countries: Bolivia 2; China; Hungary; India; Indonesia 2; Kenya 2; Mexico 21; Philippines 2; Romania; Russia 2; Spain 2; Thailand; Venezuela 2

World Mission Associates

128 East Grant St., Ste. 203
Lancaster, PA 17602 USA
Phone: (717) 299-1427
Fax: (717) 299-2943
E-mail: wmausa@wmausa.org
Web Site: www.wmausa.org
Rev. Glenn J. Schwartz, Exec. Director

A denominational service agency of Evangelical tradition engaged in mobilization of local resources for missions through seminars, training and video production/distribution.

Year Founded in US: 1983

Income for Overseas Min: NA

Fully Supported US Personnel Overseas:
 Expecting to serve more than 4 years: 2
 Nonresidential mission personnel: 10

Other personnel:
 Non-US serving in own/other country: 2
 Home ministry & office staff in US: 6

Countries: Kenya 2; Zambia

World Mission Prayer League Inc.

232 Clifton Ave.
Minneapolis, MN 55403-3497 USA
Phone: (612) 871-6843
Fax: (612) 871-6844
E-mail: wmpl@wmpl.org
Web Site: www.wmpl.org
Rev. Charles R. Lindquist, Gen. Director

A denominational sending agency of Lutheran tradition engaged in church planting, development, TEE, theological education, evangelism, leadership development and medical work.

Year Founded in US: 1937

Income for Overseas Min: $1,637,094

Fully Supported US Personnel Overseas:
 Expecting to serve more than 4 years: 58
 Expecting to serve 1 to 4 years: 2
 Nonresidential mission personnel: 2

Other personnel:
 Short-term less than 1 year from US: 12
 Non-US serving in own/other country: 5
 Home ministry & office staff in US: 21

Countries: Bangladesh 6; Bolivia 8; Central Asia–General 2; Ecuador 5; Eritrea 1; Kenya 11; Mexico 5; Mongolia 2; Nepal 4; Oceania–General 2; Pakistan 2; Peru 4; Philippines 4; Romania 2

World Missionary Assistance Plan

1419 N. San Fernando Blvd., Ste. 200
Burbank, CA 91504-4194 USA
Phone: (818) 843-7233
Fax: (818) 845-5000
E-mail: wmap01@aol.com
Web Site: www.world-map.com
Mr. Frank R. Parrish, President

A transdenominational service agency of Charismatic and Evangelical tradition engaged in leadership development, theological education, literature distribution, support of national churches, training and translation work.

WOMEN
of the Harvest

*A ministry of support and encouragement
to women serving cross-culturally*

"At your retreat I realized how many other women around the world understand and appreciate the lifestyle I live - I'm not weird and I'm not alone!" *Judy, UGANDA*

"I love reading your magazine. I have been a subscriber since the first one was sent out. I enjoy reading articles by women experiencing similar challenges to the ones I face. I am always encouraged. Your magazine helps me feel more connected to ladies in similar circumstances." *Cindy, SLOVAK REPUBLIC*

"Recently I was anguishing over our son's soon-coming flight back to the U.S. for college. I was crying out to God, asking Him for some bit of encouragement and help. When I got up the next morning, my *Women of the Harvest* magazine slipped through the mail slot. I opened it and immediately saw an article on saying goodbye to your children when you send them back the the States and how to trust God to take care of them. I cried the whole way through it, so touched by God's timing and encouragement!" *Sharon, ENGLAND*

Year Founded in US: 1964
Income for Overseas Min: $745,000
Personnel:
  Short-term less than 1 year from US: 2
  Home ministry & office staff in US: 15

World Missionary Press, Inc.
P.O. Box 120
New Paris, IN 46553 USA
Phone: (574) 831-2111
Fax: (574) 831-2161
E-mail: mailroom@wmpress.org
Web Site: www.wmpress.org
Mr. Jay E. Benson, President

An interdenominational evangelical literature ministry producing topical Scripture
booklets in 313 languages and Bible study
booklets and New Testaments in a variety
of languages for free distribution in 209
countries.
Year Founded in US: 1961
Income for Overseas Min: $1,904,575
Personnel:
  Home ministry & office staff in US: 38

World Missions Far Corners, Inc.
P.O. Box 2611
Long Beach, CA 90801 USA
Phone: (562) 402-4400
Fax: (562) 402-9039
Web Site:
www.worldmissionsfarcorners.com
Patricia L. Murdock-Cook, Exec. Secty. Treasurer

A nondenominational sending agency of
Evangelical tradition engaged in evange-
lism, church planting, literature distribu-
tion, medical work, support of national
workers and relief and/or rehabilitation.
Purpose: "A unique outreach carried on
by missionaries and an army of national
workers including medical work and
preaching the gospel on five continents."
Year Founded in US: 1958
Income for Overseas Min: $1,025,000
Fully Supported US Personnel Overseas:
  Expecting to serve more than 4 years: 36
Other personnel:
  Non-US serving in own/other country: 1,665

Home ministry & office staff in US: 10
Countries: China 2; Cote d'Ivoire 2; Cuba
1; Ecuador 8; Ethiopia; India; Kenya; Korea,
South 2; Mexico 7; Nepal; Peru 4; Philip-
pines 2; South Africa 2; Thailand 2; United
Kingdom 2; Vietnam 2

World Opportunities Intl.
1415 Cahuenga Blvd.
Hollywood, CA 90028 USA
Phone: (323) 466-7187
Fax: (323) 871-1546
E-mail: worldop@msn.com
Web Site: www.childrenscharities.org/
helpthechildren.html
Mr. Al Makhanian, Chairman

An interdenominational service agency of
Evangelical tradition engaged in relief and/
or rehabilitation, childcare/orphanage pro-
grams, disability assistance programs, litera-
ture distribution, providing medical
supplies and services for other agencies.
Year Founded in US: 1961
Income for Overseas Min: $1,000,000
Gifts-in-Kind: $871,000
Personnel:
  Home ministry & office staff in US: 20

World Outreach Ministries
P.O. Box B
Marietta, GA 30061 USA
Phone: (770) 424-1545
Fax: (770) 424-1545
E-mail: wom@worldoutreach.org
Web Site: www.worldoutreach.org
Mr. Jason R. Peebles, Founder/President

An interdenominational agency of Charis-
matic and Evangelical tradition performing
a variety of home office duties for residen-
tial missionaries engaged in church plant-
ing, evangelism and missionary training in
40 nations.
Year Founded in US: 1979
Income for Overseas Min: $1,500,000
Fully Supported US Personnel Overseas:
  Nonresidential mission personnel: 4
Other personnel:
  Home ministry & office staff in US: 8
  Bivocational/Tentmaker from US: 5

World Partners USA

P.O. Box 9127
Fort Wayne, IN 46899-9127 USA

Phone: (260) 747-2027
Fax: (260) 747-5331
E-mail: WorldPartners@compuserve.com
Web Site: www.worldpartnersusa.com

Rev. David W. Mann, Director

A denominational sending agency of Evangelical tradition engaged in church planting, agricultural programs, broadcasting, camping programs, extension education, theological education, support of national churches and Bible translation.

Year Founded in US: 1969

Income for Overseas Min: $3,588,000

Gifts-in-Kind: $13,350

Fully Supported US Personnel Overseas:
Expecting to serve more than 4 years: 72
Expecting to serve 1 to 4 years: 2
Nonresidential mission personnel: 4

Other personnel:
Short-term less than 1 year from US: 300
Non-US serving in own/other country: 2
Home ministry & office staff in US: 8
Bivocational/Tentmaker from US: 2

Countries: Brazil 4; Chad 2; China 4; Cote d'Ivoire; Cuba; Cyprus 3; Ecuador 16; Germany 4; Guinea 12; Haiti; India; Indonesia 2; Jamaica 2; Portugal 4; Russia 5; Sierra Leone; Spain 1; Thailand 5; Turkey 4; Vietnam 4

World Reach, Inc.

P.O. Box 26155
Birmingham, AL 35260-6155 USA

Phone: (205) 979-2400
Fax: (205) 979-6289
E-mail: info@world-reach.org
Web Site: www.world-reach.org

Rev. Timothy Q. Prewitt, Gen. Director

An interdenominational sending agency of Evangelical tradition engaged in church planting, evangelism, leadership development, support of national churches, short-term programs and correspondence courses.

Purpose: "...targeting unreached peoples in both remote and urban areas for the purpose of evangelizing and discipling."

Year Founded in US: 1982

Income for Overseas Min: $1,108,795

Fully Supported US Personnel Overseas:
Expecting to serve more than 4 years: 11
Nonresidential mission personnel: 5

Other personnel:
Short-term less than 1 year from US: 54
Non-US serving in own/other country: 32
Home ministry & office staff in US: 16

Countries: Albania; El Salvador 4; Germany; Honduras 4; Kenya; Peru 1; Romania; Russia 2

World Relief Corporation

P.O. Box 868
Baltimore, MD 21203-0868 USA

Phone: (443) 451-1900
Fax: (443) 451-1975
E-mail: WorldRelief@wr.org
Web Site: www.wr.org

Dr. Clive Calver, President

An interdenominational service agency of Evangelical tradition engaged in relief and/or rehabilitation, development and technical assistance. Ongoing programs in 14 countries. Home staff figure from 1998.

Purpose: "...to work with the church in alleviating human suffering worldwide in the name of Christ."

Year Founded in US: 1944

Income for Overseas Min: $17,083,313

Personnel:
Home ministry & office staff in US: 544

World Servants

7130 Portland Ave. S.
Richfield, MN 55423 USA

Phone: (612) 866-0010
Fax: (612) 866-0078
E-mail: worldservant@worldservants.org
Web Site: www.worldservants.org

Rev. Timothy N. Gibson, Exec. Director

A nondenominational specialized agency of Evangelical and Ecumenical tradition engaged in short-term programs, church construction, evangelism, leadership development and training. Short-term teams serving in 22 countries.

Purpose: "To mobilize a global network of people who will impact the world for Jesus Christ through responding to physical and spiritual need."

Year Founded in US: 1986
Income for Overseas Min: $674,987
Gifts-in-Kind: $76,308
Fully Supported US Personnel Overseas:
  Nonresidential mission personnel: 4
Other personnel:
  Non-US serving in own/other country: 8
  Home ministry & office staff in US: 3
Countries: Dominican Republic; Ecuador; Jamaica; Kenya; Kosovo

World Team
1431 Stuckert Rd.
Warrington, PA 18976 USA
Phone: (215) 491-4900
Fax: (215) 491-4910
E-mail: WT-USA@worldteam.org
Web Site: www.worldteam.org
Dr. Lee Maliska, USA Director
A nondenominational sending agency of Evangelical tradition engaged in church planting, aviation services, evangelism, support of national churches, Bible translation and training.
Purpose: "Glorifying God by working together to plant reproducing churches among the unreached people groups of the world."
Year Founded in US: 1928
Income for Overseas Min: $7,752,078
Gifts-in-Kind: $18,477
Fully Supported US Personnel Overseas:
  Expecting to serve more than 4 years: 203
  Expecting to serve 1 to 4 years: 1
  Nonresidential mission personnel: 9
Other personnel:
  Short-term less than 1 year from US: 19
  Non-US serving in own/other country: 2
  Home ministry & office staff in US: 17
  Bivocational/Tentmaker from US: 17
Countries: Australia 1; Brazil 9; Cambodia 15; Cameroon 25; Chile 6; Dominican Republic 4; Europe–General 18; France 14; Guadeloupe 2; Haiti 7; Indonesia 18; Italy 2; Peru 2; Philippines 21; Saint Vincent and the Grenadines 2; Spain 9; Suriname 10; Taiwan 6; Trinidad and Tobago 9; United Kingdom; Unspecified Country 23

World Thrust Intl., Inc.
3545 Cruse Rd., Ste. 309-A
Lawrenceville, GA 30044 USA
Phone: (770) 923-5215
Fax: (770) 923-3933
E-mail: info@worldthrust.com
Web Site: www.worldthrust.com
Dr. Bill H. Boerop, President
A transdenominational support agency engaged in mobilization for mission, theological education, leadership development and services for other agencies.
Purpose: "...to serve...as a catalyst to help mobilize the local church toward a more effective involvement in the evangelization of the world."
Year Founded in US: 1984
Income for Overseas Min: $154,714
Personnel:
  Home ministry & office staff in US: 1

World Vision Inc.
P.O. Box 9716
Federal Way, WA 98063-9716 USA
Phone: (253) 815-1000
Fax: (253) 815-3343
E-mail: info@worldvision.org
Web Site: www.worldvision.org
Mr. Richard E. Stearns, President
An interdenominational service agency of Evangelical tradition engaged in development, agricultural programs, childcare/orphanage programs, evangelism, funds transmission and relief and/or rehabilitation.
Purpose: "...to follow our Lord and Savior Jesus Christ in working with the poor and oppressed to promote human transformation, seek justice and bear witness to the good news of the Kingdom of God."
Year Founded in US: 1950
Income for Overseas Min: $358,703,000
Gifts-in-Kind: $88,610,000
Personnel:
  Home ministry & office staff in US: 679
Countries: Bangladesh; Colombia; El Salvador; Ethiopia; Ghana; Haiti; Honduras; India; Indonesia; Kenya; Mexico; Mozambique; Sierra Leone; Zambia

World Vision International
800 W. Chestnut Ave.
Monrovia, CA 91016-3198 USA

Phone: (626) 303-8811
Fax: (626) 301-7786
Web Site: www.wvi.org
Dr. Dean R. Hirsch, Intl. President

The international coordination office for the regional and national offices and other entities of the World Vision Partnership engaged in childcare/orphanage programs, development, evangelism, leadership development and training. North American personnel serving overseas, income for overseas ministries and countries of activity included in World Vision (USA) and World Vision Canada.

Purpose: "...working with the poor and oppressed to promote human transformation, seek justice and bear witness to the good news of the Kingdom of God."

Year Founded in US: 1978

Income for Overseas Min: NA

Personnel:
Home ministry & office staff in US: 165

World Witness, the Foreign Mission Board of the Associate Reformed Presbyterian Church

One Cleveland St.
Greenville, SC 29601-4799 USA
Phone: (864) 233-5226
Fax: (864) 233-5326
E-mail: worldwitness@worldwitness.org
Web Site: www.worldwitness.org
Mr. John E. Mariner, Exec. Director

A denominational sending agency of Presbyterian tradition engaged in church planting, theological education, evangelism, medical work, support of national churches and short-term programs.

Purpose: "Proclaim Christ as the only Savior and Lord through the means of evangelism, church planting, theological education and works of compassion."

Year Founded in US: 1876

Income for Overseas Min: $3,349,849

Gifts-in-Kind: $3,199

Fully Supported US Personnel Overseas:
Expecting to serve more than 4 years: 43
Nonresidential mission personnel: 2

Other personnel:

Non-US serving in own/other country: 414
Home ministry & office staff in US: 7
Countries: Germany 8; Iran 2; Mexico 13; Pakistan 7; Russia 10; Turkey 3

WorldTeach

4201 N. Peachtree Rd
Atlanta, GA 30341 USA
Phone: (770) 458-9300
Fax: (770) 454-9313
E-mail: WorldTeach@mail.com
Web Site: www.WorldTeach.net
Mr. William H. Watson, Exec. Vice President

An interdenominational support agency of Evangelical tradition engaged in leadership development, support of national churches, support of national workers and video/film production/distribution.

Income for Overseas Min: $2,997,983

Countries: India; Latin America–General; Singapore; South Africa; Ukraine

Worldwide Discipleship Assoc.

110 Carnegie Place, Ste.100
Fayetteville, GA 30214 USA
Phone: (770) 460-1337
Fax: (770) 460-1339
E-mail: Headquarters@wdausa.org
Web Site: www.wdausa.org
Mr. Robert D. Dukes, President

An interdenominational support agency of Evangelical tradition engaged in training, evangelism and missions information service.

Year Founded in US: 1974

Income for Overseas Min: $98,416

Personnel:
Home ministry & office staff in US: 13

Worldwide Lab Improvement, Inc.

3607 Gembrit Circle
Kalamazoo, MI 49001 USA
Phone: (616) 323-8407
Fax: (616) 323-2030
E-mail: mail@wwlab.org
Web Site: www.wwlab.org
Mr. Edwin J. Bos, President

A transdenominational non-profit agency of Evangelical tradition which assists any evangelical mission hospital or clinic or short-term medical missionary.

Purpose: "...to serve Jesus Christ by providing mission hospitals and clinics in developing countries with quality medical laboratory testing equipment and supplies, and train the staff in the appropriate techniques of use."

Year Founded in US: 1988

Income for Overseas Min: $312,830

Gifts-in-Kind: $78,860

Personnel:
Home ministry & office staff in US: 6

World-Wide Missions
P.O. Box 2300
Redlands, CA 92373 USA
Phone: (909) 793-2009
Fax: (909) 793-6880
E-mail: wwmiss@gte.net
Web Site: www.world-widemissions.org
Rev. Fred M. Johnson, Exec. Director

An interdenominational support agency of Evangelical tradition engaged in support of national workers, Bible distribution, childcare/orphanage programs, church planting, Christian education and medical work.

Year Founded in US: 1950

Income for Overseas Min: NA

Gifts-in-Kind: $3,126,561

Personnel:
Non-US serving in own/other country: 252
Home ministry & office staff in US: 3

Countries: Bangladesh; Bolivia; Brazil; Cameroon; Chile; Colombia; Congo, Republic of the; Egypt; El Salvador; Guatemala; Haiti; Honduras; Hong Kong; India; Italy; Jordan; Kenya; Korea, South; Liberia; Malawi; Middle East; Nigeria; Papua New Guinea; Paraguay; Philippines; Syria; Taiwan; Turkey

Worldwide Tentmakers, Inc.
423 Townes St.
Greenville, SC 29601 USA
Phone: (864) 370-0475
Fax: (864) 235-3369
E-mail: wtijobs@aol.com
Web Site: www.worldwidetentmakers.com
Mr. Thomas Stultz, President

A nondenominational service agency of

Baptist and Fundamental tradition engaged in tentmaking and evangelism.

Purpose: "...committed to assisting local fundamentalist churches in the promotion, preparation and placement of self-supporting witnesses worldwide."

Year Founded in US: 1987

Income for Overseas Min: $225,000

Fully Supported US Personnel Overseas:
Nonresidential mission personnel: 2

Other personnel:
Short-term less than 1 year from US: 60
Home ministry & office staff in US: 2
Bivocational/Tentmaker from US: 23

Countries: Austria; China; Hong Kong; Korea, South; Micronesia, Federated States of; Poland; Thailand; Turkey; United Arab Emirates; United Kingdom

Wycliffe Associates USA
P.O. Box 2000
Orange, CA 92859 USA
Phone: (714) 639-9950
Fax: (714) 771-5262
E-mail: wa@wycliffe.org
Web Site: www.wycliffeassociates.org
Mr. Martin Huyett, President

A nondenominational service agency of Evangelical tradition engaged in short-term programs, funds transmission, furloughed missionary support, mobilization for mission, supplying equipment and technical assistance. Statistics from 1998.

Purpose: "...supports Wycliffe Bible Translators through programs and services that enable God's people to become involved in Bible translation through their prayers and resources."

Year Founded in US: 1967

Income for Overseas Min: $2,959,290

Gifts-in-Kind: $64,862

Fully Supported US Personnel Overseas:
Expecting to serve 1 to 4 years: 10
Nonresidential mission personnel: 2

Other personnel:
Short-term less than 1 year from US: 7
Home ministry & office staff in US: 59

Countries: Guatemala; Indonesia; Kenya; Papua New Guinea; Senegal

Wycliffe Bible Translators International

7500 W. Camp Wisdom Rd.
Dallas, TX 75236 USA
Phone: (972) 708-7400
Fax: (972) 708-7350
E-mail: corporation_secretary@sil.org
Web Site: www.wycliffe.net

Dr. John Watters, Exec. Director

An interdenominational support agency of Evangelical tradition that is the international coordination center for 31 Wycliffe national sending agencies and 14 affiliates around the world. Wycliffe is engaged in Bible translation, linguistics, literacy work and other activities needed to support these primary ministries. Income and overseas personnel totals from the USA and Canada shown under Wycliffe USA and Wycliffe Canada.

Purpose: "...to integrate Scripture translation, scholarship and service so that all people will have access to God's Word in their own language."

Year Founded in US: 1934

Income for Overseas Min: $666,328

Wycliffe Bible Translators USA

P.O. Box 628200
Orlando, FL 32862-8200 USA
Phone: (407) 852-3600
Fax: (407) 852-3601
E-mail: hq@wycliffe.org
Web Site: www.wycliffe.org

Mr. Bob Creson, President

A nondenominational sending agency of Evangelical and Independent tradition engaged in Bible translation, linguistics, literacy work and translation work.

Purpose: "...to assist the church in making disciples of all nations through Bible translation."

Year Founded in US: 1934

Income for Overseas Min: $82,457,000

Gifts-in-Kind: $202,000

Fully Supported US Personnel Overseas:
Expecting to serve more than 4 years: 3,907
Nonresidential mission personnel: 2

Other personnel:

Short-term less than 1 year from US: 127
Home ministry & office staff in US: 121

Countries: Africa–General 132; Asia–General 564; Australia 134; Austria 5; Belgium 3; Brazil 126; Burkina Faso 57; Cameroon 187; Caribbean–General 4; Central African Republic 14; Chad 58; Colombia 58; Congo, Democratic Republic of 22; Cote d'Ivoire 97; Ethiopia 55; Europe–General 20; Finland 2; France 8; Germany 17; Ghana 38; Hong Kong 1; Hungary 2; Indonesia 267; Japan 4; Kenya 42; Latin America –General 137; Malaysia 44; Mexico 226; Mozambique 45; Netherlands 17; New Zealand 14; Niger 32; Nigeria 31; Norway 1; Oceania–General 22; Papua New Guinea 621; Peru 139; Philippines 224; Senegal 58; Singapore 8; Solomon Islands 30; South Africa 7; Sudan 69; Sweden 2; Switzerland 12; Togo 75; Uganda 69; United Kingdom 83; Vanuatu 24

Young Life

P.O. Box 520
Colorado Springs, CO 80901 USA
Phone: (719) 381-1800
Fax: (719) 381-1750
E-mail: MAT@sc.younglife.org
Web Site: www.younglife.org

Mr. Denny Rydberg, President

A nondenominational sending agency of Evangelical tradition engaged in evangelism, camping programs and youth programs in more than 40 countries.

Year Founded in US: 1941

Income for Overseas Min: NR

Youth Encounter

2500 39th Ave. NE, #222
Minneapolis, MN 55418 USA
Phone: (612) 789-3556
Fax: (612) 789-6027
E-mail: encounter@youthencounter.org
Web Site: www.youthencounter.org

Dr. Larry Dean Johnson, President

A denominational specialized agency of Lutheran tradition engaged in youth programs and short-term programs.

Year Founded in US: 1965

Income for Overseas Min: $420,000

Personnel:
    Short-term less than 1 year from US: 75
    Home ministry & office staff in US: 60

Youth for Christ/USA, World Outreach Division

P.O. Box 228822
Denver, CO 80222 USA

Phone: (303) 843-9000
Fax: (303) 843-6793
E-mail: info@yfc.org
Web Site: www.yfc.org/worldoutreach

Dr. Roger Cross, President/CEO

A nondenominational sending agency of Evangelical tradition engaged in evangelism and youth programs.

Purpose: "...facilitate USA citizens to serve the YFC International movement in reaching youth in nearly 100 countries in the world."

Year Founded in US: 1945

Income for Overseas Min: $3,815,276

Fully Supported US Personnel Overseas:
    Expecting to serve more than 4 years: 56

Other personnel:
    Home ministry & office staff in US: 36

Countries: Australia 5; Brazil 1; France 2; Germany 10; Guinea-Bissau 4; Honduras 2; Italy 2; Kenya 3; Lebanon 2; Namibia 1; Netherlands 1; New Zealand 1; Portugal 2; South Africa 2; Spain 1; Switzerland 8; Thailand 1; United Kingdom 8

Youth With A Mission (YWAM), N. American Office

7085 Battlecreek Rd. SE
Salem, OR 97301 USA

Phone: (503) 364-3837
Fax: (503) 378-7026
E-mail: YWAMNAO@compuserve.com
Web Site: www.ywam.org

Mr. Peter Iliyn, N. American Regional Director

An interdenominational sending agency of Evangelical tradition engaged in evangelism, church planting, relief and/or rehabilitation, missionary training and youth programs. YWAM has some 30,000 staff serving internationally in more than 75 countries. See also Mercy Ships.

Year Founded in US: 1960

Income for Overseas Min: NA
Fully Supported US Personnel Overseas:
    Expecting to serve more than 4 years: 1,000
Other personnel:
    Short-term less than 1 year from US:
100,000
    Home ministry & office staff in US: 1,200
Countries: Unspecified Country 1,000

YUGO Ministries

P.O. Box 25
San Dimas, CA 91773-0025 USA

Phone: (909) 592-6621
Fax: (909) 394-1210
E-mail: outreach@yugo.org
Web Site: www.yugo.org

Mr. Leonard K. Janssen, Exec. Director

A nondenominational sending agency of Evangelical tradition engaged in short-term programs, church planting, evangelism and youth programs.

Year Founded in US: 1964

Income for Overseas Min: $1,500,000

Zion Evangelical Ministries of Africa

Box 727
Zion, IL 60099 USA

Phone: (847) 872-7363
E-mail: zemausa@aol.com
Web Site: www.zema.org

Mr. Clint Newman, Home Office Director

An interdenominational sending agency of Evangelical tradition engaged in theological education, leadership development, support of national churches and support of national workers.

Year Founded in US: 1900

Income for Overseas Min: $212,032

Fully Supported US Personnel Overseas:
    Expecting to serve more than 4 years: 6
Other personnel:
    Short-term less than 1 year from US: 28
    Non-US serving in own/other country: 5
    Home ministry & office staff in US: 3
Countries: South Africa 6

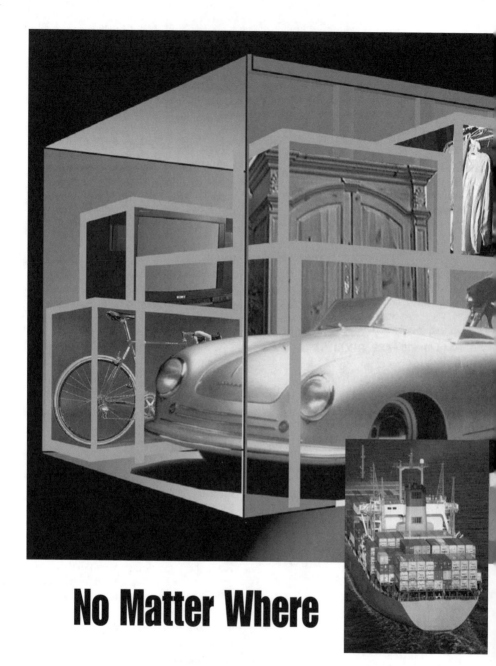

No Matter Where

We ship anywhere

At World Air & Ocean Services, Inc., transportation specialists will help you plan the methods and routes to transport your personal belongings from your home to your foreign destination.

- Years of experience in international shipping
- Personalized service anywhere in the world
- Complete line of international services

We'll Get it There

World Air & Ocean Services

448 Grandview Drive
South San Francisco, CA 94080
800-213-9267   650-952-1041
Fax: 650-952-1146
EMail: Ming@worldsfo.com
www.worldairocean.com

Our services include:

- Shipping by Air or Sea
- Pickup from any City Nationwide
- Door to Door Service to most countries

- Full Insurance coverage
- Act as your receiving station
- Short Term Warehousing
- Preparation of all export documents

Chapter 3
Indices to U.S. Protestant Agencies

M any *Handbook* users find it valuable to locate agencies by particular categories of church tradition or ministry activity. This chapter provides the user with those indices. Agency responses on the Mission Handbook survey questionnaire helped define the listed categories. The organizations in each category appear in alphabetical order by organization name.

Index by Church Tradition

If an agency needed more than one generic or denominational category to describe its traditional doctrinal and/or ecclesiastical stance, the agency may appear under as many as two of the given categories. We have arranged the list alphabetically by category and within each category by agency name. See question #7 of the survey questionnaire reproduced in the Appendix for the actual wording of the question and the check-off list of choices.

Index by Ministry Activity

Almost all agencies are involved in several types of ministry activities. Each agency may be listed under as many as six primary categories of activity. We asked those with more than six primary activities to indicate the six activities toward which they had committed the largest amount of resources.

We have divided the broad activities of education and evangelism into subcategories. For example, the evangelism category appears as "evangelism, mass" and "evangelism, student," and so on. See question #8 of the survey questionnaire in the Appendix for the actual wording of the question and the check-off list of activities.

Agencies sometimes have written in new categories under the "other" choice in previous surveys. Some of these, if used often enough, may be included in the check-off list for the next edition's survey questionnaire. Sometimes categories are dropped because of lack of use. The most used categories, however, have remained the same over the years.

Seven new categories added during this edition (which will appear as options on the next survey) are: adoption, apologetics, discipleship, justice & related, tentmaking & related, TESOL, and urban ministry.

Church Tradition

Adventist
Advent Christian Gen. Conf.
Seventh-day Adventists Gen. Conf.

Anglican
Reformed Episcopal Bd. of Foreign Msns.

Baptist
ABWE
American Baptist Chs. in the USA
Anis Shorrosh Evangelistic Assoc.
Baptist Bible Fellowship Intl.
Baptist Bible Translators Institute
Baptist General Conference
Baptist Intl. Evangelistic Mins.
Baptist Intl. Missions, Inc. (BIMI)
Baptist International Outreach
Baptist Medical & Dental Msn. Intl.
Baptist Mid-Missions
Baptist Missions to Forgotten Peoples
Baptist World Mission
Biblical Ministries Worldwide
Carver International Missions, Inc.
CBInternational
Children's Medical Ministries
Christ to the Nations
Christian Discipleship Ministries, Inc.
Christian Missions Unlimited
East-West Ministries International
Final Frontiers Foundation, Inc.
Free Will Baptists, Inc.
FRIENDS in Action, International
Fundamental Baptist Msn. Trinidad
General Assoc. Regular Baptist Chs.
General Baptists International
Gospel Furthering Fellowship
Gospel Mission of South America
Grace Baptist Missions International
Handclasp International, Inc.
In Touch Mission International
Independent Faith Mission
Independent Gospel Missions
International Bd. of Jewish Missions, Inc.
International Partnership Mins., Inc.
International Street Kids Outreach Mns.
JARON Ministries International
Macedonia World Baptist Missions, Inc.
Macedonian Missionary Service
Medical Missions Philippines
Mission Nannys
Mission ONE, Inc.
Mission to the Americas
Missionary Flights International
National Baptist Convention of America
National Baptist Conv. USA
North American Baptist Conf. Intl.
Open Door Baptist Missions
Outreach To Asia Nationals
Pan American Missions
Prakash Association USA
Priority One International
Progressive National Baptist Conv. USA
Romanian Missionary Society
Russian Bible Society, Inc.
Seventh Day Baptist Missionary Society
Son Shine Ministries International
Source of Light Ministries Intl. Inc.
Southern Baptist Conv. Int. Mission Bd.
Spiritual Growth Resources, Inc.
Sports & Rec Plus
The Master's Harvest
The Master's Mission, Inc.
Third World Baptist Missions
Training Evangelistic Leadership
Waymarks International Radio Ministries
World Baptist Fellowship Mission Agency
Worldwide Tentmakers, Inc.

Brethren
Brethren Church Missionary Bd.
Church of the Brethren
Grace Brethren International Missions
India Evangelical Mission, Inc.

Charismatic
Advancing Indigenous Missions
AIMS
Apostolic Team Ministries, Intl.
Bethany Fellowship Missions
Bethel Christian Ministries
Calvary Commission, Inc.
Calvary International
Celebrant Singers
Christ for India, Inc.
Christ for the Nations, Inc.
Christian Fellowship Union
Christian Laymen's Msny. Evangelism Assoc.
Christian Ministries Intl. (C.M.I.)
Covenant Celebration Ch. Global Outreach
Elim Fellowship, International Dept.
Family Aid International, Inc.
Foundation For His Ministry
Global Strategy Mission Assoc.
Globe Missionary Evangelism
Good News for India
Hundredfold Ministries International
International Leadership Seminars
International Outreach Ministries
International Pentecostal Ch. of Christ
Living Water Teaching International

Mahesh Chavda Ministries Intl.
Ministry to Eastern Europe
Mission Possible Foundation, Inc.
Missionary Revival Crusade
New Life League International
Omega World Missions
Open Bible Standard
Oriental Missionary Crusade
Pass the Torch Ministries
Precious Seed Ministries
Shield of Faith Ministries
Surfing the Nations
The Master's Harvest
Tribes and Nations Outreach
United Evangelical Churches
University of the Family
Vineyard International Consortium
World Horizons
World Indigenous Missions
World Missionary Assistance Plan
World Outreach Ministries

Christian (Restoration Movement)
ACM International
African Mission Evangelism
AMOR Ministries
Christian Ch. (Disciples of Christ)
Christian Churches/Churches of Christ
Churches of Christ
CMF International
European Evangelistic Society
Flwshp. of Assoc. of Medical Evangelism
Good News Productions Intl.
Health Teams International
Key Communications
Mission Services Association
Missions Resource Center
Missions Resource Network
Muslim Hope
Pioneer Bible Translators
Southern Mexico Missions
TCM International
Team Expansion, Inc.
Turkish World Outreach

Christian/Plymouth Brethren
Brethren Assemblies
Christian Mission for the Deaf
Christian Missions in Many Lands
Grace and Truth, Inc.
Ireland Outreach International Inc.
United Church Board of World Mins.

Congregational
Armenian Missionary Association
Congregational Christian Chs.

Conservative Cong. Christian Conf.
United Church Board of World Mins.

Ecumenical
Bread for the World
Christian Blind Mission Intl.
Christian Dental Society
Christian Literacy Associates
Church World Service & Witness
East Gates Ministries International
Habitat for Humanity International
Interchurch Medical Assistance
Intl. Found. for EWHA Woman's University
International Students
Ludhiana Christian Medical College Bd.
MAP International
Middle East Media–USA
Moravian Church in N. America
Overseas Ministries Study Center
Self-Help International
United Bd. for Christian Higher Ed. in Asia
United Church Board for World Mins.
Vellore Christian Medical College Bd (USA)

Episcopal
Anglican Frontier Missions
Episcopal Church Msny. Community
Episcopal Ch., Domestic & Frgn. Msny. Soc.
Rock the World Youth Mission Alliance
Society of St. Margaret
South American Missionary Society

Evangelical
ACMC
Action International Ministries
ACTS International Ministries
Adopt-A-People Clearinghouse
Advancing Indigenous Missions
Advancing Native Missions
Adventures in Missions
Africa Inland Mission International
African Bible Colleges, Inc.
African Enterprise, Inc.
African Leadership
AIMS
Alberto Mottesi Evangelistic Assoc.
Amazon Focus
Ambassadors for Christ Intl.
Ambassadors for Christ, Inc.
American Leprosy Missions, Inc.
American Missionary Fellowship
American Scripture Gift Mission
AmeriTribes
AMF International
AMG International
Anis Shorrosh Evangelistic Association

Arab World Ministries
ARISE International
Armenian Msny. Assoc. of America, Inc.
Artists In Christian Testimony
Asian Outreach U.S.A.
ASSIST
Audio Scripture Ministries
Awana Clubs International
Back to the Bible International
Barnabas International
BCM International
Bethany Fellowship Missions
Bible League, The
Bible Literature International
Bible Training Centre for Pastors
Bibles For The World, Inc.
Biblical Literature Fellowship
BILD International
Billy Graham Center, The
Blessings International
Bridge Builders International
Bright Hope International
Cadence International
Caleb Project
Calvary Comission
Calvary Evangelistic Mission, Inc.
CAM International
Campus Crusade for Christ, Intl.
Caring Partners International, Inc.
Carpenter's Tools International
Carver International Missions
Cedar Lane Missionary Homes
CEIFA Ministries International
Celebrant Singers
Centers for Apologetics Research
Childcare International
China Connection
China Ministries International
Chosen, Inc.
Christ Community Church
Christ for the City International
Christ for the Lost World
Christar
Christian Aid Mission
Christian and Missionary Alliance
Christian Associates International
Christian Broadcasting Network, the
Christian Info. Service, Inc. Mns. Div.
Christian Leadership Dev., Inc.
Christian Literature International
Christian Outreach International
Christian Pilots Association
Christian Resources International
Christian Service International
Christian World Publishers
Christians In Action, Inc.

Church Ministries International
Church Missions Link
Church of God (Seventh Day) Gen. Conf.
Church of the United Brethren in Christ
Church Planting International
Church Resource Ministries
Churches of God, General Conference
CityTeam Ministries
Clark Theol. College (India) Tribal Mns., USA
CLC Ministries International
CMTS Ministries, Inc.
ComCare International
Commission to Every Nation
Connecting Businessmen to Christ
Cook Communications Ministries Intl.
Correll Missionary Ministries
Crisis Consulting International
Crossover Communications Intl.
D & D Missionary Homes, Inc.
Dawn Ministries
Dayspring Enterprises International
Daystar U.S.
Deaf Missions International
Development Associates Intl. (DAI)
Disciples International
Donetsk Christian University
DualReach
East Gates Ministries Intl.
East West Ministries
Eastern European Outreach, Inc.
ECHO
EFMA
Emmanuel Intl. Mission (U.S.)
Empowering Lives International
Engineering Ministries International
EQUIP
Equip, Inc.
Equipping the Saints
European Christian Mission NA, Inc.
Evangelical Covenant Ch., Bd. of Wld. Msn.
Evangelical Free Church Mission
Evangelical Friends Church Southwest
Evangelical Friends Mission
Evangelical Greenhouse Mins. Intl.
Evangelical Methodist Ch., Bd. of Mns.
Evangelical Presbyterian Church
Evangelism and Missions Info. Service
Evangelism Explosion International
Evangelism Resources
Every Child Ministries, Inc.
Every Home for Christ International
Far East Broadcasting Company, Inc.
FARMS International, Inc.
Food for the Hungry, Inc.
Forward Edge International
Foursquare Missions International

Friends Church Southwest
Friends of Israel Gospel Ministry
Friendship International
Global Advance
Global Fellowship
Global Focus
Global Harvest Ministries
Global Mapping International
Global Opportunities
Global Outreach, Ltd.
Global Youth Ministry Network
Go Ye Fellowship
Good News for India
Gospel Communications Intl.
Gospel for Asia
Gospel Literature Intl., Inc.
Gospel Missionary Union
Gospel Outreach Ministries Intl.
Gospel Recordings
Grace Ministries International
Grand Old Gospel Fellowship
Great Commission Center Intl.
Great Commission Ministries, Inc.
Greater Europe Mission
Greater Grace World Outreach
Hands for Christ
Harvest
Harvest Evangelism, Inc.
HBI Global Partners
HCJB World Radio
Health Emergent Intl. Services
Heart of God Ministries
Heart to Heart Intl. Ministries
Hellenic Ministries
Help for Christian Nationals, Inc.
Helps International Ministries
Hermano Pablo Ministries
High Adventure Mns.
Holt Intl. Children's Services, Inc.
Hope for the Hungry
Hope Missions Outreach Intl.
IFMA
Impact International
India Gospel League Inc., N. America
India Gospel Outreach
India Rural Evangelical Fellowship
Institute for Intl. Christian Communication
Institute of Theological Studies
INTENT
InterAct Ministries
Interaction International Inc.
INTERCOMM
Intercristo
INTERDEV
International Aid
International Bible Institute

International Bible Society
International Cassette Bible Institute
International Child Care
Intl. Christian Leprosy Msn., Inc. (USA)
International Christian Ministries
International Cooperating Ministries
International Family Missions
International Gospel Outreach
International Health Services
Intl. Institute for Christian Studies
International Messengers
International Needs–USA
International Students, Inc
International Teams, U.S.A.
International Urban Associates
InterServe/USA
InterVarsity Christian Fellowship/USA
Iranian Christians International
Italy for Christ
JAARS, Inc.
Japanese Evangelical Msny. Society
Japanese Evangelization Center
Jews for Jesus
Joni and Friends
Josue Yrion Ministries
Kids Alive International
Kids Around the World, Inc.
Kingdom Building Ministries
Larry Jones Intl. Mins. (Feed the Children)
Latin America Assistance, Inc.
Latin America Mission
Latin American Indian Ministries
Leadership Ministries Worldwide
Liberty Corner Mission
Liebenzell USA
LIFE Ministries
LIGHT International, Inc.
Link Care Foundation
Literacy & Evangelism International
Luis Palau Evangelistic Assoc.
Luke Society, The
Lutheran Brethren World Missions
M/E International, Inc.
Media Associates International
Medical Ambassadors International
Men for Missions International
Mercy Ships
Mexican Medical Ministries
Middle East Christian Outreach
Ministries In Action
Mission Aviation Fellowship
Mission India
Mission Ministries, Inc.
Mission of Mercy
Mission ONE, Inc.
Mission Possible, Inc.

Mission Safety International
Mission To Unreached Peoples
Mission Training and Resource Center
Mission: Moving Mountains, Inc.
Missionaire International
Missionary Athletes International
Missionary Gospel Fellowship
Missionary Retreat Fellowship Inc.
Missionary Revival Crusade
Missionary Ventures International
Missions To Japan, Inc.
MMS Aviation
Morelli Ministries International
Mustard Seed, Inc., The
Narramore Christian Foundation
National Religious Broadcasters
Navigators, U.S. Intl. Missions Group
Network of Intl. Christian Schools
New Directions International
New Hope International
New Life League International
New Tribes Mission
New Way Missions
No Greater Love Ministries, Inc.
Northwest Medical Teams
OC International, Inc.
OMF International
OMS International, Inc.
On The Go Ministries
Open Air Campaigners–Overseas Mins.
Open Doors with Brother Andrew USA
Operation Blessing International
Operation Mobilization, Inc.
Outreach Incorporated
Overseas Council International
Overseas Ministries Study Center
Overseas Radio & Television, Inc.
Paraclete, Inc.
Partners in Christ International
Partners International
People International
Peoples Mission International
Peter Deyneka Russian Ministries
Pioneer Clubs
Pioneers
Pocket Testament League
Precept Ministries International
Presbyterian Order for Wld. Evangelization
Prison Mission Association
Progressive Vision
Project AmaZon
Project Mercy, Inc.
Project Partner with Christ
Providence Mission Homes, Inc.
Radio Voice of Christ, Inc.
Ramabai Mukti Mission

Ramesh Richard Intl.
Ravi Zacharias International Ministries
RBC Ministries
Reach Ministries International
Reciprocal Ministries International
Red Sea Team International
Rio Grande Bible Institute
Ripe for Harvest, Inc.
Russian Christian Radio
Russian Language Ministries
Samaritan's Purse
SAND International
SEND International
Sending Experienced Retired Volunteers
ServLife International
Share International
Shield of Faith Mission Intl.
SIM USA
Slavic Gospel Association
Slavic Missionary Service
South America Mission
Sowers International, The
SP Ministries
Spanish World Ministries
STEER, Inc.
STEM
TEAM (The Evangelical Alliance Mission)
Teen Missions International
Tentmakers International Exchange–T.I.E
TMA Ministries
Touch the World Ministries
Trans World Missions
Trans World Radio
UFM International
VELA Ministries International
Venture International
Vineyard International Consortium
Voice of the Martyrs, The
Walk Thru The Bible Ministries
Waymakers International
WEC International
Word To Russia
World Bible Translation Center
World Concern
World Harvest Mission
World Harvest Now, Inc.
World Help
World Mission Associates
World Missionary Press, Inc.
World Missions Far Corners, Inc.
World Opportunities International
World Partners USA
World Reach, Inc.
World Relief Corporation
World Servants
World Team

World Vision Inc.
World Vision International
WorldTeach
Worldwide Discipleship Assoc.
Worldwide Lab Improvement, Inc.
World-Wide Missions
Wycliffe Associates USA
Wycliffe Bible Translators International
Wycliffe Bible Translators USA
Young Life
Youth for Christ/USA, World Outreach Div.
Youth With A Mission, N. Am. Office
YUGO Ministries
Zion Evangelical Ministries of Africa

Friends

Central Yearly Meeting of Friends Missions
Evangelical Friends Mission
Friends Church Southwest
Friends United Meeting, World Ministries

Fundamental

Baptist International Outreach
Baptist Mid-Missions
Baptist World Mission
Brazil Gospel Fellowship Mission
Christian Fellowship Union
FOM (Fellowship of Missions)
Fundamental Baptist Msn. Trinidad
Gideons International, The
Good Shepherd Ministries
Gospel Fellowship Association
Gospel Mission of South America
Helps International Mins.
India National Inland Mission
MATS International, Inc.
Missionary Athletes International
Missionary TECH Team
Pilgrim Fellowship, Inc.
Project Christ International
Russian Bible Society, Inc.
Spanish World Ministries
Things To Come Mission, Inc.
Third World Baptist Missions
World Baptist Fellowship Mission

Holiness

Allegheny Wesleyan Methodist Missions
Church of God (Anderson, IN)
Ch. of the Nazarene, Wld. Msn. Dept.
Congregational Holiness Church
Evangelical Bible Mission
Evangelistic Faith Missions
International Pentecostal Holiness Church
Pentecostal Free Will Baptist Church
Pillar of Fire Missions Intl.

Salvation Army, U.S.A.
World Gospel Mission

Independent

Aurora Mission
Baptist International Missions Inc. (BIMI)
Biblical Ministries Worldwide
Chosen People Ministries
Christ to the Nations
Christian Union Churches of N. AM.
Church Missions Link
Church of God (Holiness), World Mission Bd.
David Livingstone KURE Foundation
Evangelical Baptist Missions
Fellowship International Mission
Galcom International (U.S.)
Global Outreach Mission
Have Christ Will Travel Ministries
Independent Gospel Missions
International Bd. of Jewish Missions
Mailbox Club International
Missions to Military, Inc.
Mutual Faith Ministries Intl.
New Tribes Mission
Partners in Asian Missions
Shelter for Life International, Inc.
Strategic Ventures Network
Village Ministries International, Inc.
Word of Life Fellowship

Lutheran

Advancing Renewal Ministries
American Association of Lutheran Chs.
Assoc. of Free Luth. Congregations
Concordia Gospel Outreach
Evangelical Lutheran Church in America
Global Health Ministries
Haiti Lutheran Mission Society
Intl. Lutheran Laymen's League/Lutheran
    Hour Ministries
Latin America Lutheran Mission
Lutheran Bible Translators
Lutheran Brethren World Missions
Lutheran Church—Missouri Synod
Lutheran Literature Soc. for the Chinese
Lutheran World Relief
Wisconsin Evangelical Lutheran Synod
World Mission Prayer League Inc.
Youth Encounter

Mennonite

Africa Inter-Mennonite Mission
Children's Haven International
Christian Aid Ministries
Church of God in Christ, Mennonite
Eastern Mennonite Missions

General Conf. Mennonite Church
MBMS International
Mennonite Central Committee
Mennonite Mission Network
PNMC Missions
Rosedale Mennonite Missions
Virginia Mennonite Board of Missions

Methodist
African Methodist Episcopal Church
Primitive Methodist Church
Salvation Army
Servants in Faith & Technology (SIFAT)
The Mission Society (United Methodist)
United Methodist Ch., General Bd. Global
    Ministries

Other Tradition
American Bible Society
Apostolic Christian Ch. Foundation, Inc.
Evangelical Mennonite Ch. Intl. Mins.
Frontier Mission Fellowship
Global Action
International Justice Mission

Pentecostal
All God's Children International
Assemblies of God World Missions
Bethel Christian Ministries
Christian Advance International
Christian Church of N. America Missions
Ch. of God (Cleveland, TN)
Church of God of Prophecy
Congregational Holiness Church
Evangel Bible Translators
Faith Christian Fellowship Intl.
FOCAS
Free Gospel Church, Missions Dept.
Full Gospel Evangelistic Association
Full Gospel Grace Fellowship
Global University
Gospel Revival Ministries
International Pentecostal Church of Christ
International Pentecostal Holiness Church
Open Bible Standard Churches
Pentecostal Church of God Msns.
Rehoboth Ministries, Inc
Teen World Outreach
The Ch. of God of the Apostolic Faith, Inc.
Tribes and Nations Outreach
United Pentecostal Church Intl.

Presbyterian
Arabic Communication Center
Audio Scriptures International
China Outreach Ministries

Church Planting International
Cities for Christ Worldwide
Cumberland Presbyterian Church Msns.
Evangelical Presbyterian Church
Floresta USA, Inc.
Flying Doctors of America
Mission to the World (PCA), Inc.
Orthodox Presbyterian Church
Perimeter Church, Global Outreach
Presbyterian Center for Mission Studies
Presbyterian Church (USA)
Presbyterian Evangelistic Fellowship
Presbyterian Missionary Union
Reformed Churches in America
Seed International
Spiritual Growth Resources
Westminister Biblical Missions
World Witness, Assoc. Reformed Presb. Ch.

Reformed
Christian Reformed World Missions
Christian Reformed World Relief Comte.
Cities for Christ Worldwide
LOGOI, Inc./FLET
Orthodox Presbyterian Church
Presbyterian Evangelistic Fellowship
Project Care
Reformation Translation Flwshp.
Reformed Ch. in America, Gen. Synod

Wesleyan
Allegheny Wesleyan Methodist Missions
Bible Missionary Church
Brethren in Christ World Missions
Congregational Methodist Church
Cornerstone International
Evangelical Congregational Church
Evangelistic Faith Missions
Free Methodist World Missions
GO InterNational
International Gospel Outreach
Pan American Missions
Primitive Methodist Church in the USA
Salvation Army
Wesleyan World Missions
World Gospel Mission

Ministry Activity

Adoption
Holt International Children's Services, Inc.

Agricultural programs
China Connection
Christ for the Nations, Inc.
Christar
Christian Blind Mission Intl.
Christian Medical & Dental Society
Church World Service & Witness
Christ in the U.S.A.
Congregational Christian Churches
ECHO
Empowering Lives International
Equip, Inc.
FARMS International, Inc.
Floresta USA, Inc.
Food for the Hungry, Inc.
Heifer International
Lutheran World Relief
Medical Ambassadors International
Mennonite Central Committee
Mercy Ships
Mission To Unreached Peoples
Mustard Seed, Inc., The
Prakash Association USA
Project Mercy, Inc.
Red Sea Team International
SAND International
Self-Help International
STEER, Inc.
Tribes and Nations Outreach
World Concern
World Partners USA
World Vision Inc.

Apologetics
Anis Shorrosh Evangelistic Association, Inc.
Centers for Apologetics Research (CFAR)

Association of Missions
ACMC
Congregational Christian Chs., Natl. Assoc.
EFMA
Evangelical Mennonite Church Intl. Mins.
FOM (Fellowship of Missions)
Full Gospel Evangelistic Assoc.
IFMA
Seventh Day Baptist Missionary Society

Audio recording/distribution
Audio Scripture Ministries
Audio Scriptures International
Carpenter's Tools International

Celebrant Singers
Christian Resources International
Derek Prince Ministries, Intl.
East Gates Ministries Intl.
Edwin L. Hodges Ministries
Emmaus Road, International
Far East Broadcasting Company, Inc.
Friendship International
Gospel Recordings (Global Recordings Net.)
Grand Old Gospel Fellowship
Hands for Christ
Hosanna / Faith Comes By Hearing
INTERCOMM
International Cassette Bible Institute
Josue Yrion World Evangelism Missions, Inc.
Lutheran Bible Translators
Lutheran Literature Society for the Chinese
Middle East Media–USA
Missionary Revival Crusade
Overseas Radio & Television, Inc.
Pilgrim Fellowship, Inc.
Russian Christian Radio
Trans World Radio
Waymarks International Radio Ministries
Word To Russia

Aviation services
Assoc. of Free Luth. Congregations Wld. Msn.
Christian Pilots Association
Church of the Nazarene, Wld. Msn. Dept.
Global Outreach Mission
JAARS, Inc.
Living Water Teaching International
Mission Aviation Fellowship
Mission Safety International
Missionaire International
Missionary Flights International
MMS Aviation
South America Mission
World Gospel Mission
World Team

Bible distribution
Advancing Renewal Ministries
African Bible Colleges, Inc.
African Methodist Episcopal Church
Allegheny Wesleyan Methodist Missions
Ambassadors for Christ, Inc.
American Bible Society
AMF International
AMG International
Arabic Communication Center
Armenian Msny. Assoc. of America, Inc.
Asian Outreach U.S.A.
Assemblies of God World Missions
ASSIST

Audio Scriptures International
Aurora Mission
Baptist Bible Translators Institute
Baptist International Evangelistic Ministries
Baptist International Missions, Inc. (BIMI)
Bethel Christian Ministries
Bible League, The
Bible Literature International
Bibles For The World, Inc.
Biblical Literature Fellowship
Calvary Evangelistic Mission, Inc.
Central Yearly Meeting of Friends Missions
China Connection
China Ministries International
China Outreach Ministries
Christ to the Nations
Christian Aid Ministries
Christian Discipleship Ministries, Inc.
Christian Literature International
Christian Missions Unlimited
Christian Resources International
Church of God (Seventh Day) Gen. Conf.
Ch. of God in Christ, Mennonite Gen. Msn. Bd.
CLC Ministries International
Congregational Methodist Church
Cook Communications Ministries Intl.
East Gates Ministries Intl.
Edwin L. Hodges Ministries
Evangel Bible Translators
Evangelical Bible Mission
Final Frontiers Foundation, Inc.
Free Gospel Church, Missions Dept.
Full Gospel Evangelistic Association
Gideons International, The
Go Ye Fellowship
Gospel Revival Ministries
Hands for Christ
Hosanna / Faith Comes By Hearing
In Touch Mission International
India National Inland Mission
India Rural Evangelical Fellowship
International Bible Society
International Board of Jewish Missions, Inc.
International Family Missions
Iranian Christians International
Ireland Outreach International Inc.
Italy for Christ
Key Communications
Lutheran Literature Society for the Chinese
Macedonian Missionary Service
Missionary Athletes International
Muslim Hope
New Life League International
Open Door Baptist Missions
Open Doors with Brother Andrew USA
Outreach To Asia Nationals

Pan American Missions
Partners in Christ International
Pentecostal Ch. of God
Pocket Testament League
Presbyterian Missionary Union
Prison Mission Association
Progressive National Baptist Conv USA
Project Christ International
Project Mercy, Inc.
Reformed Baptist Mission Services
Ripe for Harvest, Inc.
Russian Bible Society, Inc.
Slavic Gospel Association
Spanish World Ministries
The Ch. of God of the Apostolic Faith, Inc.
Third World Baptist Missions
Trans World Missions
Tribes and Nations Outreach
Turkish World Outreach
Voice of the Martyrs, The
Waymarks International Radio Ministries
World Bible Translation Center
World Help
World-Wide Missions

Bible memorization
Awana Clubs International
Disciples International
Navigators, U.S. Intl. Missions Group

Broadcasting, radio and/or TV
African Bible Colleges, Inc.
Alberto Mottesi Evangelistic Association
Anis Shorrosh Evangelistic Association, Inc.
Arab World Ministries
Back to the Bible International
Baptist International Missions, Inc. (BIMI)
Brazil Gospel Fellowship Mission
Calvary Evangelistic Mission, Inc.
CAM International
Celebrant Singers
China Outreach Ministries
Christian and Missionary Alliance
Christian Broadcasting Network, the
Christian Info. Service, Inc. Msns. Div.
Commission to Every Nation
Correll Missionary Ministries
Dayspring Enterprises International
Derek Prince Ministries, Intl.
European Christian Mission NA, Inc.
Evangelistic Faith Missions
Far East Broadcasting Company, Inc.
Friends of Israel Gospel Ministry
Galcom International (U.S.)
Global Outreach Mission
Go Ye Fellowship

Good News Productions Intl.
Gospel for Asia
Gospel Mission of South America
Grand Old Gospel Fellowship
HBI Global Partners
HCJB World Radio
Hellenic Ministries
Hermano Pablo Ministries
High Adventure Ministries
Impact International
India Gospel Outreach
International Board of Jewish Missions, Inc.
International Cooperating Ministries
International Lutheran Laymen's League
Joni and Friends
Key Communications
Luis Palau Evangelistic Assoc.
Macedonia World Baptist Missions, Inc.
Macedonian Missionary Service
Missionary Gospel Fellowship
Missionary Revival Crusade
National Religious Broadcasters
OMS International, Inc.
Overseas Radio & Television, Inc.
Partners in Christ International
Precept Ministries International
Radio Voice of Christ, Inc.
Ramesh Richard Evangelism
Raul Zaldivar Evangelistic Ministry
RBC Ministries
Romanian Missionary Society
Russian Christian Radio
SAT-7 North America
SIM USA
Slavic Missionary Service
Spanish World Ministries
Trans World Radio
Turkish World Outreach
Waymarks International Radio Ministries
Wisconsin Evangelical Lutheran Synod
Word of Life Fellowship
Word To Russia
World Concern

Camping programs

Action International Ministries
American Missionary Fellowship
Armenian Msny. Assoc. of America, Inc.
BCM International
Brazil Gospel Fellowship Mission
CAM International
Christ Community Church
CityTeam Ministries
Eastern European Outreach, Inc.
Evangelical Baptist Missions
Gospel Fellowship Association

Greater Europe Mission
InterAct Ministries
International Messengers
Intl. Street Kids Outreach Ministries
Joni and Friends
Latin America Assistance, Inc.
New Hope International
Peter Deyneka Russian Ministries
Pioneer Clubs
Presbyterian Evangelistic Fellowship
Romanian Missionary Society
Salvation Army, U.S.A.
Third World Baptist Missions
TITUS International
Word of Life Fellowship
World Partners USA
Young Life

Childcare/orphanage

Advancing Native Missions
African Leadership
All God's Children International
AMG International
Association of Free Lutheran Congregations
Baptist Medical & Dental Mission Intl.
Bibles For The World, Inc.
Brethren Church Missionary Bd.
Calvary Commission, Inc.
CEIFA Ministries International
Childcare International
Children's Cross Connection USA
Children's Haven International
China Connection
Christ for India, Inc.
Christ for the City International
Christar
Christian Aid Ministries
Christian Church of N. America Msns.
Christians In Action, Inc.
Church of God (Cleveland, TN)
Cities for Christ Worldwide
Commission to Every Nation
Eastern European Outreach, Inc.
Elim Fellowship, International Dept.
Evangelical Baptist Missions
Evangelical Congregational Church
Every Child Ministries, Inc.
Family Aid International, Inc.
Fellowship International Mission
Final Frontiers Foundation, Inc.
Foundation For His Ministry
Free Methodist World Missions
General Baptists International
Global Fellowship
Global Outreach, Ltd.
HBI Global Partners

Heart to Heart Intl. Ministries
Holt International Children's Services, Inc.
Hope for the Hungry
Independent Gospel Missions
India Evangelical Mission, Inc.
India National Inland Mission
India Partners
India Rural Evangelical Fellowship
International Messengers
International Outreach Ministries
International Pentecostal Church of Christ
International Street Kids Outreach Mins.
Kids Alive International
Larry Jones International Mins.
Latin America Mission
Living Water Teaching International
Mission Nannys
Mission of Mercy
Mission Possible Foundation, Inc.
Mustard Seed, Inc., The
New Life League International
N. American Baptist Conf. Intl. Msns. Dept.
Pan American Missions
Precious Seed Ministries
Project Christ International
Project Mercy, Inc.
Project Partner with Christ
Ramabai Mukti Mission
Sowers International, The
The Mission Society
TITUS International
Trans World Missions
WEC International
World Opportunities International
World Vision Inc.
World Vision International
World-Wide Missions

Childrens programs

Action International Ministries
African Methodist Episcopal Church, Dept.
  Global Witness
American Missionary Fellowship
American Scripture Gift Mission
Armenian Msny. Assoc. of America, Inc.
Assemblies of God World Missions
Awana Clubs International
BCM International
Cadence International
Childcare International
Children's Medical Ministries
Christ to the Nations
Christian Advance International
Christian Mission for the Deaf
Cook Communications Mins. Intl.
Cornerstone International

D & D Missionary Homes, Inc.
Empowering Lives International
Every Child Ministries, Inc.
Family Aid International, Inc.
Food for the Hungry, Inc.
Global Action
Global Outreach, Ltd.
Globe Missionary Evangelism
GO InterNational
Holt International Children's Services, Inc.
Hope for the Hungry
Interaction International Inc.
International Family Missions
International Messengers
Kids Around the World, Inc.
Larry Jones International Mins.
M/E International, Inc.
Mailbox Club International
Ministry to Eastern Europe
Mission India
Mission Ministries, Inc.
Mission of Mercy
Mission Training International
Northwest Medical Teams
Operation Blessing International
Progressive National Baptist Conv USA
Ramabai Mukti Mission
Salvation Army, U.S.A.
Samaritan's Purse
Society of St. Margaret
SP Ministries
TITUS International
Trans World Missions
Venture International

Church construction

African Methodist Episcopal Church
Apostolic Christian Ch. Foundation, Inc.
Baptist Intl. Evangelistic Ministries
Baptist Medical & Dental Msn. Intl.
China Connection
Christ for India, Inc.
Christ for the Nations, Inc.
Christian and Missionary Alliance
Christian Church of North America Missions
Christian Missions Unlimited
Christian Union Churches of N. AM.
Church Ministries International
Church Planting International
Congregational Christian Chs., Ntl. Assoc.
Congregational Holiness Church
Correll Missionary Ministries
East Gates Ministries Intl.
Evangel Bible Translators
Free Gospel Church, Missions Department
Hope Missions Outreach International

India Partners
International Cooperating Ministries
International Messengers
Macedonian Missionary Service
Men for Missions International
National Baptist Convention of America,
    Foreign Mission Board
National Baptist Convention USA, Inc.,
    Foreign Mission Board
New Directions International
N. American Baptist Conf. Intl. Missions Dept.
Open Bible Standard Chs., Intl. Mins.
Oriental Missionary Crusade
Pentecostal Church of God, World Msns.
Pentecostal Free Will Baptist Church
Pillar of Fire Missions Intl.
Progressive National Baptist Conv USA
Project Care
Reciprocal Ministries International
STEM
The Ch. of God of the Apostolic Faith, Inc.
Third World Baptist Missions
TITUS International
United Methodist Church
World Help
World Servants

Church establishing/planting
ABWE
Action International Ministries
Advent Christian General Conf.
Africa Inland Mission International
Africa Inter-Mennonite Mission
African Mission Evangelism
Allegheny Wesleyan Methodist Missions
American Association of Lutheran Churches
American Missionary Fellowship
AmeriTribes
AMG International
Anglican Frontier Missions
Apostolic Team Ministries, Intl.
Arab World Ministries
Armenian Msny. Assoc. of America, Inc.
Artists In Christian Testimony
Asian Outreach U.S.A.
Assemblies of God World Missions
Assoc. of Free Lutheran Congregations
Aurora Mission
Baptist Bible Fellowship Intl.
Baptist Bible Translators Institute
Baptist General Conference
Baptist International Evangelistic Ministries
Baptist International Missions, Inc. (BIMI)
Baptist International Outreach
Baptist Medical & Dental Mission Intl.
Baptist Mid-Missions

Baptist Missions to Forgotten Peoples
Baptist World Mission
BCM International
Bethel Christian Ministries
Bible League, The
Bible Missionary Church
Biblical Ministries Worldwide
BILD International
Brazil Gospel Fellowship Mission
Brethren Assemblies
Brethren Church Missionary Bd.
Brethren in Christ World Missions
Bridge Builders International
Bright Hope International
Calvary International
CAM International
CBInternational
Central Yearly Meeting of Friends Missions
Childcare International
Chosen People Ministries
Christ for India, Inc.
Christ for the City International
Christ to the Nations
Christar
Christian Aid Mission
Christian and Missionary Alliance
Christian Associates International
Christian Church of N. America Missions
Christian Churches/ Churches of Christ
Christian Discipleship Ministries, Inc.
Christian Fellowship Union
Christian Mission for the Deaf
Christian Reformed World Missions
Christians In Action, Inc.
Church Ministries International
Church of God (Anderson, Indiana)
Church of God (Cleveland, TN)
Church of God (Holiness)
Church of God of Prophecy
Church of the Nazarene, World Msn. Dept.
Church of the United Brethren in Christ
Church Planting International
Church Resource Ministries
Churches of Christ
Churches of God, General Conference
CMF International
Congregational Methodist Church
Cornerstone International
Correll Missionary Ministries
Covenant Celebration Ch. Global Outreach
Crossover Communications International
Cumberland Presbyterian Ch. Bd. of Msns.
Dawn Ministries
Eastern European Outreach, Inc.
Eastern Mennonite Missions
East-West Ministries International

Elim Fellowship, International Dept.
European Evangelistic Society
Evangelical Baptist Missions
Evangelical Bible Mission
Evangelical Congregational Church
Evangelical Covenant Church
Evangelical Free Church Mission
Evangelical Friends Church Southwest
Evangelical Friends Mission
Evangelical Greenhouse Ministries Intl.
Evangelical Mennonite Church Intl.
Evangelical Methodist Church
Evangelical Presbyterian Church
Every Home for Christ International
Faith Christian Fellowship Intl.
Fellowship International Mission
Flwshp. of Assoc. of Medical Evangelism
Final Frontiers Foundation, Inc.
Foundation For His Ministry
Foursquare Missions International
Free Gospel Church, Missions Dept.
Free Methodist World Missions
Free Will Baptists, Inc., National Assoc.
Frontiers
Full Gospel Evangelistic Association
Fundamental Baptist Mission Trinidad
Galcom International (U.S.)
General Baptists International
General Conf. Mennonite Church
Global Action
Global Fellowship
Global Outreach Mission
Global Outreach, Ltd.
Global Strategy Mission Assoc.
Globe Missionary Evangelism
GO InterNational
Go Ye Fellowship
Good News for India
Gospel Fellowship Association
Gospel for Asia
Gospel Furthering Fellowship
Gospel Mission of South America
Gospel Missionary Union
Gospel Outreach Ministries Intl.
Grace Baptist Missions International
Grace Brethren International Missions
Grace Ministries International
Grand Old Gospel Fellowship
Great Commission Ministries, Inc.
Greater Europe Mission
Greater Grace World Outreach
Haiti Lutheran Mission Society
HBI Global Partners
Health Teams International
Heart of God Ministries
Hellenic Ministries

Impact International
Independent Faith Mission
Independent Gospel Missions
India Evangelical Mission, Inc.
India Gospel Outreach
India National Inland Mission
India Rural Evangelical Fellowship
InterAct Ministries
International Board of Jewish Missions, Inc.
International Outreach Ministries
International Partnership Ministries, Inc.
International Pentecostal Holiness Church
International Teams, U.S.A.
InterServe/USA
Iranian Christians International
Ireland Outreach International Inc.
Japanese Evangelization Center
Latin American Indian Ministries
Liebenzell Mission USA
LIFE Ministries
Lutheran Brethren World Missions
Lutheran Church—Missouri Synod
M/E International, Inc.
Macedonia World Baptist Missions, Inc.
MBMS International
Mennonite Mission Network
Mission India
Mission Ministries, Inc.
Mission Possible Foundation, Inc.
Mission to the Americas
Mission to the World (PCA), Inc.
Mission To Unreached Peoples
Missionary Gospel Fellowship
Missionary Revival Crusade
Missionary Ventures International
Missions Resource Network
Missions to Military, Inc.
Moravian Church in North America
Morelli Ministries International
Mustard Seed, Inc., The
National Baptist Convention USA, Inc.
New Life League International
New Tribes Mission
N. American Baptist Conf. Intl. Missions Dept.
Omega World Missions
OMF International
OMS International, Inc.
Open Air Campaigners - Overseas Ministries
Open Bible Standard Churches, Intl. Mins.
Open Door Baptist Missions
Operation Mobilization, Inc.
Orthodox Presbyterian Church
Pan American Missions
Partners in Asian Missions
Partners International
Pass the Torch Ministries

Pentecostal Ch. of God, World Msns. Dept.
Pentecostal Free Will Baptist Church
People International
Perimeter Church, Global Outreach
Peter Deyneka Russian Ministries
Pilgrim Fellowship, Inc.
Pioneers
PNMC Missions
Prakash Association USA
Precious Seed Ministries
Presbyterian Ch. (USA), Worldwide Mins.
Primitive Methodist Church in the USA
Project AmaZon
Project Christ International
Project Mercy, Inc.
Red Sea Team International
Reformed Baptist Mission Services
Reformed Episcopal Bd. of Foreign Msns.
Ripe for Harvest, Inc.
Rosedale Mennonite Missions
Seed International
SEND International
ServLife International
Seventh Day Baptist Missionary Society
Seventh-day Adventists General Conference
Shield of Faith Ministries
Shield of Faith Mission Intl.
SIM USA
Slavic Missionary Service
South America Mission
South American Missionary Society
Southern Baptist Conv. Intl. Msn. Bd.
Sowers International, The
Sports & Rec Plus
TEAM (The Evangelical Alliance Mission)
Team Expansion, Inc.
The Ch. of God of the Apostolic Faith, Inc.
The Master's Mission, Inc.
The Mission Society
Things To Come Mission, Inc.
Third World Baptist Missions
TITUS International
Trans World Missions
Trans World Radio
Tribes and Nations Outreach
Turkish World Outreach
UFM International
United Evangelical Churches
United Pentecostal Church Intl.
VELA Ministries International
Vineyard International Consortium
Virginia Mennonite Board of Missions
Waymarks International Radio Ministries
WEC International
Wisconsin Evangelical Lutheran Synod
World Baptist Fellowship Mission Agency

World Harvest Mission
World Harvest Now, Inc.
World Help
World Horizons
World Indigenous Missions
World Mission Prayer League Inc.
World Missions Far Corners, Inc.
World Partners USA
World Reach, Inc.
World Team
World Witness, Assoc. Reformed Presb. Ch.
World-Wide Missions
Youth With A Mission (YWAM)
YUGO Ministries

Correspondence courses

African Bible Colleges, Inc.
Asian Outreach U.S.A.
BCM International
Calvary Evangelistic Mission, Inc.
Child Evangelism Fellowship, Inc.
Christian and Missionary Alliance
CLC Ministries International
Congregational Methodist Church
Every Home for Christ International
Global University
Go Ye Fellowship
Gospel Fellowship Association
High Adventure Ministries
International Bible Institute
International Cassette Bible Institute
Ireland Outreach International Inc.
Macedonian Missionary Service
Mailbox Club International
Missionary Gospel Fellowship
Missionary Revival Crusade
Missions to Military, Inc.
Pocket Testament League
Primitive Methodist Church in the USA
Prison Mission Association
Rio Grande Bible Institute
Son Shine Ministries International
Source of Light Ministries Intl., Inc.
Spanish World Ministries
Trans World Radio
World Reach, Inc.

Development, community and/or other

Action International Ministries
Advancing Native Missions
African Enterprise, Inc.
African Leadership
Amazon Focus
American Baptist Churches in the U.S.A.
AmeriTribes

Baptist General Conference
Bright Hope International
CBInternational
Christ for the City International
Christian and Missionary Alliance
Christian Church (Disciples of Christ)
Christian Reformed World Relief Committee
Church of the Brethren
Church Resource Ministries
Church World Service & Witness
CMF International
Commission to Every Nation
Compassion International, Inc.
Congregational Christian Churches
Eastern Mennonite Missions
Emmanuel Intl. Mission (U.S.)
Empowering Lives International
Engineering Ministries International
Episcopal Ch., Domestic & Fgn. Msny. Soc.
Equip, Inc.
Evangelical Covenant Church
Evangelical Lutheran Church in America
Faith Christian Fellowship Intl.
FARMS International, Inc.
Floresta USA, Inc.
FOCAS
Food for the Hungry, Inc.
For Haiti with Love Inc.
Free Will Baptists, Inc., Natl. Assoc.
FRIENDS in Action, International
Friends United Meeting, World Ministries
General Conf. Mennonite Church
Global Outreach, Ltd.
GO InterNational
Gospel Outreach Ministries Intl.
Habitat for Humanity International
HCJB World Radio
Health Emergent International Services
Heifer International
INTERDEV
International Child Care
International Outreach Ministries
International Teams, U.S.A.
InterServe/USA
Kids Around the World, Inc.
Larry Jones International Ministries
Latin America Mission
Latin American Indian Ministries
Liebenzell Mission USA
Lifewater International
Luke Society, The
Lutheran World Relief
MAP International
MBMS International
Medical Ambassadors International
Medical Missions Philippines

Mennonite Central Committee
Mennonite Mission Network
Middle East Christian Outreach
Ministries In Action
Mission Ministries, Inc.
Mission: Moving Mountains, Inc.
New Directions International
New Life League International
New Way Missions
Northwest Medical Teams
Operation Blessing International
Opportunity Intl./Women's Opportunity Fund
Partners International
People International
Pioneer Bible Translators
Prakash Association USA
Presbyterian Ch. (USA), Worldwide Mins.
Project Care
Project Mercy, Inc.
Salvation Army, U.S.A.
SAND International
Seed International
Self-Help International
Servants in Faith & Technology (SIFAT)
ServLife International
SIM USA
Society of St. Margaret
South American Missionary Society
Sowers International, The
Sports & Rec Plus
United Church Board for World Ministries
United Methodist Church, Global Mins.
Vellore Christian Medical College Bd. (USA)
Venture International
World Concern
World Mission Prayer League Inc.
World Relief Corporation
World Vision Inc.
World Vision International

Disability assistance programs

American Leprosy Missions, Inc.
Baptist International Outreach
Christian Blind Mission Intl.
Deaf Missions International
Holt International Children's Services, Inc.
International Child Care
Joni and Friends
Venture International
World Concern
World Opportunities International

Discipleship

Campus Crusade for Christ, Intl.
Christian Medical & Dental Society
Every Home for Christ International

International Christian Ministries
InterVarsity Christian Fellowship/USA
Radio Voice of Christ
Southern Baptist Conv. Intl. Mission Bd.
Training Evangelistic Leadership

**Education, church/school
general Christian**
ACMC
Africa Inland Mission International
African Bible Colleges, Inc.
African Leadership
Allegheny Wesleyan Methodist Missions
American Missionary Fellowship
Bible Training Centre for Pastors
Bibles For The World, Inc.
Brazil Gospel Fellowship Mission
Caleb Project
Campus Crusade for Christ, Intl.
Children's Medical Ministries
Christian Mission for the Deaf
Christian Reformed World Missions
Christian Reformed World Relief Committee
Church Planting International
Churches of Christ
Churches of God, General Conference
Commission to Every Nation
Compassion International, Inc.
Congregational Holiness Ch. World Msns.
Cook Communications Ministries Intl.
Correll Missionary Ministries
Crossover Communications International
Cumberland Presbyterian Ch. Bd. of Msns.
Every Child Ministries, Inc.
Fellowship International Mission
FOCAS
Foundation For His Ministry
Foursquare Missions International
Friends United Meeting, World Ministries
Frontier Mission Fellowship
Good News for India
Good Shepherd Ministries
Gospel Missionary Union
Grace Brethren International Missions
Grace Ministries International
Haiti Lutheran Mission Society
Have Christ Will Travel Ministries
India Partners
India Rural Evangelical Fellowship
Institute for Intl. Christian Communication
Institute of Theological Studies
Interaction International Inc.
International Bible Institute
International Cassette Bible Institute
Intl. Christian Leprosy Mission, Inc. (USA)
International Pentecostal Church of Christ

InterServe/USA
Kids Alive International
Kids Around the World, Inc.
LOGOI, Inc./FLET
Macedonia World Baptist Missions, Inc.
Middle East Christian Outreach
Ministry to Eastern Europe
Mission Possible, Inc.
Missions To Japan, Inc.
Mustard Seed, Inc., The
National Baptist Convention of America
National Baptist Convention USA, Inc.
Network of International Christian Schools
Open Doors with Brother Andrew USA
Pillar of Fire Missions Intl.
Presbyterian Center for Mission Studies
Presbyterian Ch. (USA), Worldwide Mins.
Project AmaZon
Project Mercy, Inc.
Reciprocal Ministries International
Rehoboth Ministries, Inc
Seventh-day Adventists General Conference
Shield of Faith Ministries
Society of St. Margaret
South American Missionary Society
SP Ministries
Team Expansion, Inc.
The Mission Society
TITUS International
UFM International
United Church Board for World Ministries
Walk Thru The Bible Ministries
WEC International
World Harvest Mission
World-Wide Missions

Education, extension (other)
Africa Inland Mission International
Alberto Mottesi Evangelistic Association
Assemblies of God World Missions
Child Evangelism Fellowship, Inc.
China Ministries International
Daystar U.S.
Development Associates International (DAI)
Evangelical Baptist Missions
Frontier Mission Fellowship
Global University
Grace Baptist Missions International
Grace Ministries International
Handclasp International, Inc.
Heifer International
IFMA
International Bible Institute
International Christian Ministries
International Institute for Christian Studies
Mennonite Central Committee

Missionary Gospel Fellowship
Overseas Council International
Peter Deyneka Russian Ministries
Precept Ministries International
Red Sea Team International
Self-Help International
Word of Life Fellowship
World Partners USA
Zion Evangelical Ministries of Africa

Education, missionary (certificate/degree)

Baptist Bible Translators Institute
Bethany Fellowship Missions
Bible Training Centre for Pastors
Calvary Commission, Inc.
Christ for the Nations, Inc.
Church of the Nazarene, World Msn. Dept.
Donetsk Christian University
Equip, Inc.
Global Fellowship
Good News for India
Greater Grace World Outreach
India Evangelical Mission, Inc.
Literacy & Evangelism International
Overseas Ministries Study Center
Project Christ International
Rio Grande Bible Institute
Russian Language Ministries
Tentmakers International Exchange–T.I.E
The Master's Mission, Inc.
United Evangelical Churches
WEC International
World Harvest Mission

Education, theological

ABWE
ACM International
ACTS International Ministries
Advent Christian General Conf.
African Leadership
African Mission Evangelism
American Baptist Churches in the U.S.A.
AMG International
Arabic Communication Center
Armenian Msny. Assoc. of America, Inc.
Asian Outreach U.S.A.
Assemblies of God World Missions
Association of Free Lutheran Congregations
Aurora Mission
Baptist Bible Fellowship Intl.
Baptist General Conference
Baptist International Evangelistic Ministries
Baptist International Outreach
Baptist Medical & Dental Mission Intl., Inc.
Baptist Mid-Missions

Baptist World Mission
Bethany Fellowship Missions
Bible Missionary Church
Bible Training Centre for Pastors
Bibles For The World, Inc.
Biblical Ministries Worldwide
Brazil Gospel Fellowship Mission
CAM International
CBInternational
Centers for Apologetics Research (CFAR)
China Ministries International
Christ Community Church
Christ for India, Inc.
Christ for the Nations, Inc.
Christar
Christian Aid Mission
Christian and Missionary Alliance
Christian Fellowship Union
Christian Reformed World Missions
Church of God (Cleveland, TN)
Church of God (Holiness)
Clark Theol. College (India) Tribal Mins. USA
Congregational Methodist Church
Crossover Communications International
Daystar U.S.
Donetsk Christian University
Eastern Mennonite Missions
Elim Fellowship, International Dept.
European Evangelistic Society
Evangelical Congregational Church
Evangelical Free Church Mission
Evangelical Friends Mission
Evangelical Greenhouse Ministries Intl.
Evangelical Lutheran Church in America
Evangelical Methodist Church
Evangelical Presbyterian Church
Free Gospel Church, Missions Dept.
Free Methodist World Missions
Free Will Baptists, Inc., Natl. Assoc.
Friends of Israel Gospel Ministry
General Conf. Mennonite Church
Global Outreach Mission
Global Outreach, Ltd.
Global University
Globe Missionary Evangelism
Good News for India
Gospel Fellowship Association
Gospel Furthering Fellowship
Gospel Mission of South America
Greater Europe Mission
Greater Grace World Outreach
Haiti Lutheran Mission Society
HBI Global Partners
Help for Christian Nationals, Inc.
Hundredfold Ministries International
India Gospel Outreach

India National Inland Mission
India Rural Evangelical Fellowship
Institute of Theological Studies
International Cassette Bible Institute
International Christian Ministries
International Institute for Christian Studies
International Justice Mission
International Missionary Center
International Outreach Ministries
International Pentecostal Church of Christ
International Pentecostal Holiness Church
International Urban Associates
JARON Ministries International
Latin America Mission
Liebenzell Mission USA
Living Water Teaching International
Lutheran Church–Missouri Synod
MBMS International
Ministry to Eastern Europe
Moravian Church in North America
Mustard Seed, Inc., The
New Tribes Mission
N. Am. Baptist Conf. Intl. Missions Dept.
OMF International
Orthodox Presbyterian Church
Outreach Incorporated
Outreach To Asia Nationals
Overseas Council International
Partners in Christ International
Perimeter Church, Global Outreach
Pillar of Fire Missions Intl.
Primitive Methodist Church in the USA
Ravi Zacharias International Ministries
Reformed Church in America, Gen. Synod
Rehoboth Ministries, Inc
Rio Grande Bible Institute
Rock the World Youth Mission Alliance
Romanian Missionary Society
Seed International
SEND International
Seventh Day Baptist Missionary Society
Seventh-day Adventists Gen. Conf.
SIM USA
Slavic Gospel Association
Southern Baptist Conv. Intl. Msn. Bd.
TCM International
TEAM (The Evangelical Alliance Mission)
The Ch. of God of the Apostolic Faith, Inc.
The Master's Mission, Inc.
Things To Come Mission, Inc.
Third World Baptist Missions
TMA Ministries
UFM International
United Church Board for World Ministries
United Pentecostal Church Intl.
Village Ministries International, Inc.

Virginia Mennonite Board of Missions
WEC International
Wesleyan World Missions
Westminister Biblical Missions
Wisconsin Evangelical Lutheran Synod
World Gospel Mission
World Harvest Mission
World Mission Prayer League Inc.
World Missionary Assistance Plan
World Partners USA
World Thrust International, Inc.
World Witness, Assoc. Reformed Presb. Ch.
Zion Evangelical Ministries of Africa

Education, Theological by Extension (TEE)

Advent Christian General Conf.
Arab World Ministries
Bible Literature International
Brethren in Christ World Missions
CBInternational
CEIFA Ministries International
China Ministries International
Christian Leadership Development, Inc.
Church of God (Anderson, Indiana)
Church of God (Cleveland, TN)
Church of the Nazarene, World Msn. Dept.
Congregational Methodist Church
Cornerstone International
East-West Ministries International
Emmanuel Intl. Mission (U.S.)
Evangelical Friends Church Southwest
Evangelistic Faith Missions
Foursquare Missions International
Global University
Grace and Truth, Inc.
Grace Ministries International
Institute of Theological Studies
International Bible Institute
International Cassette Bible Institute
International Christian Ministries
International Gospel Outreach
Latin American Indian Ministries
LOGOI, Inc./FLET
Ministries In Action
Mission Possible Foundation, Inc.
Mission to the World (PCA), Inc.
OMS International, Inc.
Open Bible Standard Churches
Overseas Council International
Partners in Christ International
Primitive Methodist Church in the USA
Project Care
Raul Zaldivar Evangelistic Ministry
SEND International
Seventh Day Baptist Missionary Society

WEC International
Wesleyan World Missions
World Gospel Mission
World Harvest Mission
World Mission Prayer League Inc.

Evangelism, mass

Action International Ministries
Advancing Native Missions
Advent Christian General Conf.
Africa Inland Mission International
African Bible Colleges, Inc.
African Enterprise, Inc.
Alberto Mottesi Evangelistic Association
Anis Shorrosh Evangelistic Association, Inc.
Apostolic Christian Church Foundation, Inc.
Artists In Christian Testimony
Assemblies of God World Missions
Baptist Medical & Dental Mission Intl. Inc.
Bethel Christian Ministries
Bible Literature International
Billy Graham Center, The
Bridge Builders International
Campus Crusade for Christ, Intl.
Carpenter's Tools International
CEIFA Ministries International
Celebrant Singers
Centers for Apologetics Research (CFAR)
Child Evangelism Fellowship, Inc.
Chosen People Ministries
Christ for the Lost World
Christian Advance International
Christian Aid Mission
Christian Broadcasting Network, the
Christian Church of North America Missions
Christian Laymen's Msny. Evangelism Assoc.
Church of God of Prophecy
Church of the Nazarene, World Msn. Dept.
Church Planting International
Churches of Christ
Covenant Celebration Ch. Global Outreach
Dayspring Enterprises International
Disciples International
East-West Ministries International
Emmanuel Intl. Mission (U.S.)
Engineering Ministries International
Evangelical Covenant Church
Evangelical Friends Church Southwest
Far East Broadcasting Company, Inc.
FARMS International, Inc.
FOCAS
Foursquare Missions International
Free Methodist World Missions
Friendship International
Fundamental Baptist Mission Trinidad
Galcom International (U.S.)

Global Action
Global Fellowship
GO InterNational
Go Ye Fellowship
Good News Productions Intl.
Gospel Outreach Ministries Intl.
Gospel Recordings
Gospel Revival Ministries
Grand Old Gospel Fellowship
Harvest Evangelism, Inc.
Hellenic Ministries
Hermano Pablo Ministries
High Adventure Ministries
Impact International
India Evangelical Mission, Inc.
India Gospel Outreach
India Rural Evangelical Fellowship
INTERCOMM
International Bible Society
International Board of Jewish Missions, Inc.
International Family Missions
International Lutheran Laymen's League
International Partnership Ministries, Inc.
Iranian Christians International
Italy for Christ
Joni and Friends
Josue Yrion World Evangelism Missions, Inc.
Kingdom Building Ministries
Larry Jones International Ministries
Latin America Assistance, Inc.
Luis Palau Evangelistic Assoc.
Lutheran Church—Missouri Synod
M/E International, Inc.
Mahesh Chavda Ministries Intl.
Mexican Medical Ministries
Middle East Christian Outreach
Middle East Media - USA
Middle Eastern Outreach
Missionary Athletes International
Missionary Revival Crusade
Morelli Ministries International
National Baptist Convention of America
National Baptist Convention USA, Inc.
Network of International Christian Schools
New Life League International
No Greater Love Ministries, Inc.
On The Go Mins./Keith Cook Evangelistic Assoc.
Open Air Campaigners - Overseas Ministries
Open Doors with Brother Andrew USA
Operation Mobilization, Inc.
Orthodox Presbyterian Church
Partners in Asian Missions
Pentecostal Church of God
Perimeter Church, Global Outreach
Pioneer Bible Translators
Pioneers

Pocket Testament League
Precious Seed Ministries
Presbyterian Ch. (USA), Worldwide Mins.
Presbyterian Evangelistic Fellowship
Progressive Vision
Project AmaZon
Radio Voice of Christ, Inc.
Ramesh Richard Evangelism
Raul Zaldivar Evangelistic Ministry
Ripe for Harvest, Inc.
Samaritan's Purse
Seventh-day Adventists General Conf.
Son Shine Ministries International
Southern Baptist Conv. Intl. Msn. Bd.
Spiritual Growth Resources, Inc.
Sports & Rec Plus
STEM
The Ch. of God of the Apostolic Faith, Inc.
Things To Come Mission, Inc.
Training Evangelistic Leadership
Trans World Radio
United Pentecostal Church Intl.
VELA Ministries International
Village Ministries International, Inc.
Waymakers International
Wesleyan World Missions
Word of Life Fellowship
World Harvest Mission
World Indigenous Missions
World Missions Far Corners, Inc.
World Reach, Inc.
World Witness, Assoc. Reformed Presb. Ch.
Youth for Christ / USA

Evangelism, personal and small group
ABWE
Adventures in Missions
Africa Inter-Mennonite Mission
African Enterprise, Inc.
Allegheny Wesleyan Methodist Missions
Ambassadors for Christ Intl.
American Baptist Churches in the U.S.A.
American Missionary Fellowship
American Scripture Gift Mission
AMF International
Arab World Ministries
Arabic Communication Center
Armenian Msny. Assoc. of America, Inc.
Asian Outreach U.S.A.
Assemblies of God World Missions
Assoc. of Free Lutheran Cong. Wld. Msn.
Aurora Mission
Awana Clubs International
Baptist Bible Fellowship Intl.
Baptist General Conference
Baptist International Missions, Inc. (BIMI)

Baptist International Outreach
Baptist Missions to Forgotten Peoples
BCM International
Bethany Fellowship Missions
Bible League, The
Biblical Ministries Worldwide
Brazil Gospel Fellowship Mission
Brethren Church Missionary Bd.
Brethren in Christ World Missions
Cadence International
Calvary Evangelistic Mission, Inc.
Calvary International
CAM International
Campus Crusade for Christ, Intl.
Caring Partners International, Inc.
CBInternational
Central Yearly Meeting of Friends Missions
Children's Medical Ministries
China Ministries International
Chosen People Ministries
Christ Community Church
Christar
Christian and Missionary Alliance
Christian Church of North America Missions
Christian Ministries International (C.M.I.)
Christian Mission for the Deaf
Christian Missions Unlimited
Christian Outreach International
Christian Reformed World Missions
Christian Service International
Christian Union Churches of N. AM.
Christians In Action, Inc.
Church of God (Cleveland, TN)
Church of God (Holiness)
Church of God in Christ, Mennonite
Church of God of Prophecy
Church of the United Brethren in Christ
Churches of Christ
CityTeam Ministries
CMF International
Congregational Methodist Church
Connecting Businessmen to Christ
Cornerstone International
Dayspring Enterprises International
Disciples International
European Christian Mission NA, Inc.
European Evangelistic Society
Evangelical Bible Mission
Evangelical Free Church Mission
Evangelical Friends Mission
Evangelical Greenhouse Ministries Intl.
Evangelical Lutheran Church in America
Evangelical Mennonite Church Intl. Mins.
Evangelical Methodist Church
Evangelical Presbyterian Church
Evangelism Explosion International

Evangelistic Faith Missions
Every Home for Christ International
Final Frontiers Foundation, Inc.
Floresta USA, Inc.
FOCAS
For Haiti with Love Inc.
Forward Edge International
Foundation For His Ministry
Free Gospel Church, Missions Dept.
Free Will Baptists, Inc., Natl. Assoc.
Friends of Israel Gospel Ministry
Friends United Meeting, World Ministries
Friendship International
Frontiers
Full Gospel Evangelistic Association
General Conf. Mennonite Church
Global Outreach Mission
Global Strategy Mission Assoc.
Global University
Globe Missionary Evangelism
Go Ye Fellowship
Good News Productions Intl.
Gospel Fellowship Association
Gospel for Asia
Gospel Furthering Fellowship
Gospel Missionary Union
Grace Brethren International Missions
Great Commission Ministries, Inc.
Greater Europe Mission
Greater Grace World Outreach
Harvest Evangelism, Inc.
Have Christ Will Travel Ministries
HBI Global Partners
Health Teams International
Hope for the Hungry
Hosanna / Faith Comes By Hearing
India Evangelical Mission, Inc.
InterAct Ministries
INTERCOMM
International Christian Leprosy Mission, Inc.
International Family Missions
International Gospel Outreach
International Health Services
International Institute for Christian Studies
Ireland Outreach International Inc.
Japanese Evangelization Center
Jews for Jesus
Key Communications
Kids Alive International
Latin America Mission
Latin American Indian Ministries
Liberty Corner Mission
Liebenzell Mission USA
LIFE Ministries
Literacy & Evangelism International
Living Water Teaching International

Mailbox Club International
MBMS International
Medical Ambassadors International
Medical Missions Philippines
Men for Missions International
Mercy Ships
Mexican Medical Ministries
Middle Eastern Outreach
Mission Ministries, Inc.
Mission Possible, Inc.
Mission to the World (PCA), Inc.
Missionary Athletes International
Missionary Gospel Fellowship
Missions To Japan, Inc.
Muslim Hope
Navigators, U.S. Intl. Mins. Group
New Life League International
No Greater Love Ministries, Inc.
OMF International
OMS International, Inc.
Open Bible Standard Churches, Intl. Mins.
Open Door Baptist Missions
Operation Mobilization, Inc.
Pass the Torch Ministries
Pentecostal Church of God
Pentecostal Free Will Baptist Church
People International
Perimeter Church, Global Outreach
Peter Deyneka Russian Ministries
Presbyterian Evangelistic Fellowship
Prison Mission Association
Project AmaZon
Project Mercy, Inc.
Reach Ministries International
Red Sea Team International
Reformed Baptist Mission Services
Reformed Church in America, Gen. Synod
Rehoboth Ministries, Inc
Ripe for Harvest, Inc.
Salvation Army, U.S.A.
Seed International
SEND International
Seventh Day Baptist Missionary Society
Shield of Faith Ministries
Shield of Faith Mission Intl.
Son Shine Ministries International
South American Missionary Society
Southern Mexico Missions
Spanish World Ministries
Spiritual Growth Resources, Inc.
Sports & Rec Plus
TEAM (The Evangelical Alliance Mission)
Teen Missions International
Teen World Outreach
Tentmakers International Exchange–T.I.E
The Ch. of God of the Apostolic Faith, Inc.

The Master's Harvest
The Mission Society
Things To Come Mission, Inc.
TMA Ministries
Touch the World Ministries
Training Evangelistic Leadership
Trans World Missions
Turkish World Outreach
UFM International
United Methodist Church, Global Mins.
United Pentecostal Church Intl., Fgn. Mins.
VELA Ministries International
Vineyard International Consortium
Virginia Mennonite Board of Missions
Voice of the Martyrs, The
Walk Thru The Bible Ministries
World Baptist Fellowship Mission Agency
World Concern
World Gospel Mission
World Harvest Now, Inc.
World Horizons
World Mission Prayer League Inc.
World Servants
World Team
World Vision Inc.
World Vision International
Worldwide Tentmakers, Inc.
Youth for Christ/USA, World Outreach Div.
Youth With A Mission (YWAM)
YUGO Ministries

Evangelism, student
Adventures in Missions
Ambassadors for Christ, Inc.
Baptist Mid-Missions
Calvary Commission, Inc.
Campus Crusade for Christ, Intl.
Carpenter's Tools International
China Outreach Ministries
Chosen People Ministries
Compassion International, Inc.
Evangelism Explosion International
Fellowship International Mission
Frontiers
Global Youth Ministry Network
Grace Brethren International Missions
Great Commission Ministries, Inc.
International Institute for Christian Studies
International Messengers
International Students, Inc
InterVarsity Christian Fellowship/USA
Italy for Christ
Japanese Evangelical Missionary Society
Kids Alive International
Kingdom Building Ministries
LIFE Ministries

Mission Ministries, Inc.
Mission to the Americas
Missions To Japan, Inc.
Navigators, U.S. Intl. Msns. Group
New Hope International
No Greater Love Ministries, Inc.
On The Go Mins./Keith Cook Evangelistic Assoc.
Project Mercy, Inc.
Ravi Zacharias International Ministries
Rock the World Youth Mission Alliance
Surfing the Nations–Targeting 10/40 Window
Things To Come Mission, Inc.
Touch the World Ministries
Worldwide Discipleship Assoc.
Young Life
Youth for Christ/USA, World Outreach Div.

Funds transmission
Advancing Native Missions
American Association of Lutheran Churches
Apostolic Christian Church Foundation, Inc.
Christian Discipleship Ministries, Inc.
Christian Info. Service, Inc. Msns. Div.
Christian Missions in Many Lands
Church of God (Seventh Day) Gen. Conf.
Church of the United Brethren in Christ
Congregational Christian Churches
Episcopal Ch., Domestic & Fgn. Msny. Soc.
Evangelical Lutheran Church in America
Faith Christian Fellowship Intl.
Full Gospel Grace Fellowship
Global Health Ministries
Global Strategy Mission Assoc.
Gospel Revival Ministries
India Gospel League Inc., N. America
International Gospel Outreach
International Missionary Center
Ludhiana Christian Medical College Bd., USA
Luke Society, The
MATS International, Inc.
Moravian Church in North America
National Baptist Convention of America
Pilgrim Fellowship, Inc.
Presbyterian Missionary Union
Ramabai Mukti Mission
Reciprocal Ministries International
Ripe for Harvest, Inc.
ServLife International
STEER, Inc.
Vellore Christian Medical College Bd. (USA)
World Baptist Fellowship Mission Agency
World Outreach Ministries
World Vision Inc.

Furloughed missionary support
Bible Missionary Church

Cedar Lane Missionary Homes
CMTS Ministries, Inc.
Cumberland Presbyterian Ch. Bd. Msns.
D & D Missionary Homes, Inc.
FRIENDS in Action, International
International Missionary Center
Intl. Pentecostal Holiness Ch. World Msns.
Men for Missions International
Mission Training International
Missionary Retreat Fellowship Inc.
National Baptist Convention USA, Inc.
Overseas Ministries Study Center
Providence Mission Homes, Inc.
Sending Experienced Retired Volunteers
World Harvest Mission
Wycliffe Associates USA

Information services
ACMC
Adopt-A-People Clearinghouse
Billy Graham Center, The
China Connection
ChinaSource
Christian Aid Mission
Christian Info. Service, Inc. Msns. Div.
Christian Missions in Many Lands
Church Missions Link
Church of the Nazarene, World Msn. Dept.
Congregational Christian Chs., Ntl. Assoc.
Cumberland Presbyterian Ch. Bd. Msns.
D & D Missionary Homes, Inc.
Envoy International
Episcopal Church Missionary Community
Evangelical Friends Mission
Evangelism and Missions Information Service
FOM (Fellowship of Missions)
Frontier Mission Fellowship
General Association of Regular Baptist Chs.
General Baptists International
Global Mapping International
Grace Baptist Missions International
IFMA
International Missionary Center
Japanese Evangelization Center
LIGHT International, Inc.
MATS International, Inc.
Middle Eastern Outreach
Mission Aviation Fellowship
Mission Services Association
Mission Training and Resource Center
Missions Resource Center
Missions Resource Network
OC International, Inc.
Seventh Day Baptist Missionary Society
Tentmakers International Exchange - T.I.E
World Mission Associates

Worldwide Discipleship Assoc.

Justice & Related
Bread for the World
Christian Medical & Dental Society
Compassion International, Inc.
International Justice Mission

Leadership development
ABWE
ACM International
ACMC
ACTS International Ministries
Advent Christian General Conf.
Africa Inland Mission International
Africa Inter-Mennonite Mission
African Bible Colleges, Inc.
African Enterprise, Inc.
African Leadership
AIMS
Alberto Mottesi Evangelistic Association
Amazon Focus
American Baptist Churches in the U.S.A.
Arab World Ministries
Asian Outreach U.S.A.
Aurora Mission
Awana Clubs International
Baptist General Conference
Barnabas International
Bible Training Centre for Pastors
BILD International
Billy Graham Center, The
Brethren Church Missionary Bd.
Brethren in Christ World Missions
Calvary International
CAM International
Carpenter's Tools International
CBInternational
CEIFA Ministries International
Christ for the City International
Christar
Christian and Missionary Alliance
Christian Church (Disciples of Christ)
Christian Fellowship Union
Christian Leadership Development, Inc.
Christian Ministries International (C.M.I.)
Christian Outreach International
Christian Reformed World Missions
Christian Reformed World Relief Committee
Church of God (Anderson, IN)
Church of God of Prophecy
Church Planting International
Church Resource Ministries
Churches of Christ
Churches of God, General Conference
CityTeam Ministries

Partners in Asian Missions
Partners International
Pioneers
Precept Ministries International
Presbyterian Ch. (USA), Worldwide Mins.
Progressive Vision
Project AmaZon
Project Care
Project Partner with Christ
Raul Zaldivar Evangelistic Ministry
Ravi Zacharias International Ministries
Reach Ministries International
Reformed Baptist Mission Services
Reformed Church in America, Gen. Synod
Rehoboth Ministries, Inc
Rock the World Youth Mission Alliance
Rosedale Mennonite Missions
Seed International
SEND International
Seventh Day Baptist Missionary Society
Shield of Faith Ministries
Slavic Gospel Association
Society of St. Margaret
South America Mission
South American Missionary Society
Southern Baptist Conv. Intl. Msn. Bd.
Spiritual Growth Resources, Inc.
Strategic Ventures Network
Surfing the Nations/Targeting 10/40 Window
TCM International
TEAM (The Evangelical Alliance Mission)
Teen Missions International
The Master's Mission, Inc.
Training Evangelistic Leadership
Trans World Missions
UFM International
United Bd. for Christian Higher Ed. in Asia
United Church Board for World Ministries
United Evangelical Churches
United Pentecostal Church Intl.
VELA Ministries International
Vineyard International Consortium
Virginia Mennonite Board of Missions
Walk Thru The Bible Ministries
Wesleyan World Missions
World Concern
World Gospel Mission
World Harvest Now, Inc.
World Help
World Mission Associates
World Mission Prayer League Inc.
World Missionary Assistance Plan
World Reach, Inc.
World Servants
World Thrust International, Inc.
World Vision International

WorldTeach
Zion Evangelical Ministries of Africa

Linguistics

Africa Inter-Mennonite Mission
Baptist Bible Translators Institute
Commission to Every Nation
Evangel Bible Translators
Lutheran Bible Translators
New Tribes Mission
Russian Language Ministries
Wycliffe Bible Translators International
Wycliffe Bible Translators USA

Literacy

Baptist Bible Translators Institute
Bible League, The
Christian Literacy Associates
Christian Literature International
Christian Mission for the Deaf
CLC Ministries International
Evangel Bible Translators
Floresta USA, Inc.
General Baptists International
Gospel Outreach Ministries Intl.
Literacy & Evangelism International
Lutheran Bible Translators
Mission India
New Tribes Mission
Omega World Missions
Pioneer Bible Translators
Society of St. Margaret
World Bible Translation Center
Wycliffe Bible Translators International
Wycliffe Bible Translators USA

Literature distribution

Advancing Renewal Ministries
All God's Children International
Allegheny Wesleyan Methodist Missions
Ambassadors for Christ, Inc.
American Scripture Gift Mission
AMF International
Arab World Ministries
Arabic Communication Center
Asian Outreach U.S.A.
ASSIST
Aurora Mission
Back to the Bible International
Baptist International Evangelistic Ministries
Bible Literature International
Biblical Literature Fellowship
Calvary Evangelistic Mission, Inc.
Carver International Missions, Inc.
CBInternational
CEIFA Ministries International

Literature production

Biblical Literature Fellowship
BILD International
CEIFA Ministries International
Centers for Apologetics Research (CFAR)
Child Evangelism Fellowship, Inc.
Christian Leadership Development, Inc.
Christian Medical & Dental Society
Christian Union Churches of N. AM.
Derek Prince Ministries, Intl.
Disciples International
East Gates Ministries Intl.
Edwin L. Hodges Ministries
Evangelism and Missions Information Service
Every Home for Christ International
Friends of Israel Gospel Ministry
Global Focus
Gospel Literature International, Inc.
Gospel Mission of South America
Grace and Truth, Inc.
Great Commission Center International
Hands for Christ
Harvest
Hundredfold Ministries International
INTENT
InterVarsity Christian Fellowship/USA
Ireland Outreach International Inc.
Italy for Christ
Jews for Jesus
Josue Yrion World Evangelism Missions, Inc.
Key Communications
Leadership Ministries Worldwide
Luis Palau Evangelistic Assoc.
Lutheran Brethren World Missions
Lutheran Literature Society for the Chinese
Macedonia World Baptist Missions, Inc.
Macedonian Missionary Service
Mahesh Chavda Ministries Intl.
Mailbox Club International
MAP International
Middle East Media - USA
Mission Possible Foundation, Inc.
Missionary TECH Team
Narramore Christian Foundation
OMF International
Orthodox Presbyterian Church
Precept Ministries International
Prison Mission Association
RBC Ministries
Reformation Translation Flwshp.
Romanian Missionary Society
Russian Bible Society, Inc.
Russian Christian Radio
Seventh-day Adventists General Conference
Source of Light Ministries International, Inc.
SP Ministries
Spiritual Growth Resources, Inc.

Turkish World Outreach
United Pentecostal Church Intl.
Walk Thru The Bible Ministries
Waymakers International
WEC International
Westminister Biblical Missions
Wisconsin Evangelical Lutheran Synod
World Evangelization Research Center
World Missionary Press, Inc.

Management consulting/training

ChinaSource
Christian Ministries International (C.M.I.)
Christian World Publishers
Church Missions Link
Crisis Consulting International
Daystar U.S.
Development Associates International (DAI)
DualReach
Engineering Ministries International
Enterprise Development Intl.
Global Focus
Great Commission Ministries, Inc.
Health Emergent International Services
India Gospel League Inc., North America
Intercristo
International Gospel Outreach
LIGHT International, Inc.
Literacy & Evangelism International
Media Associates International
Medical Ambassadors International
Men for Missions International
Mission: Moving Mountains, Inc.
Overseas Council International
Paraclete, Inc.
Partners International
Peoples Mission International
Perimeter Church, Global Outreach
Project Partner with Christ
Shelter for Life International, Inc.
Strategic Ventures Network
TCM International
Tentmakers International Exchange–T.I.E
World Mission Associates

Medical supplies

All God's Children International
American Leprosy Missions, Inc.
Baptist International Outreach
Blessings International
Caring Partners International, Inc.
Children's Cross Connection USA
Children's Medical Ministries
Chosen, Inc.
Christian Aid Ministries
Christian Blind Mission Intl.

Christian Pilots Association
Church of the Nazarene, World Msn. Dept.
Congregational Holiness Ch. World Msns.
Equip, Inc.
Flwshp. of Assoc. of Medical Evangelism
Flying Doctors of America
Global Health Ministries
Health Emergent International Services
International Aid
International Child Care
Living Water Teaching International
Ludhiana Christian Medical College Bd., USA
Medical Missions Philippines
National Baptist Convention USA, Inc.
Northwest Medical Teams
Project Mercy, Inc.
Reformed Church in America, Gen. Synod
Samaritan's Purse
The Ch. of God of the Apostolic Faith, Inc.
Vellore Christian Medical College Bd. (USA)
World Concern
World Help
World Opportunities International
Worldwide Lab Improvement, Inc.

**Medicine, incl. dental
and public health**
ACM International
Africa Inland Mission International
AIMS
Amazon Focus
AmeriTribes
Baptist Medical & Dental Msn. Intl., Inc.
Baptist Mid-Missions
Blessings International
Brethren Church Missionary Bd.
Calvary International
Caring Partners International, Inc.
CBInternational
Childcare International
Children's Cross Connection USA
Children's Medical Ministries
China Connection
Christ for India, Inc.
Christar
Christian Advance International
Christian Aid Ministries
Christian Dental Society
Christian Service International
Church of the Nazarene, World Msn. Dept.
Churches of God, General Conference
CMF International
ComCare International
Correll Missionary Ministries
Crossover Communications International
Empowering Lives International

Equip, Inc.
Evangelical Covenant Church
Evangelical Lutheran Church in America
Evangelical Methodist Church
Flwshp. of Assoc. of Medical Evangelism
FOCAS
For Haiti with Love Inc.
Foundation For His Ministry
General Baptists International
Global Health Ministries
Global Outreach Mission
Gospel Fellowship Association
Grace Ministries International
Haiti Lutheran Mission Society
HCJB World Radio
Health Emergent International Services
Health Teams International
India Partners
Interchurch Medical Assistance
International Aid
Intl. Christian Leprosy Mission, Inc. (USA)
International Health Services
International Outreach Ministries
InterServe/USA
Lifewater International
Ludhiana Christian Medical College Bd., USA
Luke Society, The
Macedonian Missionary Service
MAP International
Medical Ambassadors International
Medical Missions Philippines
Men for Missions International
Mennonite Mission Network
Mercy Ships
Mexican Medical Ministries
Mission of Mercy
Missionary Ventures International
Moravian Church in North America
Mustard Seed, Inc., The
N. Am. Baptist Conf. Intl. Missions Dept.
Northwest Medical Teams
Operation Blessing International
Partners in Christ International
Presbyterian Church (USA), Worldwide
Primitive Methodist Church in the USA
Project AmaZon
Project Christ International
Project Mercy, Inc.
Ramabai Mukti Mission
Red Sea Team International
Reformed Episcopal Bd. of Fgn. Msns.
Samaritan's Purse
Seventh-day Adventists Gen. Conference
SIM USA
Surfing the Nations/Targeting 10/40 Window
TEAM (The Evangelical Alliance Mission)

Teen World Outreach
The Mission Society
Tribes and Nations Outreach
UFM International
United Church Board for World Ministries
Vellore Christian Medical College Bd. (USA)
World Gospel Mission
World Mission Prayer League Inc.
World Missions Far Corners, Inc.
World Witness, Assoc. Reformed Presb. Ch.
World-Wide Missions

Member Care
Barnabas International
Commission to Every Nation
D & D Missionary Homes, Inc.
Interaction International Inc.
Liebenzell Mission USA
Missions Resource Network
Providence Mission Homes, Inc.
University of the Family

National church nurture/support
ABWE
ACTS International Ministries
Advancing Indigenous Missions
Advancing Native Missions
Advancing Renewal Ministries
Africa Inter-Mennonite Mission
African Mission Evangelism
AIMS
Amazon Focus
American Baptist Churches in the U.S.A.
AmeriTribes
AMOR Ministries
Anglican Frontier Missions
Baptist Bible Fellowship Intl.
Barnabas International
Bible Missionary Church
Bibles For The World, Inc.
Brethren in Christ World Missions
Bridge Builders International
Caring Partners International, Inc.
Christ Community Church
Christ for the City International
Christ to the Nations
Christian Associates International
Christian Church (Disciples of Christ)
Christian Fellowship Union
Christian Info. Service, Inc. Msns. Div.
Christian Reformed World Missions
Christians In Action, Inc.
Church of God (Holiness), World Msn. Bd.
Church of God (Seventh Day) Gen. Conf.
Ch. of God in Christ, Mennonite Gen. Msn. Bd.
Church of God of Prophecy

Church of the Brethren
Church of the United Brethren in Christ
Church Planting International
Churches of Christ
Churches of God, General Conference
Conservative Congregational Christian Conf.
Cumberland Presbyterian Ch. Bd Msns.
East West Ministries
Emmanuel Intl. Mission (U.S.)
Envoy International
Episcopal Ch., Domestic & Fgn. Msny. Soc.
European Christian Mission NA, Inc.
Evangelical Congregational Church
Evangelical Lutheran Church in America
Evangelical Mennonite Ch. Intl. Mins.
Evangelical Presbyterian Ch. - Wld. Outreach
Family Aid International, Inc.
Forward Edge International
Foursquare Missions International
Free Gospel Church, Missions Dept.
Full Gospel Evangelistic Association
Global Advance
Global Youth Ministry Network
Globe Missionary Evangelism
Gospel Furthering Fellowship
Grace Brethren International Missions
Harvest Evangelism, Inc.
Have Christ Will Travel Ministries
Help for Christian Nationals, Inc.
In Touch Mission International
India Gospel Outreach
Intl. Christian Leprosy Mission, Inc. (USA)
International Cooperating Ministries
International Pentecostal Church of Christ
International Pentecostal Holiness Church
International Teams, U.S.A.
InterServe/USA
Iranian Christians International
Japanese Evangelical Missionary Society
Kingdom Building Ministries
Latin America Lutheran Mission
Latin American Indian Ministries
Liberty Corner Mission
Liebenzell Mission USA
LIFE Ministries
LOGOI, Inc./FLET
Lutheran Brethren World Missions
Mahesh Chavda Ministries Intl.
Mercy Ships
Middle East Christian Outreach
Middle Eastern Outreach
Ministries In Action
Mission ONE, Inc.
Mission to the World (PCA), Inc.
Missionary Ventures International
Missions To Japan, Inc.

Moravian Church in North America
Morelli Ministries International
Navigators, U.S. Intl. Msns. Group
New Directions International
New Tribes Mission
New Way Missions
Open Bible Standard Chs., Intl. Mins.
Open Door Baptist Missions
Outreach To Asia Nationals
Partners in Asian Missions
Pentecostal Ch. of God, World Msns. Dep.
Pentecostal Free Will Baptist Church
Pioneer Bible Translators
Prakash Association USA
Presbyterian Ch. (USA), Worldwide Mins.
Presbyterian Missionary Union
Primitive Methodist Church in the USA
Ramesh Richard Evangelism
Reciprocal Ministries International
Reformed Church in America, Gen. Synod
Rosedale Mennonite Missions
Samaritan's Purse
SEND International
ServLife International
Slavic Gospel Association
Slavic Missionary Service
Society of St. Margaret
South American Missionary Society
Sowers International, The
STEM
TCM International
TEAM (The Evangelical Alliance Mission)
Teen World Outreach
The Master's Harvest
The Mission Society
TMA Ministries
Turkish World Outreach
United Methodist Ch., Gen. Bd. Global Mins.
Venture International
Vineyard International Consortium
Virginia Mennonite Board of Missions
Wesleyan World Missions
Westminister Biblical Missions
Wisconsin Evangelical Lutheran Synod
World Gospel Mission
World Harvest Now, Inc.
World Help
World Missionary Assistance Plan
World Partners USA
World Reach, Inc.
World Team
World Witness, Assoc. Reformed Presb. Ch.
WorldTeach
Zion Evangelical Ministries of Africa

Partnership development

AIMS
Awana Clubs International
Bridge Builders International
Christ Community Church
Evangelical Mennonite Ch. Intl. Mins.
Good News Productions Intl.
Harvest
India Gospel League Inc., North America
India Partners
Intl. Christian Leprosy Mission, Inc. (USA)
International Cooperating Ministries
Kids Alive International
Latin America Lutheran Mission
Lutheran Church—Missouri Synod
Mailbox Club International
Mission ONE, Inc.
Missionary Ventures International
New Directions International
SP Ministries
Venture International

Psychological counseling

Barnabas International
Link Care Foundation
Narramore Christian Foundation

Purchasing services

Hundredfold Ministries International
Interchurch Medical Assistance
JAARS, Inc.
MATS International, Inc.
Seventh Day Baptist Missionary Society

Recruiting/Mobilizing

ACMC
Action International Ministries
AIMS
Ambassadors for Christ, Inc.
American Baptist Churches in the U.S.A.
Artists In Christian Testimony
Baptist Bible Translators Institute
Cadence International
Caleb Project
Calvary International
CAM International
Christian Medical & Dental Society
Christian Ministries International (C.M.I.)
Christian Missions Unlimited
Christian Outreach International
Church of the United Brethren in Christ
Cornerstone International
DualReach
Emmaus Road, International
Episcopal Church Missionary Community
Evangelical Friends Church Southwest

Evangelism Explosion International
Flwshp. of Assoc. of Medical Evangelism
Forward Edge International
Free Will Baptists, Inc., Bd. of Fgn. Msn.
Friendship International
Frontier Mission Fellowship
Frontiers
Global Focus
Global Opportunities
Global Strategy Mission Assoc.
Grace Brethren International Missions
Great Commission Center International
Harvest Evangelism, Inc.
Health Teams International
Heart of God Ministries
Hope Missions Outreach International
India Gospel League Inc., North America
INTENT
Intercristo
International Gospel Outreach
Intl. Pentecostal Holiness Ch. World Msns.
International Students, Inc
Kingdom Building Ministries
Ludhiana Christian Medical College Bd., USA
Mennonite Mission Network
Mission ONE, Inc.
Mission To Unreached Peoples
Mission: Moving Mountains, Inc.
Missions Resource Network
Navigators, U.S. Intl. Missions Group
New Life League International
New Way Missions
N. American Baptist Conf. Intl. Msns. Dept.
OMS International, Inc.
Operation Mobilization, Inc.
Overseas Ministries Study Center
People International
Pioneer Bible Translators
Presbyterian Center for Mission Studies
Presbyterian Order for World Evangelization
Priority One International
Rock the World Youth Mission Alliance
Sending Experienced Retired Volunteers
Seventh-day Adventists General Conference
Share International
STEM
Team Expansion, Inc.
Turkish World Outreach
Wesleyan World Missions
World Harvest Mission
World Horizons
World Thrust International, Inc.
Wycliffe Associates USA

Relief and/or rehabilitation
African Enterprise, Inc.

All God's Children International
American Association of Lutheran Chs.
AMG International
AMOR Ministries
Apostolic Christian Ch. Foundation, Inc.
ASSIST
Baptist Mid-Missions
Blessings International
Bread for the World
Bright Hope International
Childcare International
Christ for the City International
Christian Aid Ministries
Christian Aid Mission
Christian Blind Mission Intl.
Christian Broadcasting Network, the
Christian Church of North America Missions
Christian Reformed World Relief Committee
Christians In Action, Inc.
Ch. of God in Christ, Mennonite Gen. Msn. Bd.
Church of the Brethren
Church of the Nazarene, World Msn. Dept.
Church World Service & Witness
Congregational Christian Chs., Natl. Assoc.
Cumberland Presbyterian Ch. Bd. Msns.
Dayspring Enterprises International
Eastern Mennonite Missions
Emmanuel Intl. Mission (U.S.)
Flying Doctors of America
Food for the Hungry, Inc.
For Haiti with Love Inc.
Forward Edge International
Frontiers
Globe Missionary Evangelism
Haiti Lutheran Mission Society
Health Emergent International Services
Heart to Heart Intl. Ministries
International Aid
International Teams, U.S.A.
Kids Alive International
Larry Jones International Ministries
Latin America Assistance, Inc.
Lutheran World Relief
MAP International
Mennonite Central Committee
Mercy Ships
Ministries In Action
Mission of Mercy
Mission Possible, Inc.
Mission To Unreached Peoples
Muslim Hope
New Life League International
Northwest Medical Teams
Operation Blessing International
People International
Project Mercy, Inc.

Ramabai Mukti Mission
Reformed Church in America, Gen. Synod
Romanian Missionary Society
Rosedale Mennonite Missions
Samaritan's Purse
Seventh Day Baptist Missionary Society
Seventh-day Adventists General Conference
Shelter for Life International, Inc.
Southern Baptist Conv. Intl. Msn. Bd.
TCM International
United Methodist Church
Venture International
Wisconsin Evangelical Lutheran Synod
World Concern
World Missions Far Corners, Inc.
World Opportunities International
World Relief Corporation
World Vision Inc.
Youth With A Mission (YWAM)

Research

AmeriTribes
Anglican Frontier Missions
Billy Graham Center, The
Caleb Project
Centers for Apologetics Research (CFAR)
China Ministries International
ChinaSource
Daystar U.S.
Envoy International
European Evangelistic Society
FOM (Fellowship of Missions)
Frontier Mission Fellowship
Global Fellowship
Global Mapping International
Good News Productions Intl.
Gospel Outreach Ministries Intl.
Gospel Recordings
Grace Baptist Missions International
Handclasp International, Inc.
Institute for Intl. Christian Communication
INTENT
InterAct Ministries
Japanese Evangelization Center
LIGHT International, Inc.
Mission Training and Resource Center
Missions Resource Center
Missions Resource Network
OC International, Inc.
Paraclete, Inc.
Russian Language Ministries
Sentinel Group, The
VELA Ministries International
World Evangelization Research Center

Services for other agencies

ACM International
Audio Scripture Ministries
Barnabas International
Blessings International
Caleb Project
Calvary Evangelistic Mission, Inc.
Children's Haven International
ChinaSource
Christian Info. Service, Inc. Msns. Div.
Church Ministries International
Crisis Consulting International
Disciples International
DualReach
ECHO
Episcopal Ch., Domestic & Fgn. Msny. Soc.
Galcom International (U.S.)
Global Mapping International
Global Opportunities
Gospel Communications International
Gospel Literature International, Inc.
Gospel Recordings
Handclasp International, Inc.
Health Teams International
Helps International Ministries
IFMA
Interaction International Inc.
Intercristo
INTERDEV
International Aid
Kids Around the World, Inc.
Lifewater International
MATS International, Inc.
Media Associates International
Middle East Media–USA
Mission Nannys
Mission Safety International
Mission Services Association
Mission To Unreached Peoples
Missionaire International
Missionary Retreat Fellowship Inc.
Missionary TECH Team
New Way Missions
Paraclete, Inc.
Progressive Vision
Sending Experienced Retired Volunteers
STEER, Inc.
Teen Missions International
Tentmakers International Exchange–T.I.E
The Master's Mission, Inc.
TMA Ministries
United Evangelical Churches
World Concern
World Mission Associates
World Opportunities International
World Outreach Ministries
World Thrust International, Inc.

Short-term programs coordination

Adventures in Missions
Amazon Focus
AMF International
AMOR Ministries
Artists In Christian Testimony
Asian Outreach U.S.A.
Aurora Mission
Biblical Literature Fellowship
Blessings International
Caleb Project
Calvary Commission, Inc.
CAM International
Caring Partners International, Inc.
Children's Haven International
Children's Medical Ministries
Christian Advance International
Christian Medical & Dental Society
Christian Missions Unlimited
Christian Outreach International
Christian Service International
Church of God (Anderson, Indiana)
CMTS Ministries, Inc.
Conservative Congregational Christian Conf.
Cornerstone International
Crossover Communications International
Eastern European Outreach, Inc.
Emmaus Road, International
Empowering Lives International
Envoy International
Evangelical Mennonite Ch. Intl. Mins.
Family Aid International, Inc.
Flwshp. of Assocs. of Medical Evangelism
Floresta USA, Inc.
Flying Doctors of America
FOCAS
FRIENDS in Action, International
Friends United Meeting, World Ministries
Friendship International
Global Action
GO InterNational
Great Commission Center International
Greater Grace World Outreach
Harvest Evangelism, Inc.
Health Teams International
Heart to Heart Intl. Ministries
Hope for the Hungry
Hope Missions Outreach International
In Touch Mission International
Independent Gospel Missions
India Gospel League Inc., North America
India Partners
International Family Missions
International Messengers
International Outreach Ministries
Japanese Evangelical Missionary Society

JARON Ministries International
Kids Alive International
Kingdom Building Ministries
Larry Jones International Ministries
Latin America Lutheran Mission
Latin America Mission
Macedonian Missionary Service
Men for Missions International
Mennonite Mission Network
Mexican Medical Ministries
Missionary Athletes International
Missionary TECH Team
Missionary Ventures International
Mutual Faith Ministries Intl.
New Tribes Mission
New Way Missions
No Greater Love Ministries, Inc.
On The Go Mins./Keith Cook Evangelistic. Assoc.
Operation Blessing International
Partners in Christ International
Pass the Torch Ministries
Pioneers
Precious Seed Ministries
Project Christ International
Project Mercy, Inc.
Project Partner with Christ
Raul Zaldivar Evangelistic Ministry
Rock the World Youth Mission Alliance
Rosedale Mennonite Missions
SAND International
Sending Experienced Retired Volunteers
Seventh Day Baptist Missionary Society
Sowers International, The
STEM
Surfing the Nations-Targeting 10/40 Window
Team Expansion, Inc.
Teen Missions International
Teen World Outreach
The Master's Harvest
Touch the World Ministries
Tribes and Nations Outreach
United Evangelical Churches
Village Ministries International, Inc.
Virginia Mennonite Board of Missions
Word of Life Fellowship
World Horizons
World Indigenous Missions
World Reach, Inc.
World Servants
World Witness, Assoc. Reformed Presb. Ch.
Wycliffe Associates USA
Youth Encounter
YUGO Ministries

Supplying equipment

Audio Scripture Ministries

Chosen, Inc.
Christ for the Lost World
CMTS Ministries, Inc.
ComCare International
Dayspring Enterprises International
Equip, Inc.
Equipping the Saints
Evangelical Bible Mission
FRIENDS in Action, International
Galcom International (U.S.)
Global Health Ministries
Gospel Revival Ministries
Have Christ Will Travel Ministries
HCJB World Radio
International Aid
Kids Around the World, Inc.
Ludhiana Christian Medical College Bd., USA
Morelli Ministries International
Operation Blessing International
Progressive National Baptist Conv USA
Project Care
Vellore Christian Medical College Bd. (USA)
Worldwide Lab Improvement, Inc.
Wycliffe Associates USA

Support of national workers

Advancing Native Missions
Advent Christian General Conf.
Amazon Focus
Ambassadors for Christ Intl.
AMG International
Apostolic Christian Church Foundation, Inc.
Assoc. of Free Lutheran Congregations
Back to the Bible International
Baptist International Evangelistic Ministries
Bible League, The
Bible Missionary Church
Bibles For The World, Inc.
BILD International
Brethren Church Missionary Bd.
Calvary Commission, Inc.
Campus Crusade for Christ, Intl.
Carver International Missions, Inc.
Child Evangelism Fellowship, Inc.
Christ Community Church
Christ for the Lost World
Christ to the Nations
Christian Church of N. America Missions
Christian Info. Service, Inc. Msns. Div.
Christian Missions Unlimited
Church of God (Anderson, Indiana)
Church of God (Cleveland, TN)
Church of God (Holiness)
Church of God of Prophecy
Church of the United Brethren in Christ
Churches of God, General Conference

Cities for Christ Worldwide
Clark Theol. College (India) Tribal Mins., USA
Congregational Holiness Ch. World Msns.
Cook Communications Ministries Intl.
Correll Missionary Ministries
Covenant Celebration Ch. Global Outreach
David Livingstone KURE Foundation
Dayspring Enterprises International
East Gates Ministries Intl.
Eastern European Outreach, Inc.
East-West Ministries International
European Christian Mission NA, Inc.
Evangel Bible Translators
Evangelical Covenant Church
Evangelical Presbyterian Ch.–Wld. Outreach
Evangelism Explosion International
Evangelistic Faith Missions
Family Aid International, Inc.
Flwshp. of Assoc. of Medical Evangelism
Final Frontiers Foundation, Inc.
Foundation For His Ministry
Fundamental Baptist Mission of Trinidad
General Baptists International
General Conf. Mennonite Church
Global Fellowship
Global Youth Ministry Network
Good News for India
Gospel for Asia
Gospel Outreach Ministries Intl.
Gospel Recordings
Gospel Revival Ministries
Grace Baptist Missions International
HBI Global Partners
Heart to Heart Intl. Ministries
Help for Christian Nationals, Inc.
Hope for the Hungry
Hosanna / Faith Comes By Hearing
In Touch Mission International
Independent Gospel Missions
India Evangelical Mission, Inc.
India Gospel Outreach
India National Inland Mission
International Missionary Center
International Needs–USA
International Partnership Ministries, Inc.
Josue Yrion World Evangelism Missions, Inc.
Latin America Lutheran Mission
Latin American Indian Ministries
LIFE Ministries
M/E International, Inc.
MBMS International
Medical Ambassadors International
Medical Missions Philippines
Mennonite Mission Network
Mission Ministries, Inc.
Mission ONE, Inc.

Mission Possible, Inc.
Mission: Moving Mountains, Inc.
National Baptist Convention of America
New Directions International
New Hope International
New Way Missions
Omega World Missions
Outreach To Asia Nationals
Overseas Ministries Study Center
Partners in Asian Missions
Partners International
Pentecostal Church of God
Peter Deyneka Russian Ministries
Pillar of Fire Missions Intl.
Precious Seed Ministries
Presbyterian Evangelistic Fellowship
Project Care
Project Christ International
Project Partner with Christ
Reach Ministries International
Romanian Missionary Society
ServLife International
Seventh Day Baptist Missionary Society
Share International
Slavic Gospel Association
Source of Light Ministries International, Inc.
Sowers International, The
Spanish World Ministries
Spiritual Growth Resources, Inc.
Team Expansion, Inc.
Teen Missions International
Third World Baptist Missions
Walk Thru The Bible Ministries
World Missions Far Corners, Inc.
WorldTeach
World-Wide Missions
Zion Evangelical Ministries of Africa

Technical assistance
Audio Scripture Ministries
Chosen, Inc.
Christian Reformed World Relief Committee
CMTS Ministries, Inc.
ComCare International
ECHO
Engineering Ministries International
Enterprise Development Intl.
Equip, Inc.
FARMS International, Inc.
Global Mapping International
Gospel Communications International
Gospel Recordings
HCJB World Radio
Helps International Ministries
Hosanna / Faith Comes By Hearing
Hundredfold Ministries International

Interchurch Medical Assistance
International Child Care
JAARS, Inc.
Lifewater International
Literacy & Evangelism International
MATS International, Inc.
Media Associates International
Mennonite Central Committee
Missionary TECH Team
Open Doors with Brother Andrew USA
Paraclete, Inc.
Partners International
Progressive Vision
Self-Help International
Servants in Faith & Technology (SIFAT)
Shelter for Life International, Inc.
Tech Serve International
TMA Ministries
Trans World Radio
United Bd. for Christian Higher Ed. in Asia
World Relief Corporation
Worldwide Lab Improvement, Inc.
Wycliffe Associates USA

Tentmaking & Related
INTENT
Worldwide Tentmakers, Inc.

TESOL
Christian Outreach International
Overseas Radio & Television, Inc.

Training, other
ABWE
AIMS
Ambassadors for Christ Intl.
Artists In Christian Testimony
Asian Outreach U.S.A.
BCM International
Bible League, The
Bible Training Centre for Pastors
BILD International
Billy Graham Center, The
Bridge Builders International
Campus Crusade for Christ, Intl.
Carver International Missions, Inc.
China Outreach Ministries
Christ for India, Inc.
Christian Dental Society
Christian Discipleship Ministries, Inc.
Christian Ministries International (C.M.I.)
Christian World Publishers
CMTS Ministries, Inc.
ComCare International
Cook Communications Ministries Intl.
Crisis Consulting International

Derek Prince Ministries, Intl.
East West Ministries
ECHO
Emmaus Road, International
Empowering Lives International
Enterprise Development Intl.
Envoy International
Equip, Inc.
Evangelical Covenant Church
Evangelism Resources
Faith Christian Fellowship Intl.
Friendship International
Global Action
Global Advance
Global Focus
Global Harvest Ministries
Global Opportunities
Global Youth Ministry Network
Gospel Literature International, Inc.
Great Commission Center International
Harvest
HCJB World Radio
Heifer International
Help for Christian Nationals, Inc.
IFMA
Independent Gospel Missions
India Gospel League Inc., North America
Institute of Theological Studies
International Aid
International Christian Ministries
International Street Kids Outreach Ministries
International Students, Inc.
International Urban Associates
Joni and Friends
Kids Around the World, Inc.
Kingdom Building Ministries
Leadership Ministries Worldwide
M/E International, Inc.
Media Associates International
Medical Missions Philippines
Mennonite Central Committee
Middle East Media–USA
Mission to the Americas
Missionaire International
MMS Aviation
National Religious Broadcasters
New Hope International
On The Go Mins./Keith Cook Evangelistic Assoc.
Oriental Missionary Crusade
Pass the Torch Ministries
Peoples Mission International
Prakash Association USA
Precept Ministries International
Project Mercy, Inc.
Radio Voice of Christ, Inc.
Ravi Zacharias International Ministries

Reciprocal Ministries International
Rio Grande Bible Institute
Russian Language Ministries
Self-Help International
Sentinel Group, The
Servants in Faith & Technology (SIFAT)
Share International
Son Shine Ministries International
South America Mission
SP Ministries
Sports & Rec Plus
The Ch. of God of the Apostolic Faith, Inc.
Things To Come Mission, Inc.
TITUS International
United Bd. for Christian Higher Ed. in Asia
United Evangelical Churches
University of the Family
VELA Ministries International
Vellore Christian Medical College Bd. (USA)
Walk Thru The Bible Ministries
World Mission Associates
World Missionary Assistance Plan
World Servants
World Team
World Vision International
Worldwide Discipleship Assoc.
Worldwide Lab Improvement, Inc.
Wycliffe Bible Translators International

Training/Orientation, missionary
ACM International
Adventures in Missions
African Enterprise, Inc.
Ambassadors for Christ, Inc.
AMF International
AMOR Ministries
Anglican Frontier Missions
Apostolic Team Ministries, Intl.
Baptist Bible Fellowship Intl.
Barnabas International
Bethany Fellowship Missions
Caleb Project
Calvary Commission, Inc.
Calvary International
China Ministries International
ChinaSource
Chosen People Ministries
Christ to the Nations
Christian Blind Mission Intl.
Christian Churches/Churches of Christ
Christian Outreach International
Christians In Action, Inc.
Church Missions Link
Church of the Nazarene, World Msn. Dept.
CityTeam Ministries
Clark Theol. College (India) Tribal Mins., USA

CLC Ministries International
CMF International
Daystar U.S.
Deaf Missions International
DualReach
Elim Fellowship, International Department
Episcopal Church Missionary Community
Episcopal Ch., Domestic & Fgn. Msny. Soc.
Equip, Inc.
Evangelical Friends Church Southwest
Evangelism Explosion International
Food for the Hungry, Inc.
Frontier Mission Fellowship
Global Mapping International
Global Strategy Mission Assoc.
Gospel for Asia
Greater Grace World Outreach
Harvest Evangelism, Inc.
Heart of God Ministries
Hope for the Hungry
India National Inland Mission
Institute for Intl. Christian Communication
Interaction International Inc.
International Family Missions
International Gospel Outreach
International Messengers
International Teams, U.S.A.
JAARS, Inc.
Japanese Evangelical Missionary Society
Jews for Jesus
Larry Jones International Ministries
Literacy & Evangelism International
Living Water Teaching International
Macedonian Missionary Service
Mexican Medical Ministries
Middle Eastern Outreach
Mission Training and Resource Center
Mission Training International
Missions Resource Network
Narramore Christian Foundation
Navigators, U.S. Intl. Missions Group
New Tribes Mission
OC International, Inc.
OMS International, Inc.
Operation Mobilization, Inc.
Paraclete, Inc.
Peoples Mission International
Project Christ International
Project Partner with Christ
Raul Zaldivar Evangelistic Ministry
Reach Ministries International
Russian Language Ministries
SAND International
Seventh Day Baptist Missionary Society
Seventh-day Adventists General Conference
Shield of Faith Mission Intl.

Son Shine Ministries International
Teen Missions International
Tentmakers International Exchange–T.I.E
The Master's Mission, Inc.
Touch the World Ministries
Training Evangelistic Leadership
Tribes and Nations Outreach
United Methodist Church
World Harvest Now, Inc.
World Horizons
Youth With A Mission (YWAM)

Translation, Bible
Africa Inter-Mennonite Mission
American Association of Lutheran Churches
American Bible Society
Aurora Mission
Baptist Bible Translators Institute
Baptist Mid-Missions
Bible League, The
CAM International
Christian Aid Mission
Christian Literature International
Evangel Bible Translators
Evangelical Congregational Church
Fellowship International Mission
FRIENDS in Action, International
Frontiers
International Bible Society
Leadership Ministries Worldwide
Lutheran Bible Translators
Lutheran Brethren World Missions
Ministry to Eastern Europe
New Tribes Mission
People International
Pioneer Bible Translators
Red Sea Team International
Reformed Episcopal Bd. of Foreign Msns.
Russian Bible Society, Inc.
SIM USA
World Bible Translation Center
World Partners USA
World Team
Wycliffe Bible Translators International
Wycliffe Bible Translators USA

Translation, other
African Leadership
Arabic Communication Center
Gospel Literature International, Inc.
Iranian Christians International
Key Communications
Outreach To Asia Nationals
Progressive Vision
RBC Ministries
Reformation Translation Flwshp.

Russian Bible Society, Inc.
Slavic Gospel Association
Team Expansion, Inc.
World Missionary Assistance Plan
Wycliffe Bible Translators USA

Urban Ministry
Church Resource Ministries
Cities for Christ Worldwide
International Teams, U.S.A.
LIGHT International, Inc.

Video/Film production/distribution
Anis Shorrosh Evangelistic Association, Inc.
Arabic Communication Center
China Outreach Ministries
Christian Resources International
CMTS Ministries, Inc.
Derek Prince Ministries, Intl.
Emmaus Road, International
Evangelical Baptist Missions
Friends of Israel Gospel Ministry
Good News Productions Intl.
Gospel Communications International
Handclasp International, Inc.
In Touch Mission International
INTERCOMM
International Board of Jewish Missions, Inc.
JAARS, Inc.
Josue Yrion World Evangelism Missions, Inc.
Lutheran Bible Translators
Middle East Christian Outreach
Middle East Media–USA
Overseas Radio & Television, Inc.
Priority One International
Progressive Vision
Project Mercy, Inc.
Rio Grande Bible Institute
Sentinel Group, The
The Ch. of God of the Apostolic Faith, Inc.
World Mission Associates
WorldTeach

Youth programs
AMOR Ministries
Awana Clubs International
Bridge Builders International
Cadence International
Carpenter's Tools International
Christ for the Lost World
Christ for the Nations, Inc.
Christian Advance International
Christian Union Churches of N. AM.
CityTeam Ministries
Compassion International, Inc.
Eastern Mennonite Missions

Every Child Ministries, Inc.
Forward Edge International
Global Action
Global Youth Ministry Network
Great Commission Ministries, Inc.
Hellenic Ministries
Interaction International Inc.
International Teams, U.S.A.
Italy for Christ
MBMS International
Mennonite Central Committee
Mexican Medical Ministries
Mission Possible Foundation, Inc.
Mission To Unreached Peoples
Navigators, U.S. Intl. Missions Group
New Hope International
On The Go Mins./Keith Cook Evangelistic Assoc.
Pioneer Clubs
Presbyterian Evangelistic Fellowship
Rock the World Youth Mission Alliance
Rosedale Mennonite Missions
Salvation Army, U.S.A.
Shield of Faith Ministries
Surfing the Nations–Targeting 10/40 Window
Teen World Outreach
The Ch. of God of the Apostolic Faith, Inc.
The Master's Harvest
Touch the World Ministries
Word of Life Fellowship
Young Life
Youth Encounter
Youth for Christ / USA, World Outreach Div.
Youth With A Mission (YWAM)
YUGO Ministries

Chapter 4
Countries of Activity
for U.S. Protestant Agencies

I n this chapter you will find the countries where agencies reported field personnel in answer to question #12 of the Survey Questionnaire (see the Appendix for details). The few exceptions to this are agencies whose whole program supports (with funds raised in the USA, but which may not be designated to specific personnel on a regular basis) churches or other initiatives in a country.

All countries are listed in alphabetical order according to the name most commonly recognized in North America. Countries that are part of the Commonwealth of Independent States (most of the former Soviet Union) have been listed separately. Examples of this include Armenia, Kyrgyzstan and Belarus. In a few cases we have listed a territory or other administrative district of a country because it is commonly viewed as a separate entity and mission agencies report it that way. An example would be the Azores, located in the Atlantic Ocean 900 miles west of mainland Portugal.

We have separated the personnel totals for all agencies into five categories. Under the "personnel from U.S." heading, the term of expected service has been divided into three categories: 4+ years, 2-4 years and 1-2 years for fully supported personnel. For non-U.S. personnel in the "other countries" heading, the categories are those who are citizens of that ministry country and those who are not citizens, and are fully or partially supported by funds raised in the U.S. by the associated agency. For example, a Korean with specific mission/ministry duties serving in Korea would be included in an agency's "citizens" column of the Korea section. A Korean serving in Russia would be listed in the "not citizen" column of the Russia section.

At the end of each country section, totals of each category for that country are given. Please note that the totals for the "other countries" heading do not necessarily reflect all non-U.S. mission personnel who draw support from U.S. agencies. Some agencies give grants for ongoing institutions and other programs without specifying individual recipients. This may be in addition to U.S. mission personnel based in that country or the agency may not have U.S. personnel living in that country.

Please note also that the totals will be minimum numbers only because of the bigger number of large agencies in this edition that reported their personnel only by general regions and not by specific countries. Therefore, their numbers are not included in this "countries of activity" section.

	First Year	4+ yrs.	2-4 yrs.	1-2 yrs.	Other Countries Citizens	Not Citizens
Afghanistan						
Engineering Ministries International	2002	-	-	2	-	-
Evangelical Presb. Ch. - World Outreach	1991	2	-	-	-	-
Health Emergent International Services	1999	2	10	2	-	1
International Teams, U.S.A.	-	-	-	1	-	-
InterServe/USA	1967	12	-	-	-	-
Medical Ambassadors International	2001	-	-	-	-	-
Mennonite Mission Network	1966	4	-	-	-	-
Northwest Medical Teams	2001	-	-	-	-	-
Samaritan's Purse	2001	-	-	3	-	1
Shelter for Life International, Inc.	1982		1	-	-	-
	Totals:	20	11	8	-	2
Africa—General						
Africa Inland Mission International	2001	2	-	-	-	
Bethany Fellowship Missions		1	-	-	-	-
Bible Training Centre for Pastors	1998	1	-	-	2	-
Calvary International	1993	4	-	-	-	4
Campus Crusade for Christ, Intl.		16	-	21	72	2
CBInternational	1993	20	-	3	-	-
Christian and Missionary Alliance	1996	4	-	-	-	-
Christian Churches / Churches of Christ		4	-	-	-	-
Church World Service & Witness	1946	5	-	-	35	10
Eastern Mennonite Missions		6	1	-	-	-
Evangelical Covenant Ch. Bd. of World Msn.	1999	2	-	-	-	-
Final Frontiers Foundation, Inc.	1992	-	-	-	148	-
Free Methodist World Missions		2	-	-	-	-
Globe Missionary Evangelism	1993	3	-	-	-	-
Good News Productions Intl.	1995	2	-	-	8	-
Hope for the Hungry		2	1	-	1	-
India Partners		-	-	-	-	-
International Bible Society		-	-	-	117	-
Intl. Christian Leprosy Mission, Inc. (USA)	1988	-	-	-	2	-
Intl. Pentecostal Holiness Ch. World Mins.	1992	6	-	-	-	2
Mennonite Central Committee		187	-	-	-	-
Middle East Christian Outreach		1	-	-	1	14
Mission Aviation Fellowship		10	-	-	-	-
Operation Mobilization, Inc.		7	3	1	-	-
Opportunity Intl./Women's Opportunity		-	2	-	-	-
Pentecostal Ch. of God, World Msns. Dept.		4	-	-	-	-
Red Sea Team International	1975	3	-	-	-	-
Southern Baptist Conv. Intl. Mission Bd.		-	-	-	-	-
TEAM (The Evangelical Alliance Mission)		33	-	2	-	-
Team Expansion, Inc.	2001	2	-	-	-	-
WEC International		2	-	-	-	21
World Horizons	2001	5	-	-	-	7
Wycliffe Bible Translators USA		132	-	-	-	-
	Totals:	466	7	27	386	60
Albania						
AMG International	1992	2	-	-	-	-
Apostolic Team Ministries, Intl.		5	-	-	3	-
Assemblies of God World Missions		8	-	-	-	-

		Personnel from U.S.			Other Countries	
	First Year	4+ yrs.	2-4 yrs.	1-2 yrs.	Citizens	Not Citizens
Baptist Bible Fellowship Intl.	1995	2	-	-	-	-
Bible League, The	1997	-	-	-	4	-
Brethren Assemblies		6	-	-	-	-
CAM International	1995	2	-	-	-	2
Campus Crusade for Christ, Intl.	1991	10	-	1	58	9
CBInternational	1992	2	-	-	-	-
Child Evangelism Fellowship, Inc.	1992	1	-	-	-	-
Christar	1994	6	8	2	-	-
Christian Aid Mission		-	-	-	8	-
Church of God (Cleveland, TN)	1993	-	-	-	-	2
Church of the Nazarene	1993	2	2	-	-	-
Churches of Christ	1991	25	-	-	4	-
Eastern Mennonite Missions		4	-	2	-	-
East-West Ministries International	1998	-	2	1	3	-
Evangelical Mennonite Church	1984	2	4	-	-	-
Every Home for Christ International	1992	-	-	-	9	-
Foursquare Missions International	1996	2	-	-	-	-
Globe Missionary Evangelism	1990	1	-	-	-	-
Gospel Fellowship Association	1997	2	-	-	-	-
Greater Europe Mission	1992	-	-	-	-	-
International Teams, U.S.A.		4	-	-	-	2
Larry Jones Intl. Ministries	1999	-	-	-	2	2
Medical Ambassadors International	1995	2	-	-	3	-
Mission Possible Foundation, Inc.		-	-	-	-	-
Operation Mobilization, Inc.	1991	2	1	-	-	-
Perimeter Church, Global Outreach	1995	-	-	-	2	-
Pioneers	1992	3	-	-	-	1
Presbyterian Ch. (USA), Worldwide Mins.		7	-	-	-	-
Reformed Church in America, Gen. Syn.	2000	2	-	-	-	-
SEND International	1993	2	-	-	-	-
Seventh-day Adventists Gen. Conf.	1992	-	-	-	-	6
Spiritual Growth Resources, Inc.	1994	-	-	-	3	-
Virginia Mennonite Board of Missions	1991	-	3	-	-	1
WEC International	1993	-	-	-	-	6
Wesleyan World Missions	1992	-	4	-	-	-
Wisconsin Evangelical Lutheran Syn.	1995	-	2	-	-	-
World Reach, Inc.	1999	-	-	-	-	2
	Totals:	104	26	6	99	33

Algeria

Mission ONE, Inc.		-	-	-	-	-
	Totals:	-	-	-	-	-

American Samoa

Church of the Nazarene	1958	2	-	-	-	-
Churches of Christ		2	-	-	-	-
Faith Christian Fellowship Intl.	1994	-	2	-	-	-
	Totals:	4	2			

Andorra

Faith Christian Fellowship Intl.	1993	-	2	-	-	-
	Totals:	-	2	-	-	-

		Personnel from U.S.			Other Countries	
	First Year	4+ yrs.	2-4 yrs.	1-2 yrs.	Citizens	Not Citizens

Angola

	First Year	4+ yrs.	2-4 yrs.	1-2 yrs.	Citizens	Not Citizens
Assemblies of God World Missions	1985	6	-	-	-	-
Campus Crusade for Christ, Intl.	1997	-	-	-	10	-
Child Evangelism Fellowship, Inc.	1993	-	-	-	1	-
Church of God of Prophecy		-	-	-	2	-
Church of the Nazarene	1992	2	-	-	-	2
Evangelism Resources	2001	-	-	-	-	-
Every Child Ministries, Inc.	2000	-	-	-	-	1
Larry Jones Intl. Ministries	1995	-	-	-	7	-
MBMS International	1990	-	-	-	-	2
SIM USA	1914	5	-	-	-	-
	Totals:	13	-	-	20	5

Antigua

	First Year	4+ yrs.	2-4 yrs.	1-2 yrs.	Citizens	Not Citizens
Assemblies of God World Missions		2	-	2	-	-
BCM International		-	-	-	1	-
Church of the Nazarene	1973	-	-	-	-	-
Churches of Christ	1971	2	-	-	-	-
Habitat for Humanity International	1996	-	1	-	-	-
Independent Faith Mission	1950	2	-	-	-	-
Salvation Army, U.S.A.	1903	1	-	-	-	-
Seventh-day Adventists Gen. Conf.	1944	-	-	-	-	1
	Totals:	7	1	2	1	1

Argentina

	First Year	4+ yrs.	2-4 yrs.	1-2 yrs.	Citizens	Not Citizens
ABWE		9	-	-	-	-
Apostolic Christian Church Foundation, Inc.	1969	1	-	-	11	-
Armenian Msny. Assoc. of America, Inc.	1950	-	-	-	-	-
Assemblies of God World Missions	1910	16	-	3	-	-
Baptist Bible Fellowship Intl.	1959	20	4	-	-	-
Baptist General Conference	1957	8	-	-	-	-
Baptist Mid-Missions	1987	3	-	-	-	-
Biblical Ministries Worldwide	1979	3	-	-	1	5
Brethren Assemblies		8	-	-	-	-
Brethren Church Missionary Bd.	1911	1	-	-	-	-
Campus Crusade for Christ, Intl.	1963	4	-	12	23	1
CBInternational	1947	15	-	-	-	-
Child Evangelism Fellowship, Inc.	1944	1	-	-	-	-
Chosen People Ministries	1942	-	-	-	-	-
Christian Aid Mission		-	-	-	15	-
Christian and Missionary Alliance	1897	16	-	-	-	-
Christian Churches/Churches of Christ		4	-	-	4	-
Church of God of Prophecy		-	-	-	3	2
Church of the Nazarene	1909	8	7	-	-	2
Churches of Christ	1957	13	-	-	2	-
Elim Fellowship, Intl. Dept.	1956	3	-	-	-	3
Evangelical Baptist Missions		8	-	-	-	-
Evangelical Covenant Church	1999	-	-	-	-	2
Evangelical Lutheran Church in America	1948	1	-	-	-	-
Evangelical Presbyterian Church	1991	5	-	-	2	-
Evangelism Explosion International		-	-	-	-	2
Every Home for Christ International	1958	-	-	-	3	-

	First Year	Personnel from U.S.			Other Countries	
		4+ yrs.	2-4 yrs.	1-2 yrs.	Citizens	Not Citizens
Full Gospel Grace Fellowship	1940	-	-	-	3	-
Global Outreach, Ltd.		2	-	-	-	-
Gospel Fellowship Association		2	-	-	-	-
Gospel Mission of South America	1970	10	-	-	-	-
Gospel Missionary Union	1975	17	-	-	-	-
Grace Brethren International Missions	1909	7	2	2	-	2
Greater Grace World Outreach	1996	-	-	-	-	2
HCJB World Radio		-	-	-	1	1
Impact International	1959	-	-	-	2	-
International Cassette Bible Institute	1987	-	-	-	4	-
Latin America Mission	1976	2	-	2	-	4
Luis Palau Evangelistic Assoc.	1978	-	-	-	4	-
Lutheran Church—Missouri Synod	1902	-	-	2	-	-
Medical Ambassadors International	1995	-	-	-	6	-
Mennonite Mission Network	1917	4	-	-	-	-
Mission to the World (PCA), Inc.	1983	2	2	-	-	-
Missionary Revival Crusade	1991	3	-	-	-	-
Navigators, U.S. Intl. Missions Group		6	-	5	-	-
OC International, Inc.	1956	-	-	-	2	1
Open Bible Standard Chs., Intl. Mins.	1982	1	-	-	-	-
Presbyterian Church (USA)		13	-	-	-	-
Reformed Baptist Mission Services		2	-	-	-	1
Seventh-day Adventists Gen. Conf.	1890	2	-	-	-	7
Source of Light Ministries Intl., Inc.	1999	-	-	-	3	-
Team Expansion, Inc.	1990	-	-	-	-	-
United Church Board for World Mins.		-	2	-	-	-
Word of Life Fellowship	1971	8	-	-	139	-
World Gospel Mission	1970	10	-	-	-	-
Totals:		238	17	26	228	35

Armenia

	First Year	4+ yrs.	2-4 yrs.	1-2 yrs.	Citizens	Not Citizens
Armenian Msny. Assoc. of America, Inc.	1988	2	-	-	-	4
Bible League, The	1996	-	-	-	4	-
Child Evangelism Fellowship, Inc.	1992	2	-	-	-	1
Christian Aid Mission		-	-	-	4	-
Church of the Nazarene	2002	-	-	-	-	-
Evangelism Explosion International		-	-	-	-	3
Every Home for Christ International	1991	-	-	-	1	-
Walk Thru The Bible Ministries	2000	-	-	-	1	-
Totals:		4	-	-	10	8

Aruba

	First Year	4+ yrs.	2-4 yrs.	1-2 yrs.	Citizens	Not Citizens
Church of God (Cleveland, TN)	1968	2	-	-	-	-
Church of the Nazarene	2000	-	-	-	-	-
Totals:		2	-	-	-	-

Asia - General

	First Year	4+ yrs.	2-4 yrs.	1-2 yrs.	Citizens	Not Citizens
Anglican Frontier Missions	1994	8	8	-	-	-
Arab World Ministries		116	-	6	-	-
Artists In Christian Testimony	1996	-	2	-	-	-
Assemblies of God World Missions		89	-	59	-	-
Baptist Mid-Missions		7	-	-	2	-

	Personnel from U.S.			Other Countries	
	First Year	4+ yrs.	2-4 yrs.	1-2 yrs.	Citizens	Not Citizens
Bethany Fellowship Missions		11	-	-	-	2
Bible Training Centre for Pastors	2001	1	-	-	-	-
Caleb Project	1994	6	-	1	-	-
Calvary International	1999	1	-	-	-	1
Campus Crusade for Christ, Intl.		131	-	223	3721	200
CBInternational	1993	22	2	-	-	-
Christar	1988	13	1	-	-	-
Christian Chs./ Chs. of Christ		6	-	-	2	-
Church Resource Ministries	1998	2	-	-	-	-
Church World Service & Witness	1946	-	10	17	-	-
CLC Ministries International	1956	-	3	-	-	-
Eastern Mennonite Missions		12	9	-	-	-
Elim Fellowship, International Dept.		13	-	-	1	12
Evangelical Covenant Church	1999	2	-	-	-	-
Evangelical Mennonite Church Intl.	1991	2	1	-	-	-
Final Frontiers Foundation, Inc.	1986	-	-	-	265	-
Free Methodist World Missions		2	-	-	-	-
Global Action	1998	-	-	-	1	-
Globe Missionary Evangelism	1986	2	-	-	-	-
Greater Grace World Outreach	1981	-	-	-	-	1
Heart of God Ministries	1998	-	-	-	-	15
Heifer International	1954	35	26	20	111	4
International Bible Society		-	-	-	128	-
International Cassette Bible Institute	1997	-	-	-	18	-
Intl. Christian Leprosy Mission, Inc. (USA)	1980	-	-	-	5	-
International Institute for Christian Studies	1995	-	-	-	-	2
Intl. Pentecostal Holiness Ch. World Mins.	1995	-	2	-	-	-
InterServe/USA		3	-	-	-	-
Lutheran Brethren World Missions		2	-	-	-	-
Mennonite Central Committee		451	-	-	-	-
Mennonite Mission Network		2	-	-	-	-
Middle East Christian Outreach		3	-	2	1	28
Mission Aviation Fellowship		4	-	-	-	6
Mission Ministries, Inc.	1994	2	-	-	-	2
Mission to the World (PCA), Inc.		55	6	-	-	-
Moravian Church in North America	1994	3	-	-	-	2
Muslim Hope		1	-	-	-	-
Navigators, U.S. Intl. Missions Group		4	-	2	-	-
OMF International		44	10	-	-	-
OMS International, Inc.		-	1	-	-	-
Operation Mobilization, Inc.	1995	14	8	14	-	-
Opportunity Intl./Women's Opportunity		-	5	-	-	-
Partners in Asian Missions	1972	-	-	-	50	-
Pilgrim Fellowship, Inc.	1947	1	-	-	-	1
Pioneers		172	-	-	28	7
Radio Voice of Christ, Inc.	1986	1	-	1	-	-
Red Sea Team International	1999	2	-	-	-	-
Seed International	1992	4	2	-	-	-
Southern Baptist Conv. Intl. Mission Bd.		-	-	-	-	-
Surfing the Nations		4	3	-	-	3
TEAM (The Evangelical Alliance Mission)		-	-	3	-	-
Team Expansion, Inc.	1996	20	4	-	1	1

	First Year	Personnel from U.S. 4+ yrs.	2-4 yrs.	1-2 yrs.	Other Countries Citizens	Not Citizens
TMA Ministries	1989	2	-	-	-	-
UFM International	2001	2	-	-	-	-
United Church Board for World Mins.		-	1	-	-	-
WEC International		27	-	-	-	126
World Harvest Now, Inc.		2	3	-	4	4
World Horizons	1990	4	1	-	-	2
Wycliffe Bible Translators USA		564	-	-	-	-
Totals:		1874	108	348	4338	419

Australia

	First Year	4+ yrs.	2-4 yrs.	1-2 yrs.	Citizens	Not Citizens
ABWE	1970	13	-	-	-	-
Apostolic Christian Ch. Foundation, Inc.	1978	2	-	-	-	-
Armenian Missionary Assoc. of America	1975	-	-	-	-	-
Asian Outreach U.S.A.		-	-	-	-	-
Back to the Bible International	1957	-	-	-	3	-
Baptist Bible Fellowship Intl.	1968	28	2	4	-	-
Baptist Mid-Missions	1968	18	-	-	-	-
Biblical Ministries Worldwide	1981	2	-	-	-	-
Campus Crusade for Christ, Intl.	1967	4	-	6	105	-
Child Evangelism Fellowship, Inc.	1944	2	-	-	-	-
Chosen People Ministries		-	-	-	-	-
Christ to the Nations	1998	2	-	-	-	2
Christian Churches / Churches of Christ		20	-	-	4	-
Christian Literature International		-	-	-	-	-
Church of God (Anderson, IND)		4	-	-	-	-
Church of God (Cleveland, TN)	1976	2	-	-	-	4
Church of God of Prophecy		2	-	-	1	-
Church of the Nazarene	1946	2	-	-	-	-
Churches of Christ	1847	-	-	3	30	-
Eastern Mennonite Missions		-	2	-	-	-
Elim Fellowship, Intl. Dept.		2	-	-	-	2
Fellowship International Mission	1983	3	-	-	-	2
Global Outreach Mission	1994	2	-	-	-	-
Gospel Fellowship Association	1973	4	-	1	-	-
Grace Baptist Missions International	1991	2	-	-	-	-
Grace Ministries International	1976	6	-	-	-	-
Intl. Pentecostal Holiness Ch. World Mins.	1995	4	-	-	-	-
International Teams, U.S.A.		1	-	1	12	4
Jews for Jesus	1998	1	-	-	-	-
Mennonite Mission Network	2000	-	-	-	-	-
Mission to the World (PCA), Inc.	1984	14	4	-	-	-
Missionary Ventures International	1997	4	-	-	-	-
Navigators, U.S. Intl. Missions Group		4	-	-	-	-
OC International, Inc.	1973	-	2	-	-	-
Operation Mobilization, Inc.		2	-	-	-	-
Pocket Testament League	1987	1	-	-	-	-
Precept Ministries International	1988	-	-	-	3	-
Presbyterian Ch. (USA), Worldwide Mins.		2	-	-	-	-
Seventh-day Adventists Gen. Conf.	1885	4	-	-	-	5
Teen Missions International	1986	3	-	-	-	-
Things To Come Mission, Inc.	1995	1	-	-	1	-
Trans World Radio		-	4	-	-	-

	First Year	Personnel from U.S. 4+ yrs.	2-4 yrs.	1-2 yrs.	Other Countries Citizens	Not Citizens
Turkish World Outreach	1999	2	-	-	2	-
United Church Board for World Mins.		-	2	-	-	-
Walk Thru The Bible Ministries	2002	-	-	-	4	-
WEC International	1942	-	-	-	-	86
Wesleyan World Missions	1945	-	8	-	-	-
Word of Life Fellowship	1970	8	-	-	5	-
World Baptist Fellowship Mission Agency		-	2	-	-	-
World Team	1942	1	-	-	-	-
Wycliffe Bible Translators USA		134	-	-	-	-
Youth for Christ /USA, World Outreach		5	-	-	-	-
	Totals:	311	26	15	170	105

Austria

	First Year	4+ yrs.	2-4 yrs.	1-2 yrs.	Citizens	Not Citizens
Apostolic Team Ministries, Intl.		-	-	-	2	-
Assemblies of God World Missions	1967	9	-	1	-	-
Baptist Bible Fellowship Intl.	2000	-	2	4	-	-
Baptist Mid-Missions	1965	4	-	-	-	-
BCM International		1	-	-	-	-
Biblical Ministries Worldwide	1964	2	-	-	-	-
Brethren Assemblies		6	-	-	1	-
Campus Crusade for Christ, Intl.	1974	1	-	-	-	1
CBInternational	1969	22	-	-	-	-
Child Evangelism Fellowship, Inc.	1955	1	-	-	-	-
Christian Churches / Churches of Christ		6	2	-	9	-
Churches of Christ	1953	14	-	-	-	-
Elim Fellowship, Intl. Dept.	1991	2	-	-	-	2
Evangelical Free Church Mission	1971	4	-	-	-	-
Every Home for Christ International	1960	-	-	-	2	-
Global Outreach Mission		1	-	-	-	-
Gospel Fellowship Association	1997	4	-	-	-	-
Gospel Missionary Union	1966	4	-	-	-	-
Greater Europe Mission	1964	11	1	-	-	-
International Teams, U.S.A.		30	7	-	-	12
MBMS International	1953	-	2	-	-	-
Mission to the World (PCA), Inc.	1991	7	-	-	-	-
Navigators, U.S. Intl. Missions Group		2	-	-	-	-
Network of International Christian Schools	1995	8	40	-	-	-
Precept Ministries International	1992	1	-	-	1	-
TEAM (The Evangelical Alliance Mission)	1932	15	-	2	-	-
Trans World Radio		10	-	-	-	2
UFM International	1984	4	-	1	-	-
Walk Thru The Bible Ministries	2002	-	-	-	2	-
Word of Life Fellowship	1997	2	-	-	1	3
Worldwide Tentmakers, Inc.	2001	-	-	-	-	-
Wycliffe Bible Translators USA		5	-	-	-	-
	Totals:	176	54	8	18	20

Azerbaijan

	First Year	4+ yrs.	2-4 yrs.	1-2 yrs.	Citizens	Not Citizens
Church of God of Prophecy		-	-	-	1	-
Greater Grace World Outreach	1991	-	-	-	-	3
InterVarsity Christian Fellowship/USA		-	1	-	-	-
Seventh-day Adventists Gen. Conf.	1886	-	-	-	-	1
	Totals	-	1	-	1	4

	First Year	Personnel from U.S.			Other Countries	
		4+ yrs.	2-4 yrs.	1-2 yrs.	Citizens	Not Citizens
Azores						
Baptist Bible Fellowship Intl.	1993	2	-	-	-	-
Church of the Nazarene	1984	-	-	-	-	-
Gospel Fellowship Association	1978	2	-	-	-	-
Totals:		4	-	-	-	-
Bahamas, The						
American Baptist Churches in the U.S.A.	2000	2	-	-	-	-
Assemblies of God World Missions	1942	-	-	1	-	-
Baptist Bible Fellowship International	1999	-	2	-	-	-
Christian Churches/Churches of Christ		2	-	-	-	-
Church of the Nazarene	1971	-	-	-	-	-
Churches of Christ	1959	4	-	-	-	-
Gospel Missionary Union	1967	8	-	-	-	-
Grand Old Gospel Fellowship		-	-	-	1	-
National Baptist Convention USA	1946	-	-	-	1	-
Precept Ministries International	2001	-	-	-	2	-
Totals:		16	2	1	4	-
Bahrain						
Church of God (Cleveland, TN)	1984	-	-	-	-	2
Reformed Church in America, Gen. Syn.	1970	4	-	1	1	-
University of the Family	1993	-	-	-	-	2
Totals:		4	-	1	1	4
Bangladesh						
ABWE		56	-	-	-	-
AMG International		-	-	-	9	-
Assemblies of God World Missions	1949	-	-	1	-	-
Baptist Mid-Missions	1979	-	-	-	-	2
Campus Crusade for Christ, Intl.	1975	-	-	-	421	-
Christian Aid Mission		-	-	-	36	-
Christian Churches / Churches of Christ		-	-	-	2	-
Christian Reformed World Missions	2001	-	-	2	-	
Christian Reformed World Relief Comte.	1972	1	1	-	1	-
Church of the Nazarene	1992	-	-	-	-	-
Churches of Christ	1970	1	-	-	-	-
Churches of God, General Conference	1905	-	-	-	330	-
Evangelical Lutheran Ch. in America	1993	2	-	-	-	1
Evangelism Resources	1997	-	-	-	-	-
Every Home for Christ International	1973	-	-	-	15	-
Food for the Hungry, Inc.	1972	-	1	-	-	-
Global Fellowship		-	-	-	5	2
Global Outreach Mission		-	-	-	6	-
Gospel for Asia	1979	-	-	-	-	-
International Gospel Outreach	1990	2	-	-	2	-
International Needs - USA	1974	-	-	-	93	-
InterServe/USA	1971	7	-	-	-	-
Medical Ambassadors International	1998	-	-	-	20	-
Operation Mobilization, Inc.	1964	2	-	-	-	-
Partners International	1975	-	-	-	-	-
Presbyterian Church (USA)		6	-	-	-	-

	First Year	4+ yrs.	2-4 yrs.	1-2 yrs.	Citizens	Not Citizens
		Personnel from U.S.			Other Countries	

	First Year	4+ yrs.	2-4 yrs.	1-2 yrs.	Citizens	Not Citizens
Seventh-day Adventists Gen. Conf.	1906	2	2	-	-	8
SIM USA	1957	8	-	2	-	-
Walk Thru The Bible Ministries	2000	-	-	-	1	-
World Concern	1978	-	-	-	208	-
World Mission Prayer League Inc.	1972	6	-	-	-	1
World Vision Inc.	1970	-	-	-	-	-
World-Wide Missions	1975	-	-	-	4	-
Totals:		93	4	5	1153	14

Barbados

	First Year	4+ yrs.	2-4 yrs.	1-2 yrs.	Citizens	Not Citizens
Christian Churches / Churches of Christ	1953	6	-	-	-	-
Church of God of Prophecy		-	-	-	4	-
Church of the Nazarene	1926	-	-	-	-	-
Churches of Christ	1957	1	-	-	-	-
National Baptist Convention USA, Inc.	1975	-	-	-	1	-
Totals:		7	-	-	5	-

Belarus

	First Year	4+ yrs.	2-4 yrs.	1-2 yrs.	Citizens	Not Citizens
Assemblies of God World Missions		4	-	-	-	-
Baptist International Outreach	1994	4	-	-	-	-
Baptist Mid-Missions	1975	2	-	-	-	-
Bible League, The	1994	-	-	-	6	-
Campus Crusade for Christ, Intl.	1992	7	-	6	7	10
Childcare International	1995	-	-	-	1	-
Christian Aid Mission		-	-	-	15	-
Church of God of Prophecy		-	-	-	2	2
Churches of Christ	1991	2	-	-	-	-
Full Gospel Grace Fellowship	1990	-	-	-	-	1
Greater Grace World Outreach	1996	-	-	-	-	1
InterVarsity Christian Fellowship/USA		2	-	-	-	-
Mission Ministries, Inc.	1994	2	-	-	-	-
Peter Deyneka Russian Ministries		-	-	-	-	-
Village Ministries International, Inc.	1992	-	-	-	1	-
Walk Thru The Bible Ministries	2000	-	-	-	4	-
World Baptist Fellowship Mission Agency		-	2	-	-	-
Totals:		23	2	6	36	14

Belau

	First Year	4+ yrs.	2-4 yrs.	1-2 yrs.	Citizens	Not Citizens
Assemblies of God World Missions	1983	2	-	-	-	-
Church of the Nazarene	1995	-	-	-	-	-
High Adventure Ministries/Voice of Hope	1991	1	-	-	7	2
Seventh-day Adventists General Conference	1946	-	5	4	-	-
Totals:		3	5	4	7	2

Belgium

	First Year	4+ yrs.	2-4 yrs.	1-2 yrs.	Citizens	Not Citizens
Armenian Msny. Assoc. of America, Inc.	1988	-	-	-	-	-
Assemblies of God World Missions	1949	20	-	24	-	-
Baptist Bible Fellowship Intl.	1962	9	-	-	1	-
Biblical Literature Fellowship	1958	6	-	-	-	-
CBInternational	1989	6	-	-	-	-
Child Evangelism Fellowship, Inc.	1955	2	-	-	3	-
Christian Churches / Churches of Christ		1	-	-	-	-

	First Year	Personnel from U.S.			Other Countries	
		4+ yrs.	2-4 yrs.	1-2 yrs.	Citizens	Not Citizens
Church of God (Cleveland, TN)	1973	4	-	-	-	2
Church of God of Prophecy		-	-	-	1	-
Churches of Christ	1947	12	-	-	-	-
Development Associates Intl. (DAI)	1999	-	-	-	1	-
Evangelical Free Church Mission	1977	15	3	-	-	-
Evangelism Explosion International		-	-	-	-	2
Every Home for Christ International	1961	-	-	-	1	-
Fellowship International Mission	1991	-	-	-	-	1
Free Methodist World Missions		2	-	-	-	-
Global Outreach Mission		2	-	-	-	-
Gospel Missionary Union	1966	4	-	-	-	-
Greater Europe Mission	1972	6	-	-	-	-
International Outreach Ministries	1986	6	-	-	-	-
Intl. Pentecostal Holiness Ch. World Mins.	1999	-	2	-	-	2
Mennonite Mission Network	1950	-	-	-	-	-
Operation Mobilization, Inc.	1961	8	-	1	-	-
Pilgrim Fellowship, Inc.	1990	1	-	-	1	-
Presbyterian Church (USA)		3	-	-	-	-
WEC International	2000	-	-	-	-	4
Wycliffe Bible Translators USA		3	-	-	-	-
	Totals:	110	5	25	7	11

Belize

	First Year	Personnel from U.S.			Other Countries	
		4+ yrs.	2-4 yrs.	1-2 yrs.	Citizens	Not Citizens
Amazon Focus	1995	-	-	-	1	-
Assemblies of God World Missions	1956	12	-	7	-	-
Baptist Bible Fellowship Intl.	1979	6	2	-	-	-
BCM International		2	-	-	1	-
Calvary Commission, Inc.	1984	6	-	-	-	-
Child Evangelism Fellowship, Inc.	1997	2	-	-	-	-
Christian Advance International	1989	-	-	-	2	-
Church of God (Anderson, IND)		2	-	-	-	-
Church of God of Prophecy		-	-	-	3	2
Church of the Nazarene	1934	-	-	-	-	-
Churches of Christ		8	-	-	-	-
Eastern Mennonite Missions		-	-	-	-	-
Equip, Inc.		2	-	-	2	-
Full Gospel Grace Fellowship	1989	-	-	-	-	2
Global Outreach Mission		2	-	-	-	2
Global Outreach, Ltd.		9	-	-	-	-
Gospel Missionary Union	1955	6	2	-	-	-
Hope for the Hungry		1	-	-	-	1
Intl. Pentecostal Holiness Ch. World Mins.	2000	1	-	-	-	-
Mission to the Americas	1960	2	-	-	2	-
Mission to the World (PCA), Inc.	1996	3	4	-	-	-
Pentecostal Church of God		2	-	-	-	-
Pioneers	1986	3	1	-	-	-
Rock the World Youth Mission Alliance		-	-	-	1	-
STEM International	1996	-	-	-	-	-
	Totals:	69	9	7	11	7

Benin

	First Year	Personnel from U.S.			Other Countries	
		4+ yrs.	2-4 yrs.	1-2 yrs.	Citizens	Not Citizens
Assemblies of God World Missions	1937	6	-	-	-	-

		Personnel from U.S.			Other Countries	
	First Year	4+ yrs.	2-4 yrs.	1-2 yrs.	Citizens	Not Citizens
Campus Crusade for Christ, Intl.	1988	-	-	-	15	-
Child Evangelism Fellowship, Inc.	1987	-	-	-	2	-
Christian Aid Mission		-	-	-	18	-
Church of God of Prophecy		-	-	-	4	-
Church of the Nazarene	1998	2	-	-	-	-
Churches of Christ	1988	6	-	-	1	-
Evangel Bible Translators	1989	-	-	-	1	-
Evangelical Baptist Missions		2	-	-	-	-
Every Home for Christ International	1991	-	-	-	16	-
International Missionary Center		-	-	-	-	4
Mennonite Mission Network	1986	3	-	-	-	1
Pioneers	1998	2	-	-	4	-
Seventh-day Adventists Gen. Conf.	1957	-	-	-	-	2
SIM USA	1946	12	-	-	-	-
	Totals:	33	0	0	61	7

Bermuda

Church of God of Prophecy		-	-	-	1	-
Church of the Nazarene	1970	-	-	-	-	-
Word of Life Fellowship	1986	-	-	-	4	-
	Totals:	-	-	-	5	-

Bhutan

East-West Ministries International		-	-	-	10	-
Global Fellowship		-	-	-	5	5
Good News for India	1997	-	-	-	-	1
Gospel for Asia	1979	-	-	-	-	-
International Partnership Ministries, Inc.	2000	-	-	-	-	2
Josue Yrion World Evangelism Missions, Inc.	1999	-	-	-	-	1
New Directions International	1998	-	-	-	10	-
New Life League International		-	-	-	4	-
Outreach To Asia Nationals	1989	2	-	-	2	-
	Totals:	2	-	-	31	9

Bolivia

Amazon Focus	1995	-	-	-	3	-
American Baptist Churches in the U.S.A.	1986	2	-	-	-	-
Apostolic Team Ministries, Intl.		2	-	-	-	-
Assemblies of God World Missions	1946	12	-	2	-	-
Baptist Bible Fellowship Intl.	1978	4	4	-	-	-
BCM International		-	-	-	2	-
Bethany Fellowship Missions	2001	4	-	-	-	-
Brethren Assemblies		17	-	-	-	1
Campus Crusade for Christ, Intl.	1965	-	-	-	16	1
Central Yearly Meeting of Friends Missions		5	2	-	-	-
Child Evangelism Fellowship, Inc.	1943	-	-	-	1	-
Christian Aid Mission		-	-	-	13	-
Christian and Missionary Alliance	1981	6	-	-	-	-
Church of God (Holiness)	1945	3	-	-	-	3
Church of God of Prophecy		-	-	-	2	-
Church of the Nazarene	1945	2	-	-	-	-
Commission to Every Nation	2002	1	-	-	-	-

	First Year	Personnel from U.S. 4+ yrs.	2-4 yrs.	1-2 yrs.	Other Countries Citizens	Not Citizens
Compassion International, Inc.	1975	-	-	-	27	-
Congregational Methodist Church	2000	1	-	-	-	-
Correll Missionary Ministries	1978	-	-	-	4	-
Envoy International	1998	-	-	-	-	2
Evangelical Methodist Church		4	-	-	-	-
Evangelistic Faith Missions	1977	-	2	-	-	-
Fellowship International Mission	1998	2	-	-	-	-
Food for the Hungry, Inc.	1978	3	8	-	-	-
Global Outreach Mission		3	-	-	2	-
Gospel Missionary Union	1975	32	3	-	-	-
Grace Ministries International	1951	6	-	-	-	-
Habitat for Humanity International	1984	-	2	-	22	-
Hosanna / Faith Comes By Hearing	1996	-	-	-	4	-
International Cassette Bible Institute	1991	-	-	-	3	-
International Justice Mission		-	-	-	-	-
International Missionary Center		4	-	-	-	-
International Partnership Ministries, Inc.	2001	-	-	-	1	1
International Teams, U.S.A.		1	1	-	-	2
Latin America Mission	1992	2	-	-	-	2
Leadership Ministries Worldwide	1998	-	-	-	1	-
MAP International	1989	-	-	-	18	-
Medical Ambassadors International	1999	-	-	-	-	-
Mennonite Mission Network	1971	1	-	-	-	-
Missionary Ventures International	2002	1	-	-	-	-
New Tribes Mission	1942	97	-	8	2	3
Partners International	1976	-	-	-	-	-
Pentecostal Church of God		2	-	-	-	-
Pioneers	1984	8	-	-	-	-
Precept Ministries International	1993	-	-	-	1	-
Ripe for Harvest, Inc.	1990	2	-	-	-	-
Seventh-day Adventists Gen. Conf.	1907	-	-	-	-	8
SIM USA	1907	50	-	5	-	-
Source of Light Ministries Intl., Inc.	1993	-	-	-	2	-
South America Mission	1922	36	-	5	-	41
South American Missionary Society	1996	3	2	-	-	-
United Evangelical Churches		2	-	-	-	2
Walk Thru The Bible Ministries	2001	-	-	-	2	-
Word of Life Fellowship	1989	-	-	-	12	2
World Concern	1997	1	2	2	16	3
World Gospel Mission	1944	39	-	-	-	4
World Indigenous Missions	1993	2	-	-	2	-
World Mission Prayer League Inc.	1939	8	-	-	-	-
World-Wide Missions	1962	-	-	-	6	-
Totals:		368	26	22	162	75

Bosnia and Herzegovina

	First Year	4+ yrs.	2-4 yrs.	1-2 yrs.	Citizens	Not Citizens
ABWE		1	-	-	-	-
Christian and Missionary Alliance	1998	10	-	-	-	-
Christian Churches / Churches of Christ		2	1	-	-	-
Churches of Christ		2	-	-	-	-
Elim Fellowship, Intl. Dept.	1987	3	-	-	-	3
Every Home for Christ International	1997	-	-	-	1	-

	First Year	Personnel from U.S.			Other Countries	
		4+ yrs.	2-4 yrs.	1-2 yrs.	Citizens	Not Citizens
International Teams, U.S.A.		3	-	-	-	2
InterVarsity Christian Fellowship/USA		1	-	-	-	-
Pioneers	1992	15	-	-	4	-
Samaritan's Purse	1993	-	-	-	3	2
UFM International	1996	4	-	-	-	-
Totals:		41	1	-	8	7

Botswana

	First Year	4+ yrs.	2-4 yrs.	1-2 yrs.	Citizens	Not Citizens
Africa Inter-Mennonite Mission	1975	3	-	2	-	4
Assemblies of God World Missions	1963	4	-	-	-	-
Baptist Bible Fellowship Intl.	2001	2	-	-	-	-
Baptist International Outreach	1996	-	-	-	-	1
Baptist Mid-Missions	1999	2	-	-	-	-
Campus Crusade for Christ, Intl.	1993	-	-	-	2	8
Child Evangelism Fellowship, Inc.	1996	1	-	-	-	-
Church of God (Cleveland, TN)	1951	2	-	-	-	-
Church of God of Prophecy		-	-	-	3	2
Church of the Nazarene	1984	-	-	-	-	-
Churches of Christ	1974	-	-	-	1	-
Evangelical Mennonite Ch. Intl. Mins.	1972	2	-	-	-	-
Faith Christian Fellowship Intl.	1994	2	-	-	-	1
General Conf. Mennonite Church	1975	3	-	-	-	3
Gospel Fellowship Association	2002	2	-	-	-	-
Habitat for Humanity International	1992	-	6	-	12	-
Intl. Pentecostal Holiness Ch. World Mins.	1953	2	-	-	-	-
Lutheran Bible Translators	1993	6	-	-	5	-
Lutheran Church—Missouri Synod	1984	2	-	-	-	-
MBMS International	1985	-	2	-	-	-
Mennonite Mission Network	1975	2	-	-	-	2
Seventh-day Adventists Gen. Conf.	1921	-	-	-	-	6
SIM USA	1973	9	-	-	-	-
United Church Board for World Ministries		-	2	-	-	-
Walk Thru The Bible Ministries	1999	-	-	-	2	-
Totals:		44	10	2	25	27

Brazil

	First Year	4+ yrs.	2-4 yrs.	1-2 yrs.	Citizens	Not Citizens
ABWE	1942	102	-	-	-	-
Action International Ministries	1997	5	-	-	-	-
American Baptist Churches in the U.S.A.	1999	1	-	-	-	-
Apostolic Christian Church Foundation, Inc.	1961	17	-	-	3	2
Apostolic Team Ministries, Intl.		2	-	-	-	-
Armenian Msny. Assoc. of America, Inc.	1956	-	-	-	-	-
Assemblies of God World Missions	1925	15	-	2	-	-
Assoc. of Free Lutheran Congregations		6	-	-	-	-
Back to the Bible International	2000	-	-	-	3	-
Baptist Bible Fellowship Intl.	1952	33	4	1	-	-
Baptist General Conference	1955	9	-	-	-	-
Baptist International Outreach	1993	3	-	-	-	-
Baptist Mid-Missions	1935	149	-	-	1	-
BCM International		-	-	-	4	-
Bethany Fellowship Missions	1963	20	-	-	-	1
Bible Training Centre for Pastors	2000	-	-	-	1	-

	First Year	Personnel from U.S.			Other Countries	
		4+ yrs.	2-4 yrs.	1-2 yrs.	Citizens	Not Citizens
Brazil Gospel Fellowship Mission	1938	51	-	-	9	42
Brethren Assemblies		7	-	-	1	1
Campus Crusade for Christ, Intl.	1968	5	-	5	54	-
CBInternational	1946	22	-	1	-	-
Centers for Apologetics Research (CFAR)	1997	-	-	-	2	-
Child Evangelism Fellowship, Inc.	1941	-	-	-	-	2
Christian Advance International		-	-	-	2	-
Christian and Missionary Alliance	1962	30	1	-	-	-
Christian Churches / Churches of Christ		28	4	1	6	-
Christian Ministries International (C.M.I.)		2	-	-	-	-
Christian Missions Unlimited	1973	-	-	-	-	-
Christians In Action, Inc.	1960	2	-	-	4	2
Church of God (Anderson, IND)		4	-	-	-	-
Church of God (Cleveland, TN)	1951	7	-	-	-	-
Church of God of Prophecy		-	-	-	5	-
Church of the Nazarene	1958	4	-	-	-	4
Churches of Christ	1927	79	-	-	17	-
Churches of God, General Conference	1994	3	-	-	15	-
CMF International	1957	4	-	-	-	-
Compassion International, Inc.	1974	-	-	-	17	-
Crossover Communications International	1994	1	-	-	1	-
Cumberland Presbyterian Ch. Bd. of Msns.	2002	-	-	1	-	-
Eastern Mennonite Missions		-	-	3	-	-
Emmanuel Intl. Mission (U.S.)		-	-	-	-	-
Equip, Inc.		7	-	-	1	-
Evangelical Baptist Missions		4	-	-	-	-
Evangelical Free Church Mission	1986	4	-	-	-	-
Evangelical Lutheran Church in America	1958	4	-	-	-	-
Every Home for Christ International	1963	-	-	-	4	-
Fellowship International Mission	1960	16	-	-	6	-
Food for the Hungry, Inc.	1997	-	1	-	-	-
Foursquare Missions International	1946	2	-	-	-	-
Free Methodist World Missions	1928	2	-	-	-	-
Free Will Baptists, Inc.,	1958	16	-	-	-	-
General Conf. Mennonite Church	1964	1	-	-	1	6
Global Outreach Mission	1973	2	-	-	-	-
Global Outreach, Ltd.		1	-	-	-	-
Go Ye Fellowship	1962	4	-	-	-	-
Gospel Fellowship Association	1965	4	-	-	-	-
Gospel Missionary Union	1975	21	-	-	-	-
Grace Brethren International Missions	1949	6	-	-	-	-
Greater Grace World Outreach	1983	-	-	-	1	-
Habitat for Humanity International	1987	-	2	-	7	-
Harvest		-	-	-	2	1
International Justice Mission		-	-	-	-	-
Intl. Street Kids Outreach Mins.		1	-	-	-	-
Japanese Evangelical Msny. Society	1961	1	-	-	-	-
Jews for Jesus		1	-	-	-	-
Josue Yrion Wld. Evangelism Missions, Inc.	1993	-	-	-	1	-
Latin America Mission	1973	4	-	-	2	2
Latin American Indian Ministries	1997	-	-	-	-	-
Literacy & Evangelism International		-	-	-	2	-

	Personnel from U.S.				Other Countries	
	First Year	4+ yrs.	2-4 yrs.	1-2 yrs.	Citizens	Not Citizens
Lutheran Church—Missouri Syn.	1900	1	1	1	-	-
MBMS International	1946	-	4	-	-	-
Medical Ambassadors International	1999	-	-	-	-	-
Mennonite Mission Network	1954	-	-	-	-	-
Mission Aviation Fellowship	1957	4	-	4	-	-
Mission to the World (PCA), Inc.	1993	4	2	-	-	-
Navigators, U.S. Intl. Missions Group		10	-	-	-	-
Network of International Christian Schools	1996	-	31	-	-	-
New Life League International	1984	1	-	-	-	-
New Tribes Mission	1946	160	-	5	3	11
N. American Baptist Conf. Intl. Msns. Dept.	1966	3	-	-	-	4
Northwest Medical Teams	2001	-	-	-	-	-
OC International, Inc.	1963	13	-	-	8	2
OMS International, Inc.		7	-	-	-	3
Open Air Campaigners - Overseas Mins.	1990	-	-	-	3	-
Overseas Radio & Television, Inc.		-	-	-	-	-
Pilgrim Fellowship, Inc.	1948	5	-	-	-	1
Pocket Testament League	1965	-	-	-	2	2
Precept Ministries International	2000	-	-	-	6	-
Presbyterian Church (USA)		14	23	7	-	-
Project AmaZon	1976	25	-	-	-	-
Reformed Episcopal Bd. of Foreign Msns.		1	-	-	-	-
Ripe for Harvest, Inc.	1998	1	-	-	-	-
Salvation Army, U.S.A.	1922	4	-	-	-	-
Seventh-day Adventists Gen. Conf.	1894	-	2	-	-	6
Source of Light Ministries Intl., Inc.	1982	-	-	-	1	-
South America Mission	1913	16	-	2	-	18
Sowers International, The	2000	1	-	-	1	-
TEAM (The Evangelical Alliance Mission)		6	-	-	-	-
Teen Missions International	1985	-	-	-	13	1
Things To Come Mission, Inc.	1958	4	-	-	5	4
UFM International	1931	66	-	-	2	7
United Church Board for World Mins.		-	1	-	-	-
WEC International	1957	-	4	-	-	58
Wesleyan World Missions	1958	-	6	-	-	-
Wisconsin Evangelical Lutheran Syn.	1987	4	-	-	-	-
Word of Life Fellowship	1958	50	-	-	99	-
World Baptist Fellowship Mission Agency		28	2	-	-	-
World Horizons	2000	2	-	-	-	-
World Partners USA	1955	4	-	-	-	-
World Team	1957	9	-	-	-	-
World-Wide Missions	1965	-	-	-	10	-
Wycliffe Bible Translators USA		126	-	-	-	-
Youth for Christ /USA, World Outreach Div.	1950	1	-	-	-	-
Totals:		1282	88	33	325	180

Bulgaria

	First Year	4+ yrs.	2-4 yrs.	1-2 yrs.	Citizens	Not Citizens
All God's Children International	1992	-	-	-	2	-
American Baptist Churches in the U.S.A.	2001	2	-	-	-	-
AMG International		-	-	-	3	-
Armenian Msny. Assoc. of America, Inc.	1950	-	-	-	-	-
Assemblies of God World Missions	1926	-	-	-	-	-

	First Year	Personnel from U.S. 4+ yrs.	2-4 yrs.	1-2 yrs.	Other Countries Citizens	Not Citizens
Baptist Bible Fellowship Intl.	1995	2	-	-	-	-
Baptist General Conference	1994	1	-	-	-	-
Bible League, The	1992	-	-	-	9	-
Campus Crusade for Christ, Intl.	1991	11	-	-	28	-
Christian Aid Mission		-	-	-	74	-
Church of God (Cleveland, TN)	1982	2	-	-	-	-
Church of God of Prophecy		-	-	-	4	-
Church of the Nazarene	1994	2	-	-	-	-
Churches of Christ	1990	3	-	-	2	-
Envoy International		-	-	-	-	-
Greater Europe Mission	1993	-	-	-	-	-
International Teams, U.S.A.		4	-	-	-	-
Mission Possible Foundation, Inc.		-	-	-	-	-
Mission to the World (PCA), Inc.	1994	7	-	-	-	-
Navigators, U.S. Intl. Missions Group		6	-	-	-	-
Precept Ministries International	1991	-	-	-	1	-
Presbyterian Evangelistic Fellowship		2	-	-	8	-
SEND International	1992	6	-	-	-	-
WEC International	1998	-	-	-	-	11
Wisconsin Evangelical Lutheran Synod	1992	6	-	-	-	-
Total:		54	-	-	131	11

Burkina Faso

	First Year	4+ yrs.	2-4 yrs.	1-2 yrs.	Citizens	Not Citizens
Africa Inter-Mennonite Mission	1978	4	-	-	-	6
Assemblies of God World Missions	1919	7	-	-	-	-
Baptist Bible Fellowship Intl.	1994	2	-	2	-	-
Campus Crusade for Christ, Intl.	1991	2	-	-	13	-
Child Evangelism Fellowship, Inc.	1982	-	-	-	2	-
Christian and Missionary Alliance	1923	20	2	-	-	-
Church of God of Prophecy		-	-	-	2	-
Church of the Nazarene	1997	-	-	-	-	-
Churches of Christ	1986	6	-	-	-	-
Evangelical Covenant Church	1998	2	-	-	-	-
Every Home for Christ International	1995	-	-	-	2	-
General Conf. Mennonite Church	1977	3	-	-	-	4
MBMS International	1994	-	2	-	-	-
Mennonite Mission Network	1977	-	-	-	-	-
Northwest Medical Teams	2001	-	-	-	-	-
Seventh-day Adventists Gen. Conf.	1972	-	-	2	-	-
SIM USA	1930	11	-	-	-	-
WEC International	1939	-	-	-	-	12
Wycliffe Bible Translators USA		57	-	-	-	-
Totals:		114	4	4	19	22

Burundi

	First Year	4+ yrs.	2-4 yrs.	1-2 yrs.	Citizens	Not Citizens
Brethren Assemblies		4	-	-	-	-
Campus Crusade for Christ, Intl.	1980	-	-	-	27	-
Child Evangelism Fellowship, Inc.	1952	-	-	-	1	-
Church of the Nazarene	1999	-	-	-	-	-
Covenant Celebration Ch. Global Outreach		-	-	-	-	-
Free Methodist World Missions	1935	2	-	-	-	-
International Justice Mission		-	-	-	-	-

	First Year	Personnel from U.S.			Other Countries	
		4+ yrs.	2-4 yrs.	1-2 yrs.	Citizens	Not Citizens
Seventh-day Adventists Gen. Conf.	1931	-	-	2	-	-
	Totals:	6	-	2	28	-

Cambodia

	First Year	4+ yrs.	2-4 yrs.	1-2 yrs.	Citizens	Not Citizens
ABWE	1998	8	-	-	-	-
Africa Inland Mission International		-	-	-	-	-
American Baptist Chs. in the U.S.A.	1996	4	-	-	-	-
Asian Outreach U.S.A.		-	-	-	-	-
Assemblies of God World Missions		25	-	14	-	-
Baptist Bible Fellowship Intl.	1997	4	2	2	-	-
Baptist Mid-Missions	1998	4	-	-	-	-
Bethany Fellowship Missions	1999	2	-	-	-	-
Bible League, The	1995	-	-	-	8	-
Campus Crusade for Christ, Intl.	1989	-	-	-	111	-
Christian Aid Mission		-	-	-	71	-
Christian and Missionary Alliance	1923	18	8	-	-	-
Christian Reformed World Relief Comte.	1995	-	1	-	-	2
Church of the Nazarene	1992	2	-	-	-	-
Church Resource Ministries	1995	7	-	1	-	1
Church World Service & Witness		1	-	-	10	4
Eastern Mennonite Missions		3	-	-	-	-
Evangelical Friends Church Southwest	1995	4	-	2	-	-
Every Home for Christ International	1993	-	-	-	8	-
Far East Broadcasting Company, Inc.	1993	-	-	-	12	-
Food for the Hungry, Inc.	1991	1	3	-	-	-
Foursquare Missions International	1995	2	-	-	-	-
Free Methodist World Missions	1996	2	-	-	-	-
Gospel Fellowship Association	2000	2	-	-	-	-
Grace Brethren International Missions	1998	2	-	-	-	16
International Justice Mission		-	-	-	-	-
Intl. Pentecostal Holiness Ch. World Mins.	1996	-	-	-	-	3
International Teams, U.S.A.		3	-	-	-	2
Medical Ambassadors International	1998	-	-	-	1	-
Mission To Unreached Peoples	1989	10	-	-	1	-
Missionary Gospel Fellowship	2000	-	-	-	2	-
OMF International		2	-	-	-	-
Outreach To Asia Nationals	1987	2	-	-	14	-
Partners International	1993	-	-	-	-	-
Seventh-day Adventists General Conference	1991	4	3	1	-	4
TEAM (The Evangelical Alliance Mission)		-	-	1	-	-
Trans World Radio		2	-	-	-	-
UFM International	2001	2	-	-	-	-
Walk Thru The Bible Ministries	2002	-	-	-	2	-
WEC International	1992	3	-	-	-	16
Wesleyan World Missions	1994	-	2	-	-	4
World Baptist Fellowship Mission Agency		-	-	2	-	-
World Concern	1985	1	-	1	1	1
World Horizons	1998	2	-	-	-	6
World Team	1996	15	-	-	-	-
	Totals:	137	19	24	241	59

		Personnel from U.S.			Other Countries	
	First Year	4+ yrs.	2-4 yrs.	1-2 yrs.	Citizens	Not Citizens

Cameroon

	First Year	4+ yrs.	2-4 yrs.	1-2 yrs.	Citizens	Not Citizens
Assemblies of God World Missions	1976	6	-	3	-	-
Baptist General Conference	1982	7	2	-	-	1
Bible League, The	1995	-	-	-	13	-
Campus Crusade for Christ, Intl.	1992	-	-	-	53	2
Child Evangelism Fellowship, Inc.	1995	-	-	-	2	-
Christian Blind Mission Intl.	1982	-	1	-	-	-
Church of God of Prophecy		-	-	-	5	-
Church of the Nazarene	1999	-	-	-	-	-
Churches of Christ	1960	-	-	1	-	-
Commission to Every Nation	2000	-	-	-	1	-
Evangelical Covenant Church	1998	2	2	-	-	-
Evangelical Lutheran Church in America	1923	18	-	4	-	1
Evangelism Resources	1999	-	2	-	1	2
Global Outreach, Ltd.		2	-	-	-	-
Gospel Fellowship Association	1987	11	-	2	-	-
Gospel Revival Ministries	1998	-	-	-	1	-
International Missionary Center		1	-	-	-	10
Lutheran Bible Translators	1980	4	-	-	6	-
Navigators, U.S. Intl. Missions Group		2	-	-	-	-
N. American Baptist Conf. Intl. Msns. Dept.	1891	12	-	2	-	8
Presbyterian Ch. (USA), Worldwide Mins.		4	-	-	-	-
Prison Mission Association	1975	-	-	-	1	-
Seventh-day Adventists Gen. Conf.	1928	2	-	-	-	5
Teen Missions International	2002	-	-	-	2	-
Things To Come Mission, Inc.	1995	-	2	-	1	-
Wisconsin Evangelical Lutheran Syn.	1997	-	2	-	-	-
World Team	1985	25	-	-	-	-
World-Wide Missions	1961	-	-	-	15	-
Wycliffe Bible Translators USA		187	-	-	-	-
Totals:		283	11	12	101	29

Cape Verde

	First Year	4+ yrs.	2-4 yrs.	1-2 yrs.	Citizens	Not Citizens
Assemblies of God World Missions		4	-	-	-	-
Church of the Nazarene	1901	-	-	-	-	-
Totals:		4	-	-	-	-

Caribbean - General

	First Year	4+ yrs.	2-4 yrs.	1-2 yrs.	Citizens	Not Citizens
Brethren Assemblies		3	-	-	-	1
Calvary Evangelistic Mission, Inc.	1953	6	5	3	-	1
Church of God (Cleveland, TN)		2	-	-	-	-
Church of God of Prophecy		-	-	-	7	-
Final Frontiers Foundation, Inc.	1993	-	-	-	14	-
Southern Baptist Conv. Intl. Mission Bd.		-	-	-	-	-
World Baptist Fellowship Mission Agency		8	-	-	-	-
Wycliffe Bible Translators USA		4	-	-	-	-
Totals:		23	5	3	21	2

Caucasus

	First Year	4+ yrs.	2-4 yrs.	1-2 yrs.	Citizens	Not Citizens
Operation Mobilization, Inc.	1998	-	2	-	-	-
Totals:		-	2	-	-	-

		Personnel from U.S.			Other Countries	
	First Year	4+ yrs.	2-4 yrs.	1-2 yrs.	Citizens	Not Citizens
Cayman Islands						
Christian Churches / Churches of Christ		2	-	-	-	-
Church of God (Holiness)	1954	4	-	-	2	2
Totals:		6	-	-	2	2
Central African Republic						
Africa Inland Mission International	1924	1	-	-	-	-
Assemblies of God World Missions		4	-	-	-	-
Baptist Mid-Missions	1920	13	-	-	-	-
Campus Crusade for Christ, Intl.	1987	-	-	-	30	-
CBInternational	1988	-	2	-	-	-
Church of God of Prophecy		-	-	-	1	-
Churches of Christ	1990	-	-	-	1	-
Evangelical Covenant Church	1997	12	-	-	-	-
Evangelical Free Church Mission	1997	15	-	-	-	-
Evangelical Lutheran Church in America	1974	5	-	-	-	-
Grace Brethren International Missions	1918	12	1	7	-	1
Habitat for Humanity International	1991	-	3	-	9	-
International Missionary Center		-	-	-	-	6
SIM USA	1978	1	-	-	-	-
Wycliffe Bible Translators USA		14	-	-	-	-
Totals:		77	6	7	41	7
Central Asia						
Baptist General Conference		4	2	-	-	-
Bethany Fellowship Missions		3	-	-	-	5
Bible League, The	1992	-	-	-	31	-
CBInternational	1993	6	-	5	-	-
Liebenzell Mission USA	1995	8	-	-	-	-
Mission Aviation Fellowship		14	-	-	-	-
Paraclete, Inc.		-	4	-	-	-
People International	1989	27	2	3	-	-
Pioneers		32	-	3	8	1
TEAM (The Evangelical Alliance Mission)		104	-	-	-	-
World Mission Prayer League Inc.	1968	2	-	-	-	-
Totals:		200	8	11	39	6
Chad						
Africa Inland Mission International	1986	8	-	-	-	-
Assemblies of God World Missions		4	-	-	-	-
Baptist Mid-Missions	1925	7	-	-	-	-
Bible League, The	1996	-	-	-	7	-
Brethren Assemblies		-	1	-	-	-
Campus Crusade for Christ, Intl.	1996	-	-	-	12	-
Child Evangelism Fellowship, Inc.	1997	-	-	-	1	1
Christian Mission for the Deaf	1978	-	-	-	1	-
Church of God of Prophecy		-	-	-	1	-
Gospel Revival Ministries	1997	-	-	-	5	-
Grace Brethren International Missions	1966	-	-	-	-	2
International Missionary Center		-	-	-	-	4
Lutheran Brethren World Missions		8	-	-	-	-
Seed International	1997	2	-	-	-	-

		Personnel from U.S.			Other Countries	
	First Year	4+ yrs.	2-4 yrs.	1-2 yrs.	Citizens	Not Citizens
Seventh-day Adventists Gen. Conf.	1870	-	-	-	-	1
TEAM (The Evangelical Alliance Mission)	1969	19	-	1	-	-
WEC International	1962	3	-	-	-	20
World Partners USA	1996	2	-	-	-	-
Wycliffe Bible Translators USA		58	-	-	-	-
Totals:		111	1	1	27	28

Chile

	First Year	4+ yrs.	2-4 yrs.	1-2 yrs.	Citizens	Not Citizens
ABWE	1953	30	-	-	-	-
American Baptist Churches in the U.S.A.	1993	6	-	-	-	-
Assemblies of God World Missions	1941	20	-	4	-	-
Baptist Bible Fellowship Intl.	1954	11	-	-	-	-
Baptist Mid-Missions	1992	8	-	-	-	-
Brethren Assemblies		1	-	-	2	1
Campus Crusade for Christ, Intl.	1963	-	-	-	1	-
Child Evangelism Fellowship, Inc.	1942	-	-	1	-	-
Christian Aid Mission		-	-	-	2	-
Christian and Missionary Alliance	1897	16	-	-	-	-
Christian Churches / Churches of Christ		32	-	-	4	-
Church of God (Cleveland, TN)	1954	3	-	-	-	-
Church of God of Prophecy		-	-	-	1	-
Church of the Nazarene	1962	2	-	-	-	-
Churches of Christ	1958	19	-	-	2	-
CMF International	1988	2	-	-	-	-
Evangelical Lutheran Church in America	1982	1	-	1	-	-
Foursquare Missions International	1947	1	-	-	-	-
Free Methodist World Missions	1986	3	-	-	-	-
Global Outreach, Ltd.		2	-	-	-	-
Gospel Fellowship Association	1963	4	-	1	-	-
Gospel Mission of South America	1923	14	-	-	-	-
Grace Brethren International Missions	1999	-	-	-	-	3
International Cassette Bible Institute	1991	-	-	-	2	-
International Gospel Outreach	1975	-	-	-	2	-
International Partnership Ministries, Inc.	1992	-	-	-	5	-
MBMS International	2001	-	-	-	-	-
Mennonite Mission Network	1963	-	-	-	2	-
Mission to the World (PCA), Inc.	1977	16	-	-	-	-
Navigators, U.S. Intl. Missions Group		4	2	-	-	-
Presbyterian Church (USA)		7	-	-	-	-
Presbyterian Evangelistic Fellowship		1	-	-	-	-
Salvation Army, U.S.A.	1909	6	-	-	-	-
Seventh-day Adventists General Conference	1895	4	-	2	-	-
SIM USA	1986	7	-	-	-	-
Source of Light Ministries Intl., Inc.	1979	-	-	-	2	-
South American Missionary Society	1979	2	-	-	-	2
United Ch. Board for World Mins.		-	1	-	-	-
Word of Life Fellowship	1976	-	-	-	27	9
World Harvest Mission	2000	2	-	-	-	-
World Team	1982	6	-	-	-	-
World-Wide Missions	1964	-	-	-	14	-
Totals:		230	3	9	66	15

	Personnel from U.S.				Other Countries	
	First Year	4+ yrs.	2-4 yrs.	1-2 yrs.	Citizens	Not Citizens

China

	First Year	4+ yrs.	2-4 yrs.	1-2 yrs.	Citizens	Not Citizens
All God's Children International	1995	-	-	-	1	-
Ambassadors for Christ, Inc.	1963	-	-	-	-	-
American Baptist Churches in the U.S.A.	1843	1	-	1	-	-
Asian Outreach U.S.A.		-	-	-	-	-
Back to the Bible International	1994	-	-	-	8	-
Baptist International Outreach	1993	4	-	-	-	-
Bible League, The	1979	-	-	-	31	-
Calvary International	1995	2	-	-	-	2
Caring Partners International, Inc.	1989	-	-	-	-	-
Christar	1914	17	12	10	-	-
Christian Aid Mission		-	-	-	347	-
Christian and Missionary Alliance	1897	20	-	-	-	-
Christian Ministries International (C.M.I.)		-	12	-	-	-
Christian Reformed World Missions	1986	2	-	-	-	-
Church of God (Cleveland, TN)	1937	4	-	-	-	-
Church of God of Prophecy		2	-	-	-	-
Church of the Nazarene	2001	9	-	-	-	1
Churches of Christ	1930	6	-	-	2	-
CMF International	2001	-	-	1	-	-
East Gates Ministries Intl.	1990	-	-	-	1	-
East-West Ministries International		-	-	-	5	-
Evangelical Free Church Mission	1887	19	4	-	5	-
Evangelical Lutheran Church in America	1986	1	-	5	-	-
Evangelical Presbyterian Church	1993	4	-	-	-	-
Food for the Hungry, Inc.	1992	6	1	-	-	-
General Conf. Mennonite Church	1909	2	-	-	-	2
Global Outreach, Ltd.		12	-	3	-	-
Global Strategy Mission Assoc.	1996	-	-	4	-	-
Gospel for Asia	1979	-	-	-	-	-
Great Commission Center Intl.	2000	-	-	-	-	1
Hope for the Hungry		1	-	-	-	1
International Outreach Ministries	1996	-	5	-	-	-
Intl. Pentecostal Holiness Ch. World Mins.	1911	4	-	-	-	-
International Teams, U.S.A.		-	-	-	-	21
InterServe/USA	1989	7	-	-	-	-
Literacy & Evangelism International		-	-	-	-	-
Lutheran Church—Missouri Syn.	1913	15	4	38	-	-
MBMS International	1911	-	-	3	-	-
Medical Ambassadors International	1998	-	-	-	-	-
Mennonite Mission Network	1909	4	-	-	-	4
Mission ONE, Inc.		-	-	-	-	-
Mission Possible Foundation, Inc.		-	-	-	-	-
Mission To Unreached Peoples	1986	15	-	-	-	-
Missions To Japan, Inc.		3	-	-	-	-
Network of International Christian Schools	1999	-	8	-	-	-
New Life League International		-	-	-	-	-
OC International, Inc.	1983	-	2	1	-	-
Outreach To Asia Nationals	1986	-	-	2	45	-
Overseas Radio & Television, Inc.		-	-	-	-	-
Partners International	1943	-	-	-	-	-
Presbyterian Ch. (USA), Worldwide Mins.		4	-	20	-	-

	First Year	Personnel from U.S. 4+ yrs.	2-4 yrs.	1-2 yrs.	Other Countries Citizens	Not Citizens
Project Partner with Christ	1984	-	-	-	1	-
Reformed Church in America, Gen. Syn.		-	-	-	2	-
Ripe for Harvest, Inc.	1999	2	-	-	-	-
Seventh-day Adventists Gen. Conf.	1902	12	1	8	-	3
Sowers International, The	1994	-	-	-	3	-
The Mission Society	1994	3	-	-	-	-
Training Evangelistic Leadership	1976	12	4	-	11	3
United Church Board for World Ministries		-	2	-	-	-
World Help	1992	-	-	-	1	-
World Indigenous Missions		-	-	-	-	-
World Missions Far Corners, Inc.	1988	2	-	-	2	-
World Partners USA	1998	4	-	-	-	-
Worldwide Tentmakers, Inc.	1993	-	-	-	-	-
Totals:		199	55	96	465	38

CIS - General

	First Year	4+ yrs.	2-4 yrs.	1-2 yrs.	Citizens	Not Citizens
MBMS International	1994	-	-	-	12	-
Pioneers	1993	16	-	3	8	-
Totals:		16	-	3	20	-

Colombia

	First Year	4+ yrs.	2-4 yrs.	1-2 yrs.	Citizens	Not Citizens
ABWE		16	-	-	-	-
Action International Ministries	1990	1	-	-	1	1
Assemblies of God World Missions	1962	23	-	6	-	-
Baptist Bible Fellowship Intl.	1971	4	-	-	-	-
Bible League, The	1989	-	-	-	23	-
Brethren Assemblies		19	-	-	-	1
Brethren in Christ World Missions	1984	4	-	-	3	-
Calvary International	2001	1	-	-	-	1
Campus Crusade for Christ, Intl.	1963	-	-	-	31	-
Child Evangelism Fellowship, Inc.	1943	-	-	-	1	-
Christ for the City International	1988	-	-	-	-	-
Christian Aid Mission		-	-	-	47	-
Christian and Missionary Alliance	1923	17	-	-	-	-
Christian Ch. of N. America Missions	1965	1	-	-	-	-
Christians In Action, Inc.	1970	3	-	-	1	3
Church Ministries International	1992	1	-	-	1	-
Church of God (Cleveland, TN)	1954	3	-	-	-	-
Church of God of Prophecy		-	-	-	3	-
Church of the Nazarene	1975	-	-	-	-	-
Churches of Christ	1958	-	-	-	-	-
CLC Ministries International	1973	2	-	-	-	-
Compassion International, Inc.	1976	-	-	-	25	-
Cumberland Presbyterian Church		3	-	-	-	-
Elim Fellowship, Intl. Dept.	1964	2	-	-	1	1
Evangelical Covenant Church	1968	9	2	-	-	-
Fellowship International Mission	1994	2	-	-	-	-
General Conf. Mennonite Church	1947	-	-	2	1	4
Habitat for Humanity International	1994	-	3	-	2	-
Hope for the Hungry		1	-	-	1	-
Impact International	1990	2	-	-	3	-
International Cassette Bible Institute	1976	2	-	-	7	-

		Personnel from U.S.			Other Countries	
	First Year	4+ yrs.	2-4 yrs.	1-2 yrs.	Citizens	Not Citizens
International Missionary Center		2	-	-	-	-
International Needs - USA	1994	-	-	-	8	-
International Outreach Ministries	1986	2	-	-	-	-
Intl. Pentecostal Holiness Ch. World Mins.	1993	1	-	-	-	-
International Teams, U.S.A.		3	-	-	-	2
Latin America Mission	1953	8	3	1	10	2
MBMS International	1945	-	2	-	-	-
Mennonite Mission Network	1945	2	-	-	-	2
Mission to the World (PCA), Inc.	1979	5	-	-	-	-
Missionary Revival Crusade	1974	4	-	-	2	-
Missionary Ventures International	2001	1	-	-	-	-
New Tribes Mission	1944	55	-	2	3	4
OMS International, Inc.		12	-	-	-	2
Precept Ministries International	1995	-	-	-	2	-
Presbyterian Ch. (USA), Worldwide Mins.		7	-	-	-	-
Reformed Baptist Mission Services		2	-	-	-	1
Ripe for Harvest, Inc.	2001	1	-	-	-	-
Seventh-day Adventists Gen. Conf.	1921	-	2	-	-	3
South America Mission	1934	8	-	-	-	8
Sowers International, The	1985	-	-	-	-	4
TEAM (The Evangelical Alliance Mission)		14	-	-	-	-
Team Expansion, Inc.	1989	3	-	-	1	-
The Mission Society	1985	2	-	-	-	-
WEC International	1933	-	-	-	-	8
Wesleyan World Missions	1941	-	6	-	-	-
Wisconsin Evangelical Lutheran Syn.	1974	3	-	-	-	-
Word of Life Fellowship	1980	-	-	-	-	6
World Baptist Fellowship Msn. Agency		4	2	2	-	-
World Vision Inc.	1960	-	-	-	-	-
World-Wide Missions	1966	-	-	-	1	-
Wycliffe Bible Translators USA		58	-	-	-	-
Totals:		313	20	13	178	53

Comoros

Africa Inland Mission International	1975	8	-	-	-	-
Totals:		8	-	-	-	-

Congo, Democratic Republic of

Africa Inter-Mennonite Mission	1912	-	-	-	-	-
American Baptist Churches in the U.S.A.	1884	15	-	-	-	1
Assemblies of God World Missions		4	-	-	-	-
Baptist Bible Fellowship Intl.	1957	6	-	-	-	-
Brethren Assemblies		8	-	-	-	2
Campus Crusade for Christ, Intl.	1979	-	-	-	184	12
CBInternational	1946	2	1	-	-	-
Child Evangelism Fellowship, Inc.	1952	-	-	-	3	-
Christian Mission for the Deaf	1978	-	-	-	4	-
Church of God of Prophecy		-	-	-	20	-
Church of the Nazarene	1990	-	-	-	-	-
Compassion International, Inc.	1980	-	-	-	23	-
Evangelical Covenant Church	1937	2	-	-	-	-
Evangelical Free Church Mission	1922	-	-	-	-	-

	First Year	4+ yrs.	2-4 yrs.	1-2 yrs.	Citizens	Not Citizens
			Personnel from U.S.		Other Countries	
Evangelism Resources	1980	-	-	-	5	-
Every Child Ministries, Inc.	1981	-	-	-	12	-
Free Methodist World Missions		-	-	-	-	1
General Conf. Mennonite Church	1906	1	-	-	-	1
Grace Ministries International	1928	5	-	-	12	-
Habitat for Humanity International	1974	-	1	-	58	-
Independent Faith Mission		8	-	-	-	-
International Outreach Ministries	1986	6	-	-	-	-
MBMS International	1912	-	2	-	-	-
Medical Ambassadors International	1987	-	-	-	28	-
Mennonite Mission Network	1906	-	-	-	-	-
Mission Aviation Fellowship	1960	· 14	-	2	-	-
Navigators, U.S. Intl. Missions Group	1982	2	-	-	-	-
Presbyterian Ch. (USA), Worldwide Mins.		12	10	-	-	-
Seventh-day Adventists Gen. Conf.	1965	-	2	-	-	13
The Masters' Mission	1970	1	-	-	1	-
UFM International	1931	3	-	-	-	-
Walk Thru The Bible Ministries	2002	-	-	-	1	-
WEC International	1913	-	-	-	-	6
Wycliffe Bible Translators USA		22	-	-	-	-
Totals:		111	16	2	351	36

Congo, Republic of the

	First Year	4+ yrs.	2-4 yrs.	1-2 yrs.	Citizens	Not Citizens
Africa Inland Mission International	1912	4	-	-	-	-
African Enterprise, Inc.	1994	-	-	-	5	-
Assemblies of God World Missions		3	-	-	-	-
Campus Crusade for Christ, Intl.	1990	-	-	-	13	2
Christian and Missionary Alliance	1992	4	-	-	-	-
Christian Blind Mission Intl.	1991	-	1	-	-	-
Church of God of Prophecy		-	-	-	2	-
Church of the Nazarene	1997	-	-	-	-	-
Every Child Ministries, Inc.	1993	-	-	-	1	-
Global Outreach Mission	1974	5	-	-	-	-
World-Wide Missions	1961	-	-	-	15	-
Totals:		16	1	-	36	2

Costa Rica

	First Year	4+ yrs.	2-4 yrs.	1-2 yrs.	Citizens	Not Citizens
ABWE	1998	5	-	-	-	-
American Baptist Churches in the U.S.A.	1980	5	-	-	-	-
Artists In Christian Testimony	1994	-	-	-	-	2
Assemblies of God World Missions	1943	25	-	3	-	-
Baptist Bible Fellowship Intl.	1970	11	-	2	-	-
Baptist International Outreach	1990	-	-	-	2	-
Calvary International	1982	4	-	-	-	3
CAM International	1891	13	-	-	-	13
Campus Crusade for Christ, Intl.	1976	-	-	1	3	-
Christ for the City International	1985	5	-	-	-	6
Christian and Missionary Alliance	1975	1	-	-	-	-
Christian Leadership Development, Inc.	1992	2	-	-	1	1
Christian Reformed World Missions	1981	3	3	-	-	-
Church of God (Anderson, Indiana)		2	-	-	-	-
Church of God of Prophecy		-	-	-	3	2

		Personnel from U.S.			Other Countries	
	First Year	4+ yrs.	2-4 yrs.	1-2 yrs.	Citizens	Not Citizens
Church of the Nazarene	1964	6	4	-	-	5
Churches of Christ	1967	4	-	-	1	-
Commission to Every Nation	2000	2	-	-	-	-
Envoy International	2001	1	-	-	1	1
Evangelical Free Church Mission	1999	4	-	-	-	-
Evangelical Lutheran Ch. in America	1998	2	-	-	-	-
Evangelistic Faith Missions	1982	-	-	-	-	2
Foursquare Missions International	1953	2	-	-	-	-
Global Outreach, Ltd.		-	2	1	-	-
Go Ye Fellowship	1998	2	-	-	-	-
Gospel Fellowship Association	1991	2	-	1	-	-
Grace Ministries International	1984	5	-	1	-	-
Habitat for Humanity International	1987	-	3	-	-	-
Hope for the Hungry		1	-	-	-	1
Impact International		1	-	-	2	-
International Outreach Ministries	1994	6	-	1	-	-
Intl. Pentecostal Holiness Church	1951	2	-	-	-	-
International Teams, U.S.A.		5	2	-	4	2
Latin America Assistance, Inc.		-	-	-	3	-
Latin America Mission	1921	55	10	2	4	63
Living Water Teaching International	1983	-	-	-	1	3
MBMS International	2000	-	-	-	-	-
Medical Ambassadors International	1999	-	-	-	-	-
Mission to the Americas	1967	2	-	-	-	-
Missionary Ventures International	2001	2	-	-	-	-
Mutual Faith Ministries Intl.		1	-	-	-	-
Navigators, U.S. Intl. Missions Group		2	-	-	-	-
Precept Ministries International	1994	-	-	-	-	1
Presbyterian Ch. (USA), Worldwide Mins.		4	8	2	-	-
Presbyterian Evangelistic Fellowship		1	-	-	-	-
Project Partner with Christ	1979	-	-	-	1	-
Ripe for Harvest, Inc.	2000	1	-	-	-	-
Rosedale Mennonite Missions	1962	2	-	-	-	-
Salvation Army, U.S.A.	1907	7	-	-	-	-
Seed International	1996	2	1	-	-	-
Seventh-day Adventists Gen. Conf.	1903	4	1	-	-	5
South American Missionary Society	1982	-	1	-	-	-
The Mission Society	1985	2	-	-	-	-
Wesleyan World Missions	1995	-	8	-	-	-
Word of Life Fellowship	1986	-	-	-	15	6
	Totals:	206	43	14	41	116

Cote d'Ivoire

Assemblies of God World Missions	1968	6	-	-	-	-
Baptist Bible Fellowship Intl.	1988	2	-	1	-	-
Baptist General Conference	1977	8	-	-	-	1
Baptist Mid-Missions	1974	21	-	-	-	-
Campus Crusade for Christ, Intl.	1975	-	-	-	36	8
CBInternational	1947	47	4	7	-	-
Child Evangelism Fellowship, Inc.	1976	-	-	-	4	-
Christian and Missionary Alliance	1930	42	18	-	-	-
Christian Churches / Churches of Christ		6	-	-	-	-

	First Year	4+ yrs.	2-4 yrs.	1-2 yrs.	Personnel from U.S. Citizens	Other Countries Not Citizens
Church of God (Anderson, IND)		5	-	-	-	-
Church of God (Cleveland, TN)	1992	2	-	-	-	-
Church of God of Prophecy		-	-	-	7	-
Church of the Nazarene	1987	10	-	-	-	2
Churches of Christ		3	-	-	-	-
CMF International	1999	-	4	-	-	2
Development Associates Intl. (DAI)	1998	-	-	-	1	-
Evangelical Baptist Missions		9	-	3	-	-
Evangelical Free Church Mission	1997	3	-	-	-	-
Evangelism Resources	2001	-	-	-	-	-
Every Home for Christ International	1991	-	-	-	3	-
Free Will Baptists, Inc., National Assoc.	1958	17	-	1	-	-
FRIENDS in Action, International		-	2	-	-	-
Global Fellowship		-	-	-	5	-
Gospel Missionary Union	1969	2	1	-	-	-
HCJB World Radio		2	-	-	-	2
International Justice Mission		-	-	-	-	-
International Missionary Center		2	-	-	-	4
International Partnership Ministries, Inc.	1998	-	-	-	10	-
Intl. Pentecostal Holiness Ch. World Mins.	1993	2	2	-	-	-
Lutheran Bible Translators	1997	4	-	-	-	-
MAP International	1995	-	-	-	3	-
Mennonite Mission Network	1978	2	-	-	1	-
Mission to the World (PCA), Inc.	1985	12	-	-	-	-
Navigators, U.S. Intl. Missions Group		4	-	-	-	-
New Tribes Mission	1982	61	-	7	-	7
Partners International	1990	-	-	-	-	-
Seventh-day Adventists General Conference	1946	-	-	4	-	6
SIM USA	1968	13	-	2	-	-
Source of Light Ministries International, Inc.	2001	-	-	-	1	-
WEC International	1934	9	-	-	-	23
World Missions Far Corners, Inc.	1992	2	-	-	-	-
World Partners USA	2000	-	2	-	-	-
Wycliffe Bible Translators USA		97	-	-	-	-
Totals:		393	33	25	71	55

Croatia

	First Year	4+ yrs.	2-4 yrs.	1-2 yrs.	Citizens	Not Citizens
Advent Christian General Conf.	1996	-	-	-	2	-
Assemblies of God World Missions		2	-	-	-	-
Bethany Fellowship Missions	1999	-	1	-	-	1
Campus Crusade for Christ, Intl.	1993	10	-	10	13	1
Child Evangelism Fellowship, Inc.	1989	2	-	-	2	-
Christian Aid Mission		-	-	-	11	-
Church of God (Cleveland, TN)	1968	2	-	-	-	-
Church of the Nazarene	1999	-	-	-	-	-
Churches of Christ	1969	2	-	-	8	-
Envoy International		-	-	-	-	-
Every Home for Christ Intl.	1993	-	-	-	1	-
Foursquare Missions International	1997	2	-	-	-	-
Greater Europe Mission	1974	6	-	-	-	-
Pioneers	1992	2	-	-	-	-
Presbyterian Ch. (USA), Worldwide Mins.		2	-	-	-	-

	Personnel from U.S.			Other Countries	
	First Year	4+ yrs.	2-4 yrs.	1-2 yrs.	Citizens	Not Citizens

	First Year	4+ yrs.	2-4 yrs.	1-2 yrs.	Citizens	Not Citizens
Seed International	1999	2	-	-	-	-
SEND International	1995	5	-	-	-	-
TEAM (The Evangelical Alliance Mission)		2	-	-	-	-
Wesleyan World Missions	1992	-	5	-	-	-
Totals:	39	6	10	37	2	

Cuba

	First Year	4+ yrs.	2-4 yrs.	1-2 yrs.	Citizens	Not Citizens
ABWE		4	-	-	-	-
American Baptist Churches in the U.S.A.	1898	1	-	-	-	-
BCM International		1	-	-	-	-
Bright Hope International	2001	-	-	-	152	-
Caring Partners International, Inc.	1996	-	-	-	-	-
Child Evangelism Fellowship, Inc.	1949	-	-	-	2	-
Christ to the Nations	1995	10	-	-	6	4
Christian Aid Mission		-	-	-	84	-
Church of God of Prophecy		-	-	-	4	-
Church of the Nazarene	1902	-	-	-	-	-
Correll Missionary Ministries	1978	-	-	-	60	-
Elim Fellowship, Intl. Dept.	1943	-	-	-	-	-
International Gospel Outreach	1999	-	-	-	4	-
International Partnership Ministries, Inc.	1999	-	-	-	21	-
Living Water Teaching International	2001	-	-	-	-	2
Medical Ambassadors International	2001	-	-	-	-	-
New Life League International		-	-	-	-	-
Partners International	1995	-	-	-	-	-
SAND International	2001	-	-	-	1	-
Touch the World Ministries	2000	1	-	-	-	-
University of the Family	1993	-	-	-	2	-
Wisconsin Evangelical Lutheran Syn.	1995	1	-	-	-	-
World Help	1997	-	-	-	2	-
World Missions Far Corners, Inc.	1977	1	-	-	-	-
World Partners USA	1998	-	-	-	-	-
Totals:	19	-	-	338	6	

Cyprus

	First Year	4+ yrs.	2-4 yrs.	1-2 yrs.	Citizens	Not Citizens
AMG International	1984	2	-	-	-	-
Armenian Msny. Assoc. of America, Inc.	1950	-	-	-	-	-
Biblical Ministries Worldwide	1963	4	-	-	-	-
Child Evangelism Fellowship, Inc.	1952	7	-	-	-	-
Church of God of Prophecy		-	-	-	2	2
Church of the Nazarene	1985	-	-	-	-	-
Evangelical Lutheran Church in America	1996	3	-	-	-	-
InterServe/USA	1984	2	-	-	-	-
Middle East Christian Outreach	1975	-	-	-	-	19
Reformed Ch. in America, Gen. Syn.	1966	-	2	-	-	-
Ripe for Harvest, Inc.	2001	3	-	-	-	-
Seventh-day Adventists Gen. Conf.	1932	-	2	6	-	4
Venture International	1986	-	-	-	1	-
World Partners USA	1966	3	-	-	-	-
Totals:	24	4	6	3	25	

	Personnel from U.S.			Other Countries	
	First Year	4+ yrs.	2-4 yrs.	1-2 yrs.	Citizens	Not Citizens

Czech Republic

American Baptist Chs. in the U.S.A.	1995	2	-	-	-	2
Apostolic Christian Ch. Foundation, Inc.	1998	1	-	-	-	-
Assemblies of God World Missions		4	-	2	-	-
Campus Crusade for Christ, Intl.	1981	12	-	1	17	-
CBInternational	1991	3	-	-	-	-
Christian Aid Mission		-	-	-	16	-
Christian Churches/Churches of Christ		2	-	-	-	-
Christian Outreach International	1992	7	-	-	1	3
Churches of Christ	1990	4	-	2	-	-
Envoy International		-	-	-	-	-
Evangelical Covenant Church	1999	2	-	-	-	-
Evangelical Free Church Mission	1991	13	-	-	-	-
Every Home for Christ International	1991	-	-	-	4	-
Faith Christian Fellowship Intl.	1997	-	2	-	-	-
Grace Brethren International Missions	1994	2	-	-	-	2
Greater Europe Mission	1991	6	-	-	-	-
Greater Grace World Outreach	1991	-	-	-	-	2
HCJB World Radio		2	-	-	-	-
International Institute for Christian Studies	1994	10	2	-	1	-
International Messengers	1994	-	-	-	2	-
International Needs - USA	1993	-	-	-	6	-
International Teams, U.S.A.		12	-	6	8	1
Mission to the World (PCA), Inc.	1989	4	2	-	-	-
Missionary Athletes International		2	-	-	-	-
Operation Mobilization, Inc.		2	-	-	-	-
Project Care		-	-	-	-	-
Salvation Army, U.S.A.	1990	2	-	-	-	-
SEND International	1992	4	-	-	-	2
Seventh-day Adventists General Conference	1919	1	-	-	-	-
TEAM (The Evangelical Alliance Mission)		12	-	-	-	-
Wesleyan World Missions	1992	-	5	-	-	-
Word of Life Fellowship	1997	4	1	-	6	-
	Totals:	113	12	11	61	12

Denmark

Assemblies of God World Missions		2	-	5	-	-
Baptist Bible Fellowship Intl.	1980	2	-	-	-	-
Child Evangelism Fellowship, Inc.	1947	2	-	-	-	-
Church of the Nazarene	1960	-	-	-	-	-
Churches of Christ	1950	-	-	-	1	-
Evangelical Lutheran Church in America	1995	2	-	2	-	-
Greater Europe Mission	1976	-	-	-	-	-
Ripe for Harvest, Inc.	2001	1	-	-	-	-
	Totals:	9	-	7	1	-

Djibouti

Project Mercy, Inc.	1977	-	-	-	-	23
Seventh-day Adventists Gen. Conf.	1980	-	-	-	-	4
SIM USA	1996	3	-	-	-	-
	Totals:	3	-	-	-	27

		Personnel from U.S.			Other Countries	
	First Year	4+ yrs.	2-4 yrs.	1-2 yrs.	Citizens	Not Citizens

Dominica

Assemblies of God World Missions		2	-	-	-	-
Bible Training Centre for Pastors	1998	-	-	-	1	-
Christian Churches/Churches of Christ		5	-	-	15	-
Church of the Nazarene	1974	-	-	-	-	-
Gospel Fellowship Association	1994	2	-	-	-	-
World Gospel Mission	1996	4	-	-	-	-
Totals:		13	-	-	16	-

Dominican Republic

American Baptist Chs. in the U.S.A.	1980	5	-	-	-	-
Assemblies of God World Missions	1922	13	-	6	-	-
Baptist Bible Fellowship Intl.	1996	4	-	-	-	-
Baptist Mid-Missions	1950	-	-	-	-	-
BCM International		-	-	-	2	-
Bethany Fellowship Missions	1978	2	-	-	-	-
Bible League, The	1989	-	-	-	15	-
Brethren Assemblies		2	-	-	-	-
Campus Crusade for Christ, Intl.	1977	-	-	-	39	-
Christian and Missionary Alliance	1969	13	-	-	-	-
Christian Blind Mission Intl.	1985	-	-	1	-	-
Christian Churches / Churches of Christ		12	-	-	-	-
Christian Reformed World Missions	1979	8	2	4	-	-
Christian Reformed World Relief Comte.	1982	1	-	-	-	-
Church of the Nazarene	1974	-	-	-	-	4
Churches of Christ	1963	5	-	-	3	-
Compassion International, Inc.	1970	-	-	-	29	-
Correll Missionary Ministries	2001	-	-	-	2	-
Evangelistic Faith Missions	1981	-	2	-	-	-
Floresta USA, Inc.	1984	-	-	-	8	-
Food for the Hungry, Inc.	1979	-	2	-	-	-
Foursquare Missions International	1996	2	-	-	-	-
Free Methodist World Missions	1889	2	-	-	-	-
Habitat for Humanity International	1987	-	4	-	5	-
Harvest		-	-	-	3	-
International Partnership Ministries, Inc.	2000	-	-	-	5	-
Intl. Pentecostal Holiness Ch. World Mins.	1996	2	-	-	-	-
Kids Alive International	1989	9	1	-	1	-
Literacy & Evangelism International		-	-	-	-	2
Medical Ambassadors International	1988	-	-	-	4	-
Mennonite Mission Network	1906	-	-	-	-	-
Ministries In Action	1995	-	-	-	-	1
Mission Possible, Inc.	1987	-	-	-	12	-
Mission to the Americas	1981	-	-	-	2	-
Missionary Ventures International	1999	1	-	-	-	-
Presbyterian Church (USA)		3	-	-	-	-
Primitive Methodist Ch. in the USA		2	-	-	-	-
Seventh-day Adventists Gen. Conf.	1908	-	-	-	-	9
South American Missionary Society	1987	3	-	-	-	-
STEM	1994	-	-	-	-	-
UFM International	1949	17	-	3	-	-
United Church Board for World Ministries		-	1	-	-	-

	Personnel from U.S.			Other Countries	
	First Year	4+ yrs.	2-4 yrs.	1-2 yrs.	Citizens	Not Citizens

	First Year	4+ yrs.	2-4 yrs.	1-2 yrs.	Citizens	Not Citizens
Walk Thru The Bible Ministries	2001	-	-	-	2	-
Wisconsin Evangelical Lutheran Syn.	1993	2	-	-	-	-
Word of Life Fellowship	1994	-	-	-	5	9
World Servants	1987	-	-	-	3	-
World Team	1939	4	-	-	-	-
	Totals:	112	12	14	140	25

Dubai

	First Year	4+ yrs.	2-4 yrs.	1-2 yrs.	Citizens	Not Citizens
Church of God (Cleveland, TN)	1992	-	-	-	-	2
	Totals:	-	-	-	-	2

East Timor

	First Year	4+ yrs.	2-4 yrs.	1-2 yrs.	Citizens	Not Citizens
Church of the Nazarene	2001	-	-	-	-	-
WEC International	1999	-	-	-	-	6
	Totals	-	-	-	-	6

Eastern Europe - General

	First Year	4+ yrs.	2-4 yrs.	1-2 yrs.	Citizens	Not Citizens
Pioneers		9	-	-	-	-
	Totals:	9	-	-	-	-

Ecuador

	First Year	4+ yrs.	2-4 yrs.	1-2 yrs.	Citizens	Not Citizens
Action International Ministries	1993	2	-	-	-	-
Assemblies of God World Missions	1962	28	-	6	-	-
Back to the Bible International	1970	-	-	-	8	-
Baptist Bible Fellowship Intl.	1975	12	-	1	-	-
Baptist Mid-Missions	1988	11	-	-	1	-
Bible League, The	2001	-	-	-	12	-
Brethren Assemblies		14	-	-	-	-
Campus Crusade for Christ, Intl.	1965	-	-	-	30	-
Caring Partners International, Inc.	1998	-	-	-	-	-
Child Evangelism Fellowship, Inc.	1941	-	-	-	2	-
Christian Aid Mission		-	-	-	5	-
Christian and Missionary Alliance	1897	32	32	-	-	-
Christian Blind Mission Intl.	1980	-	1	-	-	-
Christian Churches / Churches of Christ		4	4	-	-	-
Christian Reformed World Relief Comte.	1983	-	-	-	-	1
Christians In Action, Inc.	1979	2	-	-	-	2
Church Ministries International	2000	-	-	-	-	2
Church of God (Anderson, Indiana)		4	-	-	-	-
Church of God (Cleveland, TN)	1971	6	-	-	20	-
Church of God of Prophecy		-	-	-	2	2
Church of the Nazarene	1972	4	-	-	-	2
Churches of Christ	1966	12	-	-	4	-
Compassion International, Inc.	1974	-	-	-	26	-
Evangelical Covenant Church	1947	9	1	-	-	-
Fellowship International Mission	1972	2	-	-	-	-
Foursquare Missions International	1956	2	-	-	-	-
Free Methodist World Missions	1981	2	-	-	-	-
Global Outreach, Ltd.		9	-	-	-	-
Gospel Missionary Union	1896	52	-	-	-	-
HCJB World Radio		139	-	-	11	27
International Cassette Bible Institute	2000	-	-	-	2	-

	Personnel from U.S.			Other Countries	
First Year	4+ yrs.	2-4 yrs.	1-2 yrs.	Citizens	Not Citizens
Intl. Pentecostal Holiness Ch. World Mins.	2000	2	-	-	-	-
International Teams, U.S.A.		12	-	-	7	2
Latin America Mission	1974	4	-	-	2	2
Liebenzell Mission USA	1989	7	-	-	-	-
Lutheran Bible Translators		-	-	-	-	-
MAP International	1981	-	-	-	10	-
Mennonite Mission Network	1969	2	-	-	2	-
Mission Aviation Fellowship	1948	23	-	2	-	-
Mission to the World (PCA), Inc.	1975	18	8	-	-	-
OMS International, Inc.		18	-	-	-	4
Open Air Campaigners - Overseas Mins.	2001	-	-	-	2	-
Reformed Church in America, Gen. Syn.	1987	-	-	-	1	-
Rosedale Mennonite Missions	1980	7	-	-	-	-
SIM USA	1989	8	-	-	-	-
South American Missionary Society	2001	-	1	-	-	-
Team Expansion, Inc.	1990	6	-	-	-	-
Teen Missions International	1999	2	-	-	2	-
UFM International		10	-	-	-	-
United Church Bd. for World Mins.		-	2	-	-	-
Walk Thru The Bible Ministries	2001	-	-	-	1	-
Word of Life Fellowship	1970	2	-	-	6	5
World Baptist Fellowship Mission Agency		12	2	-	-	-
World Mission Prayer League Inc.	1951	5	-	-	-	-
World Missions Far Corners, Inc.	1984	8	-	-	-	-
World Partners USA	1945	16	-	-	-	-
World Servants	1990	-	-	-	1	-
Totals:		508	51	9	157	49

Egypt

ABWE		1	-	-	-	-
Armenian Msny. Assoc. of America, Inc.	1950	-	-	-	-	-
Assemblies of God World Missions	1908	-	-	1	-	-
Back to the Bible International	1998	-	-	-	10	-
BCM International		-	-	-	11	-
Campus Crusade for Christ, Intl.	1972	3	-	-	113	2
Christ Community Church	1979	1	-	-	-	-
Christar	1984	4	-	-	-	-
Christian Aid Mission		-	-	-	72	-
Church of God of Prophecy		-	-	-	6	-
Church of the Nazarene	1986	-	-	-	-	-
Churches of Christ	1960	2	-	-	-	-
Development Associates Intl. (DAI)	2001	-	-	-	-	-
Evangelical Lutheran Ch. in America	1967	6	-	1	-	-
Evangelical Presbyterian Church	2001	2	-	-	-	-
Go Ye Fellowship	1997	1	-	-	-	-
Habitat for Humanity International	1989	-	1	-	1	-
International Christian Ministries	2002	-	-	-	4	-
International Missionary Center		3	-	-	-	-
International Needs - USA	1997	-	-	-	2	-
Medical Ambassadors International	1999	-	-	-	-	-
Mennonite Mission Network	1985	2	-	-	-	-
Missionary Ventures International	1997	1	-	-	-	-

	First Year	4+ yrs.	2-4 yrs.	1-2 yrs.	Citizens	Not Citizens
		Personnel from U.S.			Other Countries	
Operation Mobilization, Inc.		6	3	2	-	-
Partners International	1989	-	-	-	-	-
Presbyterian Ch. (USA), Worldwide Mins.		13	10	-	-	-
Reformed Church in America, Gen. Syn.	2001	2	-	-	-	-
Seventh-day Adventists Gen. Conf.	1879	-	2	2	-	-
University of the Family	1992	-	-	-	1	1
Venture International	1994	-	-	-	1	-
Walk Thru The Bible Ministries	2001	-	-	-	2	-
World-Wide Missions	1963	-	-	-	16	-
Totals:		47	16	6	239	3

El Salvador

	First Year	4+ yrs.	2-4 yrs.	1-2 yrs.	Citizens	Not Citizens
American Baptist Chs. in the U.S.A.	1911	2	-	-	-	-
Assemblies of God World Missions	1925	10	-	39	-	-
Brethren Assemblies		6	-	-	-	-
CAM International	1896	8	-	-	-	8
Campus Crusade for Christ, Intl.	1966	-	-	-	20	-
Child Evangelism Fellowship, Inc.	1942	-	-	-	1	-
Christian Reformed World Missions	1996	1	-	-	-	-
Christian Reformed World Relief Comte.	1976	-	1	-	-	-
Church of God of Prophecy		-	-	-	4	-
Church of the Nazarene	1964	-	-	-	-	-
Churches of Christ	1964	-	-	-	5	-
Compassion International, Inc.	1977	-	-	-	19	-
Correll Missionary Ministries	1998	-	6	-	-	-
Evangelical Lutheran Church in America	1987	-	-	1	-	-
Evangelistic Faith Missions	1964	-	-	-	-	2
Foursquare Missions International	1973	2	-	-	-	-
Greater Grace World Outreach	1974	-	-	-	2	-
Habitat for Humanity International	1992	-	-	-	13	-
International Justice Mission		-	-	-	-	-
Larry Jones International Ministries	1983	-	-	-	6	-
Latin America Mission	2001	-	2	-	-	2
Living Water Teaching International	1985	-	-	-	-	-
Medical Ambassadors International	1984	-	-	-	6	-
Mission to the Americas	1994	-	-	-	2	-
Northwest Medical Teams	2000	-	-	-	-	-
Open Bible Standard Chs., Intl. Mins.	1973	2	-	-	-	-
Precept Ministries International	1988	-	-	-	1	-
Samaritan's Purse	2001	-	-	5	-	-
United Church Board for World Ministries		-	2	-	-	-
Walk Thru The Bible Ministries	2000	-	-	-	1	-
Word of Life Fellowship	1993	2	-	-	1	4
World Reach, Inc.	1996	4	-	-	2	-
World Vision Inc.	1975	-	-	-	-	-
World-Wide Missions	1970	-	-	-	8	-
Totals:		37	11	45	91	16

Equatorial Guinea

	First Year	4+ yrs.	2-4 yrs.	1-2 yrs.	Citizens	Not Citizens
Assemblies of God World Missions	1987	6	-	2	-	-
Christian Churches / Churches of Christ		2	-	-	-	-
Church of the Nazarene	2002	-	-	-	-	-

	Personnel from U.S.			Other Countries	
	First Year	4+ yrs.	2-4 yrs.	1-2 yrs.	Citizens	Not Citizens
Evangelical Covenant Church	1999	2	-	-	-	-
Every Home for Christ International	1988	-	-	-	5	-
Gospel Fellowship Association	1999	2	-	-	-	-
Seventh-day Adventists Gen. Conf.	1986	-	-	2	-	2
WEC International	1933	-	-	-	-	8
	Totals:	12	-	4	5	10
Eritrea						
Assemblies of God World Missions		4	-	-	-	-
Church of the Nazarene	1993	-	-	-	-	-
CMF International	1997	1	3	1	-	-
International Needs—USA	1980	-	-	-	-	-
Lutheran Church—Missouri Syn.	1975	2	-	-	-	-
World Mission Prayer League Inc.	1996	1	-	-	-	1
	Totals:	8	3	1	-	1
Estonia						
Baptist General Conference		2	-	-	-	-
Campus Crusade for Christ, Intl.	1991	4	-	4	3	-
Child Evangelism Fellowship, Inc.	1989	-	-	-	1	-
Churches of Christ	1990	10	-	-	4	-
International Teams, U.S.A.		2	-	-	-	-
Navigators, U.S. Intl. Missions Group		4	-	-	-	-
Precept Ministries International	1994	-	-	-	1	-
Reformed Ch. in America, Gen. Syn.	1994	2	-	-	2	-
Walk Thru The Bible Ministries	2001	-	-	-	1	-
	Totals:	24	-	4	12	-
Ethiopia						
ACM International	1996	1	-	-	-	-
African Enterprise, Inc.	1995	-	-	-	3	-
Assemblies of God World Missions	1968	11	-	1	-	-
Baptist Bible Fellowship Intl.	1960	6	-	-	-	-
Baptist General Conference	1950	8	-	-	-	-
Baptist International Outreach	1985	-	-	-	40	-
Baptist Mid-Missions	1993	5	-	-	-	-
Bible League, The	1995	-	-	-	3	-
Campus Crusade for Christ, Intl.	1980	-	-	-	72	-
Christian Churches / Churches of Christ		8	-	-	2	-
Church of God of Prophecy		-	-	-	9	-
Church of the Nazarene	1992	2	4	-	-	-
Churches of Christ	1961	-	-	-	1	-
CMF International	1963	4	2	2	-	2
Compassion International, Inc.	1993	-	-	-	30	-
Eastern Mennonite Missions		4	-	-	-	-
Emmanuel Intl. Mission (U.S.)		-	-	-	-	-
Equip, Inc.		2	-	-	-	-
Evangelical Lutheran Ch. in America	1957	4	-	3	-	-
Habitat for Humanity International	1990	-	5	-	5	-
Harvest		-	-	-	2	-
International Needs - USA	1996	-	-	-	50	-
Larry Jones International Ministries	1983	-	-	-	12	-

| | Personnel from U.S. | | | Other Countries | |
	First Year	4+ yrs.	2-4 yrs.	1-2 yrs.	Citizens	Not Citizens
MBMS International	2000	-	-	-	-	-
Medical Ambassadors International	1993	-	-	-	4	-
Mission ONE, Inc.		-	-	-	-	-
Mission to the World (PCA), Inc.	1990	2	-	-	-	-
New Directions International	1991	-	-	-	8	-
Orthodox Presbyterian Church	1994	2	-	-	-	-
Presbyterian Ch. (USA), Worldwide Mins.		4	18	2	-	-
Project Mercy, Inc.	1977	2	-	-	17	-
Reformed Ch. in America, Gen. Syn.	1995	4	-	-	-	-
Seventh-day Adventists Gen. Conf.	1907	4	2	-	-	17
SIM USA	1927	70	-	9	-	-
World Concern	1983	3	-	2	16	1
World Missions Far Corners, Inc.	1982	-	-	-	2	-
World Vision Inc.	1971	-	-	-	-	-
Wycliffe Bible Translators USA		55	-	-	-	-
Totals:		201	31	19	276	20

Europe - General

Caleb Project	2001	4	-	2	-	-
Campus Crusade for Christ, Intl.		-	-	-	1	-
CBInternational	1993	2	-	-	-	-
Christian and Missionary Alliance	1999	4	2	-	-	-
Christian Ch. of North America Missions	1945	2	-	-	-	-
Church of God (Cleveland, TN)		2	-	-	-	-
Church World Service & Witness	1946	1	-	-	4	1
Eastern Mennonite Missions		-	-	-	-	-
Elim Fellowship, Intl. Dept.		-	-	1	-	1
European Christian Mission NA, Inc.		15	-	-	-	-
Evangelical Covenant Church	1999	2	-	-	-	-
Final Frontiers Foundation, Inc.	1994	-	-	-	30	-
Heifer International	1992	4	14	10	31	1
International Bible Society		-	-	-	55	-
Mennonite Central Committee		29	-	-	-	-
Operation Mobilization, Inc.		11	1	3	-	-
Opportunity Intl./Women's Opportunity		-	7	-	-	-
Presbyterian Evangelistic Fellowship		9	-	-	-	-
Southern Baptist Conv. Intl. Msn. Bd.		-	-	-	-	-
Team Expansion, Inc.	1997	11	-	-	-	-
TMA Ministries	1982	4	-	-	4	-
World Team	1993	18	-	1	-	-
Wycliffe Bible Translators USA		20	-	-	-	-
Totals:		138	24	17	125	3

Fiji

Assemblies of God World Missions	1914	4	-	2	-	-
Biblical Ministries Worldwide	1990	4	-	-	-	4
Campus Crusade for Christ, Intl.	1974	-	-	-	8	-
Child Evangelism Fellowship, Inc.	1953	3	-	-	-	-
Church of God of Prophecy		-	-	-	3	-
Church of the Nazarene	1995	4	-	-	-	2
Every Home for Christ International	1964	-	-	-	4	-
Fellowship International Mission	1995	-	-	-	1	1

	Personnel from U.S.			Other Countries	
	First Year	4+ yrs.	2-4 yrs.	1-2 yrs.	Citizens	Not Citizens
Habitat for Humanity International	1991	-	2	2	2	4
Mustard Seed, Inc., The	1998	-	-	-	2	-
Presbyterian Church (USA)		2	-	-	-	-
Seventh-day Adventists Gen. Conf.	1949	-	-	-	-	1
United Church Board for World Mins.		-	2	-	-	-
WEC International	1986	-	-	-	-	17
Totals:		17	4	4	20	29

Finland

	First Year	4+ yrs.	2-4 yrs.	1-2 yrs.	Citizens	Not Citizens
Assemblies of God World Missions	2000	2	-	-	-	-
Baptist Mid-Missions	1980	2	-	-	-	-
BCM International	1968	-	-	-	2	-
Church of God of Prophecy		-	-	-	1	-
Churches of Christ	1960	1	-	2	-	-
Far East Broadcasting Company, Inc.	1999	2	-	-	-	-
Greater Europe Mission	1957	-	-	-	-	-
Greater Grace World Outreach	1975	-	-	-	12	-
International Cassette Bible Institute	1995	-	-	-	2	-
Mennonite Mission Network	1995	-	-	-	1	1
Mission Possible Foundation, Inc.	1985	-	-	-	-	-
Ripe for Harvest, Inc.	2000	2	-	-	-	-
Salvation Army, U.S.A.	1889	5	-	-	-	-
WEC International	1971	-	-	-	-	4
Wycliffe Bible Translators USA		2	-	-	-	-
Totals:		16	-	2	18	5

France

	First Year	4+ yrs.	2-4 yrs.	1-2 yrs.	Citizens	Not Citizens
ABWE	1984	6	-	-	-	-
Africa Inland Mission International	1987	2	-	-	-	-
AMF International		-	-	-	2	-
Apostolic Team Ministries, Intl.		4	-	-	1	-
Armenian Missionary Assn. of America, Inc.	1950	-	-	-	-	-
Assemblies of God World Missions	1952	13	-	1	-	-
Baptist Bible Fellowship Intl.	1970	6	-	2	-	-
Baptist General Conference	1989	4	-	-	-	-
Baptist Mid-Missions	1948	24	-	-	-	-
BCM International		2	1	-	-	-
Bethany Fellowship Missions	1987	7	-	-	-	2
Biblical Ministries Worldwide	1996	2	-	-	-	-
Brethren Assemblies		15	-	-	-	3
Campus Crusade for Christ, Intl.	1970	32	-	22	-	-
CBInternational	1962	14	2	-	-	-
Child Evangelism Fellowship, Inc.	1949	2	-	-	-	-
Chosen People Ministries		-	-	-	-	-
Christar	1988	10	5	1	-	-
Christian and Missionary Alliance	1962	21	-	-	-	-
Christian Churches/Churches of Christ		5	1	-	-	-
Christian Outreach International	1992	1	-	-	1	-
Christian Reformed World Missions	1989	2	-	-	-	-
Church of God (Cleveland, TN)	1960	1	-	-	-	4
Church of God of Prophecy		-	-	-	3	-
Church of the Nazarene	1977	3	-	-	-	1

	First Year	4+ yrs.	2-4 yrs.	1-2 yrs.	Other Countries Citizens	Not Citizens
		Personnel from U.S.				
Church Resource Ministries	1996	4	-	-	-	-
Churches of Christ	1949	18	-	-	4	-
Elim Fellowship, Intl. Dept.	1999	2	-	-	-	2
Evangel Bible Translators	1978	2	-	-	-	-
Evangelical Baptist Missions		20	-	-	-	-
Evangelical Covenant Church	1996	3	-	-	-	-
Evangelical Free Church Mission	1988	11	-	-	-	-
Evangelical Greenhouse Ministries Intl.	1996	3	-	-	4	-
Evangelical Presbyterian Church	1992	2	-	-	-	-
Every Home for Christ International	1964	-	-	-	4	-
Fellowship International Mission	1986	-	-	-	-	1
Foursquare Missions International	1982	2	-	-	-	-
Free Will Baptists, Inc., Natl. Assoc.	1966	7	-	1	-	-
General Conf. Mennonite Church	1974	2	-	-	-	-
Global Outreach Mission	1946	33	-	-	10	-
Gospel Missionary Union	1960	8	-	-	-	-
Grace Brethren International Missions	1951	19	-	-	-	2
Greater Europe Mission	1949	31	4	-	-	-
Greater Grace World Outreach	1982	-	-	-	4	2
Hope for the Hungry		1	-	-	-	1
International Outreach Ministries	1996	4	-	-	-	-
Intl. Pentecostal Holiness Ch. World Mins.	1981	1	-	-	-	-
International Teams, U.S.A.		23	-	-	-	3
Jews for Jesus	1992	1	-	-	1	1
Mennonite Mission Network	1953	3	-	-	-	-
Mission to the World (PCA), Inc.	1978	18	7	-	-	-
Missionary Revival Crusade	1983	4	-	-	-	2
Missions to Military, Inc.	1972	5	-	-	-	-
Navigators, U.S. Intl. Missions Group		2	-	-	-	-
Operation Mobilization, Inc.	1961	2	1	-	-	-
Pocket Testament League	1988	-	-	-	2	-
Presbyterian Ch. (USA), Worldwide Mins.		2	-	-	-	-
Presbyterian Evangelistic Fellowship		5	-	-	-	-
Reformed Baptist Mission Services	1992	2	-	-	-	1
Reformed Episcopal Bd. of Foreign Msns.	1970	2	-	-	-	-
Ripe for Harvest, Inc.	2001	7	-	-	-	-
Seventh-day Adventists Gen. Conf.	1876	2	-	-	-	-
TEAM (The Evangelical Alliance Mission)	1938	40	-	-	-	-
The Mission Society	1988	9	-	-	-	-
UFM International	1962	26	-	-	-	4
WEC International	1950	2	-	-	-	21
Word of Life Fellowship	1999	2	-	-	-	2
World Baptist Fellowship Mission Agency	1954	-	-	2	-	-
World Horizons	2001	4	-	-	-	-
World Team	1980	14	-	-	-	-
Wycliffe Bible Translators USA		8	-	-	-	-
Youth for Christ/USA, World Outreach Div.	1949	2	-	-	-	-
Totals:		534	21	29	36	52

French Guiana

Brethren Assemblies		2	-	-	-	-
Church of God of Prophecy		-	-	-	1	-

		Personnel from U.S.			Other Countries	
	First Year	4+ yrs.	2-4 yrs.	1-2 yrs.	Citizens	Not Citizens
Church of the Nazarene	1988	-	-	-	-	-
Seventh-day Adventists Gen. Conf.	1946	-	-	-	-	1
Totals:		2	-	-	1	1
French Polynesia						
Assemblies of God World Missions		2	-	-	-	-
Baptist Bible Fellowship Intl.	1977	2	-	-	-	-
Seventh-day Adventists Gen. Conf.	1891	-	-	-	-	1
Totals:		4	-	-	-	1
Gabon						
Campus Crusade for Christ, Intl.	1989	-	-	-	14	-
Christian and Missionary Alliance	1934	22	12	-	-	-
Church of God of Prophecy		-	-	-	2	-
Church of the Nazarene	1999	-	-	-	-	-
InterVarsity Christian Fellowship/USA	1994	2	-	-	-	-
Medical Ambassadors International	1993	-	-	-	2	-
Totals:		24	12	-	18	-
Gambia, The						
ABWE	1978	16	-	-	-	-
Child Evangelism Fellowship, Inc.	1986	2	-	-	-	-
Church of God of Prophecy		-	-	-	1	-
General Conf. Mennonite Church	1995	2	-	-	-	1
International Missionary Center		-	-	-	-	4
Reformed Church in America, Gen. Syn.		4	-	-	-	-
Seventh-day Adventists Gen. Conf.	1973	-	-	2	-	2
WEC International	1957	1	-	-	-	38
Totals:		25	-	2	1	45
Georgia						
Armenian Msny. Assoc. of America, Inc.	1988	-	-	-	-	-
Assemblies of God World Missions		-	-	3	-	-
Every Home for Christ International	1999	-	-	-	9	-
Salvation Army, U.S.A.	1993	6	-	-	-	-
Seventh-day Adventists Gen. Conf.	1886	-	1	1	-	1
Walk Thru The Bible Ministries	2001	-	-	-	1	-
World Concern	1998	-	-	-	17	-
Totals:		6	1	4	27	1
Germany						
ABWE	1989	7	-	-	-	-
Apostolic Team Ministries, Intl.		-	-	-	2	-
Assemblies of God World Missions	1950	41	-	12	-	-
Baptist Bible Fellowship Intl.	1970	18	2	-	-	-
Baptist Mid-Missions	1952	19	-	-	-	-
BCM International		3	-	-	3	-
Bible Missionary Church	1995	2	-	-	-	-
Biblical Ministries Worldwide	1958	7	-	-	-	-
Brethren Assemblies		3	-	-	-	-
Cadence International		-	36	-	-	36
Campus Crusade for Christ, Intl.	1966	23	-	10	-	15

		Personnel from U.S.			Other Countries	
	First Year	4+ yrs.	2-4 yrs.	1-2 yrs.	Citizens	Not Citizens
CBInternational		2	-	1	-	-
Child Evangelism Fellowship, Inc.	1949	4	-	-	-	-
Chosen People Ministries	1995	-	-	-	-	-
Christian and Missionary Alliance	1975	13	2	-	-	-
Christian Associates International	1996	4	-	-	1	-
Christian Churches/Churches of Christ		8	2	-	-	-
Christians In Action, Inc.	1972	3	-	-	1	3
Church of God (Cleveland, TN)	1936	9	-	-	-	4
Church of God of Prophecy		4	-	-	1	-
Church of the Nazarene	1958	6	-	-	-	7
Churches of Christ	1947	34	-	-	22	-
Eastern Mennonite Missions		4	-	-	-	1
Evangelical Baptist Missions		12	-	-	-	-
Evangelical Covenant Church	1991	3	2	-	-	-
Evangelical Free Church Mission	1958	8	-	-	-	-
Evangelical Lutheran Ch. in America	1972	5	-	2	-	-
Evangelical Mennonite Ch. Intl. Mins.	1997	1	-	2	-	-
Every Home for Christ International	1964	-	-	-	5	-
Fellowship International Mission	1984	-	-	-	-	2
Foursquare Missions International	1981	2	-	-	-	-
General Conf. Mennonite Church	1994	-	-	-	-	4
Global Outreach Mission	1946	7	-	-	8	-
Globe Missionary Evangelism	1977	-	2	-	-	-
Gospel Fellowship Association	1963	18	-	1	-	-
Gospel Missionary Union	1961	4	1	-	-	-
Grace Baptist Missions International	1990	1	-	-	-	-
Grace Brethren International Missions	1969	10	-	-	-	2
Great Commission Ministries, Inc.		2	4	-	-	-
Greater Europe Mission	1954	47	7	-	-	-
Greater Grace World Outreach	1983	-	-	-	-	2
International Christian Ministries	1998	2	-	-	-	-
International Messengers	1996	-	1	-	2	-
International Missionary Center		3	-	-	-	-
Intl. Pentecostal Holiness Ch. World Mins.	1987	2	2	-	-	-
Lutheran Church—Missouri Syn.	1972	4	-	1	-	-
MBMS International	1953	-	2	-	-	-
Mennonite Mission Network	1994	-	-	-	-	2
Mission to the World (PCA), Inc.	1991	10	2	-	-	-
Missionary Revival Crusade	1979	3	-	-	-	2
Navigators, U.S. Intl. Missions Group		1	-	-	-	-
New Tribes Mission	1991	2	-	-	-	-
OC International, Inc.	1981	10	5	1	-	Not
Operation Mobilization, Inc.		2	-	-	-	-
Pocket Testament League	1986	2	-	-	-	-
Precept Ministries International	1992	-	-	-	1	-
Presbyterian Church (USA)		2	8	-	-	-
Reformed Episcopal Bd. of Foreign Missions		2	-	-	-	-
Ripe for Harvest, Inc.	1996	2	-	-	-	-
Rosedale Mennonite Missions	1975	-	-	-	-	2
Salvation Army, U.S.A.	1886	2	-	-	-	-
SEND International	1980	-	-	-	1	-
Seventh-day Adventists Gen. Conf.	1875	-	-	1	-	8

	Personnel from U.S.			Other Countries	
	First Year	4+ yrs.	2-4 yrs.	1-2 yrs.	Citizens	Not Citizens

	First Year	4+ yrs.	2-4 yrs.	1-2 yrs.	Citizens	Not Citizens
TEAM (The Evangelical Alliance Mission)		24	-	8	-	-
Trans World Radio		-	-	-	-	1
Turkish World Outreach	1988	2	-	-	2	-
UFM International	1976	20	-	3	1	-
United Church Board for World Ministries		-	2	-	-	-
WEC International	1951	1	-	-	-	47
Word of Life Fellowship	1965	6	-	-	44	-
World Harvest Mission	1996	3	1	-	-	-
World Partners USA	2001	4	-	-	-	-
World Reach, Inc.	1988	-	-	-	2	-
World Witness, Assoc. Reformed Presb. Ch.	1994	8	-	-	-	-
Wycliffe Bible Translators USA		17	-	-	-	-
Youth for Christ /USA, World Outreach Div.		10	-	-	-	-
Totals:		478	81	42	96	138

Ghana

	First Year	4+ yrs.	2-4 yrs.	1-2 yrs.	Citizens	Not Citizens
ABWE	1993	12	-	-	-	-
Advent Christian Gen. Conference	1995	-	-	-	10	-
African Enterprise, Inc.	1995	-	-	-	4	-
African Mission Evangelism	1966	9	-	-	10	-
AMG International		-	-	-	1	-
Apostolic Christian Ch. Foundation, Inc.	1975	-	-	-	2	-
Assemblies of God World Missions	1931	2	-	-	-	-
Baptist Mid-Missions	1946	12	-	-	-	-
BCM International		-	-	-	2	-
Bethany Fellowship Missions	1995	2	-	-	-	2
Bible League, The	1986	-	-	-	12	-
Bible Missionary Church		2	-	-	-	-
Campus Crusade for Christ, Intl.	1967	-	-	-	63	3
Child Evangelism Fellowship, Inc.	1971	-	-	-	12	-
Christ to the Nations	1999	2	-	-	2	-
Christian Churches / Churches of Christ		13	1	-	2	-
Christians In Action, Inc.	1994	4	-	-	-	4
Church of the Nazarene	1990	-	1	-	-	-
Churches of Christ	1961	8	-	-	-	-
Correll Missionary Ministries	1992	1	-	-	-	-
Development Associates Intl. (DAI)	1997	-	-	-	-	-
East West Ministries	1994	-	-	-	1	-
Elim Fellowship, Intl. Dept.	2000	-	-	2	-	2
Evangel Bible Translators	1992	2	-	-	-	-
Evangelism Explosion International		-	-	-	-	2
Evangelism Resources	2001	-	-	-	-	-
Every Child Ministries, Inc.	1999	-	-	-	12	-
Every Home for Christ International	1976	-	-	-	2	-
Flwshp. of Assoc. of Medical Evangelism	1987	-	-	-	16	-
Gospel Revival Ministries	1996	-	-	-	4	-
Grace Baptist Missions International	1990	-	-	-	1	-
Greater Grace World Outreach	1988	-	-	-	10	-
Habitat for Humanity International	1987	-	3	-	16	-
Harvest		-	-	-	1	-
Hosanna / Faith Comes By Hearing	1995	-	-	-	8	-
Hundredfold Ministries International	1988	-	-	-	-	-

	Personnel from U.S.			Other Countries	
	First Year	4+ yrs.	2-4 yrs.	1-2 yrs.	Citizens	Not Citizens
International Aid		-	-	-	-	-
International Christian Ministries	2000	-	-	-	1	-
International Missionary Center		-	-	-	-	4
International Needs - USA	1986	-	-	-	91	-
International Partnership Ministries, Inc.	1987	2	-	-	17	-
Intl. Pentecostal Holiness Church	1992	4	-	-	-	-
Ireland Outreach International Inc.	1997	-	-	-	3	-
Josue Yrion Wld. Evangelism Msns., Inc.	2001	-	-	-	1	-
Literacy & Evangelism International		-	-	-	-	-
Lutheran Church—Missouri Syn.	1960	4	2	-	-	-
M/E Intl., Inc. (Missionary Electronics)	1999	-	-	-	3	-
Mennonite Mission Network	1957	-	-	-	-	-
National Baptist Convention of America	1984	-	-	-	14	-
Navigators, U.S. Intl. Missions Group		1	-	-	-	-
Network of Intl. Christian Schools	2002	-	5	-	-	-
New Directions International	1985	-	-	-	1	-
Partners International	1973	-	-	-	-	-
Presbyterian Ch. (USA), Worldwide Mins.	1964	4	-	-	-	-
Self-Help International	1990	-	-	-	5	-
Seventh-day Adventists Gen. Conf.	1894	-	2	-	-	4
SIM USA	1956	10	-	-	-	-
Source of Light Ministries Intl., Inc.	1995	-	-	-	2	-
The Mission Society	1985	8	-	2	-	-
Village Ministries International, Inc.	1991	-	-	-	6	-
Walk Thru The Bible Ministries	2001	-	-	-	4	-
WEC International	1946	2	-	-	-	16
World Vision Inc.	1958	-	-	-	-	-
Wycliffe Bible Translators USA	1962	38	-	-	-	-
	Totals:	142	14	4	339	37

Greece

	First Year	4+ yrs.	2-4 yrs.	1-2 yrs.	Citizens	Not Citizens
AMG International	1945	13	-	-	2	-
Armenian Msny. Assoc. of America, Inc.	1950	-	-	-	-	-
Assemblies of God World Missions	1931	-	-	2	-	-
Baptist Bible Fellowship Intl.	1993	2	-	-	-	-
BCM International		-	-	-	1	-
Brethren Assemblies		3	-	-	-	-
Campus Crusade for Christ, Intl.	1978	5	-	-	-	1
Child Evangelism Fellowship, Inc.	1971	2	-	-	2	-
Church of God of Prophecy		-	-	-	1	-
Church of the Nazarene	2002	-	-	-	-	-
Churches of Christ	1960	2	-	-	12	-
European Christian Mission NA, Inc.		7	-	-	-	-
Free Methodist World Missions	1998	2	-	-	-	-
Global Outreach Mission	1994	2	-	-	-	-
Gospel Missionary Union	1959	5	-	-	-	-
Greater Europe Mission	1966	14	-	-	-	-
Greater Grace World Outreach	1984	-	-	-	2	-
Hellenic Ministries	1980	3	2	-	6	1
International Teams, U.S.A.		7	3	-	3	5
InterVarsity Christian Fellowship/USA		-	2	-	-	-
OC International, Inc.	1967	-	-	-	2	-

| | Personnel from U.S. | | | | Other Countries |
	First Year	4+ yrs.	2-4 yrs.	1-2 yrs.	Citizens	Not Citizens
Presbyterian Evangelistic Fellowship		1	-	-	-	-
Ripe for Harvest, Inc.	1999	2	-	-	-	-
Seventh-day Adventists Gen. Conf.	1907	-	-	-	-	1
WEC International	1989	-	-	-	-	5
	Totals:	70	7	2	31	13

Greenland

New Tribes Mission	1988	1	-	-	-	10
	Totals:	1	-	-	-	10

Grenada

Christian Churches/Churches of Christ		2	-	-	-	-
Church of the Nazarene	1977	-	-	-	-	-
Ministries In Action	1974	1	-	-	-	-
	Totals:	3	-	-	-	-

Guadeloupe

Church of the Nazarene	1986	-	-	-	-	-
World Team	1947	2	-	-	-	-
	Totals:	2	-	-	-	-

Guam

Assemblies of God World Missions	1961	-	-	4	-	-
Biblical Ministries Worldwide	1981	4	-	-	-	-
Christian Reformed World Missions	1962	2	2	-	-	-
Church of God (Anderson, IND).		2	-	-	-	-
Church of the Nazarene	1971	2	-	-	-	-
Elim Fellowship, Intl. Dept.	1991	2	-	-	-	2
Mission to the World (PCA), Inc.	1996	4	-	-	-	-
Seventh-day Adventists Gen. Conf.	1930	45	17	16	1	5
Trans World Radio		18	-	-	-	-
	Totals:	79	19	20	1	7

Guatemala

All God's Children International		-	-	-	-	-
AMG International	1978	4	-	-	4	-
Assemblies of God World Missions	1937	14	-	5	-	-
BILD International		-	-	-	-	-
Brethren Assemblies		4	-	-	-	-
Calvary International	1987	11	-	-	-	11
CAM International	1899	68	7	-	2	66
Campus Crusade for Christ, Intl.	1963	2	-	-	38	-
Caring Partners International, Inc.	1993	-	-	-	-	-
Child Evangelism Fellowship, Inc.	1943	-	-	-	1	-
Christian Churches/Churches of Christ		2	-	-	2	-
Christian Reformed World Relief Comte.	1976	-	-	-	1	-
Christians In Action, Inc.	1970	2	-	-	5	2
Church of God (Cleveland, TN)	1934	4	-	-	-	-
Church of the Nazarene	1904	7	11	-	-	5
Churches of Christ	1960	4	-	-	8	-
Commission to Every Nation	1994	16	2	-	2	-
Compassion International, Inc.	1976	-	-	-	25	-

	First Year	Personnel from U.S. 4+ yrs.	2-4 yrs.	1-2 yrs.	Other Countries Citizens	Not Citizens
Correll Missionary Ministries	1983	5	-	-	2	-
Cumberland Presbyterian Church	2002	-	-	2	-	-
Eastern Mennonite Missions		8	2	-	-	-
Engineering Ministries International	2000	3	-	-	1	-
Evangel Bible Translators	1999	2	-	-	-	-
Evangelical Friends Church Southwest	1902	2	-	2	-	-
Evangelical Lutheran Church in America	1990	1	-	-	-	-
Evangelism Explosion International		-	-	-	-	2
Evangelistic Faith Missions	1947	-	2	-	-	-
Faith Christian Fellowship Intl.	1991	6	-	-	-	-
Fellowship International Mission	1997	1	-	-	-	-
Food for the Hungry, Inc.	1976	2	4	-	-	-
Global Fellowship		-	-	-	-	2
Global Outreach Mission		3	-	-	10	-
Global Outreach, Ltd.		-	-	1	-	-
Globe Missionary Evangelism	1976	7	-	-	-	-
Habitat for Humanity International	1979	-	2	-	15	-
Help for Christian Nationals, Inc.	1990	1	-	-	1	2
Hope for the Hungry		2	-	-	-	2
Hosanna/Faith Comes By Hearing	1998	-	-	-	4	-
Impact International	1970	2	-	-	4	-
International Gospel Outreach	1998	2	-	-	2	-
International Justice Mission		-	-	-	-	-
International Missionary Center		2	-	-	-	-
Intl. Pentecostal Holiness Ch. Wld. Mins.	1995	4	-	-	-	-
InterVarsity Christian Fellowship/USA		-	1	-	-	-
Kids Alive International	1997	-	4	-	-	2
Larry Jones International Ministries	1984	-	-	-	11	-
Living Water Teaching International	1979	-	-	-	-	-
Luis Palau Evangelistic Assoc.	1978	-	-	-	4	-
Lutheran Bible Translators	1996	8	1	-	7	-
Lutheran Church—Missouri Syn.	1947	4	2	4	-	-
Medical Ambassadors International	1983	-	-	1	8	-
Mission to the Americas	1990	2	-	-	6	-
Missionary Ventures International	1985	5	-	-	-	-
Mutual Faith Ministries Intl.		1	-	-	-	-
New Life League International	1976	6	-	-	-	-
OC International, Inc.	1979	7	6	4	9	-
Partners International	1964	-	-	-	-	-
Precept Ministries International	1983	-	-	-	1	-
Presbyterian Church (USA)		14	-	20	-	-
Primitive Methodist Church in the USA		5	-	-	-	-
Ripe for Harvest, Inc.	1995	5	2	4	-	-
SIM USA		2	-	-	-	-
The Mission Society	1985	2	-	-	-	-
UFM International	2001	2	-	-	-	-
United Church Board for World Ministries		-	1	-	-	-
Walk Thru The Bible Ministries	2000	-	-	-	2	-
Word of Life Fellowship	1998	-	-	-	2	4
World Baptist Fellowship Mission Agency		2	-	2	-	-
World-Wide Missions	1968	-	-	-	15	-
Wycliffe Associates USA	1998	-	2	-	-	-
Totals:		256	49	45	192	98

	First Year	Personnel from U.S.			Other Countries	
		4+ yrs.	2-4 yrs.	1-2 yrs.	Citizens	Not Citizens

Guinea

Campus Crusade for Christ, Intl.	1977	-	-	-	10	51
CBInternational	2003	4	-	-	-	-
Child Evangelism Fellowship, Inc.	1992	-	-	-	1	-
Christian and Missionary Alliance	1919	2	-	-	-	-
Christian Churches / Churches of Christ		15	5	-	-	-
Christian Reformed World Missions	1984	10	4	1	-	-
International Missionary Center		-	-	-	-	2
Lutheran Church—Missouri Syn.	1990	3	2	2	-	-
National Baptist Convention USA, Inc.	1990	1	-	-	-	-
New Tribes Mission	1988	23	-	-	-	-
Pioneer Bible Translators	1988	27	-	-	-	1
Seventh-day Adventists Gen. Conf.	1992	-	-	2	-	-
SIM USA	1986	13	-	-	-	-
WEC International	1984	1	-	-	-	8
World Partners USA	1995	12	-	-	-	-
	Totals:	111	11	5	11	62

Guinea-Bissau

Christian and Missionary Alliance	1991	15	8	-	-	-
Every Home for Christ International	1997	-	-	-	6	-
International Missionary Center		-	-	-	-	2
Seventh-day Adventists Gen. Conf.	1975	-	-	-	-	2
WEC International	1939	2	-	-	-	26
Youth for Christ / USA, World Outreach		4	-	-	-	-
	Totals:	21	8	-	6	30

Guyana

Baptist Mid-Missions	1954	2	-	-	-	-
BCM International		-	-	-	4	-
Bible Missionary Church		4	-	-	-	-
Campus Crusade for Christ, Intl.	1977	-	-	-	8	-
Christ Community Church	1947	-	-	-	3	-
Christian Churches / Churches of Christ		-	-	-	2	-
Church of God of Prophecy		-	-	-	2	-
Church of the Nazarene	1946	-	-	-	-	-
Churches of Christ	1982	8	-	-	-	-
Evangelical Lutheran Church in America	1916	2	-	-	-	-
Global Outreach Mission		1	-	-	-	-
Global Outreach, Ltd.		5	-	-	-	-
Habitat for Humanity International	1995	-	4	-	-	-
Seventh-day Adventists Gen. Conf.	1883	-	-	-	-	1
Source of Light Ministries Intl., Inc.	1960	-	-	-	1	-
TMA Ministries	1996	2	-	-	-	-
UFM International	1949	18	-	-	-	-
Wesleyan World Missions	1913	-	3	-	-	-
	Totals:	42	7	-	20	1

Haiti

Allegheny Wesleyan Methodist Missions	1969	9	-	-	-	-
American Baptist Churches in the U.S.A.	1923	6	-	-	-	2
AMG International		-	-	-	9	-

	First Year	Personnel from U.S. 4+ yrs.	2-4 yrs.	1-2 yrs.	Other Countries Citizens	Not Citizens
Assemblies of God World Missions	1945	4	-	4	-	-
Baptist Bible Fellowship Intl.	1982	1	4	-	-	-
Baptist Mid-Missions	1934	5	-	-	-	-
Bible League, The	2001	-	-	-	6	-
Campus Crusade for Christ, Intl.	1977	-	-	-	4	-
Child Evangelism Fellowship, Inc.	1946	2	-	-	1	-
Childcare International	1986	-	-	-	5	-
Christian Aid Ministries	1991	-	18	-	29	-
Christian Aid Mission		-	-	-	20	-
Christian Churches/Churches of Christ		4	4	-	30	-
Christian Reformed World Missions	1985	6	-	2	-	-
Christian Reformed World Relief Comte.	1975	1	-	-	1	2
Christian Service International	1963	5	-	-	17	-
Church of God (Cleveland, TN)	1933	4	-	-	-	-
Church of God of Prophecy		-	-	-	10	-
Church of the Nazarene	1950	4	4	-	-	-
Churches of Christ	1989	2	-	-	-	-
Churches of God, General Conference	1967	4	2	-	150	-
Compassion International, Inc.	1968	-	-	-	41	-
Development Associates Intl. (DAI)	2001	-	-	-	-	-
East West Ministries	1992	-	-	-	2	-
Elim Fellowship, Intl. Dept.	1986	2	-	-	-	2
Emmanuel Intl. Mission (U.S.)		-	-	-	-	-
Evangelical Baptist Missions		2	2	-	-	-
Floresta USA, Inc.	1996	-	-	-	12	-
FOCAS	1986	-	-	-	6	-
Free Methodist World Missions	1964	7	-	-	-	-
Global Outreach, Ltd.		8	-	-	-	-
Global Strategy Mission Assoc.	1988	2	-	-	-	-
Globe Missionary Evangelism	1997	2	-	-	-	-
Good Shepherd Ministries		-	-	-	49	-
Habitat for Humanity International	1981	-	3	-	-	-
Haiti Lutheran Mission Society		-	-	-	59	-
Harvest		-	-	-	3	-
Have Christ Will Travel Ministries	1966	-	-	-	10	-
Hope for the Hungry	1982	3	-	-	1	2
Hope Missions Outreach International		3	-	-	-	-
International Justice Mission		-	-	-	-	-
International Partnership Ministries, Inc.	1982	-	-	-	45	-
Intl. Pentecostal Holiness Ch. World Mins.	1976	2	-	-	-	-
Larry Jones Intl. Ministries	1979	-	-	-	7	-
Lutheran Church—Missouri Syn.	2001	-	-	1	-	-
Medical Ambassadors International	1981	-	-	-	8	2
Ministries In Action	1974	1	-	-	2	3
Mission Aviation Fellowship	1981	7	-	-	-	-
Mission Possible, Inc.	1979	-	2	2	140	1
Mission to the Americas	1992	-	-	-	4	-
Missionary Ventures International	1999	1	-	-	-	-
National Baptist Convention of America	1975	-	-	-	25	-
New Directions International	1969	-	-	-	2	-
New Life League International	1975	2	-	-	-	-
OMS International, Inc.		6	1	-	-	3

	First Year	Personnel from U.S. 4+ yrs.	2-4 yrs.	1-2 yrs.	Other Countries Citizens	Not Citizens
Open Door Baptist Missions	1995	4	-	-	-	-
Pentecostal Church of God		2	-	-	-	-
Presbyterian Ch. (USA), Worldwide Mins.		6	-	-	-	-
Rehoboth Ministries, Inc		2	-	-	-	-
Seventh-day Adventists Gen. Conf.	1905	2	-	2	-	-
Society of St. Margaret	1927	2	-	-	2	-
Source of Light Ministries Intl., Inc.	1999	-	-	-	1	-
STEM International	1985	-	2	-	-	-
UFM International	1943	26	-	-	-	-
United Church Board for World Ministries		-	2	-	-	-
Wesleyan World Missions	1948	-	8	-	-	-
World Concern	1977	2	2	-	71	-
World Gospel Mission	1962	2	-	-	-	-
World Partners USA	1945	-	-	-	-	-
World Team	1936	7	-	-	-	-
World Vision Inc.	1959	-	-	-	-	-
World-Wide Missions	1963	-	-	-	6	-
	Totals:	160	54	11	778	17

Honduras

	First Year	4+ yrs.	2-4 yrs.	1-2 yrs.	Citizens	Not Citizens
Assemblies of God World Missions	1940	18	-	4	-	-
Baptist Bible Fellowship Intl.	1974	3	2	-	-	-
Baptist Medical & Dental Mission Intl., Inc.	1974	10	-	-	45	-
Baptist Mid-Missions	1959	8	-	-	-	-
Biblical Ministries Worldwide	1949	4	-	-	-	-
Brethren Assemblies		10	-	-	-	-
Brethren in Christ World Missions	1989	2	-	-	2	-
CAM International	1896	16	-	-	-	16
Campus Crusade for Christ, Intl.	1966	-	-	-	22	-
Christian Aid Mission		-	-	-	29	-
Christian Churches / Churches of Christ		19	-	2	2	-
Christian Reformed World Missions	1971	4	-	-	-	-
Christian Reformed World Relief Comte.	1974	1	1	-	1	2
Church of God (Cleveland, TN)	1944	10	-	-	-	-
Church of the Nazarene	1970	-	-	-	-	-
Churches of Christ	1978	8	-	-	8	-
Compassion International, Inc.	1974	-	-	-	15	-
Eastern Mennonite Missions		2	-	-	-	-
Evangelical Baptist Missions		-	-	-	-	-
Evangelical Friends Church Southwest	1960	-	2	-	-	-
Evangelistic Faith Missions	1968	-	4	-	-	-
Every Home for Christ International	1962	-	-	-	4	-
Flwshp. of Assoc. of Medical Evangelism	1997	-	-	-	-	3
General Baptists International		5	-	-	-	-
Global Outreach Mission		2	-	-	1	-
Global Outreach, Ltd.		6	-	4	-	-
Globe Missionary Evangelism	1982	2	-	-	-	-
Great Commission Ministries, Inc.		-	-	-	-	2
Habitat for Humanity International	1988	-	3	-	13	-
Harvest		-	-	-	1	-
Impact International	1975	2	-	-	1	-
International Aid		-	-	-	-	-

	First Year	Personnel from U.S.			Other Countries	
		4+ yrs.	2-4 yrs.	1-2 yrs.	Citizens	Not Citizens
International Gospel Outreach	1992	6	-	-	2	-
International Justice Mission		-	-	-	-	-
Intl. Pentecostal Holiness Ch. World Mins.	1993	2	-	-	-	2
International Teams, U.S.A.		-	-	-	-	1
Kids Alive International	2001	2	-	-	-	-
Larry Jones International Ministries	1983	-	-	-	7	-
Latin America Mission	1987	1	4	-	-	5
Living Water Teaching International	1983	-	-	-	-	-
Medical Ambassadors International	1999	-	-	-	3	-
Mission to the Americas	1951	8	-	-	10	-
Missionary Ventures International	1992	3	-	-	-	-
Northwest Medical Teams	1998	-	-	-	-	-
Pentecostal Church of God	1980	2	-	-	-	-
Presbyterian Church (USA)	1973	9	-	-	-	-
Reformed Church in America, Gen. Syn.	1995	-	-	-	5	-
Ripe for Harvest, Inc.	1994	2	1	1	-	-
Rock the World Youth Mission Alliance		-	-	-	-	-
Samaritan's Purse	1998	-	-	-	2	-
Seventh-day Adventists Gen. Conf.	1891	6	-	-	-	2
Shelter for Life International, Inc.	1998	-	1	-	-	-
South American Missionary Society	1981	5	1	-	-	4
STEM International	1996	-	-	-	-	-
TEAM (The Evangelical Alliance Mission)		8	-	-	-	-
Teen Missions International	1990	3	-	-	3	-
The Ch. of God of the Apostolic Faith, Inc.	1989	1	-	-	-	-
United Church Board for World Mins.		-	2	-	-	-
Walk Thru The Bible Ministries	2002	-	-	-	2	-
Wesleyan World Missions	1957	-	2	-	-	-
Word of Life Fellowship	1998	2	-	-	-	1
World Baptist Fellowship Msn. Agency	1969	6	-	2	-	-
World Concern	1998	-	2	2	3	-
World Gospel Mission	1944	29	-	-	-	-
World Help	1994	-	-	-	1	-
World Reach, Inc.	1982	4	-	-	6	2
World Vision Inc.	1974	-	-	-	-	-
World-Wide Missions	1963	-	-	-	1	-
Youth for Christ/USA, World Outreach Div.		2	-	-	-	-
Totals:		233	25	15	189	40

Hong Kong

	First Year	4+ yrs.	2-4 yrs.	1-2 yrs.	Citizens	Not Citizens
ABWE	1950	8	-	-	-	-
American Baptist Chs. U.S.A., Intl. Mins.	1842	4	-	-	-	-
Asian Outreach U.S.A.		-	-	-	-	-
Baptist Bible Fellowship Intl.	1969	4	-	-	-	-
Biblical Ministries Worldwide	1988	5	-	-	-	1
Brethren Assemblies		2	-	-	-	-
Campus Crusade for Christ, Intl.	1972	-	-	-	119	-
CBInternational	1963	6	-	-	-	-
Child Evangelism Fellowship, Inc.	1948	1	-	-	-	2
Christian Churches/Churches of Christ		10	-	-	4	-
Church of God (Anderson, IND)		2	-	-	-	-
Church of the Nazarene	1974	-	-	-	-	-

		Personnel from U.S.			Other Countries	
	First Year	4+ yrs.	2-4 yrs.	1-2 yrs.	Citizens	Not Citizens
CLC Ministries International	1976	2	-	-	-	-
Cumberland Presbyterian Church	2001	-	1	-	-	-
East Gates Ministries Intl.	1990	-	-	-	3	-
Eastern Mennonite Missions		4	-	-	-	-
Evangelical Free Church Mission	1987	6	1	-	-	-
Evangelical Lutheran Church in America	1890	11	-	-	-	-
Free Methodist World Missions	1951	3	-	-	-	-
General Conf. Mennonite Church	1980	2	-	-	-	2
Kids Alive International	2002	-	-	-	2	-
Lutheran Church—Missouri Syn.	1950	19	12	7	-	-
Mennonite Mission Network	1980	2	-	-	-	2
Mission to the World (PCA), Inc.	1982	2	-	-	-	-
OMF International		3	-	-	-	-
OMS International, Inc.	1954	7	-	-	-	-
Partners International	1950	-	-	-	-	-
Presbyterian Church (USA)		9	-	-	-	-
SEND International	1988	4	-	-	-	2
TEAM (The Evangelical Alliance Mission)		6	-	-	-	-
Training Evangelistic Leadership	1976	9	-	-	-	-
United Church Board for World Ministries		-	1	-	-	-
WEC International	1986	-	-	-	-	6
Wisconsin Evangelical Lutheran Syn.	1964	2	-	-	-	-
World-Wide Missions	1975	-	-	-	1	-
Worldwide Tentmakers, Inc.	2001	-	-	-	-	-
Wycliffe Bible Translators USA		1	-	-	-	-
Totals:		134	15	7	129	15

Hungary

	First Year	4+ yrs.	2-4 yrs.	1-2 yrs.	Citizens	Not Citizens
ABWE	1990	30	-	-	-	-
Assemblies of God World Missions	1926	6	-	-	-	-
Baptist Bible Fellowship Intl.	1990	8	-	-	-	-
BCM International		-	-	-	4	-
Bethany Fellowship Missions	1999	2	-	-	-	-
Bible League, The	1997	-	-	-	2	-
Brethren Assemblies		1	-	-	-	-
Campus Crusade for Christ, Intl.	1978	58	-	22	65	3
CBInternational	1991	6	-	1	-	-
Centers for Apologetics Research (CFAR)	2000	-	-	-	1	-
Child Evangelism Fellowship, Inc.	1989	1	-	-	5	2
Christ to the Nations	1999	2	-	-	2	-
Christian Aid Mission		-	-	-	18	-
Christian Reformed World Missions	1990	6	-	3	-	-
Church of God (Anderson, Indiana)		2	-	-	-	-
Church of God of Prophecy		-	-	-	1	-
Church of the Nazarene	1996	-	-	-	-	-
Church Resource Ministries	1987	10	-	-	-	-
Churches of Christ	1971	11	-	3	-	-
Eastern Mennonite Missions		3	-	-	-	-
Evangelical Free Church Mission	1997	12	-	-	8	-
Free Methodist World Missions	1998	7	-	-	-	-
General Conf. Mennonite Church	1993	2	-	-	-	-
Globe Missionary Evangelism	1995	-	2	-	-	-

	Personnel from U.S.				Other Countries	
	First Year	4+ yrs.	2-4 yrs.	1-2 yrs.	Citizens	Not Citizens
Greater Europe Mission	1996	7	3	-	-	-
Greater Grace World Outreach	1990	-	-	-	1	8
Habitat for Humanity International	1994	2	1	-	-	3
International Messengers	1992	2	1	-	9	1
Intl. Pentecostal Holiness Ch. World Mins.	1989	2	-	-	-	-
International Teams, U.S.A.		1	-	-	-	1
Lutheran Church—Missouri Syn.	1991	-	-	2	-	-
Mennonite Mission Network	1993	-	-	-	-	-
Mission to the World (PCA), Inc.		-	2	-	-	-
Mission To Unreached Peoples	1996	4	-	-	-	-
Navigators, U.S. Intl. Missions Group		-	-	1	-	-
OMS International, Inc.		1	4	-	-	4
Open Bible Standard Churches, Intl. Mins.	1996	1	-	-	-	-
Operation Mobilization, Inc.		4	-	3	-	-
Pioneers	1992	5	-	-	4	-
Project Care		-	-	-	-	-
Reformed Church in America, Gen. Syn.	1996	2	-	-	1	-
Ripe for Harvest, Inc.	1996	2	-	-	-	-
SEND International	1994	6	-	1	-	-
The Mission Society	2001	2	-	-	-	-
United Church Bd. for World Mins.		-	2	-	-	-
Walk Thru The Bible Ministries	2000	-	-	-	2	-
Westminister Biblical Missions	1990	1	-	-	10	3
Word of Life Fellowship	1987	14	-	-	14	3
World Gospel Mission	1992	4	-	-	-	-
World Indigenous Missions	1999	-	3	-	-	-
Wycliffe Bible Translators USA		2	-	-	-	-
Totals:		229	18	36	147	28

Iceland

Assemblies of God World Missions		2	-	1	-	-
Baptist Bible Fellowship Intl.	1998	1	-	3	-	-
Greater Europe Mission	1985	2	-	-	-	-
Navigators, U.S. Intl. Missions Group	1967	2	-	-	-	-
Totals:		7	-	4	-	-

India

ABWE		2	-	-	-	-
Action International Ministries	1990	-	-	-	6	1
Advancing Native Missions	1993	-	-	-	2	-
Advent Christian General Conf.	1882	2	-	-	55	-
American Baptist Chs. U.S.A., Intl. Mins.	1836	6	-	-	-	-
AMG International	1970	2	-	-	115	-
Armenian Msny. Assoc. of America, Inc.	1999	-	-	-	-	-
Assoc. of Free Lutheran Congregations		-	-	-	30	-
Audio Scripture Ministries		-	-	-	5	-
Audio Scriptures International		-	-	-	-	-
Back to the Bible International	1970	-	-	-	37	-
Baptist General Conference		1	-	-	-	-
Baptist International Outreach	1993	-	-	-	2	-
Baptist Mid-Missions	1935	8	-	-	5	-
BCM International		-	-	-	298	-

	First Year	4+ yrs.	2-4 yrs.	1-2 yrs.	Other Countries Citizens	Not Citizens
		Personnel from U.S.			Other Countries	
Bible League, The	1997	-	-	-	53	-
Bible Training Centre for Pastors	1999	-	-	-	3	-
Bibles For The World, Inc.	1972	-	-	-	400	-
BILD International		-	-	-	-	-
Brethren Assemblies		7	-	-	-	-
Brethren in Christ World Missions	1904	-	-	-	17	-
Bright Hope International	1997	-	-	-	15	-
Campus Crusade for Christ, Intl.	1963	2	-	-	3649	34
Caring Partners International, Inc.	1991	-	-	-	-	-
CBInternational	1945	7	-	-	-	-
Childcare International	1981	-	-	-	74	-
Christ for India, Inc.	1981	1	-	-	1	-
Christar	1930	18	4	-	-	-
Christian Aid Mission		-	-	-	1282	-
Christian Church of North America Missions	1965	4	-	-	-	-
Christian Churches / Churches of Christ		17	-	-	35	-
Christian Discipleship Ministries, Inc.	1994	1	-	-	5	2
Christians In Action, Inc.	1972	-	-	-	4	-
Church of God of Prophecy		-	-	-	25	-
Church of the Nazarene	1898	2	-	-	-	-
Church of the United Brethren in Christ	1977	2	-	-	-	-
Churches of Christ	1960	9	-	-	10	-
Churches of God, General Conference	1898	-	-	-	15	-
Clark Theol. College (India) Tribal Mins., USA	1993	-	-	-	-	-
Commission to Every Nation	1998	-	3	10	2	-
Compassion International, Inc.	1968	-	-	-	40	-
Correll Missionary Ministries	1978	-	-	-	20	-
Dayspring Enterprises International	1979	-	-	-	-	-
Development Associates Intl. (DAI)	1995	-	-	-	2	-
East West Ministries	1993	-	-	-	10	-
East-West Ministries International		-	-	-	10	-
Engineering Ministries International	1988	2	4	-	2	-
Evangel Bible Translators	1978	6	-	-	8	-
Evangelical Free Church Mission	1995	3	-	-	15	-
Evangelical Friends Mission	1992	2	-	-	2	-
Evangelical Lutheran Ch. in America	1842	1	-	-	-	-
Evangelical Presbyterian Church	1996	2	-	-	-	-
Evangelism Explosion International		2	-	-	-	-
Evangelism Resources	1991	-	-	-	17	-
Every Home for Christ International	1965	-	-	-	325	-
Final Frontiers Foundation, Inc.	1989	-	-	-	320	-
Food for the Hungry, Inc.	1998	-	1	-	-	-
Free Will Baptists, Inc., National Assoc.	1935	1	-	-	-	-
Frontier Mission Fellowship		2	-	2	-	-
General Baptists International		-	-	1	-	-
General Conf. Mennonite Church	1900	2	-	-	-	2
Global Action	1998	-	-	-	10	-
Global Fellowship		-	-	-	290	-
Global Outreach Mission		2	-	-	16	-
Global Outreach, Ltd.		2	-	-	-	-
Globe Missionary Evangelism	1988	5	-	-	-	-
Go Ye Fellowship	2001	-	2	-	-	-

	First Year	4+ yrs.	2-4 yrs.	1-2 yrs.	Citizens	Not Citizens
		Personnel from U.S.			Other Countries	
Good News for India	1986	-	-	-	53	-
Good News Productions Intl.	1989	2	-	-	10	-
Gospel for Asia	1979	-	-	-	-	-
Gospel Outreach Ministries Intl.	1988	-	-	-	250	-
Gospel Revival Ministries	1995	-	-	-	187	-
Grace Ministries International	1969	-	-	-	-	2
Greater Grace World Outreach	1984	-	-	-	8	1
Habitat for Humanity International	1983	-	3	-	11	3
Harvest		-	-	-	1	-
Have Christ Will Travel Ministries	1995	-	-	-	18	-
HBI Global Partners	1984	1	-	-	177	-
Help for Christian Nationals, Inc.	1994	1	-	-	3	-
Hope for the Hungry		1	-	-	1	-
Hosanna / Faith Comes By Hearing	1994	-	-	-	5	-
Hundredfold Ministries International	1993	-	-	-	-	-
India Evangelical Mission, Inc.	1966	-	-	-	525	-
India National Inland Mission	1964	-	-	-	330	-
India Partners	2001	-	-	-	1	-
India Rural Evangelical Fellowship	1950	-	-	-	127	-
International Gospel Outreach	1965	-	-	-	2	-
International Justice Mission	2000	-	2	-	10	2
International Missionary Center		2	-	-	-	2
International Needs - USA	1979	-	-	-	202	-
International Partnership Ministries, Inc.	1988	-	-	-	86	-
Intl. Pentecostal Church of Christ		1	-	-	-	-
Intl. Pentecostal Holiness Ch. World Mins.	1911	2	-	-	-	-
InterServe/USA	1852	7	-	-	-	-
Josue Yrion World Evangelism Msns., Inc.	1997	-	-	-	6	-
Literacy & Evangelism International		-	-	-	-	-
Lutheran Church—Missouri Syn.	1895	2	-	2	-	-
M/E Intl., Inc. (Missionary Electronics)	1985	-	-	-	92	-
MBMS International	1898	-	3	-	80	-
Medical Ambassadors International	1982	-	-	-	38	-
Mennonite Mission Network	1899	-	-	-	-	-
Mission of Mercy	1954	1	-	1	-	-
Mission ONE, Inc.		-	-	-	-	-
Mission to the World (PCA), Inc.	1973	8	-	-	-	-
Mission To Unreached Peoples	1987	8	-	-	6	-
Missionary Gospel Fellowship	2002	1	-	-	1	-
Missionary Ventures International	1985	1	-	-	-	-
Missions To Japan, Inc.		1	-	-	-	-
Mustard Seed, Inc., The	1998	2	-	1	13	-
New Directions International	1986	-	-	-	32	-
New Life League International	1970	-	-	-	2	-
New Tribes Mission	1945	1	-	-	-	-
OC International, Inc.	1984	-	-	-	4	1
OMS International, Inc.		-	-	-	-	2
Open Air Campaigners - Overseas Ministries	1990	-	-	-	16	-
Open Door Baptist Missions	1995	-	-	-	2	-
Operation Mobilization, Inc.	1964	5	-	2	-	-
Paraclete, Inc.		-	-	-	-	-
Partners International	1969	-	-	-	-	-

	First Year	4+ yrs.	2-4 yrs.	1-2 yrs.	Other Countries Citizens	Not Citizens
Pentecostal Church of God		2	-	-	-	-
Perimeter Church, Global Outreach	1998	-	-	-	15	-
Prakash Association USA	1973	1	-	-	11	-
Precept Ministries International	2000	-	-	-	5	-
Presbyterian Ch. (USA), Worldwide Mins.		-	-	21	-	-
Presbyterian Evangelistic Fellowship		-	-	-	5	-
Project Christ International	1984	-	-	-	120	-
Project Partner with Christ	1982	-	-	-	1	-
Ramabai Mukti Mission	1929	-	-	-	100	-
Ravi Zacharias International Ministries		2	-	-	-	-
Reach Ministries International		-	-	-	2	-
Reformed Church in America, Gen. Syn.	1990	4	-	-	-	-
Ripe for Harvest, Inc.	1997	2	1	1	-	-
Salvation Army, U.S.A.	1882	2	-	-	-	-
SAND International	1985	-	-	-	1	-
Seventh-day Adventists Gen. Conf.	1895	4	4	2	-	3
SIM USA	1893	24	-	3	-	-
Source of Light Ministries International, Inc.	1978	-	-	-	13	-
TEAM (The Evangelical Alliance Mission)		2	-	-	-	-
Teen Missions International	1983	-	-	-	2	-
The Master's Mission, Inc.	1998	-	-	-	2	-
The Mission Society	1995	2	-	-	-	-
Third World Baptist Missions	1996	2	-	-	35	-
Training Evangelistic Leadership	1975	2	-	-	15	-
United Church Board for World Ministries		-	4	-	-	-
Walk Thru The Bible Ministries	1998	-	-	-	28	-
Wisconsin Evangelical Lutheran Syn.	1970	3	-	-	-	-
World Gospel Mission	1937	2	-	-	-	-
World Harvest Mission	1998	4	-	-	-	-
World Help	1996	-	-	-	100	-
World Indigenous Missions		-	-	-	-	-
World Missions Far Corners, Inc.	1965	-	-	-	1500	-
World Partners USA	1900	-	-	-	-	-
World Vision Inc.	1953	-	-	-	-	-
WorldTeach	1990	-	-	-	-	-
World-Wide Missions	1965	-	-	-	32	-
Totals:	228	31	46	11,518	55

Indonesia

	First Year	4+ yrs.	2-4 yrs.	1-2 yrs.	Citizens	Not Citizens
Advancing Native Missions	1995	-	-	-	1	-
AMG International	1975	-	-	-	124	-
Apostolic Christian Ch. Foundation, Inc.	1986	2	-	-	-	-
Asian Outreach U.S.A.		-	-	-	-	-
Assemblies of God World Missions	1937	19	-	16	-	-
Back to the Bible International	2001	-	-	-	3	-
Bethany Fellowship Missions	1971	3	-	-	-	2
Bethel Christian Ministries		2	-	-	-	-
Bible League, The	1997	-	-	-	15	-
Brethren Assemblies		3	-	-	-	-
Campus Crusade for Christ, Intl.	1968	2	-	-	506	2
CBInternational	1961	8	-	2	-	-
Christ Community Church	2001	-	-	-	-	2

	Personnel from U.S.				Other Countries	
	First Year	4+ yrs.	2-4 yrs.	1-2 yrs.	Citizens	Not Citizens
Christ for the Lost World	1983	-	-	-	101	-
Christ to the Nations	1998	2	-	-	2	-
Christian Aid Mission		-	-	-	54	-
Christian and Missionary Alliance	1929	40	1	-	-	-
Christian Churches / Churches of Christ		15	-	-	-	-
Christian Reformed World Relief Comte.	1984	-	1	-	1	-
Church of God (Cleveland, TN)	1967	2	-	-	-	-
Church of God of Prophecy		-	-	-	2	-
Church of the Nazarene	1973	4	-	-	-	-
Church World Service & Witness		-	1	-	10	-
Churches of Christ	1967	5	-	-	4	-
CMF International	1978	3	2	1	2	-
Compassion International, Inc.	1968	-	-	-	29	-
Evangelical Friends Church Southwest		-	-	-	-	-
Evangelical Lutheran Church in America	1970	2	-	-	-	-
Evangelical Presbyterian Church	2001	2	-	-	-	-
Evangelism Explosion International		-	-	-	-	10
Every Home for Christ International	1974	-	-	-	6	-
Far East Broadcasting Company, Inc.	1951	-	-	-	80	-
Go Ye Fellowship	1988	1	-	-	1	-
Hope for the Hungry		1	-	-	-	1
Hosanna / Faith Comes By Hearing	2001	-	-	-	2	-
International Gospel Outreach	1989	2	-	-	1	-
International Justice Mission		-	-	-	-	-
International Outreach Ministries	1996	1	-	-	-	-
International Teams, U.S.A.		-	-	-	-	5
Lutheran Church—Missouri Syn.	1996	2	2	3	-	-
Medical Ambassadors International	1998	-	-	-	-	2
Mission Aviation Fellowship	1952	57	3	4	-	-
Mission ONE, Inc.		-	-	-	-	-
Mission to the World (PCA), Inc.	1977	9	-	-	-	-
Missionary Ventures International	2002	1	-	-	-	-
Mustard Seed, Inc., The	1972	2	-	-	230	-
Navigators, U.S. Intl. Missions Group		8	-	1	-	-
Network of Intl. Christian Schools	1995	-	25	-	-	-
New Tribes Mission	1970	70	-	-	2	2
OC International, Inc.	1968	15	4	-	3	-
Omega World Missions		2	-	-	-	-
OMF International		15	-	-	-	-
OMS International, Inc.		6	2	-	-	3
Partners International	1971	-	-	-	-	-
Pocket Testament League	1976	-	-	-	10	-
Presbyterian Church (USA)		14	-	-	-	-
Seventh-day Adventists Gen. Conf.	1900	6	-	-	-	6
TEAM		2	-	-	-	-
Things To Come Mission, Inc.	1971	-	-	-	2	2
Training Evangelistic Leadership	1970	4	-	-	16	-
UFM International	1957	27	-	1	1	2
United Church Board for World Ministries		-	2	-	-	-
Walk Thru The Bible Ministries	2001	-	-	-	5	-
Wisconsin Evangelical Lutheran Syn.	1969	1	-	-	-	-
World Baptist Fellowship Mission Agency		5	-	-	-	-

		Personnel from U.S.			Other Countries	
	First Year	4+ yrs.	2-4 yrs.	1-2 yrs.	Citizens	Not Citizens
World Indigenous Missions	1994	2	-	-	1	-
World Partners USA	1992	2	-	-	-	-
World Team	1948	18	-	-	-	-
World Vision Inc.	1961	-	-	-	-	-
Wycliffe Associates USA	1997	-	2	-	-	-
Wycliffe Bible Translators USA		267	-	-	-	-
Totals:		654	45	28	1214	39

Iran

Armenian Msny. Assoc. of America, Inc.	1950	-	-	-	-	-
Mennonite Mission Network	2001	-	-	-	-	-
Partners International	2002	-	-	-	-	-
World Witness, Assoc. Reformed Presb. Ch.	1993	2	-	-	-	-
Totals:		2	-	-	-	-

Iraq

Mission ONE, Inc.		-	-	-	-	-
Partners International	1997	-	-	-	-	-
Totals:		-	-	-	-	-

Ireland

Assemblies of God World Missions		8	-	8	-	-
Baptist Bible Fellowship Intl.	1977	5	2	-	-	-
Baptist Mid-Missions	1978	6	-	-	-	-
BCM International		5	-	-	4	-
Biblical Ministries Worldwide	1975	5	-	-	-	2
Brethren Assemblies		9	2	-	-	2
CBInternational	1991	4	-	-	-	-
Christian Churches / Churches of Christ		6	-	1	-	-
Church of God (Cleveland, TN)	1995	5	-	-	-	1
Church of the Nazarene	1987	-	-	-	-	2
Elim Fellowship, Intl. Dept.	2001	-	-	2	-	2
European Christian Mission NA, Inc.		1	-	-	-	-
Evangelical Friends Mission	1998	3	-	-	-	-
Global Outreach Mission	1965	10	-	-	-	1
Grace Brethren International Missions	2002	2	-	-	-	-
Greater Europe Mission	1974	13	-	-	-	-
Greater Grace World Outreach	1992	-	-	-	1	-
International Teams, U.S.A.		-	2	-	-	-
Ireland Outreach International Inc.	1970	4	2	-	-	3
Mennonite Mission Network	1978	2	-	-	-	-
Mission to the World (PCA), Inc.	1995	4	-	-	-	-
Missionary Ventures International	1998	2	-	-	-	-
OMS International, Inc.		6	-	-	-	-
Operation Mobilization, Inc.		2	-	-	-	-
Reformed Baptist Mission Services		-	-	-	1	-
TEAM (The Evangelical Alliance Mission)		11	-	-	-	-
Team Expansion, Inc.	1987	7	2	1	1	-
UFM International	1980	5	-	-	1	3
Walk Thru The Bible Ministries	2000	-	-	-	1	-
World Baptist Fellowship Mission Agency		2	-	2	-	-
World Harvest Mission	1986	5	1	-	-	-
Totals:		132	11	14	9	16

		Personnel from U.S.			Other Countries	
	First Year	4+ yrs.	2-4 yrs.	1-2 yrs.	Citizens	Not Citizens

Irian Jaya

TEAM (The Evangelical Alliance Mission)		16	-	-	-	-
Totals:		16	-	-	-	-

Israel

AMF International	1930	2	-	-	3	1
Assemblies of God World Missions	1917	-	-	12	-	-
Child Evangelism Fellowship, Inc.	1951	2	-	-	2	-
Chosen People Ministries	1968	-	-	-	-	-
Christian and Missionary Alliance	1890	10	2	-	-	-
Christian Churches / Churches of Christ		2	-	-	1	-
Church of God (Cleveland, TN)	1964	7	-	-	-	4
Church of God of Prophecy		-	-	-	-	2
Church of the Nazarene	1921	3	-	-	-	2
Churches of Christ	1960	-	-	-	7	-
Commission to Every Nation	1999	2	1	-	-	-
Evangelical Lutheran Church in America	1967	4	-	-	-	-
Foursquare Missions International	1996	2	-	-	-	-
General Conf. Mennonite Church	1954	2	-	-	-	-
Global Outreach, Ltd.		2	-	-	-	-
High Adventure Mins. / Voice of Hope	1979	1	-	-	17	-
Hope for the Hungry		1	-	-	1	-
International Students, Inc		1	-	-	-	-
International Teams, U.S.A.		-	-	-	-	1
Jews for Jesus	1994	1	-	-	2	-
Mennonite Mission Network	1953	6	-	-	-	-
Missionary Ventures International	1997	1	-	-	-	-
New Life League International		-	-	-	-	-
Open Door Baptist Missions	1997	2	-	-	-	-
Operation Mobilization, Inc.		4	-	1	-	-
Presbyterian Church (USA)		4	-	-	-	-
Reformed Baptist Mission Services		2	-	-	1	-
Seed International	2000	2	-	-	-	-
Seventh-day Adventists Gen. Conf.	1898	-	-	-	-	4
The Master's Mission, Inc.	1990	-	-	-	1	-
United Church Bd. for World Mins.		-	2	-	-	-
Venture International	1987	-	-	-	1	-
Totals:		63	5	13	36	14

Italy

ABWE	1989	14	-	-	-	-
AMG International	2002	2	-	-	-	-
Assemblies of God World Missions	1949	4	-	3	-	-
Aurora Mission	1978	3	-	-	5	5
Back to the Bible International	1961	-	-	-	9	-
Baptist Mid-Missions	1951	2	-	-	-	-
BCM International		6	-	-	2	-
Biblical Ministries Worldwide	1962	8	-	-	-	-
Brethren Assemblies		5	-	-	1	-
Cadence International		-	2	-	-	2
Calvary International	2001	1	-	-	-	1
Campus Crusade for Christ, Intl.	1969	3	-	1	-	1

		Personnel from U.S.			Other Countries	
	First Year	4+ yrs.	2-4 yrs.	1-2 yrs.	Citizens	Not Citizens
CBInternational	1946	10	2	1	-	-
Christian Ch. of North America Missions	1927	1	-	-	-	-
Christian Churches / Churches of Christ		14	-	-	6	-
Church of God (Cleveland, TN)	1959	1	-	-	-	2
Church of the Nazarene	1948	2	2	-	-	-
Churches of Christ	1948	28	-	-	11	-
CLC Ministries International	1956	2	-	-	-	-
European Christian Mission NA, Inc.		2	-	-	-	-
Evangelical Baptist Missions	1983	2	-	-	-	-
Every Home for Christ International	1958	-	-	-	1	-
Foursquare Missions International	1993	2	-	-	-	-
Gospel Fellowship Association	1983	2	-	-	-	-
Gospel Missionary Union	1950	12	1	-	-	-
Great Commission Ministries, Inc.	-	4	-	-	-	
Greater Europe Mission	1956	8	-	-	-	-
Independent Faith Mission	1950	5	-	-	-	-
International Teams, U.S.A.	1980	4	-	-	-	-
InterVarsity Christian Fellowship/USA	1984	3	1	-	-	-
Italy for Christ	1983	2	-	2	1	3
Mission to the World (PCA), Inc.	1988	2	-	-	-	-
Navigators, U.S. Intl. Missions Group		4	-	-	-	-
Operation Mobilization, Inc.	1962	2	2	2	-	-
Presbyterian Church (USA)		2	-	-	-	-
Salvation Army, U.S.A.	1887	1	-	-	-	-
Seventh-day Adventists Gen. Conf.	1877	2	-	-	-	-
SIM USA	1979	2	-	-	-	-
Spiritual Growth Resources, Inc.	1984	2	-	-	6	-
TEAM (The Evangelical Alliance Mission)	1950	19	-	1	-	-
Team Expansion, Inc.	2000	9	-	-	-	-
UFM International	1974	20	-	-	1	1
Virginia Mennonite Board of Missions	1949	2	2	-	6	2
WEC International	1964	4	-	-	-	10
Word of Life Fellowship	1985		-	-	3	2
World Harvest Mission	2000	2	-	-	-	-
World Team	1997	2	-	-	-	-
World-Wide Missions	1999	-	-	-	2	-
Youth for Christ/USA, World Outreach		2	-	-	-	-
Totals:		225	16	10	54	29

Jamaica

Assemblies of God World Missions	1942	8	-	14	-	-
Back to the Bible International	1958	-	-	-	7	-
Baptist Bible Fellowship Intl.	1972	6	-	-	-	-
Baptist Mid-Missions	1939	-	-	-	-	-
BCM International		-	-	-	2	-
Calvary International	1996	1	-	-	-	1
Campus Crusade for Christ, Intl.	1990	-	-	-	2	-
Christian Churches / Churches of Christ		12	-	-	6	-
Christian Service International	1979	5	-	-	5	-
Church of the Nazarene	1966	-	-	-	-	-
Churches of Christ	1930	1	-	-	-	-
Elim Fellowship, Intl. Dept.	1998	4	-	-	-	4

	First Year	4+ yrs.	2-4 yrs.	1-2 yrs.	Citizens	Not Citizens
		Personnel from U.S.			Other Countries	
Evangelical Lutheran Ch. in America	1990	2	-	-	-	-
Faith Christian Fellowship Intl.	1989	2	-	2	-	-
General Baptists International		-	2	-	-	-
Grand Old Gospel Fellowship		-	-	-	1	-
Habitat for Humanity International	1993	-	1	-	3	-
Lutheran Church—Missouri Syn.	1993	2	-	3	-	-
Ministries In Action	1974	-	-	-	1	-
Mission to the World (PCA), Inc.	1981	5	1	-	-	-
National Baptist Convention of America	1945	-	-	-	38	-
Open Air Campaigners - Overseas Mins.	1984	-	-	-	2	-
Presbyterian Ch. (USA), Worldwide Mins.	1981	5	-	-	-	-
Reformed Baptist Mission Services	1985	2	-	-	1	-
Salvation Army, U.S.A.	1887	7	-	-	-	-
Seventh-day Adventists Gen. Conf.	1893	4	12	2	-	2
Source of Light Ministries Int., Inc.	1952	-	-	-	2	-
STEM International	1985	-	-	-	-	-
United Church Board for World Mins.		-	2	-	-	-
Virginia Mennonite Board of Missions	1955	2	-	2	-	-
World Partners USA	1946	2	-	-	-	-
World Servants	1989	-	-	-	1	-
Totals:		70	18	23	71	7

Japan

	First Year	4+ yrs.	2-4 yrs.	1-2 yrs.	Citizens	Not Citizens
ABWE	1953	15	-	-	-	-
Advent Christian General Conf.	1898	2	-	-	-	-
American Baptist Chs. in the U.S.A.	1872	12	-	-	1	-
Apostolic Christian Ch. Foundation, Inc.	1985	2	-	-	-	-
Artists In Christian Testimony	1981	2	-	-	-	-
Asian Outreach U.S.A.		-	-	-	-	-
Assemblies of God World Missions	1913	36	-	21	-	-
Baptist Bible Fellowship Intl.	1948	20	2	2	-	-
Baptist General Conference	1948	20	-	-	-	-
Baptist Mid-Missions	1949	13	-	-	4	-
Bethany Fellowship Missions	1985	2	-	-	-	4
Bethel Christian Ministries		4	2	-	-	-
Bible Missionary Church		2	-	-	-	-
Biblical Ministries Worldwide	1987	2	-	-	-	-
Brethren Assemblies		7	1	-	-	2
Cadence International		-	18	-	-	18
Calvary International	1999	1	-	-	-	1
Campus Crusade for Christ, Intl.	1962	15	-	1	31	29
CBInternational	1947	22	-	1	-	-
Child Evangelism Fellowship, Inc.	1948	-	-	-	-	2
Christ Community Church	1951	-	-	-	2	-
Christar	1950	12	-	-	-	-
Christian and Missionary Alliance	1891	10	-	-	-	-
Christian Churches / Churches of Christ		30	4	-	-	-
Christian Reformed World Missions	1951	10	4	-	-	-
Christians In Action, Inc.	1957	2	-	-	-	2
Church of God (Anderson, IND)		4	-	-	-	-
Church of God of Prophecy		2	-	-	-	-
Church of the Nazarene	1905	2	-	-	-	-

	Personnel from U.S.				Other Countries	
	First Year	4+ yrs.	2-4 yrs.	1-2 yrs.	Citizens	Not Citizens
Church Resource Ministries	1998	4	-	-	-	-
Churches of Christ	1892	11	-	-	6	-
Equip, Inc.		1	-	-	-	-
Evangelical Baptist Missions		4	-	-	-	-
Evangelical Congregational Church		-	-	-	2	-
Evangelical Covenant Church	1949	9	4	-	-	-
Evangelical Free Church Mission	1949	23	2	-	-	-
Evangelical Lutheran Ch. in America	1892	19	-	12	-	-
Evangelical Presbyterian Church	1988	2	-	-	-	-
Every Home for Christ International	1953	-	-	-	5	-
Fellowship International Mission	1975	4	-	-	3	3
Food for the Hungry, Inc.	1982	-	1	-	-	-
Foursquare Missions International	1951	2	-	-	-	-
Free Will Baptists, Inc., National Assoc.	1954	10	-	1	-	-
General Conf. Mennonite Church	1950	3	-	-	-	7
Global Strategy Mission Assoc.	1993	-	2	-	-	-
Gospel Fellowship Association	1958	1	-	-	-	-
Grace Brethren International Missions	1984	4	-	-	-	2
Hope for the Hungry		1	-	-	-	1
Intl. Pentecostal Holiness Ch. World Mins.	1989	4	2	-	-	-
International Teams, U.S.A.		-	-	-	-	4
Japanese Evangelical Missionary Society	1953	-	-	2	6	-
Liberty Corner Mission		1	-	-	-	-
LIFE Ministries	1967	21	3	1	46	-
Lutheran Brethren World Missions		6	-	5	-	-
Lutheran Church—Missouri Syn.	1948	8	10	1	-	-
MBMS International	1950	-	4	2	-	-
Mennonite Mission Network	1949	7	-	-	-	1
Mission to the World (PCA), Inc.	1985	28	18	-	-	-
Mission To Unreached Peoples	1990	6	5	2	-	-
Navigators, U.S. Intl. Missions Group		16	-	12	-	-
Network of Intl. Christian Schools	2000	-	7	-	-	-
New Life League International		-	-	-	-	-
N. American Baptist Conf. Intl. Missions	1951	9	-	-	-	2
OC International, Inc.	1985	4	-	-	-	-
OMF International		20	-	-	-	-
OMS International, Inc.		13	-	-	-	2
Orthodox Presbyterian Church	1938	8	-	2	-	-
Pioneers	1998	6	-	-	-	-
Presbyterian Ch. (USA), Worldwide Mins.		4	34	-	-	-
Presbyterian Evangelistic Fellowship		2	-	-	-	-
Project AmaZon	1989	4	-	-	-	-
Reformed Church in America	1959	5	2	2	1	-
Ripe for Harvest, Inc.	1992	2	-	-	-	-
SEND International	1948	48	5	-	-	2
Seventh-day Adventists Gen. Conf.	1896	8	-	-	2	-
Source of Light Ministries Intl., Inc.	2000	-	-	-	2	-
TEAM (The Evangelical Alliance Mission)		101	-	10	-	-
The Mission Society	1997	2	-	-	-	-
Touch the World Ministries		5	-	-	-	-
United Church Board for World Mins.		-	15	-	-	-
Walk Thru The Bible Ministries	2002	-	-	-	2	-

	First Year	4+ yrs.	2-4 yrs.	1-2 yrs.	Other Countries Citizens	Not Citizens
WEC International	1950	-	-	-	-	20
Wisconsin Evangelical Lutheran Syn.	1952	5	1	-	-	-
Word of Life Fellowship	1981	-	-	-	5	-
World Gospel Mission	1952	4	-	-	-	-
Wycliffe Bible Translators USA		4	-	-	-	-
Totals:		698	146	77	118	102

Jordan

Assemblies of God World Missions	1929	-	-	2	-	-
Calvary International	1988	1	-	-	-	1
CBInternational	1956	6	-	-	-	-
Child Evangelism Fellowship, Inc.	1991	-	-	-	2	-
Christar	1990	12	4	-	-	-
Christian Aid Mission		-	-	-	43	-
Christian and Missionary Alliance	1890	3	-	-	-	-
Christian Blind Mission Intl.	1990	-	1	-	-	-
Church of the Nazarene	1950	-	1	-	-	-
Evangelical Presbyterian Church	2000	3	-	-	-	-
Global Outreach Mission		-	-	-	2	-
International Teams, U.S.A.	1995	2	-	-	-	-
Mission ONE, Inc.		-	-	-	-	-
Mission to the World (PCA), Inc.		2	-	-	-	-
Partners International	1997	-	-	-	-	-
Seed International	1999	2	-	-	-	-
Venture International	1987	-	-	-	1	-
Walk Thru The Bible Ministries	2000	-	-	-	2	-
World-Wide Missions	1987	-	-	-	5	-
Totals:		31	6	2	55	1

Kazakhstan

Christar	1991	6	6	-	-	-
Church of God of Prophecy		-	-	-	1	-
Church of the Nazarene	1996	-	-	-	-	2
Churches of Christ	1990	2	-	-	2	-
Development Associates Intl. (DAI)	2000	-	-	-	-	-
Eastern Mennonite Missions		-	-	3	-	-
East-West Ministries International	1994	-	-	8	11	-
Evangelical Presbyterian Church	1993	6	2	-	2	-
Evangelism Explosion International		-	-	-	-	2
Every Home for Christ International	1994	-	-	-	4	-
Go Ye Fellowship	1998	-	1	-	1	-
Greater Grace World Outreach	1991	-	-	-	-	2
International Teams, U.S.A.		-	-	-	-	-
InterServe/USA	2000	2	-	-	-	-
InterVarsity Christian Fellowship/USA		2	-	-	-	-
Lutheran Church—Missouri Syn.	1993	4	-	6	-	-
Medical Ambassadors International	1994	-	-	-	-	-
Mission ONE, Inc.		-	-	-	-	-
Presbyterian Church (USA)		4	-	-	-	-
Presbyterian Evangelistic Fellowship		1	-	-	-	-
Russian Language Ministries	2000	-	-	-	-	2
Seventh-day Adventists General Conference	1886	-	-	2	-	-

	First Year	Personnel from U.S. 4+ yrs.	2-4 yrs.	1-2 yrs.	Other Countries Citizens	Not Citizens
The Master's Mission, Inc.	1999	-	-	1	-	-
The Mission Society	1993	20	1	-	-	-
Totals:		47	10	20	21	8

Kenya

ABWE		2	-	-	-	-
ACM International	1996	7	-	-	-	-
Africa Inland Mission International	1895	284	-	26	-	-
African Enterprise, Inc.	1970	-	-	-	7	-
Artists In Christian Testimony	2001	-	-	2	-	-
Assemblies of God World Missions	1967	32	-	10	-	-
Audio Scripture Ministries		-	-	-	7	1
Baptist Bible Fellowship Intl.	1971	31	6	2	-	-
Baptist International Outreach	1985	-	2	-	2	-
Bethany Fellowship Missions	1999	2	-	-	-	-
Bible League, The	1979	-	-	-	15	-
Brethren Assemblies		1	-	-	-	-
Bright Hope International	1989	-	-	-	2	-
Campus Crusade for Christ, Intl.	1972	21	-	-	120	-
Caring Partners International, Inc.	1997	-	-	-	-	-
CBInternational	1972	11	-	1	-	-
Child Evangelism Fellowship, Inc.	1966	5	-	-	27	-
Childcare International	1984	-	-	-	25	-
Christ to the Nations	1999	2	-	-	2	-
Christar	1956	2	-	-	-	-
Christian Aid Mission		-	-	-	110	-
Christian Blind Mission Intl.	1971	-	1	1	-	-
Christian Church of North America Missions	1996	-	2	-	-	-
Christian Churches / Churches of Christ		35	3	2	8	-
Christian Reformed World Relief Committee	1983	2	1	-	1	2
Church of God (Anderson, Indiana)		8	-	-	-	-
Church of God (Cleveland, TN)	1977	13	-	-	-	2
Church of God of Prophecy		-	-	-	14	-
Church of the Nazarene	1984	14	4	-	-	-
Churches of Christ	1965	29	-	-	4	-
CMF International	1977	23	3	6	-	-
Compassion International, Inc.	1980	1	-	-	36	2
Daystar U.S.		7	-	-	-	-
Eastern Mennonite Missions		15	7	-	-	-
Elim Fellowship, Intl. Dept.	1940	19	-	-	-	19
Empowering Lives International	1998	-	-	-	-	-
Equip, Inc.		-	-	-	2	-
Evangelical Free Church Mission	1996	9	-	-	-	-
Evangelical Lutheran Church in America	1974	2	-	-	-	-
Every Home for Christ International	1963	-	-	-	13	-
Faith Christian Fellowship Intl.	1996	-	2	-	-	-
Food for the Hungry, Inc.	1976	-	7	-	-	-
Free Methodist World Missions	1944	2	-	-	-	2
General Conf. Mennonite Church	1990	4	-	-	-	-
Global Outreach, Ltd.		2	-	-	-	-
Globe Missionary Evangelism	1987	1	-	-	-	-
Go Ye Fellowship	1996	4	-	2	-	-

	First Year	Personnel from U.S. 4+ yrs.	2-4 yrs.	1-2 yrs.	Other Countries Citizens	Not Citizens
Gospel Fellowship Association	2000	2	-	-	-	-
Gospel Furthering Fellowship		3	-	-	-	-
Greater Grace World Outreach	1998	-	-	-	-	2
Habitat for Humanity International	1985	-	4	-	8	1
Independent Faith Mission		8	-	-	-	-
International Christian Ministries	1986	1	-	-	12	-
International Gospel Outreach	1986	2	2	-	6	-
International Justice Mission	2001	-	2	-	3	-
International Outreach Ministries	1987	2	-	-	-	-
Intl. Pentecostal Ch. of Christ		3	-	-	-	-
Intl. Pentecostal Holiness Church	1972	6	2	-	-	-
International Teams, U.S.A.		-	1	-	-	3
InterVarsity Christian Fellowship/USA		2	-	-	-	-
Kids Alive International	2000	2	-	-	1	-
Larry Jones International Ministries	1979	-	-	-	16	1
Lifewater International	1989	-	-	-	1	-
Literacy & Evangelism International		-	-	-	-	-
Lutheran Church—Missouri Syn.	1999	-	4	2	-	-
MAP International	1980	-	-	-	16	-
Medical Ambassadors International	1987	-	-	-	16	-
Mission Ministries, Inc.	1994	1	-	-	-	-
Mission ONE, Inc.		-	-	-	-	-
Mission to the World (PCA), Inc.	1977	9	-	-	-	-
Mission: Moving Mountains, Inc.	1985	3	2	-	-	2
Navigators, U.S. Intl. Missions Group		4	-	-	-	-
New Directions International	1989	-	-	-	3	-
OC International, Inc.	1985	4	2	-	3	-
Orthodox Presbyterian Church	1979	2	-	-	-	-
Presbyterian Church (USA)		11	6	4	-	-
Presbyterian Evangelistic Fellowship		2	-	-	-	-
Reformed Baptist Mission Services		2	-	-	-	1
Reformed Church in America, Gen. Syn.	1985	6	-	-	-	-
Salvation Army, U.S.A.	1921	2	-	-	-	-
Samaritan's Purse	1994	1	-	-	-	-
Seed International	1998	-	2	-	-	-
Seventh-day Adventists Gen. Conf.	1906	16	11	2	-	26
Share International	1996	-	-	-	9	-
SIM USA	1977	16	-	-	-	-
Source of Light Ministries Intl., Inc.	1991	-	-	-	4	-
The Master's Mission, Inc.	1960	8	2	3	1	-
Things To Come Mission, Inc.	1984	5	-	-	-	4
UFM International		4	-	-	-	-
United Church Board for World Mins.		-	1	-	-	-
Walk Thru The Bible Ministries	1999	-	-	-	6	-
Word of Life Fellowship	1970	2	-	-	53	-
World Concern	1977	3	5	-	59	-
World Gospel Mission	1932	47	-	-	-	5
World Harvest Mission	1990	4	-	-	-	-
World Indigenous Missions	1994	2	-	-	-	-
World Mission Associates	1986	2	-	-	-	-
World Mission Prayer League Inc.	1968	11	-	-	-	1
World Missions Far Corners, Inc.	1992	-	-	-	6	-

	First Year	Personnel from U.S. 4+ yrs.	2-4 yrs.	1-2 yrs.	Other Countries Citizens	Not Citizens
World Reach, Inc.	1983	-	-	-	12	-
World Servants	1991	-	-	-	2	-
World Vision Inc.	1974	-	-	-	-	-
World-Wide Missions	1963	-	-	-	14	-
Wycliffe Associates USA	1999	-	-	2	-	-
Wycliffe Bible Translators USA		42	-	-	-	-
Youth for Christ/USA, World Outreach Div.		3	-	-	-	-
Totals:		833	84	65	646	74

Kiribati

	First Year	4+ yrs.	2-4 yrs.	1-2 yrs.	Citizens	Not Citizens
Assemblies of God World Missions	1989	2	-	-	-	-
Totals:		2	-	-	-	-

Korea, South

	First Year	4+ yrs.	2-4 yrs.	1-2 yrs.	Citizens	Not Citizens
Assemblies of God World Missions	1928	4	-	2	-	-
Baptist Bible Fellowship Intl.	1958	15	2	1	-	-
BCM International		-	-	-	3	-
Brethren Assemblies		1	-	-	1	-
Cadence International		-	4	-	-	4
Campus Crusade for Christ, Intl.	1958	-	-	-	860	-
CBInternational	1996	2	-	-	-	-
Christian and Missionary Alliance	1980	2	-	-	-	-
Christian Churches/Churches of Christ		4	-	-	6	-
Church of God of Prophecy		-	-	-	2	-
Church of the Nazarene	1948	6	-	-	-	-
Churches of Christ	1950	1	-	-	-	-
David Livingstone KURE Foundation		-	-	-	24	-
Far East Broadcasting Company, Inc.	1976	2	-	-	150	-
Free Methodist World Missions	1990	1	-	-	-	-
Free Will Baptists, Inc., National Assoc.	1999	2	-	-	-	-
Frontier Mission Fellowship		1	-	-	-	-
Global Outreach Mission		-	-	-	2	-
Go Ye Fellowship	1994	1	-	-	-	-
Gospel Fellowship Association	1967	6	-	-	-	-
Habitat for Humanity International	1994	1	-	-	-	1
Independent Faith Mission		2	-	-	-	-
International Gospel Outreach	1999	-	-	-	2	-
Lutheran Church—Missouri Syn.	1958	2	-	1	-	-
Medical Ambassadors International	1999	-	-	-	-	-
Mennonite Mission Network		-	-	-	-	2
Mission to the World (PCA), Inc.	1976	2	-	-	-	-
Network of Intl. Christian Schools	1983	21	83	-	-	-
New Tribes Mission	1993	2	-	-	2	-
OMF International	1960	4	-	-	-	-
OMS International, Inc.	1907	3	-	-	-	2
Orthodox Presbyterian Church	1946	2	-	-	-	-
Partners International	1976	-	-	-	-	-
Precept Ministries International	1984	-	-	-	13	-
Presbyterian Church (USA)	1884	6	19	-	-	-
Seventh-day Adventists Gen. Conf.	1904	10	4	1	-	4
Source of Light Ministries Intl., Inc.	1985	-	-	-	2	-
United Church Board for World Mins.		-	1	-	-	-

	First Year	4+ yrs.	2-4 yrs.	1-2 yrs.	Other Countries Citizens	Not Citizens
					Personnel from U.S.	**Other Countries**

	First Year	4+ yrs.	2-4 yrs.	1-2 yrs.	Citizens	Not Citizens
Walk Thru The Bible Ministries	2000	-	-	-	4	-
Westminister Biblical Missions	1973	1	-	-	15	-
Word of Life Fellowship	1989	4	-	-	12	-
World Missions Far Corners, Inc.	1976	2	-	-	7	-
World-Wide Missions	1964	-	-	-	8	-
Worldwide Tentmakers, Inc.	2000	-	-	-	-	-
Totals:		110	113	5	1113	13
Kosovo					-	
Bethany Fellowship Missions	1999	1	2	-	-	1
Christian Churches/Churches of Christ		2	-	-	1	-
Eastern European Outreach, Inc.	1999	4	-	-	3	-
Greater Europe Mission	1974	4	-	-	-	-
International Aid		-	-	-	-	-
International Teams, U.S.A.		2	-	-	-	-
Northwest Medical Teams	1998	-	-	-	-	-
Samaritan's Purse	1999	-	-	-	4	-
World Servants	1999	-	-	-	1	-
Totals:		13	2	-	9	1
Kyrgyzstan						
Christian Aid Mission		-	-	-	24	-
East-West Ministries International		-	-	-	3	-
Evangelism Explosion International		-	-	-	-	2
Grace Brethren International Missions	1998	2	-	-	-	-
Greater Grace World Outreach	1992	-	-	-	-	2
Habitat for Humanity International	1996	1	-	-	-	1
InterServe/USA	1993	18	-	-	-	1
InterVarsity Christian Fellowship/USA		6	-	-	-	-
Lutheran Church—Missouri Syn.	1998	4	-	2	-	-
Medical Ambassadors International	1999	-	-	-	-	-
Mission To Unreached Peoples	2000	1	-	-	-	-
Presbyterian Ch. (USA), Worldwide Mins.		6	-	-	-	-
Seventh-day Adventists Gen. Conf.	1886	2	-	-	-	-
Venture International	1992	-	-	-	1	-
Totals:		40	-	2	28	6
Laos						
Assemblies of God World Missions	1990	-	-	1	-	-
Christian Aid Mission		-	-	-	4	-
Christian and Missionary Alliance	1929	-	6	-	-	-
Church World Service & Witness		1	-	-	3	-
Evangelical Covenant Church	1991	2	-	-	-	-
Food for the Hungry, Inc.	1990	-	2	2	-	-
International Teams, U.S.A.		-	-	-	-	-
Medical Ambassadors International	1996	-	-	-	-	-
Mission ONE, Inc.		-	-	-	-	-
Partners International	1994	-	-	-	-	-
Seventh-day Adventists Gen. Conf.	1919	-	-	-	-	4
World Concern	1982	-	2	-	41	-
Totals:		3	10	3	48	4

	Personnel from U.S.			Other Countries	
	First Year	4+ yrs.	2-4 yrs.	1-2 yrs.	Citizens	Not Citizens

Latin America - General

Baptist Medical & Dental Mission Intl., Inc.	1974	4	-	-	-	-
Bible Training Centre for Pastors	2001	1	-	-	-	-
Calvary International	1985	4	-	-	-	4
CBInternational		2	-	-	-	-
Centers for Apologetics Research (CFAR)	1999	-	-	-	1	-
Church of God (Cleveland, TN)		1	-	-	-	-
Church World Service & Witness	1946	-	-	175	3	-
Evangelical Covenant Church	1999	2	-	-	-	-
Final Frontiers Foundation, Inc.	1989	-	-	-	165	-
Free Methodist World Missions		3	-	-	-	-
Global Action	1998	2	-	-	-	-
Go Ye Fellowship	1968	2	-	-	-	-
Heifer International	1944	14	31	25	64	6
International Bible Society		-	-	-	14	-
International Cassette Bible Institute	1987	6	-	-	-	-
Mennonite Central Committee		207	-		-	-
Mission Aviation Fellowship		4	-	-	-	-
Operation Mobilization, Inc.		4	-	-	-	-
Opportunity Intl./Women's Opportunity		-	4	-	-	-
Peoples Mission International	1993	-	-	-	-	2
Presbyterian Evangelistic Fellowship		2	-	-	-	-
Southern Baptist Conv. Intl. Msn. Bd.		-	-	-	-	-
TMA Ministries	1992	2	-	-	-	-
VELA Ministries International	1970	-	-	-	-	1
WorldTeach	2000	-	-	-	-	-
Wycliffe Bible Translators USA		137	-	-	-	-
Totals:		397	35	200	247	13

Latvia

American Baptist Chs. in the U.S.A.	1999	2	-	-	-	-
Assemblies of God World Missions		5	-	3	-	-
Bridge Builders International	1994	7	1	-	10	-
Calvary International	1992	2	-	-	1	1
Campus Crusade for Christ, Intl.	1991	7	-	5	7	5
Christian Associates International	1992	-	-	-	1	-
Churches of Christ	1991	1	-	-	2	-
Greater Europe Mission	1992	8	-	-	-	-
Peter Deyneka Russian Ministries		-	-	-	-	-
Walk Thru The Bible Ministries	2000	-	-	-	1	-
World Baptist Fellowship Mission Agency		-	2	-	-	-
Totals:		32	3	8	22	6

Lebanon

American Baptist Chs. in the U.S.A.	1998	-	-	-	-	2
Armenian Msny. Assoc. of America, Inc.	1918	2	-	1	-	-
Campus Crusade for Christ, Intl.	1968	-	-	-	18	-
CBInternational	1996	2	-	-	-	-
Christian and Missionary Alliance	1891	2	-	-	-	-
Church of God (Anderson, Indiana)		3	-	-	-	-
Church of the Nazarene	1950	2	-	-	-	-
Evangelical Presbyterian Church	1996	2	-	-	-	-

		Personnel from U.S.			Other Countries	
	First Year	4+ yrs.	2-4 yrs.	1-2 yrs.	Citizens	Not Citizens
International Partnership Mins., Inc.	1999	-	-	-	3	1
InterServe/USA		1	-	-	-	-
Kids Alive International	1950	-	1	-	1	11
Mission ONE, Inc.		-	-	-	-	-
Partners International	1994	-	-	-	-	-
Pioneers		6	-	-	-	-
Presbyterian Church (USA)		3	-	-	-	-
Seventh-day Adventists Gen. Conf.	1970	2	-	-	-	4
United Church Board for World Mins.		-	2	-	-	-
Youth for Christ/USA, World Outreach	1960	2	-	-	-	-
	Totals:	27	3	1	22	18

Lesotho

Africa Inland Mission International	1986	5	-	-	-	-
Africa Inter-Mennonite Mission	1972	-	-	-	-	-
Assemblies of God World Missions	1950	2	-	-	-	-
Campus Crusade for Christ, Intl.	1979	2	-	-	2	1
Church of the Nazarene	1993	2	-	-	-	-
Every Home for Christ International	1985	-	-	-	2	-
General Conf. Mennonite Church	1973	-	-	-	-	2
Mennonite Mission Network	1973	-	-	-	-	2
Mission Aviation Fellowship	1979	8	-	-	-	-
National Baptist Convention USA, Inc.	1961	-	-	-	-	-
Presbyterian Ch. (USA), Worldwide Mins.	1977	2	-	-	-	-
Seventh-day Adventists Gen. Conf.	1899	3	-	-	-	2
United Church Board for World Mins.	1984	-	12	-	-	-
Walk Thru The Bible Ministries	1999	-	-	-	1	-
	Totals:	24	12	-	5	7

Liberia

Advent Christian General Conf.	1988	-	-	-	4	-
Baptist Mid-Missions	1938	-	-	-	-	-
Campus Crusade for Christ, Intl.	1979	-	-	-	12	-
Child Evangelism Fellowship, Inc.	1955	-	-	-	7	-
Christian Aid Ministries		-	15	-	23	-
Christian Churches/Churches of Christ	1971	2	-	-	-	-
Church of God (Cleveland, TN)	1974	-	-	-	-	2
Church of God of Prophecy		-	-	-	6	-
Church of the Nazarene	1990	-	2	-	-	-
Equip, Inc.		-	-	-	3	3
Evangel Bible Translators	1986	-	-	-	1	-
Evangelical Lutheran Ch. in America	1862	2	-	-	-	-
Every Home for Christ International	2001	-	-	-	5	-
Global Fellowship		-	-	-	75	-
Greater Grace World Outreach	1990	-	-	-	1	-
Have Christ Will Travel Ministries	1966	-	-	-	10	-
International Missionary Center		-	-	-	-	8
International Partnership Ministries, Inc.	1998	-	-	-	6	-
Lutheran Bible Translators		-	-	-	30	-
Lutheran Church—Missouri Syn.	1978	1	-	-	-	-
Mennonite Mission Network	1988	-	-	-	-	-
Partners International	1964	-	-	-	-	-

		Personnel from U.S.			Other Countries	
	First Year	4+ yrs.	2-4 yrs.	1-2 yrs.	Citizens	Not Citizens
Presbyterian Evangelistic Fellowship		-	-	-	5	-
Seventh-day Adventists Gen. Conf.	1927	1	-	-	-	4
SIM USA	1952	4	-	-	-	-
Source of Light Ministries Intl., Inc.	1979	-	-	-	1	-
WEC International	1938	-	-	-	-	5
World-Wide Missions	1961	-	-	-	20	-
Totals:		10	17	-	209	22
Lithuania						
Assemblies of God World Missions		4	-	1	-	-
Baptist Bible Fellowship Intl.	1991	4	-	-	-	-
Campus Crusade for Christ, Intl.	1991	11	-	-	6	-
CBInternational	1996	2	-	-	-	-
Christ to the Nations	1989	13	-	-	8	5
Churches of Christ	1991	9	-	-	1	-
Eastern Mennonite Missions	1996	7	-	-	-	-
Envoy International		-	-	-	-	-
Evangelical Lutheran Church in America	1992	2	-	-	-	-
Greater Grace World Outreach	1993	-	-	-	-	2
MBMS International	1994	-	-	-	6	-
Mennonite Mission Network	1995	-	-	-	-	-
Open Door Baptist Missions	1992	4	-	-	-	-
Presbyterian Church (USA)		2	-	-	-	-
Walk Thru The Bible Ministries	2001	-	-	-	1	-
World Help	1993	-	-	-	1	-
Totals:		58	-	1	23	7
Luxembourg						
Assemblies of God World Missions	1981	4	-	-	-	-
Biblical Ministries Worldwide	1972	2	-	-	-	2
Greater Europe Mission	1989	2	-	-	-	-
Totals:		8	-	-	-	2
Macau						
Campus Crusade for Christ, Intl.	1975	-	-	-	30	1
CBInternational	1986	9	-	2	-	-
Child Evangelism Fellowship, Inc.	2000	-	-	-	1	-
Christians In Action, Inc.	1976	2	-	-	-	2
Church of the United Brethren in Christ	1987	3	-	-	-	-
Eastern Mennonite Missions		2	-	-	-	-
Evangelical Free Church Mission	1993	3	-	-	-	-
Lutheran Church—Missouri Syn.	1988	-	-	3	-	-
Mennonite Mission Network	1996	-	-	-	-	-
Partners International	1962	-	-	-	-	-
Seventh-day Adventists Gen. Conf.	1888	2	-	-	-	-
Totals:		21	-	5	31	3
Macedonia						
Assemblies of God World Missions		-	-	2	-	-
Bible League, The	1998	-	-	-	2	-
Campus Crusade for Christ, Intl.	1996	-	-	6	4	4
Christian Aid Mission		-	-	-	17	-

	Personnel from U.S.				Other Countries	
	First Year	4+ yrs.	2-4 yrs.	1-2 yrs.	Citizens	Not Citizens
Christian and Missionary Alliance	1999	8	-	-	-	-
Church of the Nazarene	2000	-	-	-	-	-
Every Home for Christ International	1995	-	-	-	1	-
Northwest Medical Teams	2000	-	-	-	-	-
Partners International	1991	-	-	-	-	-
SEND International	1993	9	1	-	-	-
Totals:		17	1	8	24	4
Madagascar						
Assemblies of God World Missions	1990	6	-	3	-	-
Campus Crusade for Christ, Intl.	1979	-	-	-	21	-
CBInternational	1966	6	2	4	-	-
Child Evangelism Fellowship, Inc.	1988	-	-	-	19	-
Christian Blind Mission Intl.	1982	-	1	-	-	-
Church of the Nazarene	1993	4	-	-	-	-
Evangelical Lutheran Ch. in America	1888	10	-	2	-	-
Presbyterian Ch. (USA), Worldwide Mins.		3	-	-	-	-
Seventh-day Adventists Gen. Conf.	1926	4	2	-	-	5
Teen Missions International	1995	-	-	-	2	-
Totals:		33	5	9	42	5
Malawi						
African Bible Colleges, Inc.		14	4	8	25	-
African Enterprise, Inc.	1982	-	-	-	5	-
Assemblies of God World Missions	1944	9	-	5	-	-
Bible Training Centre for Pastors	1998	-	-	-	1	-
Brethren in Christ World Missions	1983	3	-	-	5	-
Campus Crusade for Christ, Intl.	1979	2	-	-	23	-
Child Evangelism Fellowship, Inc.	1988	-	-	-	2	-
Christ Community Church		-	-	-	-	-
Christian Reformed World Relief Comte.	1989	-	1	-	-	-
Church of God (Cleveland, TN)	1951	-	-	-	-	2
Church of God of Prophecy		-	-	-	1	-
Church of the Nazarene	1957	2	1	-	-	1
Churches of Christ	1907	5	-	-	-	-
Emmanuel Intl. Mission (U.S.)	1985	1	-	-	-	-
Every Home for Christ International	1973	-	-	-	5	-
Foursquare Missions International	1984	2	-	-	-	-
Free Methodist World Missions	1973	2	-	-	-	-
Habitat for Humanity International	1986	-	6	-	65	-
Intl. Pentecostal Holiness Ch. World Mins.	1950	4	-	-	-	-
National Baptist Convention USA, Inc.	1900	-	-	-	1	-
Navigators, U.S. Intl. Missions Group		2	-	-	-	-
Presbyterian Ch. (USA), Worldwide Mins.		9	20	-	-	-
Reformed Church in America, Gen. Syn.	1998	2	-	-	-	-
Salvation Army, U.S.A.	1967	2	-	-	-	-
Seventh-day Adventists Gen. Conf.	1902	4	-	-	-	23
SIM USA	1906	12	-	2	-	-
Teen Missions International	1988	3	-	-	7	1
Wisconsin Evangelical Lutheran Syn.	1963	10	-	-	-	-
World-Wide Missions	1964	-	-	-	10	-
Totals:		88	32	15	150	27

		Personnel from U.S.			Other Countries	
	First Year	4+ yrs.	2-4 yrs.	1-2 yrs.	Citizens	Not Citizens
Malaysia						
Advent Christian General Conf.	1960	-	-	-	6	-
Asian Outreach U.S.A.		-	-	-	-	-
Bible League, The	1998	-	-	-	8	-
Campus Crusade for Christ, Intl.	1968	2	-	-	122	-
Christian and Missionary Alliance	1966	-	11	-	-	-
Church of God (Cleveland, TN)	1991	2	-	-	-	-
Church of God of Prophecy		-	-	-	1	-
Churches of Christ	1950	-	-	-	6	-
Compassion International, Inc.		1	-	-	-	2
Evangel Bible Translators	1989	-	-	-	1	1
Evangelical Congregational Church		1	-	-	-	-
Evangelical Free Church Mission		4	-	-	-	-
Evangelical Presbyterian Church	2000	4	-	-	-	-
Every Home for Christ International	1983	-	-	-	6	-
Food for the Hungry, Inc.	1996	-	2	-	-	-
Foursquare Missions International	1984	2	-	-	-	-
Globe Missionary Evangelism	1984	2	-	-	-	-
Gospel Revival Ministries	1999	-	-	-	2	-
International Missionary Center		2	-	-	-	-
International Teams, U.S.A.		-	-	-	-	1
Mennonite Mission Network		-	-	-	-	-
Mission To Unreached Peoples	1995	1	-	-	-	-
Navigators, U.S. Intl. Missions Group		1	4	-	-	-
New Tribes Mission	1998	2	-	-	-	-
Omega World Missions		-	-	-	-	-
OMF International		1	-	-	-	-
Partners International	1954	-	-	-	-	-
Ripe for Harvest, Inc.	1998	2	-	-	-	-
Walk Thru The Bible Ministries	2000	-	-	-	4	-
Wycliffe Bible Translators USA		44	-	-	-	-
	Totals:	71	17	-	156	4
Mali						
ACM International	1985	2	-	-	-	-
Assemblies of God World Missions	1988	4	-	-	-	-
Campus Crusade for Christ, Intl.	1972	-	-	-	36	2
CBInternational	1994	2	-	-	-	-
Child Evangelism Fellowship, Inc.	1993	-	-	-	1	-
Christian and Missionary Alliance	1923	26	-	-	-	-
Christian Churches / Churches of Christ		2	-	-	-	-
Christian Reformed World Missions	1984	7	-	-	-	-
Christian Reformed World Relief Comte.	1984	1	2	-	-	1
Evangelical Baptist Missions		11	-	2	-	-
Every Home for Christ International	1994	-	-	-	4	-
Gospel Missionary Union	1919	17	1	-	-	-
International Missionary Center		-	-	-	-	4
Mission Aviation Fellowship	1985	20	2	-	-	-
Navigators, U.S. Intl. Missions Group		2	-	-	-	-
Partners International	2001	-	-	-	-	-
Pioneers		-	-	-	5	-
Seventh-day Adventists Gen. Conf.	1982	-	-	-	-	2
	Totals:	94	5	2	46	9

	Personnel from U.S.				Other Countries	
	First Year	4+ yrs.	2-4 yrs.	1-2 yrs.	Citizens	Not Citizens

Malta

Baptist Bible Fellowship Intl.	1983	2	-	-	-	-
Church of God of Prophecy		-	-	-	-	1
Partners International	1995	-	-	-	-	-
Ripe for Harvest, Inc.	1999	1	-	-	-	-
Totals:		3	-	-	-	1

Marshall Islands

Assemblies of God World Missions	1964	-	-	2	-	-
Gospel Fellowship Association	1988	4	-	-	-	-
Missionary Ventures International	1999	1	-	-	-	-
Seventh-day Adventists Gen. Conf.	1930	2	-	2	-	-
United Church Board for World Mins.		-	2	-	-	-
Totals:		7	2	4	-	-

Martinique

Church of the Nazarene	1976	-	-	-	-	-
Totals:		-	-	-	-	-

Mauritius

Assemblies of God World Missions	1967	2	-	-	-	-
Presbyterian Church (USA)	1982	2	-	-	-	-
Reformed Baptist Mission Services		2	-	-	-	1
Totals:		6	-	-	-	1

Mexico

Action International Ministries	1990	-	-	-	2	1
Advent Christian General Conf.	1958	1	-	-	4	-
American Baptist Chs. in the U.S.A.	1870	12	-	-	-	-
AmeriTribes	1984	8	-	-	-	-
AMF International		-	-	-	3	-
AMG International	1978	5	-	-	-	-
AMOR Ministries	1980	12	5	8	6	-
Apostolic Christian Ch. Foundation, Inc.	1972	1	-	-	1	-
Assemblies of God World Missions	1915	60	-	19	-	-
Assoc. of Free Lutheran Congregations		4	-	-	5	-
Audio Scriptures International	2002	-	-	-	2	-
Baptist Bible Fellowship Intl.	1946	63	7	4	-	-
Baptist General Conference	1955	10	2	-	-	-
Baptist International Outreach	1996	-	3	-	-	-
Baptist Mid-Missions	1960	19	-	-	-	-
BCM International		-	-	-	3	-
Bethany Fellowship Missions	1972	12	-	-	-	-
Bethel Christian Ministries		2	-	-	-	-
Bible League, The	1970	-	-	-	40	-
Bible Missionary Church		2	-	-	-	-
Biblical Ministries Worldwide	1964	11	-	-	1	2
Brethren Assemblies		36	-	-	-	-
Brethren Church Missionary Bd.	1979	2	-	-	-	-
Brethren in Christ World Missions	1993	2	-	-	1	-
Calvary Commission, Inc.	1980	10	-	-	-	-
Calvary International	1986	4	-	-	-	4

	First Year	4+ yrs.	2-4 yrs.	1-2 yrs.	Citizens	Not Citizens
					Personnel from U.S.	Other Countries
CAM International	1955	60	3	9	3	53
Campus Crusade for Christ, Intl.	1961	5	-	22	41	-
Child Evangelism Fellowship, Inc.	1939	1	-	-	1	-
Childcare International	1982	-	-	-	2	-
Children's Haven International	1994	2	-	-	-	-
Chosen People Ministries		-	-	-	-	-
Christ for the City International	1988	-	-	-	-	2
Christian Advance International	1984	-	-	-	-	3
Christian Aid Mission		-	-	-	12	-
Christian and Missionary Alliance	1954	10	-	-	-	-
Christian Churches / Churches of Christ		50	4	-	20	-
Christian Outreach International	1997	3	-	-	-	3
Christian Reformed World Missions	1953	17	-	2	-	-
Christian Reformed World Relief Comte.	1969	-	3	-	-	-
Christians In Action, Inc.	1972	1	-	-	-	1
Church of the Nazarene	1903	6	-	-	-	4
Churches of Christ	1929	47	-	6	16	-
CMF International	1980	6	4	4	-	1
ComCare International	1997	2	-	-	2	-
Commission to Every Nation	1995	8	-	-	1	-
Compassion International, Inc.	1976	-	-	-	16	-
Congregational Methodist Church	1954	14	-	-	2	-
David Livingstone KURE Foundation		-	-	-	8	-
Eastern Mennonite Missions		-	2	-	-	-
Elim Fellowship, Intl. Dept.	1962	12	-	-	-	12
Equip, Inc.		2	-	4	-	-
Evangelical Baptist Missions		6	-	-	-	-
Evangelical Congregational Church		1	-	-	-	-
Evangelical Covenant Church	1946	13	1	-	-	-
Evangelical Free Church Mission	1987	12	2	-	-	-
Evangelical Friends Mission	1967	2	-	-	-	-
Evangelical Lutheran Church in America	1956	3	-	1	-	-
Evangelical Mennonite Ch. Intl. Mins.	1997	-	-	-	-	1
Evangelical Methodist Ch., Bd. of Msns.		2	-	-	-	-
Evangelism Explosion International		-	-	-	-	2
Faith Christian Fellowship Intl.	1992	6	-	-	-	-
Fellowship International Mission	1984	17	-	-	3	-
Floresta USA, Inc.	1996	-	-	-	8	-
Foundation For His Ministry	1967	-	-	-	77	47
Foursquare Missions International	1943	4	-	-	-	-
Free Methodist World Missions	1917	2	-	-	-	-
Frontier Mission Fellowship		2	-	-	-	-
Full Gospel Grace Fellowship	1950	-	-	-	-	2
General Conf. Mennonite Church	1946	-	-	-	-	6
Global Fellowship		-	-	-	5	-
Global Outreach Mission		11	-	-	-	-
Global Outreach, Ltd.		-	-	2	-	-
Global Strategy Mission Assoc.	1986	4	1	-	1	-
Globe Missionary Evangelism	1972	9	-	-	-	-
Good News Productions Intl.	1996	2	2	-	4	-
Gospel Fellowship Association	1967	13	-	-	-	-
Gospel Missionary Union	2001	7	-	-	-	-

	First Year	Personnel from U.S. 4+ yrs.	Personnel from U.S. 2-4 yrs.	Personnel from U.S. 1-2 yrs.	Other Countries Citizens	Other Countries Not Citizens
Grace Brethren International Missions	1951	2	-	1	-	2
Habitat for Humanity International	1987	-	5	-	26	-
Hope for the Hungry		1	-	-	-	1
Impact International	1990	-	-	-	2	-
Independent Faith Mission		2	-	-	-	-
International Cassette Bible Institute	2000	-	-	-	2	-
International Family Missions	1988	10	-	-	6	-
International Gospel Outreach	1990	-	2	-	-	-
International Justice Mission		-	-	-	-	-
International Missionary Center		5	-	-	-	-
International Outreach Ministries	1986	-	-	-	5	-
International Partnership Ministries, Inc.	1991	-	-	-	1	2
International Pentecostal Ch. of Christ		1	-	-	-	-
Int. Pentecostal Holiness Ch. World Mins.	1930	11	-	2	-	-
International Teams, U.S.A.		11	6	-	2	10
Josue Yrion Wld. Evangelism Msns., Inc.	2002	-	-	-	1	-
Latin America Lutheran Mission	1942	-	1	-	-	-
Latin America Mission	1952	17	3	1	2	19
Latin American Indian Ministries	1973	-	-	-	-	-
Lutheran Church—Missouri Synod	1940	-	-	2	-	-
MBMS International	1905	-	4	-	-	-
Medical Ambassadors International	1990	1	-	-	2	-
Mennonite Mission Network	1957	4	-	-	-	-
Mexican Medical Ministries	1963	12	-	-	-	-
Mission Aviation Fellowship	1946	6	-	-	-	-
Mission Ministries, Inc.	1994	2	-	-	-	-
Mission to the Americas	1951	6	-	-	16	-
Mission to the World (PCA), Inc.	1977	43	16	-	-	-
Missionary Gospel Fellowship	1943	13	-	-	2	-
Missionary Revival Crusade	1949	24	-	-	5	35
Missionary Ventures International	1992	2	-	-	-	-
Moravian Church in North America	2000	2	-	-	-	-
Navigators, U.S. Intl. Missions Group		10	1	-	-	-
New Life League International	1975	1	-	-	-	-
New Tribes Mission	1975	84	-	-	4	1
North American Baptist Conf.	1992	6	-	-	-	2
Northwest Medical Teams	1985	-	-	-	-	-
OC International, Inc.	1967	4	-	1	-	1
OMS International, Inc.		14	-	-	-	3
Open Bible Standard Churches	1965	2	-	-	-	-
Operation Mobilization, Inc.	1957	2	-	-	-	-
Pan American Missions	1960	4	1	-	-	-
Partners in Christ International	1986	1	-	-	4	-
Pentecostal Church of God		6	-	-	-	-
Pocket Testament League	1988	-	-	-	2	-
Precept Ministries International	1980	-	-	-	1	-
Precious Seed Ministries	1984	5	-	-	3	-
Presbyterian Church (USA)		4	23	7	-	-
Presbyterian Evangelistic Fellowship		8	-	-	2	-
Project Partner with Christ	1969	-	-	-	1	-
Reformed Church in America, Gen. Syn.	1969	9	-	-	1	-
Rio Grande Bible Institute		51	2	6	-	-

	Personnel from U.S.				Other Countries
	First Year	4+ yrs.	2-4 yrs.	1-2 yrs.	Citizens	Not Citizens
Ripe for Harvest, Inc.	1999	-	-	-	1	-
Rosedale Mennonite Missions	1999	-	-	-	-	2
Salvation Army, U.S.A.	1937	5	-	-	-	-
Seed International	1996	6	-	-	-	2
Seventh-day Adventists Genn. Conf.	1893	22	3	2	-	23
Source of Light Ministries Intl., Inc.	1962	-	-	-	2	-
Southern Mexico Missions	1957	8	-	2	8	2
TEAM (The Evangelical Alliance Mission)		14	-	-	-	-
The Ch. of God of the Apostolic Faith, Inc.	1950	4	-	-	-	-
The Master's Harvest		4	-	-	-	-
The Master's Mission, Inc.	1994	2	-	-	-	-
The Mission Society	1987	4	-	-	-	-
UFM International	1971	11	-	1	1	2
United Church Board for World Ministries		-	2	-	-	-
Village Ministries International, Inc.	1998	-	-	-	2	-
Walk Thru The Bible Ministries	2000	-	-	-	5	-
WEC International	1991	14	-	-	-	12
Wesleyan World Missions	1920	-	3	-	-	-
Westminister Biblical Missions	1991	-	-	-	1	2
Wisconsin Evangelical Lutheran Syn.	1968	4	1	-	-	-
Word of Life Fellowship	1983	-	-	-	18	10
World Baptist Fellowship Mission Agency		24	-	2	-	-
World Gospel Mission	1945	15	-	-	-	1
World Indigenous Missions	1980	21	4	-	5	2
World Mission Prayer League Inc.	1945	5	-	-	-	-
World Missions Far Corners, Inc.	1958	7	-	-	100	-
World Vision Inc.	1963	-	-	-	-	-
World Witness, Assoc. Reformed Presb. Ch.	1878	13	-	-	50	-
Wycliffe Bible Translators USA		226	-	-	-	-
Totals:	1433	116	108	573	278

Micronesia, Federated States of

Assemblies of God World Missions		2	-	2	-	-
Baptist Mid-Missions	1994	8	-	-	-	-
Campus Crusade for Christ, Intl.	1976	-	-	-	2	-
Child Evangelism Fellowship, Inc.	1957	2	-	-	-	-
Church of the Nazarene	2000	-	-	-	-	2
Conservative Congregational Christian Conf.	1984	2	-	-	2	1
Global Outreach Mission		2	-	-	-	-
Independent Faith Mission		2	-	-	-	-
Liebenzell Mission USA	1907	12	-	-	-	-
Mission to the World (PCA), Inc.	1985	-	2	-	-	-
Worldwide Tentmakers, Inc.	2000	-	-	-	-	-
Totals:	30	2	2	4	3

Middle East

Baptist General Conference		4	-	-	-	-
Bible League, The	1980	-	-	-	18	1
Eastern Mennonite Missions		-	-	5	-	-
Elim Fellowship, Intl. Dept.		-	-	3	1	2
Evangelical Mennonite Ch. Intl. Mins.	1993	2	-	-	-	-
Free Methodist World Missions		2	-	-	-	-

	First Year	4+ yrs.	2-4 yrs.	1-2 yrs.	Citizens	Not Citizens
			Personnel from U.S.		Other Countries	
Great Commission Center International	2001	-	-	-	-	-
Middle East Media - USA	1976	-	-	-	75	-
Navigators, U.S. Intl. Missions Group		10	-	-	-	-
Operation Mobilization, Inc.		23	4	7	-	-
Ripe for Harvest, Inc.	1992	2	-	-	-	-
Rosedale Mennonite Missions	1987	8	-	-	-	-
TMA Ministries	1982	2	-	-	-	-
WEC International		24	-	1	-	99
World-Wide Missions	1987	-	-	-	12	-
Totals:		77	4	16	106	102

Moldova

	First Year	4+ yrs.	2-4 yrs.	1-2 yrs.	Citizens	Not Citizens
Baptist International Evangelistic Mins.		-	-	-	8	2
Bible League, The	1994	-	-	-	5	-
Campus Crusade for Christ, Intl.	1995	-	-	-	26	-
Child Evangelism Fellowship, Inc.	1995	1	-	-	-	-
Christian Aid Ministries		-	-	-	1	-
Crossover Communications Intl.	1997	2	2	-	-	2
Evangelism Explosion International		-	-	-	-	3
Northwest Medical Teams	1996	-	-	-	-	-
Precept Ministries International	1994	-	-	-	5	-
Salvation Army, U.S.A.	1994	3	-	-	-	-
TITUS International	1993	-	-	-	50	-
Walk Thru The Bible Ministries	2000	-	-	-	1	-
Totals:		6	2	-	96	7

Monaco

	First Year	4+ yrs.	2-4 yrs.	1-2 yrs.	Citizens	Not Citizens
Trans World Radio		9	-	-	-	-
UFM International		2	-	-	-	-
Totals:		11	-	-	-	-

Mongolia

	First Year	4+ yrs.	2-4 yrs.	1-2 yrs.	Citizens	Not Citizens
ABWE	1998	4	-	-	-	-
Asian Outreach U.S.A.		-	-	-	-	-
Assemblies of God World Missions		8	-	3	-	-
CBInternational	1995	1	-	-	-	-
Christar	1992	6	-	-	-	-
Christian Aid Mission		-	-	-	3	-
Christian and Missionary Alliance	1997	8	1	-	-	-
Church of God (Cleveland, TN)		3	-	-	-	1
Commission to Every Nation	2000	5	5	-	-	-
Evangelical Free Church Mission	1993	9	-	-	3	-
Every Home for Christ International	1997	-	-	-	6	-
Food for the Hungry, Inc.	1997	-	2	-	-	-
InterVarsity Christian Fellowship/USA		2	-	-	-	-
Medical Ambassadors International	1993	-	1	-	-	2
Mennonite Mission Network	1993	5	-	-	-	4
Mustard Seed, Inc., The	1999	1	-	-	6	-
Navigators, U.S. Intl. Missions Group		2	-	-	-	-
New Tribes Mission	1993	7	-	-	-	2
Samaritan's Purse	1999	-	-	1	-	-
Seventh-day Adventists Gen. Conf.	1931	-	2	-	-	2

	First Year	Personnel from U.S. 4+ yrs.	2-4 yrs.	1-2 yrs.	Other Countries Citizens	Not Citizens
SIM USA	1996	1	-	-	-	-
Teen Missions International	1998	-	-	-	1	-
Walk Thru The Bible Ministries	2001	-	-	-	1	-
World Concern	1993	4	2	1	25	-
World Mission Prayer League Inc.	1993	2	-	-	-	-
Totals:		68	13	5	45	11
Morocco						
Christar	2000	-	-	2	-	-
Church of God (Cleveland, TN)		2	-	-	-	2
Fellowship International Mission	1950	13	-	-	2	-
International Needs - USA	1983	-	-	-	6	-
International Outreach Ministries	1993	2	-	-	-	-
Navigators, U.S. Intl. Msns. Group		4	-	-	-	-
Totals:		21	-	2	8	2
Mozambique						
ACM International	1996	1	-	-	-	-
Africa Inland Mission International	1985	21	-	1	-	-
Armenian Msny. Assoc. of America, Inc.	1998	-	-	-	-	-
Assemblies of God World Missions		5	-	-	-	-
Bible League, The	1995	-	-	-	10	-
Bible Training Centre for Pastors	1998	-	-	-	1	-
Brethren Assemblies		-	2	-	-	-
Bright Hope International	1999	-	-	-	1	-
Campus Crusade for Christ, Intl.	1991	-	-	-	1	-
CBInternational	2001	2	-	-	-	-
Child Evangelism Fellowship, Inc.	1994	-	-	-	4	-
Christian Churches / Churches of Christ		6	2	-	-	-
Church of God of Prophecy		-	-	-	2	-
Church of the Nazarene	1922	9	-	-	-	3
Churches of Christ	1960	2	-	-	-	-
Every Home for Christ International	1986	-	-	-	9	-
General Conf. Mennonite Church	1994	2	-	-	-	-
Global Outreach, Ltd.		2	-	-	-	-
Intl. Pentecostal Holiness Ch. World Mins.	1957	2	-	-	-	-
Medical Ambassadors International	1999	-	-	-	-	-
Mission Aviation Fellowship	2000	2	-	-	-	-
OMS International, Inc.	1994	8	-	1	-	1
Presbyterian Church (USA)		2	-	-	-	-
Samaritan's Purse	2000	-	-	1	-	-
Seventh-day Adventists Gen. Conf.	1935	-	2	-	-	-
SIM USA	1937	8	-	-	-	-
TEAM (The Evangelical Alliance Mission)	1988	2	-	-	-	-
Teen Missions International	1996	-	-	-	6	2
Walk Thru The Bible Ministries	1999	-	-	-	2	-
Wesleyan World Missions	1998	-	2	-	-	-
World Vision Inc.	1984	-	-	-	-	-
Wycliffe Bible Translators USA	1994	45	-	-	-	-
Totals:		119	8	3	36	6

	Personnel from U.S.				Other Countries	
	First Year	4+ yrs.	2-4 yrs.	1-2 yrs.	Citizens	Not Citizens

Myanmar/Burma

	First Year	4+ yrs.	2-4 yrs.	1-2 yrs.	Citizens	Not Citizens
Asian Outreach U.S.A.		-	-	-	-	-
Assemblies of God World Missions	1933	2	-	-	-	-
BCM International		-	-	-	8	-
Bible League, The	1986	-	-	-	13	-
Campus Crusade for Christ, Intl.	1972	-	-	-	139	-
Christian Aid Mission		-	-	-	179	-
Christian Churches / Churches of Christ		-	-	-	8	-
Church Planting International	1996	-	-	-	-	-
East West Ministries	1994	-	-	-	1	-
East-West Ministries International		-	-	-	2	-
Evangelism Resources	1997	-	-	-	-	-
Global Fellowship		-	-	-	-	4
Global Outreach Mission		-	-	-	2	-
Global Outreach, Ltd.		2	-	-	-	-
Good News Productions Intl.	1999	-	-	-	2	-
Gospel for Asia	1979	-	-	-	-	-
International Partnership Ministries, Inc.	1997	-	-	-	2	-
Kids Alive International	1998	-	-	-	8	-
Medical Ambassadors International	1998	-	-	-	-	-
Mission Ministries, Inc.	1997	2	-	-	1	-
Mission ONE, Inc.		-	-	-	-	-
Outreach to Asia Nationals	1987	-	-	-	14	-
Partners International	1978	-	-	-	-	-
Seventh-day Adventists Gen. Conf.	1919	-	-	-	-	2
Walk Thru The Bible Ministries	1999	-	-	-	2	-
World Concern	1993	-	1	-	50	-
World Help	1997	-	-	-	4	-
Totals:		6	1	-	435	6

N. Mariana Islands

	First Year	4+ yrs.	2-4 yrs.	1-2 yrs.	Citizens	Not Citizens
Church of the Nazarene	2000	-	-	-	-	-
Far East Broadcasting Company, Inc.	1974	7	-	-	-	-
General Baptists International	1947	2	-	-	-	-
Pioneers	1983	1	-	-	-	-
Seventh-day Adventists Gen. Conf.	1930	8	4	-	-	-
Totals:		11	4	-	-	-

Namibia

	First Year	4+ yrs.	2-4 yrs.	1-2 yrs.	Citizens	Not Citizens
Africa Inland Mission International	1981	7	-	1	-	-
Assemblies of God World Missions	1979	4	-	1	-	-
Child Evangelism Fellowship, Inc.	1994	3	-	-	1	-
Christian Aid Mission		-	-	-	3	-
Church of God of Prophecy		-	-	-	-	1
Church of the Nazarene	1973	2	-	-	-	-
Commission to Every Nation	2001	-	3	-	-	-
Evangelical Lutheran Ch. in America	1983	2	-	5	-	-
Every Home for Christ International	1995	-	-	-	1	-
General Conf. Mennonite Church	1993	-	-	-	-	1
Lutheran Bible Translators	1996	4	-	-	4	-
United Church Board for World Mins.		-	2	-	-	-
Walk Thru The Bible Ministries	1999	-	-	-	1	-

		Personnel from U.S.			Other Countries	
	First Year	4+ yrs.	2-4 yrs.	1-2 yrs.	Citizens	Not Citizens
Youth for Christ/USA, World Outreach Div.		1	-	-	-	-
Totals:		23	5	7	10	2

Nepal

Armenian Msny. Assoc. of America, Inc.	1986	-	-	-	-	-
Asian Outreach U.S.A.		-	-	-	-	-
Assemblies of God World Missions		-	-	2	-	-
BCM International	1995	-	-	-	23	-
Bible League, The	2002	-	-	-	3	-
Brethren in Christ World Missions	1992	-	-	-	11	-
Calvary International	1996	1	-	-	-	1
Campus Crusade for Christ, Intl.	1975	-	-	-	305	-
Child Evangelism Fellowship, Inc.	1988	-	-	-	1	-
Christian Aid Mission		-	-	-	261	-
Church of the Nazarene	1998	-	-	-	-	-
Churches of Christ		1	-	-	-	-
East-West Ministries International		-	-	-	10	-
Evangelical Friends Mission	1994	4	-	-	-	-
Evangelism Resources	2000	-	-	-	-	-
General Conf. Mennonite Church	1983	2	-	-	-	-
Global Fellowship		-	-	-	3	2
Good News for India	1999	-	-	-	3	-
Gospel for Asia	1979	-	-	-	-	-
Greater Grace World Outreach	1994	-	-	-	-	1
International Needs - USA	1975	-	-	-	65	-
International Partnership Ministries, Inc.	1999	-	-	-	-	1
International Teams, U.S.A.		-	-	-	-	-
InterServe/USA	1952	3	-	-	-	-
Medical Ambassadors International	1984	-	-	-	7	-
Mennonite Mission Network	1957	2	-	-	-	-
Mission ONE, Inc.		-	-	-	-	-
Mission To Unreached Peoples	1985	2	5	-	-	-
Missionary Ventures International	1993	2	-	-	-	-
Navigators, U.S. Intl. Missions Group		2	-	-	-	-
New Directions International	1991	-	-	-	75	-
New Life League International	1961	-	-	-	6	-
OC International, Inc.	1999	-	6	-	-	-
Operation Mobilization, Inc.		4	-	6	-	-
Outreach To Asia Nationals	1988	-	-	2	30	-
Paraclete, Inc.		-	-	-	-	-
Partners International	1999	-	-	-	-	-
Presbyterian Church (USA)		10	13	-	-	-
Project Christ International	1993	-	-	-	-	7
Rock the World Youth Mission Alliance		-	-	-	-	-
Seventh-day Adventists Gen. Conf.	1957	2	3	1	-	11
United Church Board for World Ministries		-	10	-	-	-
Walk Thru The Bible Ministries	1999	-	-	-	2	-
WEC International	1967	-	-	-	-	5
Wesleyan World Missions	1950	-	-	-	-	2
World Concern	1980	4	-	-	-	-
World Help	1996	-	-	-	39	-
World Mission Prayer League Inc.	1956	4	-	2	-	2

		Personnel from U.S.			Other Countries	
	First Year	4+ yrs.	2-4 yrs.	1-2 yrs.	Citizens	Not Citizens
World Missions Far Corners, Inc.	2001	-	-	-	6	1
	Totals:	43	37	13	850	33

Netherlands

	First Year	4+ yrs.	2-4 yrs.	1-2 yrs.	Citizens	Not Citizens
Assemblies of God World Missions	1965	4	-	-	-	-
Baptist Bible Fellowship Intl.	1979	2	-	-	-	-
Baptist Mid-Missions	1954	5	-	-	-	-
BCM International		1	-	-	9	-
Biblical Ministries Worldwide	1958	2	-	-	1	-
Brethren Assemblies		2	-	-	-	-
Campus Crusade for Christ, Intl.	1969	-	-	7	-	-
CBInternational	1985	2	-	1	-	-
Christian Associates International	1987	15	2	2	2	-
Church of God (Cleveland, TN)	1982	1	-	-	-	2
Church of the Nazarene	1967	-	-	-	-	-
Churches of Christ	1946	5	-	-	-	-
Evangelical Free Church Mission	1997	2	-	-	-	-
Faith Christian Fellowship Intl.	1993	-	2	-	-	-
Global Outreach Mission		-	-	-	3	-
Greater Europe Mission	1952	10	-	-	-	-
Greater Grace World Outreach	1977	-	-	-	-	4
Habitat for Humanity International	1994	1	-	-	1	-
International Missionary Center		2	-	-	-	-
International Teams, U.S.A.		-	1	-	-	-
Mennonite Mission Network	2000	-	-	-	-	-
Trans World Radio		6	-	-	-	5
WEC International	1948	-	-	-	-	34
Word of Life Fellowship	1978	-	-	-	2	-
World Harvest Mission	1989	4	-	-	-	-
Wycliffe Bible Translators USA		17	-	-	-	-
Youth for Christ/USA, World Outreach		1	-	-	-	-
	Totals:	82	5	10	18	45

Netherlands Antilles

	First Year	4+ yrs.	2-4 yrs.	1-2 yrs.	Citizens	Not Citizens
Assemblies of God World Missions	1983	2	-	2	-	-
Child Evangelism Fellowship, Inc.		2	-	-	-	-
Church of God of Prophecy		-	-	-	7	-
Global Outreach Mission		2	-	-	1	-
Trans World Radio		8	-	-	-	-
	Totals:	14	-	2	8	-

New Caledonia

	First Year	4+ yrs.	2-4 yrs.	1-2 yrs.	Citizens	Not Citizens
Seventh-day Adventists Gen. Conf.	1925	2	-	-	-	2
	Totals:	2	-	-	-	2

New Zealand

	First Year	4+ yrs.	2-4 yrs.	1-2 yrs.	Citizens	Not Citizens
Advent Christian General Conf.	1995	2	-	-	2	-
Asian Outreach U.S.A.		-	-	-	-	-
Baptist Bible Fellowship Intl.	1971	10	4	2	-	-
Baptist Mid-Missions	1973	8	-	-	-	-
Biblical Ministries Worldwide	1967	11	-	-	-	-
Campus Crusade for Christ, Intl.	1972	6	-	3	35	-

	Personnel from U.S.				Other Countries	
	First Year	4+ yrs.	2-4 yrs.	1-2 yrs.	Citizens	Not Citizens
Christian Churches/Churches of Christ		8	-	-	-	-
Church of God (Cleveland, TN)	1987	2	-	-	-	-
Church of God of Prophecy		-	-	-	-	2
Church of the Nazarene	1952	-	-	-	-	-
Churches of Christ	1844	5	-	-	21	-
Elim Fellowship, Intl. Dept.	1964	2	-	-	-	2
Every Home for Christ International	1982	-	-	-	2	-
Fellowship International Mission	1995	1	-	-	-	1
Gospel Fellowship Association	1998	2	-	-	-	-
International Teams, U.S.A.		-	-	-	-	4
Navigators, U.S. Intl. Missions Group		-	1	-	-	-
Paraclete, Inc.	1999	-	2	-	-	-
Presbyterian Church (USA)		4	-	-	-	-
Teen Missions International	1996	-	-	-	1	-
UFM International		-	-	-	2	-
WEC International	1953	2	-	-	-	47
Word of Life Fellowship	1983	-	-	-	2	-
World Baptist Fellowship Mission Agency		4	-	2	-	-
Wycliffe Bible Translators USA		14	-	-	-	-
Youth for Christ/USA, World Outreach Div.		1	-	-	-	-
Totals:		82	7	7	65	56

Nicaragua

	First Year	4+ yrs.	2-4 yrs.	1-2 yrs.	Citizens	Not Citizens
ABWE	1998	4	-	-	-	-
American Baptist Chs. in the U.S.A.	1917	10	-	-	-	-
Assemblies of God World Missions	1936	15	-	12	-	-
Baptist Bible Fellowship Intl.	1969	2	3	6	-	-
Baptist Medical & Dental Mission Intl., Inc.	1974	4	-	-	26	-
Brethren in Christ World Missions	1965	-	-	2	7	-
CAM International	1900	6	-	-	1	5
Campus Crusade for Christ, Intl.	1999	-	-	-	-	1
Caring Partners International, Inc.	1991	-	-	-	-	-
Christian Aid Ministries		-	8	-	10	-
Christian Reformed World Missions	1996	2	1	-	-	-
Christian Reformed World Relief Comte.	1973	1	-	-	2	-
Church of God (Cleveland, TN)	1950	2	-	2	-	-
Church of the Nazarene	1937	-	-	-	-	-
Churches of Christ		3	-	-	2	-
Compassion International, Inc.	2002	-	-	-	6	-
Equip, Inc.		2	-	-	2	-
Evangelical Lutheran Church in America	1980	-	-	1	-	-
Every Home for Christ International	1965	-	-	-	4	-
Food for the Hungry, Inc.	1994	1	2	1	-	-
Globe Missionary Evangelism	1997	1	-	-	-	-
Habitat for Humanity International	1984	-	2	-	21	-
International Gospel Outreach	2002	-	-	2	2	-
International Missionary Center		2	-	-	-	-
Intl. Pentecostal Holiness Ch. World Mins.	1994	3	-	-	-	-
Larry Jones International Ministries	1989	-	-	-	6	-
Living Water Teaching International	1986	-	-	-	4	-
Medical Ambassadors International	1999	-	-	-	-	-
Mission to the Americas		-	-	-	2	-

	Personnel from U.S.				Other Countries	
	First Year	4+ yrs.	2-4 yrs.	1-2 yrs.	Citizens	Not Citizens
Missionary Ventures International	1995	4	-	-	-	-
National Baptist Convention USA, Inc.	1958	-	-	-	1	-
Pentecostal Church of God		2	-	-	-	-
Presbyterian Church (USA)		4	5	6	-	-
Reformed Church in America, Gen. Syn.	1991	-	-	-	2	-
Rosedale Mennonite Missions	1973	2	-	-	-	-
Samaritan's Purse	1992	-	-	-	1	-
Self-Help International	1999	-	-	-	1	-
Seventh-day Adventists Gen. Conf.	1928	-	-	-	-	2
United Church Board for World Ministries		-	1	-	-	-
Totals:		70	22	32	100	8

Niger

	First Year	4+ yrs.	2-4 yrs.	1-2 yrs.	Citizens	Not Citizens
Assemblies of God World Missions		4	-	5	-	-
Campus Crusade for Christ, Intl.	1991	-	-	-	25	-
Child Evangelism Fellowship, Inc.	1994	-	-	-	1	-
Christian Reformed World Relief Comte.	1993	-	-	-	-	1
Elim Fellowship, Intl. Dept.	1991	8	-	-	-	8
Evangelical Baptist Missions		2	-	2	-	-
Every Home for Christ International	1996	-	-	-	5	-
Fellowship International Mission	1976	2	-	-	-	1
Gospel Revival Ministries	1997	-	-	-	5	-
Medical Ambassadors International	1997	-	-	-	3	-
Mission to the World (PCA), Inc.	1993	2	-	-	-	-
Reformed Church in America, Gen. Syn.	2000	2	-	-	-	-
Seventh-day Adventists Gen. Conf.	1987	-	-	-	-	2
SIM USA	1924	57	-	4	-	-
Wycliffe Bible Translators USA		32	-	-	-	-
Totals:		109	-	11	39	12

Nigeria

	First Year	4+ yrs.	2-4 yrs.	1-2 yrs.	Citizens	Not Citizens
ACM International	1953	3	-	-	-	-
Advent Christian General Conf.	1960	-	-	-	20	-
Assemblies of God World Missions	1939	4	-	2	-	-
Baptist Bible Fellowship Intl.	1987	4	-	-	-	-
Baptist International Outreach	1988	-	-	-	7	-
Bible League, The	1977	-	-	-	38	-
Bible Missionary Church		2	-	-	-	-
Bible Training Centre for Pastors	1998	-	-	-	1	-
BILD International		-	-	-	-	-
Brethren Assemblies		6	-	-	-	2
Campus Crusade for Christ, Intl.	1969	5	-	-	387	-
Child Evangelism Fellowship, Inc.	1982	-	-	-	7	-
Christian Aid Mission		-	-	-	98	-
Christian Blind Mission Intl.	1997	-	1	-	-	-
Christian Churches / Churches of Christ		2	-	-	-	-
Christian Mission for the Deaf	1960	-	-	-	1	-
Christian Reformed World Missions	1940	24	2	9	-	-
Christian Reformed World Relief Comte.	1969	-	-	-	1	1
Church of God (Cleveland, TN)	1951	1	-	-	-	-
Church of God (Holiness)	1988	2	-	-	-	2
Church of the Nazarene	1977	1	-	-	-	2

	First Year	Personnel from U.S. 4+ yrs.	2-4 yrs.	1-2 yrs.	Other Countries Citizens	Not Citizens
Churches of Christ	1946	14	-	-	6	-
Development Associates Intl. (DAI)	1995	-	-	-	-	-
Elim Fellowship, Intl. Dept.	1975	2	-	-	-	2
Equip, Inc.		-	-	-	2	-
Evangel Bible Translators	1982	-	-	-	1	-
Evangelical Baptist Missions		2	-	-	-	-
Evangelical Lutheran Ch. in America	1913	1	-	-	-	-
Evangelism Resources	1994	-	-	-	4	-
Every Home for Christ International	1976	-	-	-	3	-
Faith Christian Fellowship Intl.	1991	-	2	-	-	-
Fellowship International Mission	1977	4	-	-	-	-
Food for the Hungry, Inc.	2000	-	2	-	-	-
Gospel Revival Ministries	1990	-	-	-	28	-
Hundredfold Ministries International	1989	-	-	-	-	-
International Christian Ministries	2000	-	-	-	6	-
Intl. Institute for Christian Studies	1988	5	2	-	2	-
International Missionary Center		-	-	-	-	6
Ireland Outreach International Inc.	1994	-	-	-	12	-
Lutheran Church—Missouri Syn.	1936	7	-	-	-	-
Mennonite Mission Network	1959	-	-	-	-	-
Mission Ministries, Inc.	1998	-	-	-	2	-
Mission to the World (PCA), Inc.	1990	1	2	-	-	-
Missionary Ventures International	1990	1	-	-	-	-
N. American Baptist Conf. Intl. Missions	1961	2	-	-	-	2
Precept Ministries International	1996	-	-	-	2	-
Presbyterian Evangelistic Fellowship		1	-	-	2	-
Ripe for Harvest, Inc.	1998	1	-	-	-	-
Seventh-day Adventists Gen. Conf.	1914	6	-	2	-	4
SIM USA	1893	65	-	5	-	-
The Master's Mission, Inc.	1960	1	-	-	2	-
Village Ministries International, Inc.	1990	-	-	-	25	-
Walk Thru The Bible Ministries	2000	-	-	-	5	-
Word of Life Fellowship	2000	2	-	-	4	-
World-Wide Missions	1967	-	-	-	10	-
Wycliffe Bible Translators USA		31	-	-	-	-
Totals:		200	11	18	676	21

Norway

	First Year	4+ yrs.	2-4 yrs.	1-2 yrs.	Citizens	Not Citizens
ABWE	1978	8	-	-	-	-
Churches of Christ	1960	-	-	-	6	-
Evangelical Lutheran Church in America	1986	2	-	1	-	-
Foursquare Missions International		-	-	-	1	-
Intl. Pentecostal Holiness Ch. World Mins.	1992	3	-	-	-	-
Navigators, U.S. Intl. Missions Group		2	-	-	-	-
Seventh-day Adventists Gen. Conf.	1931	2	-	-	-	-
Wycliffe Bible Translators USA		1	-	-	-	-
Totals:		18	-	1	7	-

Oceania - General

	First Year	4+ yrs.	2-4 yrs.	1-2 yrs.	Citizens	Not Citizens
Final Frontiers Foundation, Inc.	1996	-	-	-	3	-
Great Commission Center International	1999	-	-	-	-	-
Southern Baptist Conv. Intl. Msn. Bd.		-	-	-	-	-

	Personnel from U.S.			Other Countries	
First Year	4+ yrs.	2-4 yrs.	1-2 yrs.	Citizens	Not Citizens
Surfing the Nations	1998	4	3	-	-	3
World Mission Prayer League Inc.	1990	2	-	-	-	-
Wycliffe Bible Translators USA		22	-	-	-	-
Totals:		28	3	-	3	3

Oman

Reformed Church in America, Gen. Syn.	1997	2	-	-	1	-
Totals:		2	-	-	1	-

Pakistan

Campus Crusade for Christ, Intl.	1960	-	-	-	175	-
CBInternational	1954	9	-	-	-	-
Child Evangelism Fellowship, Inc.	1955	-	-	-	1	-
Christar	1953	11	8	1	-	-
Christian Aid Mission		-	-	-	80	-
Christian Blind Mission Intl.	1982	-	1	-	-	-
Christian Churches / Churches of Christ		-	-	-	2	-
Church of God of Prophecy		-	-	-	2	-
Church of the Nazarene	1996	-	-	-	-	-
Church World Service & Witness	1950	-	-	-	7	-
Gospel for Asia	1979	-	-	-	-	-
Greater Grace World Outreach	1987	-	-	-	-	1
International Teams, U.S.A.		-	1	-	-	-
InterServe/USA	1852	11	-	-	1	-
Key Communications		-	-	-	1	-
MBMS International	1988	-	2	-	-	-
Mission ONE, Inc.		-	-	-	-	-
Missionary Ventures International	1996	1	-	-	-	-
Partners International	1975	-	-	-	-	-
Presbyterian Church (USA)		20	-	-	-	-
SAND International	2000	-	-	-	2	-
Seventh-day Adventists Gen. Conf.	1914	2	-	2	-	6
SIM USA	1957	1	-	-	-	-
Westminister Biblical Missions	1973	1	-	-	20	-
World Mission Prayer League Inc.	1946	2	-	-	-	-
World Witness, Assoc. Reformed Presb. Ch.	1906	7	-	-	350	-
Totals:		65	12	3	641	7

Palestine

Christ Community Church	1929	-	-	-	3	-
Helps International Ministries		2	-	-	-	-
Totals:		2	-	-	3	-

Panama

American Baptist Churches in the U.S.A.	2001	1	-	-	-	-
Assemblies of God World Missions	1967	8	-	3	-	-
Baptist Bible Fellowship Intl.	1976	8	-	-	-	-
CAM International	1940	8	-	-	-	8
Campus Crusade for Christ, Intl.	1965	2	-	-	17	-
Christian and Missionary Alliance	1999	-	4	-	-	-
Christian Churches / Churches of Christ		2	-	2	-	-
Church of God (Cleveland, TN)	1935	-	-	-	-	2

		Personnel from U.S.			Other Countries	
	First Year	4+ yrs.	2-4 yrs.	1-2 yrs.	Citizens	Not Citizens
Church of God of Prophecy		-	-	-	2	2
Church of the Nazarene	1953	-	-	-	-	-
Churches of Christ	1963	1	-	-	-	-
Engineering Ministries International	2001	1	-	-	-	-
Evangelical Lutheran Church in America	1990	2	-	-	-	-
Flwshp. of Assoc. of Medical Evangelism	1989	-	-	-	12	-
Foursquare Missions International	1928	2	-	-	-	2
Free Will Baptists, Inc., National Assoc.	1971	6	-	-	-	-
Gospel Fellowship Association	2002	2	-	-	-	-
Gospel Missionary Union	1953	5	-	-	-	-
International Missionary Center		2	-	-	-	-
Intl. Pentecostal Holiness Ch. World Mins.	1988	4	-	-	-	-
Living Water Teaching International	2001	-	-	-	-	5
Lutheran Church—Missouri Syn.	1941	-	2	8	-	-
Mission to the Americas		-	-	-	2	-
National Baptist Convention of America	1969	-	-	-	4	-
New Tribes Mission	1953	80	-	1	-	3
Word of Life Fellowship	1988	4	-	-	2	7
	Totals:	138	6	14	39	29

Papua New Guinea

ABWE	1967	21	-	-	-	-
Apostolic Christian Ch. Foundation, Inc.	1961	2	-	-	-	-
Baptist Bible Fellowship Intl.	1961	16	-	-	-	-
Bible Missionary Church		8	-	-	-	-
Brethren Assemblies		5	-	-	-	1
Campus Crusade for Christ, Intl.	1978	-	-	-	4	-
Christian Aid Mission		-	-	-	7	-
Christian Blind Mission Intl.	1988	-	2	-	-	-
Christian Churches / Churches of Christ		30	6	-	-	-
Church of the Nazarene	1955	25	3	-	-	1
Churches of Christ	1971	7	-	-	-	-
Evangelical Lutheran Church in America	1886	5	-	2	-	1
Evangelism Explosion International		-	-	-	-	10
Foursquare Missions International	1956	2	-	-	-	-
FRIENDS in Action, International		-	6	-	-	-
Gospel Fellowship Association	1997	6	-	3	-	-
Habitat for Humanity International	1983	-	9	-	7	9
Kids Alive International	1992	1	-	-	-	-
Lutheran Bible Translators	1998	2	-	-	-	-
Lutheran Church—Missouri Synod	1948	4	2	-	-	-
Mission to the World (PCA), Inc.	1987	4	-	-	-	-
Mustard Seed, Inc., The	1974	2	-	-	15	2
New Life League International		-	-	-	-	-
New Tribes Mission	1950	339	-	35	-	52
Open Bible Standard Chs., Intl. Mins.	1973	4	-	-	-	-
Operation Mobilization, Inc.		2	-	-	-	-
Pioneer Bible Translators	1977	33	-	-	-	-
Pioneers	1980	14	-	-	1	-
Presbyterian Church (USA)		3	-	-	-	-
Seventh-day Adventists Gen. Conf.	1908	4	2	4	-	25
Wesleyan World Missions	1961	-	2	-	-	4

	First Year	Personnel from U.S. 4+ yrs.	2-4 yrs.	1-2 yrs.	Other Countries Citizens	Not Citizens
Word of Life Fellowship	2000	-	-	-	2	-
World Gospel Mission	1996	11	-	-	-	-
World-Wide Missions	1975	-	-	-	6	-
Wycliffe Associates USA	1998	-	-	2	-	-
Wycliffe Bible Translators USA		621	-	-	-	-
Totals:		1171	32	46	42	105

Paraguay

	First Year	4+ yrs.	2-4 yrs.	1-2 yrs.	Citizens	Not Citizens
ABWE	1976	15	-	-	-	-
Apostolic Christian Ch. Foundation, Inc.	1978	1	-	-	1	-
Assemblies of God World Missions	1945	12	-	3	-	-
Baptist Bible Fellowship Intl.	1980	2	-	-	-	-
BCM International		-	-	-	2	-
Brethren Assemblies		12	-	-	-	-
Campus Crusade for Christ, Intl.	1966	-	-	-	4	2
Christian Aid Mission		-	-	-	34	-
Christian and Missionary Alliance	2000	2	-	-	-	-
Church of God (Cleveland, TN)	1954	2	-	-	-	-
Church of God of Prophecy		-	-	-	4	-
Church of the Nazarene	1980	-	-	-	-	2
Churches of Christ	1965	8	-	-	-	-
Full Gospel Grace Fellowship	1940	-	-	-	2	-
General Conf. Mennonite Church	1952	2	-	-	-	-
Global Outreach Mission		2	-	-	-	-
Global Outreach, Ltd.		2	-	-	-	-
Grace Brethren International Missions	1999	-	-	-	-	2
Habitat for Humanity International	1996	-	2	-	-	-
International Partnership Ministries, Inc.	1995	-	-	-	2	1
Latin America Mission	2001	-	1	-	-	1
Literacy & Evangelism International		-	-	-	1	-
Living Water Teaching International	1990	-	-	-	-	-
MBMS International	1948	-	-	-	2	-
Mennonite Mission Network	1952	-	-	-	-	-
Missionary Ventures International	2002	1	-	-	-	-
New Tribes Mission	1946	67	-	2	1	-
Open Air Campaigners - Overseas Mins.	1992	-	-	-	2	-
Seventh-day Adventists Gen. Conf.	1900		-	-	-	2
SIM USA	1987	15	-	-	-	-
South America Mission	1991	2	-	-	-	2
South American Missionary Society	1998	1	-	-	-	-
The Mission Society	1988	10	-	1	-	-
United Church Board for World Mins.		-	2	-	-	-
Word of Life Fellowship	1979	2	-	-	9	3
World Gospel Mission	1986	7	-	-	-	-
World-Wide Missions	1963	-	-	-	1	-
Totals:		165	5	6	65	15

Peru

	First Year	4+ yrs.	2-4 yrs.	1-2 yrs.	Citizens	Not Citizens
ABWE	1929	49	-	-	-	-
Allegheny Wesleyan Methodist Missions	1972	2	-	-	-	-
Amazon Focus	1995	4	-	-	25	-
AMG International		-	-	-	2	-

	Personnel from U.S.				Other Countries	
	First Year	4+ yrs.	2-4 yrs.	1-2 yrs.	Citizens	Not Citizens
Assemblies of God World Missions	1919	12	-	6	-	-
Baptist Bible Fellowship Intl.	1958	12	-	2	-	-
Baptist International Outreach	1995	6	-	-	-	-
Baptist Mid-Missions	1937	31	-	-	-	-
BCM International	1995	-	-	-	18	-
Bible Missionary Church	1988	2	-	-	-	-
Brethren Assemblies		16	1	-	-	-
Bright Hope International	1999	-	-	-	12	-
Calvary International	2002	1	-	-	1	1
Campus Crusade for Christ, Intl.	1964	-	-	-	2	4
Child Evangelism Fellowship, Inc.	1946	-	-	-	1	-
Childcare International	1986	-	-	-	12	1
Christ for the City International	1989	-	-	-	-	-
Christian Aid Mission		-	-	-	64	-
Christian and Missionary Alliance	1925	15	1	-	-	-
Church of God (Cleveland, TN)	1947	2	-	-	-	-
Church of God of Prophecy		-	-	-	2	-
Church of the Nazarene	1914	7	2	-	-	1
Churches of Christ	1958	4	-	-	1	-
Compassion International, Inc.	1977	-	-	-	26	-
Eastern Mennonite Missions		2	-	-	-	1
Elim Fellowship, Intl. Dept.	1964	3	-	-	-	3
Evangelical Free Church Mission	1975	10	-	-	-	-
Food for the Hungry, Inc.	1982	-	6	-	-	-
Foursquare Missions International	1981	-	-	-	-	2
Global Outreach Mission		-	-	-	4	-
Habitat for Humanity International	1982	-	2	-	46	-
Hosanna / Faith Comes By Hearing	1996	-	-	-	2	-
Impact International		-	-	-	2	-
International Justice Mission		-	-	-	-	-
International Partnership Ministries, Inc.	1996	-	-	-	12	-
Intl. Pentecostal Holiness Ch. World Mins.	1996	-	-	-	-	2
Josue Yrion Wld. Evangelism Missions, Inc.	1997	-	-	-	1	-
Kids Alive International	1993	-	2	-	-	2
Latin America Mission	1975	4	-	-	2	2
Latin American Indian Ministries	1994	-	-	-	-	-
Literacy & Evangelism International	1998	2	-	-	-	-
MBMS International	1954	-	4	-	-	-
Medical Ambassadors International	1999	-	-	-	-	-
Mission to the World (PCA), Inc.	1987	30	8	-	-	-
Missionary Ventures International	1999	4	-	-	-	-
Network of International Christian Schools	2001	-	5	-	-	-
Northwest Medical Teams	2001	-	-	-	-	-
Pioneers	1997	8	-	-	-	-
Precept Ministries International	1992	-	-	-	1	-
Presbyterian Evangelistic Fellowship		4	-	-	2	-
Ripe for Harvest, Inc.	1999	1	1	-	-	-
Rock the World Youth Mission Alliance		-	-	-	-	-
Seventh-day Adventists Gen. Conf.	1898	4	2	2	-	6
SIM USA	1965	11	-	1	-	-
Source of Light Ministries International, Inc.	1975	-	-	-	3	-
South America Mission	1926	24	-	1	-	25

	Personnel from U.S.				Other Countries	
	First Year	4+ yrs.	2-4 yrs.	1-2 yrs.	Citizens	Not Citizens
South American Missionary Society	1979	1	-	-	-	1
TEAM (The Evangelical Alliance Mission)	1962	8	-	2	-	-
The Mission Society	1997	8	-	2	-	-
Walk Thru The Bible Ministries	2000	-	-	-	1	-
Wesleyan World Missions	1903	-	4	-	-	-
Word of Life Fellowship	1986	-	-	-	16	3
World Concern	1987	-	-	-	1	-
World Mission Prayer League Inc.	1985	4	-	-	-	-
World Missions Far Corners, Inc.	1963	4	-	-	10	-
World Reach, Inc.	1998	1	-	-	-	4
World Team	1941	2	-	-	-	-
Wycliffe Bible Translators USA		139	-	-	-	-
Totals:		437	38	16	269	58

Philippines

	First Year	4+ yrs.	2-4 yrs.	1-2 yrs.	Citizens	Not Citizens
ABWE	1927	43	-	-	-	-
ACM International	1998	2	-	-	-	-
Action International Ministries	1961	17	-	1	-	-
Advent Christian General Conf.	1950	3	-	-	25	-
American Baptist Chs. in the U.S.A.	1900	8	-	-	-	-
AMG International	1979	2	-	-	16	-
Artists In Christian Testimony	1990	2	-	-	-	-
Asian Outreach U.S.A.		-	-	-	-	-
Assemblies of God World Missions	1925	69	-	22	-	-
Back to the Bible International	1957	-	-	-	18	-
Baptist Bible Fellowship Intl.	1948	41	8	6	-	-
Baptist General Conference	1949	24	-	-	-	-
Baptist International Outreach	1998	2	-	-	-	-
BCM International	1981	-	-	-	12	-
Bethany Fellowship Missions	1982	3	-	-	-	1
Bible League, The	1972	-	-	-	17	-
Bible Missionary Church		2	-	-	-	-
Bible Training Centre for Pastors	2001	-	-	-	3	-
Brethren Assemblies		12	2	-	-	2
Cadence International	1952	-	2	-	1	1
Calvary International	1990	10	-	-	3	9
Campus Crusade for Christ, Intl.	1965	19	-	-	301	21
CBInternational	1955	34	-	8	-	-
Child Evangelism Fellowship, Inc.	1952	-	-	-	15	-
Childcare International	1998	-	-	-	8	-
Christ Community Church	1948	-	-	-	90	-
Christ to the Nations	1993	10	-	-	8	2
Christar	1954	29	-	-	-	-
Christian Aid Mission		-	-	-	253	-
Christian and Missionary Alliance	1902	28	5	-	-	-
Christian Blind Mission Intl.	1982	-	-	1	-	-
Christian Churches / Churches of Christ		40	-	-	10	-
Christian Reformed World Missions	1961	13	5	4	-	-
Christian Reformed World Relief Comt.	1970	-	-	-	-	1
Christians In Action, Inc.	1979	-	-	-	4	-
Church of God (Cleveland, TN)	1947	15	-	-	-	2
Church of God of Prophecy		-	-	-	6	-

	Personnel from U.S.			Other Countries	
	First Year	4+ yrs.	2-4 yrs.	1-2 yrs.	Citizens	Not Citizens
Church of the Nazarene	1946	16	6	-	-	3
Churches of Christ	1928	22	-	-	12	-
Commission to Every Nation	1994	11	-	-	1	1
Compassion International, Inc.	1972	-	-	-	34	-
Correll Missionary Ministries	1995	-	-	-	50	-
Covenant Celebration Ch. Global Outreach	1974	-	-	-	-	-
David Livingstone KURE Foundation		-	-	-	42	-
Elim Fellowship, International Dept.	1997	2	-	-	-	2
Emmanuel Intl. Mission (U.S.)	1985	1	-	-	-	-
Equip, Inc.		2	-	-	-	-
Evangel Bible Translators	1981	1	-	-	-	-
Evangelical Free Church Mission	1951	15	-	-	3	-
Evangelical Friends Mission	1978	-	-	-	2	-
Every Home for Christ International	1960	-	-	-	10	-
Faith Christian Fellowship Intl.	1989	2	-	4	-	-
Far East Broadcasting Company, Inc.	1948	18	-	-	200	-
Food for the Hungry, Inc.	1982	-	4	-	-	-
Free Gospel Church, Missions Dept.	1925	-	3	-	20	-
Free Methodist World Missions	1949	6	-	-	-	-
Frontier Mission Fellowship		5	-	-	-	-
General Baptists International	1957	3	-	-	-	-
Global Fellowship		-	-	-	150	-
Global Outreach, Ltd.		2	-	-	-	-
Globe Missionary Evangelism	1988	4	-	-	-	-
Go Ye Fellowship	2000	2	-	-	2	-
Good News Productions Intl.	1995	1	-	-	4	-
Gospel Fellowship Association	1978	14	-	-	-	-
Grace Brethren International Missions	1984	5	1	-	-	2
Habitat for Humanity International	1986	-	2	-	22	2
Harvest		-	-	-	1	-
Help for Christian Nationals, Inc.	1986	2	-	-	-	2
Hundredfold Ministries International	1988	-	-	-	-	-
Independent Faith Mission		2	-	-	-	-
International Aid		-	-	-	-	-
Intl. Christian Leprosy Mission, Inc. (USA)		-	-	-	4	-
International Gospel Outreach	1997	-	2	-	-	-
International Justice Mission	2000	-	2	-	4	-
International Missionary Center		-	-	-	-	2
International Needs - USA	1977	-	-	-	71	-
International Partnership Ministries, Inc.	2001	-	-	-	13	-
Intl. Pentecostal Holiness Ch. World Mins.	1975	6	-	-	-	-
International Teams, U.S.A.		-	-	-	36	-
JARON Ministries International	1998	-	-	-	1	-
Larry Jones International Ministries	1985	-	-	-	16	-
Literacy & Evangelism International		2	-	-	1	-
Lutheran Church—Missouri Syn.	1946	2	-	-	-	-
Medical Ambassadors International	1975	-	-	-	38	-
Medical Missions Philippines	1967	-	-	-	50	-
Mennonite Mission Network	1998	-	-	-	-	-
Mission Ministries, Inc.	1980	1	-	-	2	-
Mission to the World (PCA), Inc.	1991	7	3	-	-	-
Mission To Unreached Peoples	1987	2	-	-	1	-

	Personnel from U.S.			Other Countries	
	First Year	4+ yrs.	2-4 yrs.	1-2 yrs.	Citizens	Not Citizens

	First Year	4+ yrs.	2-4 yrs.	1-2 yrs.	Citizens	Not Citizens
Missionary Ventures International	2000	1	-	-	-	-
Missions To Japan, Inc.		1	-	-	-	-
Navigators, U.S. Intl. Missions Group		7	-	6	-	-
New Life League International	2000	-	-	1	-	-
New Tribes Mission	1951	104	-	4	2	2
N. American Baptist Conf. Intl. Missions	1986	4	-	-	-	2
OC International, Inc.	1952	14	6	-	6	-
Omega World Missions	1979	5	-	-	-	-
OMF International	1952	20	4	-	-	-
OMS International, Inc.	1982	6	-	-	-	-
Open Bible Standard Chs., Intl. Mins.	1978	3	-	-	-	-
Oriental Missionary Crusade		2	-	-	-	-
Partners International	1968	-	-	-	-	-
Pentecostal Church of God		6	-	-	-	-
Pilgrim Fellowship, Inc.	1998	2	-	-	-	-
Pocket Testament League	1978	-	-	-	8	-
Precept Ministries International	1996	-	-	-	2	-
Presbyterian Church (USA)		4	14	-	-	-
Reach Ministries International	1975	5	-	-	5	-
Ripe for Harvest, Inc.	2000	1	-	-	-	-
Salvation Army, U.S.A.	1937	2	-	-	-	-
SEND International	1947	25	-	1	-	9
Seventh-day Adventists Gen. Conf.	1906	29	7	9	-	30
SIM USA	1984	8	-	-	-	-
Source of Light Ministries Intl., Inc.	1980	-	-	-	13	-
Sowers International, The	1993	-	-	-	8	-
TEAM (The Evangelical Alliance Mission)	1987	19	-	3	-	-
Teen Missions International	1982	-	-	-	3	1
The Mission Society	1988	2	-	-	-	-
Things To Come Mission, Inc.	1958	-	-	-	20	-
Third World Baptist Missions	1991	2	-	-	53	-
Training Evangelistic Leadership	1977	5	-	-	8	1
UFM International	1985	9	-	-	-	-
United Church Board for World Ministries		-	4	-	-	-
United Evangelical Churches		2	-	-	-	2
Walk Thru The Bible Ministries	2000	-	-	-	16	-
Word of Life Fellowship	1973	-	-	-	16	3
World Help	1998	-	-	-	1	-
World Indigenous Missions	1992	2	-	3	-	-
World Mission Prayer League Inc.	1984	4	-	-	-	-
World Missions Far Corners, Inc.	1976	2	-	-	20	-
World Team	1981	21	-	-	-	-
World-Wide Missions	1971	-	-	-	12	-
Wycliffe Bible Translators USA		224	-	-	-	-
Totals:		1125	80	73	1773	103

Poland

	First Year	4+ yrs.	2-4 yrs.	1-2 yrs.	Citizens	Not Citizens
Assemblies of God World Missions	1925	2	-	-	-	-
Back to the Bible International	1993	-	-	-	6	-
Baptist Bible Fellowship Intl.	2001	-	-	2	-	-
BCM International		1	-	-	1	-
Bible League, The	1999	-	-	-	3	-

	Personnel from U.S.				Other Countries	
	First Year	4+ yrs.	2-4 yrs.	1-2 yrs.	Citizens	Not Citizens
Brethren Assemblies		-	4	-	-	-
Campus Crusade for Christ, Intl.	1977	3	-	8	96	-
CBInternational	1991	13	-	4	-	-
Child Evangelism Fellowship, Inc.	1989	-	-	-	2	-
Christian Aid Mission		-	-	-	3	-
Christian and Missionary Alliance	1993	2	-	-	-	-
Christian Churches / Churches of Christ		2	-	-	60	-
Church of the Nazarene	1999	-	-	-	-	-
Church Resource Ministries	1995	4	-	-	-	-
Churches of Christ	1983	1	-	-	8	-
Elim Fellowship, Intl. Dept.	1997	2	-	-	1	1
Envoy International		-	-	-	-	-
Evangelical Free Church Mission	1993	8	-	-	-	-
Fellowship International Mission	1991	1	-	-	-	-
Global Outreach, Ltd.		-	-	2	-	-
Greater Europe Mission	1993	4	-	-	-	-
Greater Grace World Outreach	1985	-	-	-	-	1
Habitat for Humanity International	1995	1	-	-	1	-
In Touch Mission International	1984	-	2	-	2	-
International Messengers	1991	12	-	-	15	1
International Missionary Center		4	-	-	-	2
International Teams, U.S.A.	1973	5	-	-	2	4
InterVarsity Christian Fellowship/USA		-	1	-	-	-
Literacy & Evangelism International		-	-	-	-	-
Lutheran Church—Missouri Syn.	1943	-	-	1	-	-
Mission To Unreached Peoples	1989	2	2	-	-	-
Pocket Testament League	1989	-	-	-	2	-
Presbyterian Church (USA)		2	-	-	-	-
Project Care		-	-	-	-	-
Ripe for Harvest, Inc.	2000	1	1	-	-	-
SAND International	1998	-	-	-	1	-
SEND International	1991	12	-	-	-	4
TEAM (The Evangelical Alliance Mission)		1	-	-	-	-
Word of Life Fellowship	1987	6	-	-	3	-
Worldwide Tentmakers, Inc.	1990	-	-	-	-	-
Totals:		89	10	17	206	13

Portugal

	First Year	4+ yrs.	2-4 yrs.	1-2 yrs.	Citizens	Not Citizens
ABWE	1978	27	-	-	-	-
Assemblies of God World Missions	1967	9	-	3	-	-
Assoc. of Free Lutheran Congregations		-	2	-	1	-
Baptist Bible Fellowship Intl.	1987	6	-	2	-	-
BCM International		-	-	-	2	-
Brethren Assemblies		4	-	-	-	1
Campus Crusade for Christ, Intl.	1975	-	-	-	-	5
CBInternational	1945	4	-	-	-	-
Christian Associates International	1997	4	-	-	-	2
Christian Churches / Churches of Christ		4	-	-	-	-
Church of God of Prophecy		-	-	-	1	-
Church of the Nazarene	1973	-	1	-	-	3
Church Planting International	1989	-	-	-	1	-
Churches of Christ	1969	2	-	-	6	-

		Personnel from U.S.			Other Countries	
	First Year	4+ yrs.	2-4 yrs.	1-2 yrs.	Citizens	Not Citizens
CLC Ministries International		-	2	-	-	-
Evangelical Free Church Mission	1994	2	-	-	-	-
Global Outreach Mission		2	-	-	-	-
Grace Brethren International Missions	1990	7	-	-	-	2
Greater Europe Mission	1971	11	-	-	-	-
Intl. Pentecostal Holiness Ch. World Mins.	2001	-	-	-	-	1
InterVarsity Christian Fellowship/USA		1	-	-	-	-
MBMS International	1986	-	4	-	-	-
Mission to the World (PCA), Inc.	1977	8	1	-	-	-
Pocket Testament League	1985	-	-	-	-	2
Presbyterian Church (USA)		2	-	-	-	-
Salvation Army, U.S.A.	1971	1	-	-	-	-
SIM USA	1979	3	-	-	-	-
TEAM (The Evangelical Alliance Mission)		8	-	-	-	-
WEC International	1980	-	-	-	-	4
Word of Life Fellowship	1976	2	-	-	8	2
World Partners USA	1991	4	-	-	-	-
Youth for Christ/USA, World Outreach	1996	2	-	-	-	-
Totals:		113	10	5	19	22

Puerto Rico

Apostolic Christian Ch. Foundation, Inc.	1996	2	-	-	-	4
Baptist Bible Fellowship Intl.	1955	5	-	-	-	-
Baptist Mid-Missions	1959	6	-	-	-	-
Bible League, The	2002	-	-	-	2	-
Biblical Ministries Worldwide	1986	2	-	-	-	-
Brethren Assemblies		1	-	-	-	1
Christian Churches/Churches of Christ		5	-	-	5	-
Church of the Nazarene	1944	-	-	-	-	-
Evangelical Lutheran Church in America	1898	2	-	-	-	-
Gospel Fellowship Association	1963	4	-	-	-	-
Grace Ministries International	1961	6	-	-	-	-
International Partnership Ministries, Inc.	2000	-	-	-	2	-
Lutheran Church—Missouri Syn.	1993	-	2	2	-	-
Open Door Baptist Missions	1995	2	-	-	-	-
Ripe for Harvest, Inc.	1997	1	-	-	-	-
Seventh-day Adventists Gen. Conf.	1901	6	-	2	-	2
UFM International	1986	3	-	-	-	-
Wesleyan World Missions	1952	-	4	-	-	-
Wisconsin Evangelical Lutheran Syn.	1963	2	2	-	-	-
Totals:		47	8	4	9	7

Romania

ABWE	1990	9	-	-	-	-
All God's Children International	1991	-	-	-	2	-
AMG International	1992	-	-	-	13	-
Assemblies of God World Missions	1989	12	-	17	-	-
Baptist Bible Fellowship Intl.	1990	12	2	1	-	-
Baptist International Evangelistic Mins.		-	-	-	16	-
Baptist Mid-Missions	1993	4	-	-	-	-
Bible League, The	1992	-	-	-	15	-
Brethren Assemblies		5	1	-	-	-

	Personnel from U.S.			Other Countries	
	First Year	4+ yrs.	2-4 yrs.	1-2 yrs.	Citizens	Not Citizens
Calvary Commission, Inc.	1990	2	4	3	-	-
Campus Crusade for Christ, Intl.	1980	15	-	2	107	4
CBInternational	1991	8	-	-	-	-
Christian Aid Ministries		-	32	-	100	-
Christian Aid Mission		-	-	-	2	-
Christian Outreach International	2002	-	-	-	1	1
Christian Reformed World Relief Comte.	1997	1	2	-	2	-
Church of God of Prophecy		-	-	-	1	-
Church of the Nazarene	1992	1	-	-	-	-
Church Resource Ministries	1990	6	-	-	-	-
Churches of Christ	1964	17	-	-	1	-
Commission to Every Nation	2001	2	-	-	-	-
Eastern European Outreach, Inc.	1980	2	-	-	2	-
Envoy International		-	-	-	-	-
Evangelical Baptist Missions	1990	4	-	-	-	-
Evangelical Free Church Mission	1991	23	1	-	-	-
Food for the Hungry, Inc.	1991	4	8	1	-	-
Global Outreach, Ltd.		10	-	-	-	-
Globe Missionary Evangelism	1997	-	2	-	-	-
Go Ye Fellowship	1998	1	-	-	-	-
Greater Europe Mission	1993	11	3	-	-	-
Greater Grace World Outreach	1992	-	-	-	2	-
Habitat for Humanity International	1995	1	-	1	1	1
Heart to Heart Intl. Ministries	1998	1	6	-	5	-
In Touch Mission International	1967	-	-	-	5	-
International Messengers	1996	7	-	-	12	-
International Needs-USA	1992	-	-	-	11	-
Intl. Pentecostal Holiness Ch. World Mins.	1996	2	1	-	-	-
International Teams, U.S.A.	1973	6	5	-	-	-
InterVarsity Christian Fellowship/USA		2	-	-	-	-
Kids Alive International	1989	1	-	-	1	-
Larry Jones International Ministries	1989	-	-	-	5	-
Lifewater International	1992	-	-	-	1	-
Literacy & Evangelism International		-	-	-	-	-
Medical Ambassadors International	1992	2	-	-	3	-
Mission to the World (PCA), Inc.		-	-	-	-	-
Navigators, U.S. Intl. Missions Group		-	1	-	-	-
Northwest Medical Teams	1997	-	-	-	-	-
OC International, Inc.	1996	4	2	3	-	6
Open Bible Standard Churches Intl. Mins.	1992	1	-	-	-	-
Presbyterian Church (USA)		5	-	-	-	-
Project Care		-	-	-	-	-
Ripe for Harvest, Inc.	1999	1	-	-	-	-
Romanian Missionary Society	1968	-	-	-	2	-
SEND International	1993	2	-	-	-	1
Source of Light Ministries Intl., Inc.	1992	-	-	-	4	-
The Master's Mission, Inc.	1999	-	-	1	1	-
TITUS International	1998	2	-	-	8	-
UFM International	1991	2	-	-	2	-
Walk Thru The Bible Ministries	2000	-	-	-	2	-
Word of Life Fellowship	1993	-	-	-	18	2
World Help	1991	-	-	-	1	-

	First Year	4+ yrs.	2-4 yrs.	1-2 yrs.	Citizens	Not Citizens
		Personnel from U.S.			Other Countries	
World Indigenous Missions	2001	-	-	2	-	-
World Mission Prayer League Inc.	1994	2	-	-	-	-
World Reach, Inc.	1998	-	-	-	-	2
Totals:		190	70	31	346	17

Russia

	First Year	4+ yrs.	2-4 yrs.	1-2 yrs.	Citizens	Not Citizens
All God's Children International		-	-	-	-	-
Assemblies of God World Missions		24	-	6	-	-
Back to the Bible International	1995	-	-	-	10	-
Baptist International Evangelistic Mins.		3	-	-	40	2
Baptist Mid-Missions	1985	6	-	-	-	-
BCM International		-	1	-	2	-
Bible League, The	1992	-	-	-	66	-
Bible Missionary Church	1992	4	-	-	-	-
Brethren Assemblies		7	4	-	-	-
Cadence International	1997	-	25	-	21	4
Calvary International	1992	5	-	-	2	2
Campus Crusade for Christ, Intl.	1991	45	-	17	116	17
CBInternational	1991	10	2	-	-	-
Centers for Apologetics Research (CFAR)	1993	-	-	-	5	-
Child Evangelism Fellowship, Inc.	1989	-	-	-	2	2
Christ for the Lost World	1994	-	-	-	12	-
Christ to the Nations	1996	4	-	-	4	-
Christian Aid Mission		-	-	-	14	-
Christian and Missionary Alliance	1993	24	5	-	-	-
Christian Associates International	1993	1	-	-	-	-
Christian Churches / Churches of Christ		16	4	2	6	-
Christian Ministries International (C.M.I.)		-	2	-	-	-
Christian Reformed World Missions	1994	-	-	1	-	1
Church of God (Cleveland, TN)	1992	5	-	-	-	5
Church of God of Prophecy		-	-	-	3	2
Church of the Nazarene	1992	7	1	-	-	-
Church Resource Ministries	1990	11	-	-	-	-
Churches of Christ	1952	30	-	-	34	-
Development Associates Intl. (DAI)	2001	-	-	-	1	-
Eastern European Outreach, Inc.	1988	-	-	-	12	-
East-West Ministries International	1993	-	-	-	28	-
Evangelical Baptist Missions		1	-	-	-	-
Evangelical Free Church Mission	1993	21	-	-	2	-
Evangelical Lutheran Church in America	1994	2	-	5	-	1
Evangelical Mennonite Ch. Intl. Mins.	2000	2	-	-	-	-
Evangelical Presbyterian Church	1995	2	-	-	-	-
Evangelism Explosion International		-	-	-	-	10
Every Home for Christ International	1991	-	-	-	17	-
Far East Broadcasting Company, Inc.	1992	-	-	-	50	-
Free Will Baptists, Inc., National Assoc.	1999	2	-	-	-	-
General Conf. Mennonite Church	1993	-	-	-	-	3
Global Outreach Mission	1994	4	-	-	-	-
Global Outreach, Ltd.		2	-	-	-	-
Global Strategy Mission Assoc.	1991	2	28	5	1	-
Globe Missionary Evangelism	1992	1	-	-	-	-
Gospel Missionary Union	1993	7	-	-	-	-

		Personnel from U.S.			Other Countries	
	First Year	4+ yrs.	2-4 yrs.	1-2 yrs.	Citizens	Not Citizens
Greater Europe Mission	1995	1	-	-	-	-
Greater Grace World Outreach	1991	-	-	-	1	4
HCJB World Radio		2	-	-	-	-
Help for Christian Nationals, Inc.	1996	-	-	-	2	-
Hundredfold Ministries International	1998	-	-	-	-	-
InterAct Ministries	1991	9	-	-	-	-
International Cassette Bible Institute	1998	-	-	-	3	-
International Gospel Outreach	1995	2	-	-	-	-
Intl. Institute for Christian Studies	1991	-	-	1	-	3
International Teams, U.S.A.	1979	3	-	-	-	-
InterVarsity Christian Fellowship/USA	1991	6	-	-	-	-
Jews for Jesus	1993	-	-	-	10	-
Larry Jones International Ministries	1992	-	-	-	17	1
Lutheran Church—Missouri Syn.	1992	6	4	4	-	-
Mennonite Mission Network	1993	2	-	-	-	-
Mission Aviation Fellowship	1993	-	2	-	-	-
Mission Possible Foundation, Inc.		-	-	-	-	-
Mission to the World (PCA), Inc.	1992	1	-	-	-	-
Mission To Unreached Peoples	1993	3	-	-	-	-
Missionary Ventures International	1994	1	-	-	-	-
Navigators, U.S. Intl. Missions Group		40	-	2	-	-
New Tribes Mission	1992	18	-	-	-	2
OMS International, Inc.		8	-	-	-	5
Operation Mobilization, Inc.		2	-	1	-	-
Outreach To Asia Nationals	2001	-	2	-	-	-
Pentecostal Church of God		2	-	-	-	-
Perimeter Church, Global Outreach	1985	-	-	-	45	-
Peter Deyneka Russian Ministries	1991	3	-	-	403	1
Precept Ministries International	1994	-	-	-	2	-
Presbyterian Church (USA)		7	-	-	-	-
Presbyterian Evangelistic Fellowship		2	-	-	-	-
Project Care		-	-	-	-	-
Ripe for Harvest, Inc.	1996	3	1	1	-	-
Salvation Army, U.S.A.	1913	8	-	-	-	-
SEND International	1992	15	-	-	-	4
Seventh-day Adventists Gen. Conf.	1886	5	6	2	-	18
TEAM (The Evangelical Alliance Mission)		8	-	-	-	-
Team Expansion, Inc.	2002	2	-	-	-	-
The Mission Society	1995	5	-	3	-	-
VELA Ministries International	1993	-	-	1	-	-
Walk Thru The Bible Ministries	2000	-	-	-	29	-
Wesleyan World Missions	1992	-	10	-	-	-
Wisconsin Evangelical Lutheran Syn.	1991	6	-	-	-	-
World Harvest Mission	1996	-	-	-	-	-
World Harvest Now, Inc.		-	4	-	3	-
World Help	1991	-	-	-	2	-
World Indigenous Missions	1996	2	-	-	-	-
World Partners USA	1994	5	-	-	-	2
World Reach, Inc.	1991	2	-	-	-	-
World Witness, Assoc. Reformed Presb. Ch.	1993	10	-	-	10	-
Totals:		437	101	51	975	89

		Personnel from U.S.			Other Countries	
	First Year	4+ yrs.	2-4 yrs.	1-2 yrs.	Citizens	Not Citizens

Rwanda

	First Year	4+ yrs.	2-4 yrs.	1-2 yrs.	Citizens	Not Citizens
African Enterprise, Inc.	1988	-	-	-	15	-
Assemblies of God World Missions		6	-	-	-	-
Campus Crusade for Christ, Intl.	1980	-	-	-	32	-
CBInternational	1967	4	-	-	-	-
Christian Reformed World Relief Comte.	1994	-	1	-	-	-
Church of God of Prophecy		-	-	-	6	-
Church of the Nazarene	1990	3	-	-	-	1
Compassion International, Inc.	1980	-	-	-	19	-
Evangelical Friends Mission	1986	4	-	-	-	-
Free Methodist World Missions	1942	2	-	-	-	1
Global Outreach, Ltd.		1	-	-	-	-
Harvest	1998	-	-	-	1	-
International Gospel Outreach	2000	-	-	-	1	-
Mission ONE, Inc.		-	-	-	-	-
Seventh-day Adventists Gen. Conf.	1920	2	2	-	-	6
World Concern	1995	-	-	-	5	-
Totals:		22	3	-	79	8

Saint Kitts and Nevis

	First Year	4+ yrs.	2-4 yrs.	1-2 yrs.	Citizens	Not Citizens
Church of the Nazarene	1983	-	-	-	-	-
Seventh-day Adventists Gen. Conf.	1889	4	-	-	-	-
Totals:		4	-	-	-	-

Saint Lucia

	First Year	4+ yrs.	2-4 yrs.	1-2 yrs.	Citizens	Not Citizens
Church of the Nazarene	1972	-	-	-	-	-
Grace Baptist Missions International		-	-	-	2	-
Totals:		-	-	-	2	-

Saint Martin

	First Year	4+ yrs.	2-4 yrs.	1-2 yrs.	Citizens	Not Citizens
Church of the Nazarene	1994	-	-	-	-	-
Totals:		-	-	-	-	-

Saint Vincent and the Grenadines

	First Year	4+ yrs.	2-4 yrs.	1-2 yrs.	Citizens	Not Citizens
Baptist Mid-Missions	1946	4	-	-	-	-
BCM International		-	-	-	1	-
Church of the Nazarene	1975	-	-	-	-	-
Ministries In Action	1974	-	1	-	1	-
Seventh-day Adventists Gen. Conf.	1889	-	-	2	-	-
World Team	1949	2	-	-	-	-
Totals:		6	1	2	2	-

Samoa

	First Year	4+ yrs.	2-4 yrs.	1-2 yrs.	Citizens	Not Citizens
Church of God of Prophecy		2	-	-	-	-
Church of the Nazarene	1964	-	-	-	-	-
Totals:		2	-	-	-	-

Sao Tome and Principe

	First Year	4+ yrs.	2-4 yrs.	1-2 yrs.	Citizens	Not Citizens
Church of the Nazarene	1997	2	-	-	-	-
Totals:		2	-	-	-	-

| | Personnel from U.S. | | | | Other Countries | |
	First Year	4+ yrs.	2-4 yrs.	1-2 yrs.	Citizens	Not Citizens
Senegal						
Africa Inter-Mennonite Mission	1996	-	2	5	-	-
Assemblies of God World Missions	1956	6	-	-	-	-
Bible League, The	2001	-	-	-	8	-
Brethren Assemblies		3	-	-	-	-
Campus Crusade for Christ, Intl.	1985	1	-	-	13	-
CBInternational	1962	12	-	1	-	-
Christian Reformed World Relief Comte.	1992	1	-	-	-	1
Church of God of Prophecy		-	-	-	1	-
Church of the Nazarene	1988	2	-	-	-	-
Evangelical Lutheran Ch. in America	1979	9	-	-	-	-
International Missionary Center		3	-	-	-	-
Mennonite Mission Network	1996	7	-	-	-	-
Mission to the World (PCA), Inc.	1992	7	-	-	-	-
Mission: Moving Mountains, Inc.	1995	2	-	5	-	1
New Tribes Mission	1954	63	-	8	-	20
Open Door Baptist Missions	1998	2	-	-	-	-
Partners International	1991	-	-	-	-	-
Pioneers	1991	4	-	-	9	-
Reformed Ch. in America, Gen. Syn.		-	-	-	2	-
Seventh-day Adventists Gen. Conf.	1952	-	-	-	-	2
SIM USA	1984	7	-	-	-	-
Things To Come Mission, Inc.	1993	-	1	-	-	-
WEC International	1936	1	-	-	-	45
Wycliffe Associates USA	1999	-	-	2	-	-
Wycliffe Bible Translators USA		58	-	-	-	-
Totals:		188	3	21	33	69
Serbia and Montenegro						
Bible League, The	2002	-	-	-	2	-
Child Evangelism Fellowship, Inc.	1989	2	-	-	4	-
Every Home for Christ International	1994	-	-	-	3	-
Global Action	1999	-	-	-	-	1
Navigators, U.S. Intl. Missions Group		2	-	-	-	-
Precept Ministries International	1994	-	-	-	2	-
Walk Thru The Bible Ministries	2000	-	-	-	2	-
Totals:		4	-	-	13	1
Sierra Leone						
Bible Training Centre for Pastors	1998	-	-	-	1	-
Campus Crusade for Christ, Intl.	1981	-	-	-	17	-
Christian Aid Mission		-	-	-	4	-
Christian Reformed World Missions	1980	2	-	-	-	-
Christian Reformed World Relief Comte.	1979	1	-	-	-	-
Christians In Action, Inc.	1969	-	-	-	2	-
Church of God of Prophecy		-	-	-	8	-
Every Home for Christ International	1993	-	-	-	4	-
Free Gospel Church, Msns. Dept.	1928	-	-	-	25	-
International Christian Ministries	2000	-	-	-	1	1
International Missionary Center		-	-	-	-	8
Literacy & Evangelism International		-	-	-	-	-
Lutheran Bible Translators	1974	-	-	-	18	-

	Personnel from U.S.				Other Countries	
	First Year	4+ yrs.	2-4 yrs.	1-2 yrs.	Citizens	Not Citizens
Lutheran Church—Missouri Syn.	1983	-	1	-	-	-
Medical Ambassadors International	2001	-	-	-	-	-
National Baptist Conv. USA, Inc.	1950	-	-	-	2	-
Seventh-day Adventists Gen. Conf.	1905	-	-	-	-	2
Walk Thru The Bible Ministries	2001	-	-	-	1	-
World Partners USA	1945	-	-	-	-	-
World Vision Inc.	1978	-	-	-	-	-
Totals:		3	1	-	83	11

Singapore

ABWE	1991	6	-	-	-	-
Asian Outreach U.S.A.	-	-	-	-	-	-
Assemblies of God World Missions	1926	10	-	-	-	-
Baptist Bible Fellowship Intl.	1970	6	-	-	-	-
Campus Crusade for Christ, Intl.	1969	18	-	-	-	2
CBInternational	1985	4	-	-	-	-
Child Evangelism Fellowship, Inc.	1970	-	-	-	2	-
Christian Churches/Churches of Christ		4	-	-	-	-
Church of God (Cleveland, TN)	1989	-	-	-	-	2
Church Resource Ministries	2000	4	-	-	-	-
CMF International	1990	2	-	-	-	-
Eastern Mennonite Missions		-	-	5	-	-
Evangelical Free Church Mission	1957	2	-	-	-	-
Evangelical Lutheran Church in America	1966	2	-	-	-	-
Foursquare Missions International	1984	2	-	-	3	-
Global Strategy Mission Assoc.	1984	2	-	-	-	-
Good News Productions Intl.		2	-	-	2	-
Intl. Pentecostal Holiness Ch. World Mins.	1987	4	-	-	-	-
International Students, Inc		1	-	-	-	-
International Teams, U.S.A.	-	-	-	-	-	1
Network of International Christian Schools	1995	4	21	-	-	-
New Directions International	1991	-	-	-	1	-
New Tribes Mission	1994	4	-	-	-	-
OC International, Inc.	1970	4	4	-	2	-
Overseas Radio & Television, Inc.		-	-	-	-	-
Partners International	1952	-	-	-	-	-
Seventh-day Adventists Gen. Conf.	1904	4		-	-	8
SIM USA		2	-	-	-	-
Source of Light Ministries Intl., Inc.	2000	-	-	-	1	-
Trans World Radio		7	-	-	-	1
Walk Thru The Bible Ministries	1998	-	-	-	3	-
WEC International	1968	-	-	-	-	6
World Baptist Fellowship Mission Agency		2	-	-	-	-
WorldTeach	1988	-	-	-	-	-
Wycliffe Bible Translators USA		8	-	-	-	-
Totals:		104	25	5	14	20

Slovakia

ABWE	1990	15	-	-	-	-
Assemblies of God World Missions	1981	3	-	2	-	-
Baptist Mid-Missions	1992	4	-	-	-	-
Campus Crusade for Christ, Intl.	1992	10	-	15	15	1

	Personnel from U.S.			Other Countries	
	First Year	4+ yrs.	2-4 yrs.	1-2 yrs.	Citizens	Not Citizens

Child Evangelism Fellowship, Inc.	1989	-	-	-	2	-
Envoy International		-	-	-	-	-
Evangelical Free Church Mission	1993	4	1	-	-	-
Evangelical Lutheran Church in America	1991	5	1	15	-	-
Every Home for Christ International	1991	-	-	-	8	-
Global Outreach, Ltd.		2	-	-	-	-
Greater Europe Mission	1992	4	-	-	-	-
Greater Grace World Outreach	1991	-	-	-	-	2
International Messengers	1994	3	1	-	-	1
International Needs - USA	1993	-	-	-	6	-
International Teams, U.S.A.		7	-	-	14	2
Lutheran Church—Missouri Syn.	1991	-	2	7	-	-
Mission to the World (PCA), Inc.	1997	2	2	-	-	-
Precept Ministries International	1991	-	-	-	1	-
Presbyterian Church (USA)		4	-	-	-	-
Project Care		-	-	-	-	-
Trans World Radio		10	-	-	-	-
UFM International	1991	3	-	-	-	1
Totals:		76	7	39	46	7

Slovenia

Assemblies of God World Missions		2	-	-	-	-
Bethany Fellowship Missions	1992	2	-	-	-	1
Campus Crusade for Christ, Intl.	1994	4	-	7	-	-
CBInternational	1991	4	-	-	-	-
Child Evangelism Fellowship, Inc.	1997	-	-	-	2	2
Christian Aid Mission		-	-	-	1	-
Church of the Nazarene		1	-	-	-	-
Every Home for Christ International	1991	-	-	-	1	-
Greater Europe Mission	1998	-	-	-	-	-
Habitat for Humanity International	1995	-	1	-	-	1
International Teams, U.S.A.		4	-	-	-	2
Navigators, U.S. Intl. Missions Group		2	-	4	-	-
SEND International	1997	-	-	-	-	3
Totals:		19	1	11	4	9

Solomon Islands

Assemblies of God World Missions	1977	6	-	-	-	-
Campus Crusade for Christ, Intl.	1975	-	-	-	5	-
Church of the Nazarene	1992	2	-	-	-	-
Seventh-day Adventists Gen. Conf.	1914	-	-	-	-	2
Wycliffe Bible Translators USA		30	-	-	-	-
Totals:		38	-	-	5	2

Somalia

Eastern Mennonite Missions		2	-	-	-	-
World Concern	1980	-	-	-	27	-
Totals:		2	-	-	27	-

South Africa

ABWE	1980	40	-	-	-	-
ACM International	1996	2	-	-	-	-

	First Year	Personnel from U.S. 4+ yrs.	2-4 yrs.	1-2 yrs.	Other Countries Citizens	Not Citizens
Advent Christian General Conf.	1997	-	-	-	2	-
Africa Inland Mission International	1994	2	-	-	-	-
Africa Inter-Mennonite Mission	1982	-	-	-	-	2
African Enterprise, Inc.	1962	-	-	-	60	-
American Baptist Chs. in the U.S.A.	1990	5	-	-	-	-
Asian Outreach U.S.A.		-	-	-	-	-
Assemblies of God World Missions	1917	47	-	10	-	-
Baptist Bible Fellowship Intl.	1980	16	1	-	-	-
Baptist International Outreach	1995	8	-	-	-	-
Bible League, The	1996	-	-	-	10	-
Biblical Ministries Worldwide	1976	9	-	-	-	1
Brethren Assemblies		9	1	-	-	1
Brethren in Christ World Missions	1988	-	-	-	1	-
Calvary International	1995	1	-	-	1	1
Campus Crusade for Christ, Intl.	1971	4	-	-	90	15
Child Evangelism Fellowship, Inc.	1947	3	-	-	4	-
Christ Community Church	1903	-	-	-	9	-
Christian Ch. of North America Msns.	1980	4	-	-	-	-
Christian Churches/Churches of Christ		32	3	-	4	-
Christian Reformed World Relief Comte.	1996	1	-	-	-	-
Church of God (Cleveland, TN)	1951	1	-	-	-	-
Church of God of Prophecy		-	-	-	20	-
Church of the Nazarene	1919	13	3	-	-	5
Churches of Christ	1900	14	-	-	26	-
Commission to Every Nation	2002	1	-	-	-	-
Development Associates Intl. (DAI)	1998	-	-	-	-	-
Elim Fellowship, Intl. Dept.	1975	2	-	-	-	2
Emmanuel Intl. Mission (U.S.)		-	-	-	-	-
Evangelical Baptist Missions		11	-	-	-	-
Evangelical Lutheran Church in America	1844	2	-	-	-	-
Every Home for Christ International	1965	-	-	-	3	-
Faith Christian Fellowship Intl.	1994	-	3	-	-	-
Foursquare Missions International	1928	4	-	-	1	-
General Conf. Mennonite Church	1982	2	-	-	-	-
Gospel Fellowship Association	1988	6	-	1	-	-
Habitat for Humanity International	1987	-	2	-	5	-
Hope for the Hungry		1	-	-	-	1
In Touch Mission International	1977	2	-	-	-	-
Independent Faith Mission		9	-	-	-	-
Intl. Pentecostal Holiness Ch. World Mins.	1911	17	-	-	-	-
InterVarsity Christian Fellowship/USA		-	1	2	-	-
Jews for Jesus	1989	1	-	-	5	-
Lutheran Church—Missouri Syn.	1982	-	-	4	-	-
Men for Missions International		-	2	-	-	-
Mennonite Mission Network	1982	-	-	-	-	2
Mission to the World (PCA), Inc.	1997	26	6	-	-	-
National Baptist Convention USA, Inc.	1894	-	-	-	1	-
Navigators, U.S. Intl. Missions Group		2	-	3	-	-
New Directions International	1984	-	-	-	1	-
OC International, Inc.	1986	14	-	-	-	-
Operation Mobilization, Inc.		3	3	5	-	-
Partners International	1980	-	-	-	-	-

		Personnel from U.S.			Other Countries	
	First Year	4+ yrs.	2-4 yrs.	1-2 yrs.	Citizens	Not Citizens
Precept Ministries International	1990	-	-	-	17	-
Presbyterian Church (USA)		6	-	-	-	-
Reformed Church in America, Gen. Syn.	1998	2	-	-	-	-
Salvation Army, U.S.A.	1883	2	-	-	-	-
Seventh-day Adventists Gen. Conf.	1887	3	-	2	-	20
SIM USA	1906	10	-	-	-	-
Teen Missions International	1984	-	-	-	2	2
Things To Come Mission, Inc.	1989	2	-	-	-	-
Trans World Radio		11	-	-	-	2
UFM International	1979	3	-	-	2	-
United Church Board for World Ministries		-	7	-	-	-
Walk Thru The Bible Ministries	1999	-	-	-	20	-
WEC International	1955	2	-	-	-	36
Wesleyan World Missions	1901	-	10	-	-	-
Word of Life Fellowship	1998	6	-	-	4	-
World Missions Far Corners, Inc.	1958	2	-	-	-	-
WorldTeach	1990	-	-	-	-	-
Wycliffe Bible Translators USA		7	-	-	-	-
Youth for Christ / USA, World Outreach	1977	2	-	-	-	-
Zion Evangelical Ministries of Africa	1905	6	-	-	5	-
	Totals:	378	42	27	293	90

Spain

ABWE	1968	16	-	-	-	-
American Baptist Churches in the U.S.A.	2001	-	-	-	-	1
AMG International	1989	10	-	-	-	-
Assemblies of God World Missions	1923	50	-	10	-	-
Baptist Bible Fellowship Intl.	1970	16	-	-	-	-
Baptist Mid-Missions	1979	6	-	-	-	-
BCM International	1962	4	-	-	4	-
Bethany Fellowship Missions	1992	2	-	-	-	-
Biblical Ministries Worldwide	1958	5	-	-	-	-
Brethren Assemblies		9	-	-	-	-
Brethren in Christ World Missions	1985	2	2	-	-	-
Cadence International		-	2	-	-	2
CAM International	1972	10	-	-	-	10
Campus Crusade for Christ, Intl.	1970	10	-	38	-	-
CBInternational	1984	10	-	4	-	-
Christ for the City International	1994	2	-	-	-	2
Christian and Missionary Alliance	1978	10	-	-	-	-
Christian Associates International	1992	6	-	-	-	-
Christian Churches / Churches of Christ		1	-	-	-	-
Church of God (Cleveland, TN)	1937	1	-	-	-	4
Church of God of Prophecy		-	-	-	2	-
Church of the Nazarene	1981	-	-	-	-	2
Churches of Christ	1964	2	-	-	-	-
Correll Missionary Ministries	1964	-	-	-	4	-
East-West Ministries International	1997	-	-	-	-	-
European Christian Mission NA, Inc.		8	-	-	-	-
Evangelical Covenant Church	1996	4	-	-	-	-
Evangelical Free Church Mission	1994	8	3	-	-	-
Every Home for Christ International	1977	-	-	-	3	-

	First Year	4+ yrs.	2-4 yrs.	1-2 yrs.	Other Countries Citizens	Other Countries Not Citizens
		Personnel from U.S.			Other Countries	
Faith Christian Fellowship Intl.	1994	-	2	-	-	-
Foursquare Missions International		2	-	-	-	-
Free Will Baptists, Inc., National Assoc.	1974	9	-	-	-	-
Global Outreach Mission		-	-	-	5	-
Gospel Fellowship Association	1978	6	-	-	-	-
Gospel Furthering Fellowship		2	-	-	-	-
Gospel Missionary Union	1966	27	4	-	-	-
Grace Brethren International Missions	1984	4	-	-	-	-
Greater Europe Mission	1960	23	-	-	-	-
HCJB World Radio		4	-	-	-	2
Help for Christian Nationals, Inc.	1990	2	-	-	-	-
International Missionary Center		3	-	-	-	-
International Partnership Ministries, Inc.	2000	2	-	-	-	-
Intl. Pentecostal Holiness Ch. World Mins.	1988	4	-	-	-	-
International Teams, U.S.A.	1972	10	-	-	-	-
Latin America Mission	1990	5	-	1	-	6
Liebenzell Mission USA	1996	2	-	-	-	-
Mennonite Mission Network	1976	2	-	-	-	-
Mission to the World (PCA), Inc.	1983	5	-	-	-	-
Missionary Revival Crusade	1969	-	-	-	-	6
Navigators, U.S. Intl. Missions Group	1970	8	-	2	-	-
OC International, Inc.	1995	2	2	2	2	-
OMS International, Inc.	1972	7	-	-	-	3
Open Door Baptist Missions	1999	2	-	-	-	-
Operation Mobilization, Inc.	1961	-	2	-	-	-
Pilgrim Fellowship, Inc.	1976	2	-	-	-	-
Pocket Testament League	1978	-	-	-	2	-
Precept Ministries International	1992	1	-	-	-	-
Presbyterian Church (USA)		4	-	-	-	-
Salvation Army, U.S.A.	1971	2	-	-	-	-
SEND International	1987	8	-	1	-	5
South American Missionary Society	1991	5	-	-	-	-
TEAM (The Evangelical Alliance Mission)		35	-	1	-	-
UFM International	1985	4	-	-	-	-
University of the Family	1995	-	-	-	-	2
WEC International	1968	11	-	-	-	51
Word of Life Fellowship	1977	1	-	-	-	5
World Baptist Fellowship Mission Agency		4	-	-	-	-
World Harvest Mission	1998	3	-	3	-	-
World Horizons	2001	2	-	-	-	4
World Indigenous Missions	1994	2	-	-	-	-
World Partners USA	1985	1	-	-	-	-
World Team	1972	9	-	-	-	-
Youth for Christ/USA, World Outreach	1982	1	-	-	-	-
Totals:		418	17	62	22	105

Sri Lanka

	First Year	4+ yrs.	2-4 yrs.	1-2 yrs.	Citizens	Not Citizens
Back to the Bible International	1955	-	-	-	37	-
BCM International	1985	-	-	-	4	-
Campus Crusade for Christ, Intl.	1967	-	-	-	41	-
Childcare International	1984	-	-	-	4	-
Christian Aid Mission		-	-	-	5	-

	Personnel from U.S.				Other Countries	
	First Year	4+ yrs.	2-4 yrs.	1-2 yrs.	Citizens	Not Citizens
Church of God of Prophecy		-		-	1	-
Church of the Nazarene	2000	-	-	-	-	-
Every Home for Christ International	1970	-	-	-	5	-
Foursquare Missions International	1976	-	-	-	1	-
Global Fellowship		-	-	-	25	-
Gospel for Asia	1979	-	-	-	-	-
Habitat for Humanity International	1994	-	2	-	2	2
Hope for the Hungry	1989	2	-	-	2	-
International Needs–USA	1976	-	-	-	29	-
Josue Yrion Wld. Evangelism Msns., Inc.	2000	1	-	-	-	-
Presbyterian Church (USA)		2	-	-	-	-
Seventh-day Adventists Gen. Conf.	1922	2	-	2	-	2
Shelter for Life International, Inc.	1998	-	-	-	-	2
TEAM (The Evangelical Alliance Mission)	1955	2	-	-	-	-
United Church Board for World Mins.		-	3	-	-	-
Village Ministries International, Inc.	1997	-	-	-	6	-
Walk Thru The Bible Ministries	1999	-	-	-	1	-
Totals:		9	5	2	163	6

Sudan

	First Year	4+ yrs.	2-4 yrs.	1-2 yrs.	Citizens	Not Citizens
Africa Inland Mission International	1949	1	-	-	-	-
Assemblies of God World Missions	1980	-	-	6	-	-
Bible League, The	1999	-	-	-	13	1
CBInternational		-	-	-	-	-
Christian Aid Mission		-	-	-	17	-
Church of God of Prophecy		-	-	-	2	-
Emmanuel Intl. Mission (U.S.)		-	-	-	-	-
Gospel Revival Ministries	1997	-	-	-	2	-
Hope for the Hungry		-	1	-	-	1
In Touch Mission International	1998	-	-	-	-	1
International Gospel Outreach	2002	-	-	1	-	-
Mission ONE, Inc.		-	-	-	-	-
Partners International	1995	-	-	-	-	-
Presbyterian Church (USA)		10	5	-	-	-
Project Mercy, Inc.	1977	-	-	-	-	11
Reformed Church in America, Gen. Syn.	1987	2	-	-	2	-
Samaritan's Purse	1992	-	-	7	-	1
Seventh-day Adventists Gen. Conf.	1978	2	2	4	-	10
SIM USA	1938	4	-	-	-	-
Walk Thru The Bible Ministries	2001	-	-	-	1	-
Wycliffe Bible Translators USA		69	-	-	-	-
Totals:		88	8	18	37	25

Suriname

	First Year	4+ yrs.	2-4 yrs.	1-2 yrs.	Citizens	Not Citizens
Assemblies of God World Missions	1959	2	-	-	-	-
BCM International		2	-	-	3	-
Biblical Ministries Worldwide	1979	-	-	-	-	2
Campus Crusade for Christ, Intl.	1979	-	-	-	7	2
Child Evangelism Fellowship, Inc.	1973	-	-	-	-	1
Church of God of Prophecy		-	-	-	1	-
Church of the Nazarene	1984	-	-	-	-	-
Fellowship International Mission	1978	4	-	-	-	-

		Personnel from U.S.			Other Countries	
	First Year	4+ yrs.	2-4 yrs.	1-2 yrs.	Citizens	Not Citizens
Hosanna / Faith Comes By Hearing	2000	-	-	-	2	-
Independent Faith Mission		17	-	-	-	-
Network of Intl. Christian Schools	1999	-	8	-	-	-
Orthodox Presbyterian Church	1987	2	-	-	-	-
Wesleyan World Missions	1913	-	5	-	-	-
World Team	1957	10		-	2	-
Totals:		37	13	-	15	5

Swaziland
Assemblies of God World Missions	1985	4	-	4	-	-
BCM International		-	-	-	1	-
Campus Crusade for Christ, Intl.	1973	-	-	-	11	-
Church of God of Prophecy		-	-	-	4	-
Church of the Nazarene	1910	7	-	-	-	-
Churches of Christ	1966	3	-	-	-	-
Every Home for Christ International	1961	-	-	-	1	-
Greater Grace World Outreach	1998	-	-	-	-	1
Hosanna / Faith Comes By Hearing	2000	-	-	-	2	-
National Baptist Convention USA, Inc.	1971	-	-	2	-	-
Seventh-day Adventists Gen. Conf.	1920	-	-	-	-	2
TEAM (The Evangelical Alliance Mission)		2	-	-	-	-
Trans World Radio		10	-	-	-	4
United Church Board for World Ministries		-	2	-	-	-
Walk Thru The Bible Ministries	2000	-	-	-	2	-
Totals:		26	2	6	21	7

Sweden
Baptist Bible Fellowship Intl.	2001	-	-	2	-	-
Elim Fellowship, Intl. Dept.	1990	1	-	-	-	1
Evangelical Baptist Missions		2	-	-	-	-
Fellowship International Mission	1972	3	-	-	-	-
Global Outreach Mission		-	-	-	2	-
Greater Europe Mission	1955	2	-	-	-	-
Greater Grace World Outreach	1976	-	-	-	1	4
International Cassette Bible Institute	1987	-	-	-	5	-
Mennonite Mission Network		-	-	-	-	-
Mission to the World (PCA), Inc.	1999	4	-	-	-	-
Operation Mobilization, Inc.		2	-	-	-	-
UFM International	1984	2	-	-	-	-
Wisconsin Evangelical Lutheran Syn.	1999	2	-	-	-	-
Wycliffe Bible Translators USA		2	-	-	-	-
Totals:		20	-	2	8	5

Switzerland
Calvary International	2002	1	-	-	-	1
Child Evangelism Fellowship, Inc.	1950	6	-	-	-	4
Church of the Nazarene	1978	6	-	-	-	-
Churches of Christ	1959	4	-	-	3	-
Development Associates Intl. (DAI)	1995	-	-	-	-	-
Every Home for Christ International	1976	-	-	-	3	-
Seventh-day Adventists Gen. Conf.	1870	-	-	-	-	2
WEC International	1947	-	-	-	-	16

	First Year	Personnel from U.S. 4+ yrs.	2-4 yrs.	1-2 yrs.	Other Countries Citizens	Not Citizens
Wycliffe Bible Translators USA		12	-	-	-	-
Youth for Christ/USA, World Outreach	1964	8	-	-	-	-
Totals:		37	-	-	6	23

Syria

	First Year	4+ yrs.	2-4 yrs.	1-2 yrs.	Citizens	Not Citizens
Armenian Msny. Assoc. of America, Inc.	1918	-	-	-	-	-
Church of the Nazarene	1920	-	-	-	-	-
Partners International	1989	-	-	-	-	-
Walk Thru The Bible Ministries	2001	-	-	-	1	-
World-Wide Missions	1962	-	-	-	1	-
Totals:		-	-	-	2	-

Taiwan

	First Year	4+ yrs.	2-4 yrs.	1-2 yrs.	Citizens	Not Citizens
Asian Outreach U.S.A.	-	-	-	-	-	-
Assemblies of God World Missions	1948	10	-	-	-	-
Baptist Bible Fellowship Intl.	1946	10	2	-	-	-
Baptist Mid-Missions	1972	2	-	-	-	-
Brethren Assemblies		2	-	-	-	-
Campus Crusade for Christ, Intl.	1964	-	-	-	96	-
CBInternational	1952	16	-	-	-	-
Child Evangelism Fellowship, Inc.	1951	2	2	-	-	-
Christian and Missionary Alliance	1952	17	-	-	-	-
Christian Churches / Churches of Christ		21	2	-	-	-
Christian Reformed World Missions	1953	-	2	-	-	-
Church of the Nazarene	1956	-	-	-	-	2
Churches of Christ		2	-	-	-	-
Evangelical Covenant Church	1954	2	-	-	-	-
Evangelical Free Church Mission	1994	2	-	-	-	-
Every Home for Christ International	1960	-	-	-	5	-
Foursquare Missions International		2	-	-	-	-
Free Methodist World Missions	1952	6	-	-	-	-
General Conf. Mennonite Church	1954	5	-	-	1	4
Go Ye Fellowship	1951	1	-	-	-	-
International Gospel Outreach	2002	-	-	2	2	-
International Students, Inc		1	-	-	-	-
Kids Alive International	1971	2	-	-	2	-
Liberty Corner Mission		2	-	-	-	-
Lutheran Brethren World Missions		4	-	-	-	-
Lutheran Church—Missouri Syn.	1951	6	12	5	-	-
Mennonite Mission Network	1954	-	-	-	-	-
Mission to the World (PCA), Inc.	1977	8	2	-	-	-
Mustard Seed, Inc., The	1948	-	-	-	30	-
Navigators, U.S. Intl. Missions Group		8	-	-	-	-
OC International, Inc.	1951	3	-	-	2	1
OMF International		20	-	-	-	-
OMS International, Inc.		4	-	-	-	4
Open Door Baptist Missions	1999	1	-	-	-	-
Overseas Radio & Television, Inc.		-	-	-	270	-
Partners International	1959	-	-	-	-	-
Precept Ministries International	1990	-	-	-	3	2
Presbyterian Church (USA)		9	-	-	-	-
Reformed Church in America, Gen. Syn.	1968	5	-	-	-	-

	Personnel from U.S.				Other Countries	
	First Year	4+ yrs.	2-4 yrs.	1-2 yrs.	Citizens	Not Citizens
Ripe for Harvest, Inc.	1999	1	-	-	-	-
SEND International	1966	17	-	3	-	9
Seventh-day Adventists Gen. Conf.	1902	8	1	2	-	-
Sowers International, The	1995	-	-	-	4	-
TEAM (The Evangelical Alliance Mission)		19	-	-	-	-
Team Expansion, Inc.	1996	18	-	2	-	
United Church Board for World Mins.		-	5	-	-	-
WEC International	1947	-	-	-	-	6
Wisconsin Evangelical Lutheran Syn.	1968	3	-	-	-	-
World Gospel Mission	1953	2	-	-	-	-
World Team	1999	6	-	-	-	-
World-Wide Missions	1966	-	-	-	6	-
Totals:		247	28	14	421	28

Tajikistan

	First Year	4+ yrs.	2-4 yrs.	1-2 yrs.	Citizens	Not Citizens
Christar	1996	6	5	-	-	-
Christian Aid Mission		-	-	-	1	-
East-West Ministries International		-	-	-	4	-
Foursquare Missions International		1	-	-	-	-
Health Emergent International Services	1997	2	-	-	-	-
InterServe/USA	2000	3	-	-	-	-
Medical Ambassadors International	1995	-	-	-	5	-
Seventh-day Adventists Gen. Conf.	1886	-	-	-	-	2
Shelter for Life International, Inc.	1994	-	11	-	-	-
Totals:		12	16	-	10	2

Tanzania

	First Year	4+ yrs.	2-4 yrs.	1-2 yrs.	Citizens	Not Citizens
ACM International	1995	2	-	-	-	-
Africa Inland Mission International	1909	55	-	2	-	-
African Enterprise, Inc.	1970	-	-	-	9	-
Assemblies of God World Missions	1940	10	-	2	-	-
Baptist Bible Fellowship Intl.	1988	13	-	-	-	-
Brethren Assemblies		2	-	-	-	-
Campus Crusade for Christ, Intl.	1977	-	-	-	25	-
Christian Aid Mission		-	-	-	17	-
Christian Blind Mission Intl.	1971	1	1	-	-	-
Christian Churches / Churches of Christ		21	-	-	-	-
Christian Reformed World Relief Comte.	1989	-	-	-	1	3
Church of God (Anderson, Indiana)	1968	5	-	-	-	-
Church of God of Prophecy	1978	-	-	-	7	-
Church of the Nazarene	1990	-	-	-	-	2
Churches of Christ	1962	5	-	-	3	-
CMF International	1984	-	2	4	-	-
Compassion International, Inc.	1999	-	-	-	18	-
Eastern Mennonite Missions	1934	3	2	-	-	-
Elim Fellowship, Intl. Dept.	1955	9	-	-	-	9
Emmanuel Intl. Mission (U.S.)		-	-	-	-	-
Evangelical Free Church Mission	1993	10	-	-	-	-
Evangelical Lutheran Church in America	1924	22	-	13	-	-
Every Home for Christ International	1970	-	-	-	13	-
Free Methodist World Missions	1994	2	-	-	-	-
Gospel Furthering Fellowship		2	-	-	-	-

| | Personnel from U.S. | | | | Other Countries |
	First Year	4+ yrs.	2-4 yrs.	1-2 yrs.	Citizens	Not Citizens
Grace Ministries International	1952	12	-	-	-	-
Habitat for Humanity International	1986	-	4	-	47	-
Hundredfold Ministries International	1990	-	-	-	-	-
International Christian Ministries	2002	-	-	-	2	2
International Gospel Outreach	1998	1	-	-	1	-
International Needs - USA	1997	-	-	-	21	-
Intl. Pentecostal Holiness Ch. World Mins.	1996	5	-	-	-	-
Medical Ambassadors International	1987	-	-	-	3	-
Mission ONE, Inc.		-	-	-	-	-
Mission to the World (PCA), Inc.	1990	2	-	-	-	-
Mission: Moving Mountains, Inc.	1993	16	-	-	-	-
New Directions International	1998	-	-	-	2	-
Partners International	1986	-	-	-	-	-
Pioneer Bible Translators	1997	6	-	-	-	1
Seventh-day Adventists Gen. Conf.	1903	2	-	-	-	12
SIM USA	1990	2	-	-	-	-
Team Expansion, Inc.	1994	4	-	-	-	2
Walk Thru The Bible Ministries	1999	-	-	-	2	-
World Gospel Mission	1985	4	-	-	-	-
Totals:	216	9	21	171	31	

Thailand

	First Year	4+ yrs.	2-4 yrs.	1-2 yrs.	Citizens	Not Citizens
ABWE	1993	2	-	-	-	-
American Baptist Churches in the U.S.A.	1833	20	-	-	1	-
AMG International	1976	-	-	-	16	4
Asian Outreach U.S.A.		-	-	-	-	-
Assemblies of God World Missions	1968	20	-	8	-	-
Baptist Bible Fellowship Intl.	1983	8	-	-	-	-
Baptist General Conference	1990	8	2	-	-	-
Baptist Mid-Missions	1995	2	-	-	2	-
Bethany Fellowship Missions	1999	1	-	-	-	1
Bible League, The	1984	-	-	-	8	-
Campus Crusade for Christ, Intl.	1971	6	-	-	73	4
Child Evangelism Fellowship, Inc.	1957	-	-	-	1	-
Childcare International	1990	-	-	-	-	-
Christian Aid Mission		-	-	-	54	-
Christian and Missionary Alliance	1929	25	2	-	-	-
Christian Blind Mission Intl.	1982	-	-	1	-	-
Christian Churches / Churches of Christ		41	-	2	12	-
Church of God of Prophecy		-	-	-	2	-
Church of the Nazarene	1989	5	1	-	-	3
Church World Service & Witness		-	1	-	4	-
Churches of Christ	1903	22	-	-	5	-
CMF International	1994	-	2	4	-	-
Compassion International, Inc.	1970	-	-	-	27	1
Correll Missionary Ministries	2002	-	-	-	3	-
David Livingstone KURE Foundation		-	-	-	14	-
Eastern Mennonite Missions	1997	10	-	-	-	-
Evangelical Covenant Church	1971	8	3	-	-	-
Evangelical Free Church Mission	1996	4	2	-	5	-
Evangelical Lutheran Ch. in America	1975	4	-	-	-	-
Every Home for Christ International	1971	-	-	-	1	-

	Personnel from U.S.				Other Countries	
	First Year	4+ yrs.	2-4 yrs.	1-2 yrs.	Citizens	Not Citizens
Foursquare Missions International	1987	2	-	-	-	-
Global Fellowship		-	-	-	-	5
Globe Missionary Evangelism	1985	4	2	-	-	-
Good News Productions Intl.	1998	4	-	-	-	2
Greater Grace World Outreach	1989	-	-	-	-	2
International Justice Mission	2000	-	2	-	2	1
International Missionary Center		2	-	-	-	-
Intl. Pentecostal Holiness Ch. World Mins.	1988	4	-	-	-	-
International Teams, U.S.A.		-	-	-	-	10
Larry Jones International Ministries	1986	-	-	-	8	-
Lutheran Church—Missouri Syn.	1986	6	4	2	-	-
MBMS International	1992	-	8	1	2	-
Medical Ambassadors International	1999	-	-	-	-	
Mennonite Mission Network	2000	-	-	-	-	-
Mission ONE, Inc.		-	-	-	-	-
Mission to the World (PCA), Inc.		2	2	-	-	-
Mission To Unreached Peoples	1988	13	-	-	-	-
Navigators, U.S. Intl. Missions Group		4	-	-	-	-
Network of Intl. Christian Schools	1993	10	50	-	-	-
New Life League International	1989	2	-	-	-	-
New Tribes Mission	1951	66	-	1	-	4
OMF International	1952	40	4	-	-	-
Partners International	1955	-	-	-	-	-
Pioneers	1985	11	-	1	-	1
Pocket Testament League	1976	-	-	-	2	-
Presbyterian Church (USA)	1840	10	20	-	-	-
Ripe for Harvest, Inc.	2001	3	1	-	-	-
Seed International	1992	2	-	-	-	-
Seventh-day Adventists Gen. Conf.	1919	10	8	8	-	17
Sowers International, The	1999	-	-	-	-	10
United Church Board for World Mins.		-	6	-	-	-
Walk Thru The Bible Ministries	2001	-	-	-	2	-
WEC International	1947	8	2	-	-	37
Wisconsin Evangelical Lutheran Syn.	1993	1	2	-	-	-
World Baptist Fellowship Msn. Agency		1	-	-	-	-
World Concern	1979	5	-	1	13	1
World Help	1998	-	-	-	11	-
World Indigenous Missions	1999	-	2	-	-	-
World Missions Far Corners, Inc.	1996	2	-	-	8	3
World Partners USA	1992	5	-	-	-	-
Worldwide Tentmakers, Inc.	2001	-	-	-	-	-
Youth for Christ/World Outreach Div.		1	-	-	-	-
	Totals:	404	126	29	276	106

Togo

ABWE	1973	44	-	-	-	-
Assemblies of God World Missions	1937	15	-	2	-	-
Campus Crusade for Christ, Intl.	1979	-	-	-	18	-
Child Evangelism Fellowship, Inc.	1983	-	-	-	1	-
Christian Aid Mission		-	-	-	4	-
Christian Blind Mission Intl.	1980	-	1	-	-	-
Church of God of Prophecy		-	-	-	2	-

	Personnel from U.S.				Other Countries	
	First Year	4+ yrs.	2-4 yrs.	1-2 yrs.	Citizens	Not Citizens
Church of the Nazarene	1998	-	-	-	-	-
Churches of Christ	1984	20	-	-	-	-
Every Home for Christ International	1991	-	-	-	3	-
Greater Grace World Outreach	1992	-	-	-	-	3
International Missionary Center		-	-	-	-	4
International Partnership Ministries, Inc.	1991	-	-	-	11	-
Ireland Outreach International Inc.	2000	-	-	-	-	-
Lifewater International	1996	-	-	-	1	-
Lutheran Bible Translators		-	-	-	-	-
Lutheran Church—Missouri Syn.	1980	1	5	-	-	-
Mennonite Mission Network	1996	-	-	-	-	2
Seventh-day Adventists Gen. Conf.	1964	-	-	2	-	6
SIM USA	1994	2	-	-	-	-
Source of Light Ministries Intl., Inc.	1998	-	-	-	4	-
Walk Thru The Bible Ministries	2002	-	-	-	1	-
Wycliffe Bible Translators USA		75	-	-	-	-
Totals:		157	6	4	45	15

Tonga

	First Year	4+ yrs.	2-4 yrs.	1-2 yrs.	Citizens	Not Citizens
Assemblies of God World Missions	1975	2	-	-	-	-
Campus Crusade for Christ, Intl.	1974	-	-	-	4	-
Church of the Nazarene	2000	-	-	-	-	-
Faith Christian Fellowship Intl.	1995	-	2	-	-	-
Totals:		2	2	-	4	-

Trinidad and Tobago

	First Year	4+ yrs.	2-4 yrs.	1-2 yrs.	Citizens	Not Citizens
Baptist Bible Fellowship Intl.	1997	2	-	-	-	-
BCM International		-	-	-	1	-
Campus Crusade for Christ, Intl.	1977	-		-	12	-
Church of God of Prophecy	1954	-	-	-	7	-
Church of the Nazarene	1926	1	-	-	-	1
Churches of Christ		1	-	-	-	-
Fundamental Baptist Mission	1921	5	-	-	6	-
Global Outreach, Ltd.		-	-	2	-	-
Habitat for Humanity International	1996	-	2	-	-	-
Intl. Pentecostal Holiness Ch. World Mins.	1993	2	-	-	-	-
Medical Ambassadors International	1998	-	-	-	-	-
Pentecostal Church of God		2	-	-	-	-
Seventh-day Adventists Gen. Conf.	1893	-	6	-	-	5
STEM International	1986	-	-	-	-	-
TEAM (The Evangelical Alliance Mission)	1964	4	-	-	-	-
TMA Ministries	1996	2	-	-	-	-
Virginia Mennonite Board of Missions	1976	2	-	-	-	-
World Team	1953	9	-	-	-	-
Totals:		30	8	2	26	6

Tunisia

	First Year	4+ yrs.	2-4 yrs.	1-2 yrs.	Citizens	Not Citizens
Seventh-day Adventists Gen. Conf.	1928	-	-	-	-	1
Totals:		-	-	-	-	1

Turkey

	First Year	4+ yrs.	2-4 yrs.	1-2 yrs.	Citizens	Not Citizens
AMG International	1977	-	-	-	1	-

	Personnel from U.S.				Other Countries	
	First Year	4+ yrs.	2-4 yrs.	1-2 yrs.	Citizens	Not Citizens
Armenian Msny. Assoc. of America, Inc.	1951	-	-	-	-	-
Christar	1974	30	8	-	-	-
Church of God (Cleveland, TN)	1999	2	-	-	-	-
Church of the Nazarene	2002	-	-	-	-	-
Crossover Communications Intl.	2002	2	-	-	-	-
Evangelical Free Church Mission	1994	6	-	-	-	-
Go Ye Fellowship	1998	-	2	-	-	-
Grace Brethren International Missions	2002	2	-	-	-	-
International Missionary Center		4	-	-	-	-
Intl. Pentecostal Holiness Ch. World Mins.	2001	-	-	-	-	1
International Teams, U.S.A.		-	-	-	-	1
InterServe/USA	1985	13	-	-	-	-
InterVarsity Christian Fellowship/USA		1	-	3	-	-
Middle East Christian Outreach	1990	-	-	-	-	5
New Life League International	1994	2	-	-	-	-
Operation Mobilization, Inc.	1961	12	1	2	-	-
Partners International	1998	-	-	-	-	-
Presbyterian Church (USA)		2	-	-	-	-
Ripe for Harvest, Inc.	2000	2	-	-	-	-
TEAM (The Evangelical Alliance Mission)		2	-	-	-	-
Turkish World Outreach	1969	19	-	-	4	1
United Church Bd. for World Mins.		-	6	-	-	-
World Partners USA	1990	4	-	-	-	-
World Witness Assoc. Reformed Presb. Ch.	1991	3	-	-	4	-
World-Wide Missions	1970	-	-	-	1	-
Worldwide Tentmakers, Inc.	1991	-	-	-	-	-
Totals:		106	17	5	10	8

Turkmenistan

Back to the Bible International	2001	-	-	-	4	-
East-West Ministries International		-	-	-	3	-
Evangelism Explosion International		-	-	-	-	2
Greater Grace World Outreach	1996	-	-	-	-	2
Outreach To Asia Nationals	2002	-	-	4	-	-
Totals:		-	-	4	7	4

Uganda

Africa Inland Mission International	1918	24	-	2	-	-
African Bible Colleges, Inc.		-	-	-	-	-
African Enterprise, Inc.	1970	-	-	-	18	-
AMG International	1994	2	-	-	5	-
Baptist Bible Fellowship Intl.	1986	2	-	1	-	-
Baptist International Outreach	1996	-	-	-	2	-
Bible League, The	1980	-	-	-	5	-
Brethren Assemblies		2	-	-	-	-
Campus Crusade for Christ, Intl.	1971	-	-	-	61	-
CBInternational	1961	19	-	2	-	-
Child Evangelism Fellowship, Inc.	1965	-	-	-	2	-
Childcare International	1986	-	-	-	20	-
Christian Blind Mission Intl.	1978	-	2	-	-	-
Christian Reformed World Relief Comte.	1983	-	1	-	-	1
Church of God (Anderson, Indiana)	1983	4	-	-	-	-

	Personnel from U.S.				Other Countries	
	First Year	4+ yrs.	2-4 yrs.	1-2 yrs.	Citizens	Not Citizens
Church of God of Prophecy	1981	-	-	-	4	-
Church of the Nazarene	1988	2	-	-	-	-
Church Planting International	1983	-	-	-	-	-
Churches of Christ	1969	30	-	-	1	-
Compassion International, Inc.	1980	-	-	-	30	-
Congregational Methodist Church	2000	-	-	2	-	-
Development Associates Intl. (DAI)	1999	-	-	-	-	-
Elim Fellowship, Intl. Dept.	1962	1	-	-	-	1
Emmanuel Intl. Mission (U.S.)		-	-	-	-	-
Equip, Inc.		-	-	-	-	2
Evangel Bible Translators	1997	-	-	-	1	1
Evangelical Presbyterian Church	2001	2	-	-	-	-
Every Home for Christ International	1970	-	-	-	11	-
Faith Christian Fellowship Intl.	1998	-	2	-	-	-
Fellowship International Mission	1989	-	-	-	2	-
Foursquare Missions International	1997	4	-	-	-	-
Global Fellowship		-	-	-	20	-
Global Outreach, Ltd.	1979	21	-	7	-	-
Habitat for Humanity International	1984	-	3	-	43	-
Hope for the Hungry		-	-	1	-	1
Hundredfold Ministries International	1994	-	-	-	-	-
International Christian Ministries	1990	-	-	-	10	-
International Needs - USA	1994	-	-	-	74	-
Larry Jones International Ministries	1990	-	-	-	7	-
Medical Ambassadors International	1990	2	-	-	6	-
Mission Ministries, Inc.	1995	2	-	-	-	-
Mission ONE, Inc.		-	-	-	-	-
Mission to the World (PCA), Inc.	1983	4	-	-	-	-
Mission: Moving Mountains, Inc.	1982	-	-	-	5	-
Missionary TECH Team		-	2	-	-	-
Missionary Ventures International	2002	2	-	-	-	-
Orthodox Presbyterian Church	1995	10	-	3	-	-
Presbyterian Evangelistic Fellowship		2	-	-	-	-
Reformed Episcopal Bd. of Foreign Msns.	1958	2	-	-	-	-
Samaritan's Purse	1996	-	-	-	-	1
Seed International	2000	2	-	-	-	-
Seventh-day Adventists Gen. Conf.	1926	2	2	2	-	7
Source of Light Ministries Intl., Inc.	1998	-	-	-	2	-
Teen Missions International	1992	1	-	-	6	-
The Master's Mission, Inc.	1999	1	-	-	-	-
Touch the World Ministries		1	-	-	-	-
Walk Thru The Bible Ministries	1999	-	-	-	3	-
World Concern	1983	-	4	-	9	-
World Gospel Mission	1992	11	-	-	-	-
World Harvest Mission	1984	15	-	3	-	-
Wycliffe Bible Translators USA		69	-	-	-	-
Totals:		239	16	23	347	14

Ukraine

ABWE	1990	20	-	-	-	-
Action International Ministries	1996	2	-	-	-	-
Allegheny Wesleyan Methodist Msns.	1993	3	-	-	-	-

	First Year	Personnel from U.S.			Other Countries	
		4+ yrs.	2-4 yrs.	1-2 yrs.	Citizens	Not Citizens
Assemblies of God World Missions		-	-	3	-	-
Baptist Bible Fellowship Intl.	1993	2	-	-	-	-
Baptist Intl. Evangelistic Mins.		-	-	-	25	-
BCM International	1993	1	1	-	8	-
Bible League, The	1992	-	-	-	15	-
Calvary International	1992	1	-	-	-	1
Campus Crusade for Christ, Intl.	1991	14	-	7	61	16
CBInternational	1991	11	-	-	-	-
Centers for Apologetics Research (CFAR)	1999	-	2	-	2	-
Child Evangelism Fellowship, Inc.	1989	-	-	-	6	-
Chosen People Ministries	1995	-	-	-	-	-
Christian Aid Ministries		-	2	-	-	-
Christian Aid Mission		-	-	-	226	-
Christian Churches/Churches of Christ		30	-	-	8	-
Christian Ministries Intl. (C.M.I.)		2	-	-	-	-
Christian Outreach International	1993	1	-	-	2	1
Church of God (Cleveland, TN)	1992	3	-	-	-	-
Church of God (Holiness)	1996	-	-	2	-	2
Church of God of Prophecy		3	-	-	16	-
Church of the Nazarene	1992	6	-	-	-	-
Churches of Christ	1952	25	-	-	10	-
CMF International	1994	2	1	2	-	-
David Livingstone KURE Foundation		-	-	-	25	-
Donetsk Christian University		6	-	-	10	10
Eastern European Outreach, Inc.	1990	4	-	-	19	-
Evangelical Free Church Mission	1993	6	-	-	6	-
Evangelism Explosion International		-	-	-	-	10
Evangelistic Faith Missions		-	2	-	-	-
Every Home for Christ International	1991	-	-	-	6	-
Family Aid International, Inc.	1995	-	-	-	1	-
Fellowship International Mission	1994	2	-	-	-	-
Foursquare Missions International	1998	2	-	-	-	-
Free Methodist World Missions	1999	1	-	-	-	-
Global Action	2001	1	-	-	8	1
Global Outreach Mission		3	-	-	10	-
Global Outreach, Ltd.		-	2	1	-	-
Good News Productions Intl.	1997	2	-	-	2	-
Gospel Fellowship Association	2001	2	-	1	-	-
Gospel Revival Ministries	1997	-	-	-	1	-
Great Commission Ministries, Inc.		10	-	8	3	-
Greater Europe Mission	1993	2	-	-	-	-
Greater Grace World Outreach	1992	-	-	-	-	2
HCJB World Radio		2	-	-	-	-
Hosanna / Faith Comes By Hearing	1997	-	-	-	2	-
International Messengers	2000	-	1	-	-	4
International Teams, U.S.A.	1995	15	-	-	-	4
InterVarsity Christian Fellowship/USA	1998	3	6	-	-	-
Jews for Jesus	1991	-	-	-	18	-
Medical Ambassadors International	1992	-	-	-	4	-
Mennonite Mission Network	1996	-	-	-	-	-
Mission Ministries, Inc.	1997	-	1	-	-	-
Mission Possible Foundation, Inc.		-	-	-	-	-

		Personnel from U.S.			Other Countries	
	First Year	4+ yrs.	2-4 yrs.	1-2 yrs.	Citizens	Not Citizens
Mission to the World (PCA), Inc.	1993	12	24	-	-	-
Missions to Military, Inc.	1998	2	-	-	-	-
Muslim Hope	1993	2	-	-	-	-
Navigators, U.S. Intl. Missions Group		7	-	-	-	-
New Life League International		-	-	-	-	-
Open Air Campaigners - Overseas Mins.	2002	-	-	-	1	-
Peter Deyneka Russian Ministries		-	-	-	-	-
Pioneer Bible Translators	1999	4	-	-	-	1
Precept Ministries International	1994	-	-	-	9	-
SEND International	1991	28	-	-	-	4
TEAM (The Evangelical Alliance Mission)		1	-	-	-	-
Team Expansion, Inc.	1991	13	-	-	-	-
Teen Missions International	1993	-	-	-	2	-
TITUS International	1993	-	-	-	9	1
UFM International		6	-	-	-	-
Walk Thru The Bible Ministries	1998	-	-	-	30	-
Word of Life Fellowship	1992	-	-	-	16	2
World Concern	1990	-	-	-	38	-
World Gospel Mission	1997	6	-	-	-	-
World Harvest Mission	1999	2	-	-	-	-
World Help	1992	-	-	-	1	-
WorldTeach	1992	-	-	-	-	-
	Totals:	270	42	24	600	59

United Arab Emirates

International Teams, U.S.A.		-	-	-	-	1
InterVarsity Christian Fellowship/USA		6	-	-	-	-
Worldwide Tentmakers, Inc.	1992	-	-	-	-	-
	Totals:	6	-	-	-	1

United Kingdom

ABWE	1984	13	-	-	-	-
ACM International	1997	2	-	-	-	-
Apostolic Team Ministries, Intl.	1987	2	-	-	-	-
Asian Outreach U.S.A.		-	-	-	-	-
Assemblies of God World Missions		2	-	-	-	-
Back to the Bible International	1954	-	-	-	7	-
Baptist Bible Fellowship Intl.	1971	36	4	7	-	-
Baptist Mid-Missions	1972	18	-	-	-	-
BCM International		9	-	-	13	-
Biblical Ministries Worldwide	1968	19	-	-	-	2
Brethren in Christ World Missions	1980	2	-	-	-	-
Cadence International		-	2	-	-	2
Calvary International	1996	2	-	-	1	1
Campus Crusade for Christ, Intl.	1967	20	-	-	-	1
CBInternational	1994	6	-	2	-	-
Chosen People Ministries		-	-	-	-	-
Christar	1966	4	4	-	-	-
Christian and Missionary Alliance	1975	7	-	-	-	-
Christian Churches/Churches of Christ	1958	20	6	-	-	-
Christian Literature International		-	-	-	-	-
Christian Outreach International	1985	-	-	-	1	1

	First Year	4+ yrs.	2-4 yrs.	1-2 yrs.	Other Countries Citizens	Not Citizens
		Personnel from U.S.			Other Countries	
Christians In Action, Inc.	1965	5	-	-	1	5
Church of God (Cleveland, TN)	1955	2	-	-	-	2
Church of the Nazarene	1909	-	-	-	-	-
Churches of Christ	1860	51	-	-	-	-
CLC Ministries International	1941	2	-	-	-	-
CMF International	1989	12	-	-	-	-
Covenant Celebration Ch. Global Outreach		-	-	-	-	-
Elim Fellowship, Intl. Dept.	1979	2	-	-	-	2
European Christian Mission NA, Inc.		2	-	-	-	-
Evangelical Baptist Missions	1976	2	-	-	-	-
Evangelical Free Church Mission	1993	3	-	-	-	-
Evangelical Friends Mission	1998	2	-	-	-	-
Evangelical Lutheran Church in America	1974	-	-	11	-	-
Evangelical Mennonite Ch. Intl. Mins.	2000	2	-	-	-	-
Evangelical Presbyterian Church	1991	4	-	-	-	-
Every Home for Christ International	1982	-	-	-	3	-
Faith Christian Fellowship Intl.	1990	4	-	-	-	-
Far East Broadcasting Company, Inc.	1998	2	2	-	-	-
Fellowship International Mission	1993	2	-	-	-	-
Frontier Mission Fellowship		4	-	-	-	-
Global Outreach Mission	1978	14	-	-	10	-
Global Outreach, Ltd.		2	-	-	-	-
Globe Missionary Evangelism	1985	6	-	-	-	-
Gospel Fellowship Association	1972	19	-	2	-	-
Gospel Missionary Union	1963	6	-	-	-	-
Grace Brethren International Missions	1982	6	-	-	-	-
Greater Europe Mission	1970	2	-	1	-	-
Greater Grace World Outreach	1975	-	-	-	4	1
Habitat for Humanity International	1994	3	1	-	3	1
Helps International Ministries	1989	2	-	-	-	-
Independent Faith Mission	1984	2	-	-	-	-
Intl. Pentecostal Holiness Ch. World Mins.	1978	8	-	1	-	-
International Teams, U.S.A.	1986	13	-	-	16	3
InterServe/USA	1852	2	-	-	-	-
InterVarsity Christian Fellowship/USA	1996	4	5	-	-	-
Jews for Jesus	1992	1	-	-	3	1
Josue Yrion World Evangelism Msns., Inc.	2000	-	-	-	-	1
Luis Palau Evangelistic Assoc.	1980	-	-	-	1	-
Men for Missions International		2	-	-	-	-
Mennonite Mission Network	1952	2	-	-	-	-
Mission to the World (PCA), Inc.	1990	12	2	-	-	-
Missionary Athletes International		7	-	-	-	-
Missionary Ventures International	1990	4	-	-	-	-
Navigators, U.S. Intl. Missions Group		-	-	1	-	-
OC International, Inc.	2000	2	-	1	-	1
Operation Mobilization, Inc.	1961	29	8	21	-	-
Overseas Radio & Television, Inc.		-	-	-	-	-
Precept Ministries International	2002	-	-	-	1	-
Presbyterian Church (USA)		11	68	-	-	-
Presbyterian Evangelistic Fellowship		4	-	-	-	-
Ravi Zacharias International Ministries		2	-	-	-	-
Reformed Baptist Mission Services		2	-	-	-	1

	First Year	4+ yrs.	2-4 yrs.	1-2 yrs.	Citizens	Not Citizens
		Personnel from U.S.			**Other Countries**	
Ripe for Harvest, Inc.	2001	4	-	-	-	-
Salvation Army, U.S.A.	1865	17	-	-	-	-
Seventh-day Adventists Gen. Conf.	1902	5	1	4	-	29
TEAM (The Evangelical Alliance Mission)		2	-	-	-	-
TMA Ministries	1983	2	-	-	2	-
Touch the World Ministries	1999	1	-	-	-	-
UFM International		2	-	-	-	2
WEC International	1913	7	-	-	-	156
Wesleyan World Missions	1990	-	2	-	-	-
Word of Life Fellowship	1980	3	-	-	5	-
World Harvest Mission	1994	11	1	-	-	-
World Missions Far Corners, Inc.	1976	2	-	-	-	-
World Team	1986	-	-	-	-	-
Worldwide Tentmakers, Inc.	1995	-	-	-	-	-
Wycliffe Bible Translators USA		83	-	-	-	-
Youth for Christ/USA, World Outreach	1983	8	-	-	-	-
Totals:		577	106	51	71	212

Uruguay

	First Year	4+ yrs.	2-4 yrs.	1-2 yrs.	Citizens	Not Citizens
Armenian Msny. Assoc. of America, Inc.	1954	-	-	-	-	-
Assemblies of God World Missions	1946	12	-	-	-	-
Baptist Bible Fellowship Intl.	1958	2	-	-	-	-
Baptist General Conference	1991	1	-	-	-	-
Biblical Ministries Worldwide	1967	12	-	-	-	2
Brethren Assemblies		1	-	-	-	-
Campus Crusade for Christ, Intl.	1966	-	-	-	6	-
CBInternational	1995	2	-	-	-	-
Christian Aid Mission		-	-	-	10	-
Christian and Missionary Alliance	1999	2	-	-	-	-
Church of God (Cleveland, TN)	1945	2	-	-	-	-
Church of God of Prophecy		-	-	-	4	-
Church of the Nazarene	1949	-	-	-	-	-
Churches of Christ	1952	2	-	-	-	-
Free Will Baptists, Inc., National Assoc.	1961	5	-	-	-	-
Gospel Mission of South America	1970	6	-	-	-	-
International Missionary Center		2	-	-	-	-
International Partnership Ministries, Inc.	2000	-	-	-	1	1
MBMS International	1950	-	2	-	-	-
Medical Ambassadors International	1999	-	-	-	-	-
Mennonite Mission Network	1954	-	-	-	-	4
SIM USA	1995	6	-	-	-	-
Word of Life Fellowship	1977	-	-	-	-	2
Totals:		55	2	-	21	9

Uzbekistan

	First Year	4+ yrs.	2-4 yrs.	1-2 yrs.	Citizens	Not Citizens
Christian Aid Mission		-	-	-	11	-
Church of God (Cleveland, TN)		-	-	-	-	2
East-West Ministries International		-	-	-	4	-
Evangelical Free Church Mission	1995	4	1	-	-	-
Evangelism Explosion International		-	-	-	-	2
International Outreach Ministries	1992	4	-	-	-	-
International Teams, U.S.A.		-	-	-	-	5

	First Year	Personnel from U.S. 4+ yrs.	2-4 yrs.	1-2 yrs.	Other Countries Citizens	Not Citizens
InterVarsity Christian Fellowship/USA	1996	1	-	-	-	-
Medical Ambassadors International	1995	-	-	-	3	-
Northwest Medical Teams	1997	-	-	-	-	-
Outreach To Asia Nationals	2002	-	-	4	2	-
Precept Ministries International	1994	-	-	-	2	-
Presbyterian Church (USA)		-	-	3	-	-
Seed International	1992	6	2	-	-	-
Totals:		15	3	7	22	9

Vanuatu

	First Year	4+ yrs.	2-4 yrs.	1-2 yrs.	Citizens	Not Citizens
Assemblies of God World Missions	1967	6	-	4	-	-
Baptist Bible Fellowship Intl.	1999	2	-	-	-	-
Church of the Nazarene	2001	-	-	-	-	-
Faith Christian Fellowship Intl.	1998	-	-	-	-	6
FRIENDS in Action, International		-	4	-	-	-
Wycliffe Bible Translators USA		24	-	-	-	-
Totals:		32	4	4	-	6

Venezuela

	First Year	4+ yrs.	2-4 yrs.	1-2 yrs.	Citizens	Not Citizens
Assemblies of God World Missions	1920	14	-	4	-	-
Baptist Bible Fellowship Intl.	1966	6	-	-	-	-
Baptist Mid-Missions	1924	11	-	-	-	-
Bible League, The	1996	-	-	-	3	-
Bible Missionary Church		2	-	-	-	-
Brethren Assemblies		1	-	-	-	-
Brethren in Christ World Missions	1982	-	-	3	3	3
Calvary International	1995	1	-	-	-	1
Campus Crusade for Christ, Intl.	1971	-	-	5	34	-
CBInternational	1986	9	-	-	-	-
Christian and Missionary Alliance	1972	18	-	-	-	-
Christian Churches/Churches of Christ		15	-	-	-	-
Christian Outreach International	1993	1	-	-	2	-
Church of God (Anderson, Indiana)		2	-	-	-	-
Church of God (Cleveland, TN)	1966	3	-	-	-	2
Church of God of Prophecy		-	-	-	3	1
Church of the Nazarene	1982	4	2	-	-	-
Church Resource Ministries	1992	8	-	-	-	-
Churches of Christ	1957	2	-	-	-	-
Eastern Mennonite Missions		-	-	6	-	-
Evangelical Free Church Mission	1920	23	2	-	-	-
Evangelical Mennonite Ch. Intl. Mins.	1980	4	4	-	-	-
Fellowship International Mission	1970	5	-	-	1	-
Harvest		-	-	-	1	-
Impact International	1989	-	-	-	2	-
International Missionary Center		-	-	-	-	2
Intl. Pentecostal Holiness Ch. World Mins.	1978	2	-	-	-	-
Latin America Mission	1987	4	-	-	-	4
Lutheran Church—Missouri Syn.	1951	8	2	8	-	-
Medical Ambassadors International	1995	-	-	-	3	-
Mission Aviation Fellowship	1965	10	2	-	-	-
Mission Ministries, Inc.	1994	3	-	-	-	-
Navigators, U.S. Intl. Missions Group	1975	2	-	-	-	-

	First Year	4+ yrs.	2-4 yrs.	1-2 yrs.	Other Countries Citizens	Other Countries Not Citizens
New Tribes Mission	1946	111	-	6	-	6
Precept Ministries International	1998	-	-	-	1	-
Presbyterian Church (USA)	1897	2	8	-	-	-
Seventh-day Adventists Gen. Conf.	1910	2	-	-	-	-
TEAM (The Evangelical Alliance Mission)	1906	49	-	5	-	-
Team Expansion, Inc.	1987	16	-	3	3	-
WEC International	1954	2	-	-	-	1
Word of Life Fellowship	1979	-	-	-	30	2
World Indigenous Missions	1999	2	1	-	1	-
Totals:		342	21	40	87	22

Vietnam

	First Year	4+ yrs.	2-4 yrs.	1-2 yrs.	Other Countries Citizens	Other Countries Not Citizens
ABWE		2	-	-	-	-
Asian Outreach U.S.A.		-	-	-	-	-
Baptist General Conference		-	-	-	-	-
Bible League, The	1995	-	-	-	2	-
Calvary International	1996	1	-	-	-	1
Christ Community Church	2001	-	-	-	-	-
Christian Aid Mission		-	-	-	71	-
Christian and Missionary Alliance	1911	2	2	-	-	-
Church World Service & Witness		-	-	-	-	1
CMF International	1999	-	2	-	-	-
International Needs - USA	1991	-	-	-	57	-
International Teams, U.S.A.	1995	6	-	-	-	9
Lutheran Church—Missouri Syn.	1995	2	-	4	-	-
Medical Ambassadors International	1999	-	-	-	-	-
Mission ONE, Inc.		-	-	-	-	-
Mission To Unreached Peoples	1997	2	-	-	-	-
Northwest Medical Teams	2001	-	-	-	-	-
Outreach To Asia Nationals	1987	-	2	-	54	-
Partners International	1991	-	-	-	-	-
Presbyterian Church (USA)		4	-	-	-	-
Samaritan's Purse	1994	-	-	1	-	-
Seventh-day Adventists Gen. Conf.	1937	2	-	2	-	-
Training Evangelistic Leadership	1994	1	-	-	-	1
United Church Bd. for World Mins.		-	1	-	-	-
Walk Thru The Bible Ministries	2000	-	-	-	1	-
World Concern	1985	-	-	2	16	-
World Missions Far Corners, Inc.	1993	2	-	-	-	-
World Partners USA	1997	4	-	-	-	-
Totals:		28	7	9	201	12

Virgin Islands

	First Year	4+ yrs.	2-4 yrs.	1-2 yrs.	Other Countries Citizens	Other Countries Not Citizens
BCM International		-	-	-	1	-
Church of God of Prophecy		-	-	-	5	-
Church of the Nazarene	1944	-	-	-	-	-
Mission to the World (PCA), Inc.	1991	2	-	-	-	-
National Baptist Conv. of America	1978	-	-	-	6	-
Totals:		2	-	-	12	-

Yemen

	First Year	4+ yrs.	2-4 yrs.	1-2 yrs.	Other Countries Citizens	Other Countries Not Citizens
Evangelical Presbyterian Church	2000	1	-	-	-	-

	First Year	Personnel from U.S. 4+ yrs.	2-4 yrs.	1-2 yrs.	Other Countries Citizens	Not Citizens
Medical Ambassadors International	1999	-	-	-	-	-
Totals:		1	-	-	-	-
Yugoslavia						
Campus Crusade for Christ, Intl.	1979	-	-	-	10	-
Churches of Christ	1969	2	-	-	3	-
Global Outreach Mission		-	-	-	2	-
Pocket Testament League	1980	-	-	-	6	-
Totals:		2	-	-	21	-
Zambia						
Assemblies of God World Missions		9	-	1	-	-
Baptist Bible Fellowship Intl.	1989	12	2	4	-	-
Baptist International Outreach	1987	4	-	-	-	-
Baptist Mid-Missions	1990	6	-	-	-	-
Bible Training Centre for Pastors	1998	-	-	-	1	-
Brethren Assemblies		19	1	-	-	-
Brethren in Christ World Missions	1906	3	4	-	14	-
Bright Hope International	1995	-	-	-	5	-
Campus Crusade for Christ, Intl.	1975	-	-	-	27	-
CBInternational	1981	-	-	-	-	-
Child Evangelism Fellowship, Inc.	1970	-	-	-	3	-
Christian Reformed World Relief Comte.	1990	1	-	-	-	-
Church of God (Anderson, Indiana)	1990	2	-	-	-	-
Church of God (Cleveland, TN)	1965	3	-	-	-	-
Church of God of Prophecy	1977	-	-	-	2	-
Church of the Nazarene	1961	-	4	-	-	-
Churches of Christ	1919	-	-	-	3	-
Every Home for Christ International	1967	-	-	-	42	-
Grace Ministries International	1998	4	-	-	-	2
Habitat for Humanity International	1982	-	2	-	17	-
Hundredfold Ministries International	1992	-	-	-	-	-
In Touch Mission International	1995	-	-	-	1	-
Independent Faith Mission		12	-	-	-	-
International Justice Mission		-	-	-	-	-
International Needs - USA	1985	-	-	-	12	-
International Partnership Ministries, Inc.	2001	-	-	-	2	-
Intl. Pentecostal Holiness Ch. World Mins.	1950	3	-	-	-	-
Kids Alive International	2001	-	-	-	6	-
Medical Ambassadors International	1999	-	-	-	-	-
Missionary Ventures International	2000	1	-	-	-	-
National Baptist Convention USA, Inc.,	1993	-	-	-	-	-
Navigators, U.S. Intl. Missions Group		2	-	1	-	-
Overseas Ministries Study Center	2001	-	-	1	-	-
Presbyterian Church (USA)		5	-	-	-	-
Salvation Army, U.S.A.	1922	7	-	-	-	-
Seventh-day Adventists Gen. Conf.	1905	-	-	2	-	9
SIM USA	1910	35	-	2	-	-
Teen Missions International	1994	2	-	-	6	-
Walk Thru The Bible Ministries	1999	-	-	-	2	-
Wesleyan World Missions	1930	-	9	-	-	-
Wisconsin Evangelical Lutheran Synod	1953	11	-	-	-	-

		Personnel from U.S.			Other Countries	
	First Year	4+ yrs.	2-4 yrs.	1-2 yrs.	Citizens	Not Citizens
World Mission Associates		-	-	-	2	-
World Vision Inc.	1981	-	-	-	-	-
Totals:		141	22	11	145	11

Zimbabwe

	First Year	4+ yrs.	2-4 yrs.	1-2 yrs.	Citizens	Not Citizens
African Enterprise, Inc.	1980	-	-	-	12	-
AMG International		-	-	-	2	-
Assemblies of God World Missions	1964	4	-	-	-	-
BCM International		1	-	-	-	-
Bible League, The	1995	-	-	-	11	-
Bible Training Centre for Pastors	1998	-	-	-	1	-
Brethren Assemblies		1	-	-	-	2
Brethren in Christ World Missions	1898	4	3	-	26	-
Campus Crusade for Christ, Intl.	1978	14	-	-	33	-
Child Evangelism Fellowship, Inc.	1951	-	-	-	2	-
Christian Churches / Churches of Christ	1956	34	-	-	14	-
Church of God of Prophecy	1976	-	-	-	7	-
Church of the Nazarene	1963	-	-	-	-	4
Churches of Christ	1902	1	-	-	1	-
Cumberland Presbyterian Church	2000	-	1	-	-	-
Every Home for Christ International	1964	-	-	-	37	-
Faith Christian Fellowship Intl.	1987	-	2	-	-	-
Flwshp. of Assoc. of Medical Evangelism	1961	-	-	-	10	-
Free Methodist World Missions	1938	2	-	-	-	-
Habitat for Humanity International	1996	-	4	-	-	-
Independent Faith Mission		4	-	-	-	-
Intl. Pentecostal Holiness Ch. World Mins.	1950	4	1	-	-	-
InterVarsity Christian Fellowship/USA		-	2	-	-	-
Mission Aviation Fellowship	1964	2	-	-	-	-
Missionary Ventures International	2002	1	-	-	-	-
New Directions International	1984	-	-	-	1	-
Presbyterian Church (USA)		2	-	-	-	-
Salvation Army, U.S.A.	1891	2	-	-	-	-
Seventh-day Adventists Gen. Conf.	1894	10	1	2	-	14
SIM USA	1906	5	-	-	-	-
TEAM (The Evangelical Alliance Mission)	1942	22	-	4	-	-
Teen Missions International	1985	-	-	-	5	-
United Church Bd. for World Mins.		-	4	-	-	-
University of the Family	1998	-	-	-	2	-
Walk Thru The Bible Ministries	1999	-	-	-	2	-
Totals:		113	18	6	166	20

Chapter 5
Canadian Protestant Agencies

This chapter contains the basic information for Canadian Protestant agencies engaged in Christian mission ministries outside Canada and the U.S. The comprehensive coverage includes agencies that directly support the work of such ministries or the work of overseas national churches/workers. The agencies supplied the information. The Survey Questionnaire used to gather the information is reproduced in the Appendix.

The Handbook covers an agency's overseas ministry and support activities but not its mission work in Canada. Much cross-cultural mission work takes place in Canada, but due to the additional complexities of reporting such activities we have not undertaken the task for this publication. Agencies with both overseas and Canadian mission ministries, however, were asked to include Canada-based ministry personnel in the total that appears in the "home ministry and office staff" line of the "Other Personnel" section.

Each agency will have at least seven of the basic categories of information listed below, with others included as applicable.

Agency Name

Agencies are listed alphabetically. If the article "the" is in an agency's name, it will appear at the end of the name so the agency is in the most commonly referenced alphabetical order. Rare exceptions occur where the Christian public commonly uses the article "the" as the first word in the agency's name.

Agencies that have changed their name since the previous *Handbook* have their prior name listed, with a cross-reference to the current or new name. A subdivision of a larger organization may be listed separately if it is organized to also serve the larger mission community rather than just its parent organization.

Telephone and Fax Numbers

The common format of showing the area code in parentheses is used throughout. Area codes have changed rapidly in the last decade, so some may even have been changed since publication.

E-mail Address

The Internet format and emerging standards for capitalization are used. For example, upper case letters may be used to the left of the @ sign when meaningful, but characters to the right are generally lower case.

In some cases, agencies have a general e-mail address, such as Info@xxxx.org. Others have supplied an individual person's address within the organization. In cases where only a Web address is given, it generally means a Web page provides access to several e-mail addresses so an inquiry can be immediately directed to the relevant department or person.

Instead of providing a general e-mail address, an agency may indicate the format to be used to contact individuals within the agency. This may take the format of something like Firstname.Lastname@xxxx.org and could be used by the sender when the individual is known.

Mission agencies began to use e-mail on a fairly broad scale by 1995, and now nearly all the agencies use e-mail on a regular basis.

Web Address

A request for a Web address was first included in the survey for the 1998-2000 edition. This edition reports even larger numbers of Web addresses, now including most agencies.

Postal Mailing Address

A post office box number usually appears whenever the agency has one, since it is more unlikely to change over time. Exceptions occur when the agency prefers the street address.

Chief Executive Officer

In some cases where there are multiple primary contacts, or due to agency preference, two officers are listed.

Short Descriptive Paragraph

A brief description appears based on the denominational orientation and primary activities information supplied by the agency. It keeps the same general order so the reader is presented with a consistent format across agencies. Additional specific information, such as name changes, mergers, or other unique aspects may also be included.

Purpose Statement

Purpose statements are included when available. Some of the statements are concise and shown in their entirety, straight from the agency or its promotional material. For most, however, because of space considerations, common or similar phrases such as "exists for the purpose of" are replaced by ellipses to present a more concise statement.

Year Founded in Canada

This date is the year the agency or overseas mission component of a larger organization was founded or incorporated in Canada. In some cases the denomination or organization may have existed earlier in another country. For some organizations, the founding date of the missionary-sending component may be later than the founding of the larger organization. For organizations that have experienced mergers, the founding date is generally that of the oldest component involved in the merger.

Income for Overseas Ministries

This is the part of an agency's overall income used or budgeted for ministry activities outside Canada and the USA or in activities that directly facilitate overseas ministries. "NA" indicates that income in this sense is not applicable, and usually applies to specialized service agencies or agencies whose income is reported under a sister or parent organization. "NR" indicates that the agency did not report income for overseas ministries for the survey, but may make this information available on request.

Gifts-in-Kind

If applicable, this is the portion of the income received in the form of donated gifts-in-kind commodities and/or services used for overseas ministries. Please note that some agencies do not include gifts-in-kind as part of their financial audit process, so the value of such gifts may not be included in their income for overseas ministries. Gifts-in-kind amounts that were an insignificant percentage (usually 1 percent or less) are not shown as a separate item.

Fully Supported Canadian Personnel Overseas

Not all agencies have overseas personnel in the following categories, so the above heading will not always appear. If applicable, the following lines will appear with the appropriate numbers:

• "Expecting to serve more than 4 years" for persons from Canada who are fully supported by the agency

• "Expecting to serve 1 up to 4 years" for persons from Canada who are fully supported by the agency

• "Nonresidential mission personnel" for fully supported Canadian mission personnel not residing in the country or countries of their ministry, but assigned to work and travel overseas at least 12 weeks per year on operational aspects of the overseas ministry

Other Personnel

If applicable for the agency, the following lines will appear:

• "Non-Canadian serving in own/other country" for persons with either citizenship in their country of service or another non-Canadian country, who are fully or partially supported from Canada. Such individuals are not included in the specific numbers for individual countries listed under the "Countries" heading at the bottom of many entries.

- "Bivocational/Tentmaker from Canada" for persons sponsored or supervised by the agency, but who support themselves partially or fully through non-church/ non-mission vocations and live overseas for the purpose of Christian witness and/or encouraging believers
- "Short-Term less than 1 year from Canada" for persons who went on overseas projects or mission trips that lasted at least two weeks but less than one year through the agency, either fully or partially supported, or raising their own support.
- "Home Ministry and office staff in Canada" for persons assigned to ministry and/or office duties in Canada either as full-time or part-time paid staff/associates

Countries

These are the countries where the agency sends Canadian personnel or regularly supports national or other non-Canadian personnel. Following the name of the country is the number of Canadian personnel with terms of service of four years or more. In some cases a continent or other general region is shown instead of a country. This may be due to several reasons, such as mission personnel whose ministry covers several countries.

Where an agency's work is maintained by nationals of countries other than Canada or the U.S., or by personnel serving less than four years, the country of activity may be listed without a number. Refer to the chapter entitled "Countries of Activity for CANADIAN Protestant Agencies" for more detailed country personnel totals.

ABWE (Association of Baptists for World Evangelism)—Canada

980 Adelaide St. S., Ste. 34
London, ON N6E 1R3 Canada
Phone: (519)690-1009
Fax: (519) 690-1618
E-mail: office@abwecanada.org
Web Site: www.abwe.org

Mr. Frank Bale, Director

A denominational sending agency of Baptist and Independent tradition engaged in theological education, church planting,TEE, evangelism and medical work.

Year founded in CAN: 1940

Income for Overseas Mins: $1,379,189

Gifts-in-Kind: $10,220

Fully Supported CAN Personnel Overseas:
Expecting to serve more than 4 years: 24
Expecting to serve 1 to 4 years: 8

Other Personnel:
Home ministry & office staff: 3

Countries: Unspecified 24

Action Intl. Ministries

P.O. Box 280
Three Hills, AB T0M 2A0 Canada
Phone: (403) 443-2221
Fax: (403) 443-7455
E-mail: AActionCanada@compuserve.com
Web Site: www.actionintl.org

Dr. Wayne Whitbourne, Canadian Dir.

A nondenominational sending agency of Evangelical tradition engaged in children's programs, training, development, evangelism, literature distribution, support of national churches and mobilization for mission. Financial figures from 1998.

Purpose: "...networks with local churches, national organizations and other mission agencies to reach people for Christ (evangelism), train them in Christian living (discipleship) and assist them in their physical and economic needs (development)."

Year founded in CAN: 1980

Income for Overseas Mins: $1,075,458

Fully Supported CAN Personnel Overseas:
Expecting to serve more than 4 years: 19
Expecting to serve 1 to 4 years: 6

Other Personnel:
Short-term less than 1 year from CAN: 6
Home ministry & office staff: 9
Bivocational/Tentmaker from Canada: 1

Countries: Brazil 4; Colombia 3; Ecuador 2; India 2; Mexico; Philippines 8

Africa Inland Mission (Canada)

1641 Victoria Park Ave.
Scarborough, ON M1R 1P8 Canada
Phone: (416) 751-6077
Fax: (416) 751-3467
E-mail: general.can@aimint.org
Web Site: www.aimcanada.org

Dr. John Brown, Director

An interdenominational sending agency of Evangelical tradition engaged in development, theological education, evangelism, leadership development and medical work.

Purpose: "...to plant maturing churches ...through the evangelization of unreached people groups and the effective preparation of church leaders."

Year founded in CAN: 1953

Income for Overseas Mins: NR

Personnel:
Short-term less than 1 year from CAN: 3
Home ministry & office staff: 11

Countries: Angola; Central African Republic; Chad; Comoros; Democratic Republic of Congo; Kenya; Lesotho; Madagascar; Mozambique; Namibia; Seychelles; Sudan; Tanzania; Uganda

African Enterprise Association of Canada

4509 W. 11th Ave.
Vancouver, BC V6R 2M5 Canada
Phone: (604) 228-0930
Fax: (604) 228-0936
E-mail: aecanada65@cs.com
Web Site: www.africanenterprise.org

Mr. David Richardson, Exec. Director

An interdenominational support agency of Evangelical tradition engaged in funds transmission, evangelism, missions information services and mobilization for mission in more than 16 countries in Africa. Income figures from 1998.

Purpose: "To service and expand an active partnership among Canadian Christians to raise prayer, financial, material and human resources to enable African Enterprise to achieve its mission to: Evangelize the Cities of Africa, through Word and Deed, in Partnership with the Church."

Year founded in CAN: 1964

Income for Overseas Mins: $16,804

Personnel:
Home ministry & office staff: 2

Apostolic Church In Canada, The

27 Castlefield Ave.
Toronto, ON M4R 1G3 Canada
Phone: (416) 489-0453
Fax: (416) 489-6479
E-mail: castlefield@apostolic.ca
Web Site: www.apostolic.ca

A network of apostolic churches of Pentecostal and evangelical tradition engaged in church planting, Bible distribution, evangelism, funds transmission and providing medical supplies. Statistical data from 1998.

Purpose: "...to establish a network of churches in apostolic relationship and reap a harvest through church planting."

Year founded in CAN: 1930

Income for Overseas Mins: $250,000

Gifts-in-Kind: $15,000

Personnel:
Short-term less than 1 year from CAN: 4
Non-CAN serving in own/other country: 22
Home ministry & office staff: 11
Bivocational/Tentmaker from CAN: 3

Countries: Brazil; India; Jamaica

Apostolic Church of Pentecost of Canada, Inc.

119, 2340 Pegasus Way NE
Calgary, AB T2E 8M5 Canada
Phone: (403) 273-5777
Fax: (403)273-8102
E-mail: acop@acop.ca
Web Site: www.acop.ca
Rev. Gillis Killam, Moderator

A sending agency of Pentecostal tradition engaged in church construction, agricultural programs, Bible distribution, theologi-

cal education, support of national workers and training.

Purpose: "...an international network of ministers and churches providing fellowship, encouragement and accountability in the proclamation of the gospel of Jesus Christ by the power of the Holy Spirit."

Year founded in CAN: 1921

Income for Overseas Mins: $1,000,000

Gifts-in-Kind: $10,000

Fully Supported CAN Personnel Overseas:
Expecting to serve more than 4 years: 26
Nonresidential mission personnel: 5

Other Personnel:
Short-term less than 1 year from CAN: 50
Home ministry & office staff: 5
Bivocational/Tentmaker from CAN: 1

Countries: Africa—General 2; Brazil 2; Burkina Faso 4; El Salvador 2; Estonia 6; India 2; Mexico 2; Spain 1; Taiwan 2; Trinidad and Tobago 1; Zambia 2

Arab World Ministries (Canada)

P.O. Box 3398
Cambridge, ON N3H 4T3 Canada
Phone: (519) 653-3170
Fax: (519) 653-3002
E-mail: info@awmcanada.org
Web Site: www.awmcanada.org
Mr. Don Little, Canadian Director

An interdenominational sending agency of Evangelical tradition engaged in church planting, broadcasting, correspondence courses, evangelism, support of national churches and video/film production/distribution. Personnel information from 1998.

Year founded in CAN: 1967

Income for Overseas Mins: $844,032

Fully Supported CAN Personnel Overseas:
Expecting to serve more than 4 years: 16

Other Personnel:
Home ministry & office staff: 15
Bivocational/Tentmaker from CAN: 10

Countries: Africa–General 3; Asia—General 6; France 6; United Kingdom 1

Associated Gospel Churches

3228 S. Service Rd.
Burlington, ON L7N 3H8 Canada

Phone: (905) 634-8184
Fax: (905)634-6283
E-mail: admin@agcofcanada.com
Web Site: www.agcofcanada.com
Rev. A. F. (Bud) Penner, President
An association of churches of evangelical tradition encouraging mission mobilization for church planting, camping programs, evangelism, leadership development, member care and partnership development.
Purpose: "...to assist member churches in their obedience to the Great Commission of Jesus Christ."
Year founded in CAN: 1925
Income for Overseas Mins: NA
Other Personnel:
 Home ministry & office staff: 6

Association of Baptists for World Evangelism
See: ABWE Canada

Back to the Bible Missionary Agency
P.O. Box 10
Winnipeg, MB R3C 2G2 Canada
Phone: (204) 663-1782
Fax: (204) 663-1435
E-mail: bttbible@backtothebible.ca
Web Site: www.backtothebible.ca
Mr. Gerald Reimer, Canadian Director
A nondenominational service agency of Evangelical tradition engaged in broadcasting, literature distribution and support of national churches.
Year founded in CAN: 1954
Income for Overseas Mins: $301,000
Personnel:
 Home ministry & office staff: 5

Baptist General Conference of Canada (Global Ministries)
4306 97 Street
Edmonton, AB T6E 5R9 Canada
Phone: (780) 438-9127
Fax: (780) 435-2478
E-mail: bgcc@bgc.ca
Web Site: www.bgc.ca
Selmer Hanson, Interim Exec. Director

A sending agency of Baptist and Evangelical tradition engaged in church planting, development, theological education, medical work, support of national churches and partnership development.
Purpose: "To plant and grow worshiping, caring churches globally."
Year founded in CAN: 1981
Income for Overseas Mins: NR
Fully Supported CAN Personnel Overseas:
 Expecting to serve more than 4 years: 8
 Expecting to serve 1 to 4 years: 2
Other Personnel:
 Short-term less than 1 year from CAN: 1
 Home ministry & office staff: 9
Countries: Ethiopia 1; Ireland 1; Mexico; Pakistan 1; Philippines 2; Portugal 1; Vietnam 2

Barry Moore Ministries
Box 9100
London, ON N6E 3P3 Canada
Phone: (519) 661-0205
Fax: (519) 661-0206
E-mail: bmoore@odyssey.on.ca
Web Site: www.bmoore.on.ca
Rev. John Laari, Exec. Director
An interdenominational service agency of Evangelical and Fundamental tradition engaged in evangelism, leadership development, support of national churches and training. More than 900 area-wide evangelistic crusades have been conducted throughout North America, Africa, Asia, and the islands of the seas. Income figures from 1998.
Year founded in CAN: 1960
Income for Overseas Mins: $79,000
Personnel:
 Home ministry & office staff: 3

BCM Intl. (Canada), Inc.
685 Main St. East
Hamilton, ON L8M 1K4 Canada
Phone: (905) 549-9810
Fax: (905) 549-7664
E-mail: mission@bcmintl.ca
Web Site: www.bcmintl.ca
Miss Chloe Chamberlain, Exec. Secretary
A nondenominational support agency of Evangelical and Fundamental tradition engaged in Christian education, children's

programs, church planting, disability assistance programs, evangelism, literature distribution and youth programs.

Purpose: "...making disciples of all age groups for the Lord Jesus Christ through evangelism and diverse Bible-centered ministries so that churches are established and the Church strengthened."

Year founded in CAN: 1942

Income for Overseas Mins: $56,676

Personnel:
Non-CAN serving in own/other country: 5
Home ministry & office staff: 44

Countries: Italy; Netherlands; Spain

BGCC Global Ministries

4306 97th St. N.W.
Edmonton, AB T6E 5R9 Canada
Phone: (780) 438-9127
Fax: (780) 435-2478
E-mail: bgcc@bgc.ca
Web Site: www.bgc.ca
Diane Weber, Adm. Global Ministries
A denominational sending agency of Baptist tradition engaged in church planting, development, evangelism, leadership development and support of national churches. The mission agency of the Baptist General Conference of Canada. Financial data from 1996.

Purpose: "...to involve every individual and every congregation in presenting the gospel and planting churches in their communities and around the world."

Year founded in CAN: 1995

Income for Overseas Mins: $275,000

Gifts-in-Kind: $50,000

Fully Supported CAN Personnel Overseas:
Expecting to serve more than 4 years: 12

Other Personnel:
Short-term less than 1 year from CAN: 32
Home ministry & office staff: 5

Countries: Asia–General 4; Central Asia–General 1; Ethiopia 3; Portugal 1; Unspecified Country 3

Bible Holiness Movement

P.O. Box 223, Postal Station A
Vancouver, BC V6C 2M3 Canada
Phone: (250)492-3376
Evangelist Wesley H. Wakefield, Bishop-General

A denominational support agency of Wesleyan and Holiness tradition engaged in church planting, literature distribution, literature production, support of national churches, Bible distribution and evangelism. Statistical data from 1996.

Purpose: "...to establish, conduct and maintain worldwide missionary work; to spread Scriptural holiness, vital Christianity and practical Godliness through a proper qualified ministry."

Year founded in CAN: 1949

Income for Overseas Mins: $28,966

Gifts-in-Kind: $2,026

Personnel:
Home ministry & office staff: 1

Countries: Ghana; India; South Korea; Malawi; Nigeria; Philippines; Tanzania; Zambia

Bible League of Canada, The

P.O. Box 5037
Burlington ON L7R 3Y8 Canada
Phone: (905) 319-9500
Fax: (905) 319-0484
E-mail: bibleag@worldchat.com
Web Site: www.thebibleleague.ca
Rev. David J. Tigchelaar, Exec. Director
A nondenominational specialized agency of Evangelical tradition engaged in Bible distribution, correspondence courses, evangelism, literacy work and missionary training. Personnel figures from 1998.

Purpose: " To provide Scriptures that bring people into the fellowship of Christ and His Church."

Year founded in CAN: 1949

Income for Overseas Mins: $3,655,000

Personnel:
Home ministry & office staff: 17

Brethren Assemblies (CAN)

(No central office)

The Brethren Assemblies are also known as "Christian Brethren" or "Plymouth Brethren." Missionaries are sent from each local assembly (church) and not through a central agency. Personnel totals were reported by MSC Canada for 1998.

Income for Overseas Mins: NA

Fully Supported CAN Personnel Overseas:
Expecting to serve more than 4 years: 192

Other Personnel:
Home ministry & office staff: 4

Countries: Angola 1; Argentina 4; Austria 4; Belgium 6; Bolivia 10; Botswana 2; Brazil 3; Chile 14; Colombia 1; Congo, Democratic Republic of the 3; Costa Rica 2; Dominican Republic 2; Ecuador 5; El Salvador 3; Finland 2; France 19; Guatemala 2; Hong Kong 2; India 2; Ireland 12; Italy 4; Japan 7; Kenya 4; Madagascar 2; Mexico 6; Nigeria 4; Peru 4; Philippines 4; Poland 2; Portugal 6; Puerto Rico 1; Russia 3; South Africa 1; Spain 4; Saint Vincent and the Grenadines 1; Uruguay 5; Venezuela 6; Zambia 29

Calcutta Mission of Mercy
See: Mission of Mercy (CAN)

Campus Crusade for Christ of Canada

P.O. Box 300, Stn. A
Vancouver, BC V6C 2X3 Canada

Phone: (604) 514-2000
Fax: (604) 514-2002
E-mail: support@crusade.org
Web Site: www.crusade.org

Mr. Charles Price, President

A nondenominational sending agency of Evangelical tradition engaged in evangelism and video/film production/distribution.

Purpose: "...helping to fulfill the Great Commission in Canada and around the world, by developing movements of Evangelism and Discipleship."

Year founded in CAN: 1967

Income for Overseas Mins: $6,202,000

Fully Supported CAN Personnel Overseas:
Expecting to serve more than 4 years: 17
Expecting to serve 1 to 4 years: 14

Other Personnel:
Short-term less than 1 year from CAN: 270
Home ministry & office staff: 335

Countries: Africa–General 2; Asia–General Bolivia; Ecuador; India 2; Mexico; Nigeria 2; Philippines 2; Russia 1; Serbia and Montenegro 2; South Africa 4; Tanzania; Ukraine 2

Canadian Baptist Ministries

7185 Millcreek Dr.
Mississauga, ON L5N 5R4 Canada
Phone: (905) 821-3533
Fax: (905) 826-3441
Web Site: www.cbmin.org

Dr. Gary Nelson, Gen. Secretary

A denominational sending agency of Baptist tradition engaged in leadership development, church planting, development, theological education and relief and/or rehabilitation. Personnel information from 1996.

Year founded in CAN: 1874

Income for Overseas Mins: $7,763,105

Fully Supported CAN Personnel Overseas:
Expecting to serve more than 4 years: 51
Expecting to serve 1 to 4 years: 26

Other Personnel:
Short-term less than 1 year from CAN: 700
Home ministry & office staff: 27

Countries: Albania 2; Angola 2; Asia—General 3; Belgium 6; Bolivia 5; China; Democratic Republic of Congo 8; Croatia; France 2; Guyana; Hong Kong; India 4; Indonesia 3; Kenya 6; Latvia 2; Slovakia 2; Ukraine 4; Venezuela 2

Canadian Bible Society/
La Societe Biblique Canadienne

10 Carnforth Rd.
Toronto, ON M4A 2S4 Canada
Phone: (416) 757-4171
Fax: (416) 757-3376
E-mail: donorenq@biblesociety.ca
Web Site: www.biblesociety.ca

Mr. Wally Sherwin, Interim National Director

A nondenominational and interconfessional support agency serving churches of all confessions and engaged in Bible distribution, linguistics and Bible translation.

Purpose: "...to promote and encourage, without doctrinal note or comment, the translation, publication, distribution and use of the Scriptures throughout Canada and Bermuda, and to cooperate with the United Bible Societies in its worldwide work."

Year founded in CAN: 1904

Income for Overseas Mins: $3,820,000

Personnel:
Home ministry & office staff: 120

Canadian Churches' Forum for Global Ministries

230 St. Clair Ave., West
Toronto, ON M4V 1R5 Canada
Phone: (416) 924-9351
Fax: (416) 924-5356
E-mail: ccforum@web.net
Web Site: www.ccforum.ca

Mr. Robert Faris, Coord. Outreach/Comm.

An affiliated interdenominational service institution of the Canadian Council of Churches engaged in missionary training, missionary education, furloughed missionary support and services for other agencies.

Purpose: "...an agency through which the Canadian churches reflect and work together on global mission issues through programs of education, dialogue and training."

Year founded in CAN: 1921
Income for Overseas Mins: NA
Personnel:
  Home ministry & office staff: 5

Canadian Convention of Southern Baptists (CCSB)

100 Convention Way
Cochrane, AB T4C 2G2 Canada
Phone: (403) 932-5688
Fax: (403) 932-4937
E-mail: office@ccsb.ca
Web Site: www.ccsb.ca

Rev. Gerald Taillon, Exec. Director

A denominational sending agency of Baptist tradition engaged in church planting, agricultural programs, Christian education, evangelism and relief and/or rehabilitation.

Year founded in CAN: 1985
Income for Overseas Mins: $541,128
Personnel:
  Home ministry & office staff: 16

Canadian Food for the Hungry

201-2580 Cedar Park Place
Abbotsford, BC V2T 3S5 Canada
Phone: (604) 853-4262
Fax: (604) 853-4332
E-mail: info@cfh.ca
Web Site: www.cfhi.ca

Rev. David Collins, President/CEO

A service agency engaged in development, agricultural programs, childrens programs, providing medical supplies, relief and/or rehabilitation and short-term programs.

Year founded in CAN: 1988
Income for Overseas Mins: $20,543,000
Gifts-in-Kind: $17,982,000
Fully Supported CAN Personnel Overseas:
  Expecting to serve more than 4 years: 6
  Expecting to serve 1 to 4 years: 5
Other Personnel:
  Short-term less than 1 year from CAN: 75
  Non-CAN serving in own/other country: 1
  Home ministry & office staff: 27
Countries: Bolivia 1; Brazil 1; Cambodia; Guatemala 2; Myanmar/Burma 2; Peru; Rwanda

Canadian South America Mission

Box 716
Three Hills, AB T0M 2A0 Canada
Phone: (403) 443-2250
Fax: (403) 443-2099
E-mail: dcwiebe@telusplanet.net
Web Site: www.samlink.org

Mr. Dan C. Wiebe, Exec. Director

An interdenominational sending agency of Baptist and Evangelical tradition engaged in leadership development, aviation services, church planting, theological education and partnership development.

Purpose: "...to establish the church of Jesus Christ in South America by planting and nurturing churches, training church leaders, [and] developing church associations."

Year founded in CAN: 1982
Income for Overseas Mins: $163,350
Fully Supported CAN Personnel Overseas:
  Expecting to serve more than 4 years: 4
  Expecting to serve 1 to 4 years: 4
Other Personnel:
  Home ministry & office staff: 2
Countries: Bolivia 2; Brazil; Colombia; Paraguay; Peru 2

Centre for World Mission—British Columbia

P.O. Box 2436

Clearbook, BC V2T 4X3 Canada
Phone: (604) 854-3818
Fax: (604) 854-3818
E-mail: CWMBC@telus.net
Web Site: www3.telus.net/cwmbc
Mr. John Burman, Director
An interdenominational support agency of Evangelical and Fundamental tradition engaged in mobilization for mission, mission-related research, services for other agencies and missions information service.
Purpose: "...to promote information on people groups of Canada and the world isolated by social and/or language barriers from mainstream society where a viable indigenous church is not yet existing."
Year founded in CAN: 1981
Income for Overseas Mins: NA
Personnel:
    Home ministry & office staff: 4

Child Evangelism Fellowship of Canada

P.O. Box 165—Stn. Main
Winnipeg, MB R3C 2G9 Canada
Phone: (204) 943-2774
Fax: (204)943-9967
E-mail: info@cefcanada.org
Web Site: www.cefcanada.org
Rev. Don Collins, Natl. Director
An interdenominational sending agency of Evangelical tradition engaged in evangelism, childrens programs, literature distribution, literature production and training. Financial data from 1998.
Purpose: "...to assist and promote the evangelizing and discipling of children through leadership, coordination and administrative support to CEF ministries across Canada and overseas."
Year founded in CAN: 1963
Income for Overseas Mins: $555,000
Fully Supported CAN Personnel Overseas:
    Expecting to serve more than 4 years: 11
    Expecting to serve 1 to 4 years: 2
Other Personnel:
    Home ministry & office staff: 7
Countries: Albania 2; Australia; Bolivia 1; Brazil 2; Hungary 2; Japan 2; Sweden 2

Christar

P.O. Box 20164
St. Catharines, ON L2M 7W7 Canada
Phone: (905) 646-0228
Fax: (905) 646-8707
E-mail: Christar@on.aibn.com
Web Site: www.christar.org
Marty Frisk, Director
An interdenominational sending agency of Evangelical tradition engaged in evangelism and church planting. Income figure from 1998.
Purpose: "...proclaiming the gospel and establishing local indigenous churches, primarily among least-reached Asian communities worldwide."
Year founded in CAN: 1953
Income for Overseas Mins: $293,000
Fully Supported CAN Personnel Overseas:
    Expecting to serve more than 4 years: 16
Other Personnel:
    Short-term less than 1 year from CAN: 15
    Non-CAN serving in own/other country: 40
    Home ministry & office staff: 3
    Bivocational/Tentmaker from CAN: 3
Countries: Asia–General 13; France 1; United Kingdom 2

Christian Aid Mission

201 Stanton St.
Fort Erie, ON L2A 3N8 Canada
Phone: (800) 871-0882
Fax: (905) 871-5165
E-mail: friends@christianaid.ca
Web Site: www.christianaid.ca
Mr. James S. Eagles, President
A nondenominational support agency of Evangelical tradition engaged in national worker support, childcare/orphanage programs, church planting, evangelism, relief and/or rehabilitation, missionary training.
Purpose: "To aid, encourage and strengthen indigenous New Testament Christianity, particularly where Christians are impoverished, few or persecuted..."
Year founded in CAN: 1953
Income for Overseas Mins: $1,077,261
Gifts-in-Kind: $23,672
Personnel:
    Short-term less than 1 year from CAN: 1

Non-CAN serving in own/other country: 20
Home ministry & office staff: 9
Countries: Africa–General; Asia–General; China; India; Indonesia; Latin America–General; Middle East; Nepal; Pakistan; South America–General; Turkey; Ukraine

Christian and Missionary Alliance in Canada, The

30 Carrier Dr., Suite 100
Toronto, ON M9W 5T7 Canada
Phone: (416) 674-7878
Fax: (416) 674-0808
E-mail: info@cmacan.org
Web Site: www.cmacan.org
Dr. Ray Downey, Vice President Global Mins.
A denominational sending agency of Evangelical tradition engaged in church planting, TEE and evangelism. Personnel data from 1998.
Purpose: "...developing indigenous movements of reproducing churches among least reached people groups."
Year founded in CAN: 1981
Income for Overseas Mins: $14,000,000
Fully Supported CAN Personnel Overseas:
  Expecting to serve more than 4 years: 187
  Expecting to serve 1 to 4 years: 23
  Nonresidential mission personnel: 6
Other Personnel:
  Short-term less than 1 year from CAN: 8
  Home ministry & office staff: 21
Countries: Argentina 2; Benin 3; Brazil 3; Burkina Faso 2; Cambodia 6; Chile 2; Colombia 3; Costa Rica 1; Cote d'Ivoire 13; Democratic Republic of Congo 4; Ecuador 8; France 4; Gabon 9; Germany 10; Guatemala 4; Guinea 9; Hong Kong 4; Hungary 6; Indonesia 18; Israel; Japan 4; Laos 2; Lebanon 2; Malaysia; Mali 5; Mexico 14; Peru 5; Philippines 12; Poland 4; Russia 8; Serbia and Montenegro 2; Spain 2; Taiwan 4; Thailand 3; Venezuela 9

Christian Blind Mission International (Canada)

P.O. Box 800
Stouffville, ON L4A 7Z9 Canada
Phone: (800) 567-2264
Fax: (888) 845-7717

E-mail: cbmican@cbmicanada.org
Web Site: www.cbmicanada.org
Mr. David McComiskey, Natl. Director
A transdenominational medical and rehabilitational agency engaged in the cure, prevention and care of disabling afflictions, including the training of nationals.
Purpose: "...serving the blind and otherwise disabled in the developing world, irrespective of nationality, race, sex, or religion...[with] the ultimate aim of showing the love of Christ..."
Year founded in CAN: 1978
Income for Overseas Mins: $7,334,000
Gifts-in-Kind: $1,350,000
Fully Supported CAN Personnel Overseas:
  Expecting to serve more than 4 years: 122
  Nonresidential mission personnel: 4
Other Personnel:
  Home ministry & office staff: 40
Countries: Unspecified Country 122

Christian Indigenous Development Overseas

142 Dalhousie Rd., NW
Calgary, AB T3A 2H1 Canada
Phone: (403) 286-0611
Fax: (403)247-4686
E-mail: jmclean142@shaw.ca
Mr. H.A. McLean, President
A transdenominational service agency of Evangelical tradition engaged in microenterprise development and technical assistance with previously-selected nationals. Financial data from 1998.
Year founded in CAN: 1977
Income for Overseas Mins: $173,000

Christian Literature Crusade—See: Croisade du Livre Chretien

Christian Reformed World Relief Committee

P.O. Box 5070
Burlington, ON L7R 3Y8 Canada
Phone: (905) 336-2920
Fax: (905) 336-8344

E-mail: dejongwa@crcna.ca
Web Site: www.crwrc.org
Mr. Wayne DeJong, Director
A denominational service agency of Reformed tradition engaged in development, agricultural programs, leadership development, literacy work, management consulting/training and relief and/or rehabilitation. Personnel statistics from 1998.
Year founded in CAN: 1969
Income for Overseas Mins: $6,604,644
Fully Supported CAN Personnel Overseas:
Expecting to serve more than 4 years: 20
Other Personnel:
Short-term less than 1 year from CAN: 8
Home ministry & office staff: 7
Countries: Cambodia 1; Haiti 2; Honduras 3; Indonesia 1; Kenya 2; Mali 1; Niger 2; Senegal 2; Tanzania 3; Uganda 1; Zambia 2

Christian Studies International of Canada

One Massey Square, Suite 1910
Toronto, ON M4C 5L4 Canada
Phone: (416) 690-4774
E-mail: vennen@attglobal.net
Dr. Robert Vander Vennen, Exec.
A nondenominational service agency of Evangelical tradition engaged in theological education, leadership development, missionary education. An affiliate of International Institute for Christian Studies.
Purpose: " To develop leaders who think and live Christianly, by establishing Departments of Christian Studies in secular universities overseas and by providing evangelical academicians, business leaders and professionals teaching with a Christian worldview in the full range of disciplines overseas."
Year founded in CAN: 1997
Income for Overseas Mins: $112,874
Fully Supported CAN Personnel Overseas:
Expecting to serve more than 4 years: 2
Expecting to serve 1 to 4 years: 1
Other Personnel:
Home ministry & office staff: 1
Countries: China; Russia 2

Church of God (Anderson, IN), Canadian Board of Missions

4717-56th St.
Camrose, AB T4V 2C4 Canada
Phone: (780) 672-0772
Fax: (780) 672-6888
E-mail: wcdncog@cable-lynx.net
Web Site: www.chog.ca
Rev. John D. Campbell, Exec. Dir. Min. Services
A support agency of Holiness and Wesleyan tradition engaged in support of national churches, church construction, church planting and leadership development.
Purpose: "...focused on developing dynamic congregational life, effective leadership and church planting."
Year founded in CAN: 1946
Income for Overseas Mins: $177,582
Personnel:
Short-term less than 1 year from CAN: 2
Home ministry & office staff: 5
Countries: Guam; Uganda; Zambia

Compassion Canada

P.O. Box 5591
London, ON N6A 5G8 Canada
Phone: (519) 668-0224
Fax: (519) 685-1107
E-mail: compcanada@capc.ci.org
Web Site: www.compassioncanada.ca
Rev. Barry Slauenwhite, President
A transdenominational service agency of Evangelical tradition engaged in childcare/orphanage programs, children's programs, development, funds transmission and support of national churches.
Year founded in CAN: 1964
Income for Overseas Mins: $6,640,000
Personnel:
Home ministry & office staff: 20

Croisade du Livre Chretien/ Christian Literature Crusade

4257 ouest Ste-Catherine
Montreal, PQ H3Z 1P7 Canada
Phone: (514) 933-9466
Fax: (514) 933-7629
E-mail: clccanada@netcom.ca

Mr. Philippe Bonicel, Director
An interdenominational service agency of Evangelical tradition engaged in literature distribution and Bible distribution. Statistics from 1998.
Year founded in CAN: 1977
Income for Overseas Mins: $5,000
Personnel:
Home ministry & office staff: 9

Crossroads Christian Communications Inc.

P.O. Box 5100
Burlington, ON L8M 1W3 Canada
Phone: (905) 332-6400
Fax: (905) 332-1880
E-mail: missions@crossroads.ca
Web Site: www.crossroads.ca/missions
Rev. David Mainse, President
An interdenominational service agency of Evangelical and Pentecostal tradition engaged in relief and/or rehabilitation, agricultural programs, broadcasting, development, providing medical supplies, medical work and training.
Income for Overseas Mins: $1,900,000
Gifts-in-Kind: $55,000
Personnel:
Home ministry & office staff: 5

Czechoslovak Evangelical Mission

1601 Bramsey Dr.
Mississauga, ON L5J 2H8 Canada
Phone: (905) 822-8808
Rev. Joseph R. Novak, President
An interdenominational support agency of Baptist tradition engaged in literature production and literature distribution.
Year founded in CAN: 1984
Income for Overseas Mins: $30,000
Personnel:
Home ministry & office staff: 1

Emmanuel Relief and Rehabilitation International

P.O. Box 4050
Stouffville, ON L4A 8B6 Canada

Phone: (905) 640-2111
Fax: (905) 640-2186
E-mail: info@e-i.org
Web Site: www.e-i.org
Mr. Andrew Atkins, Gen. Director
An interdenominational sending agency of Evangelical tradition engaged in relief and/or rehabilitation, agricultural programs, child-care/orphanage programs, development, literacy work and support of national churches.
Purpose: " ...to encourage, strengthen and assist churches worldwide to meet the spiritual and physical needs of the poor in accordance with Holy Scriptures..."
Year founded in CAN: 1975
Income for Overseas Mins: $792,856
Fully Supported CAN Personnel Overseas:
Expecting to serve more than 4 years: 7
Expecting to serve 1 to 4 years: 13
Other Personnel:
Short-term less than 1 year from CAN: 6
Non-CAN serving in own/other country: 4
Home ministry & office staff: 17
Countries: Brazil; Haiti; Malawi 2; Philippines 3; South Africa; Tanzania 2; Uganda

Equip, Canada

P.O. Box 683
Duncan, BC V9L 3Y1 Canada
Phone: (250) 743-7171
Fax: (250) 743-0213
Web Site: www.equipinternational.com
Rev. Barrie G. Flitcroft, Gen. Director
An interdenominational sending agency of Evangelical tradition engaged in missionary training, development, and technical assistance/training.
Purpose: "...to prepare, send and support evangelical missionaries to assist the church around the world to be responsive to the poor, sensitive to the Holy Spirit, focused on personal evangelism, and practically engaged in strengthening the Body of Christ."
Year founded in CAN: 1996
Income for Overseas Mins: $195,106
Fully Supported CAN Personnel Overseas:
Expecting to serve more than 4 years: 5
Expecting to serve 1 to 4 years: 4
Other Personnel:
Short-term less than 1 year from CAN: 3

Non-CAN serving in own/other country: 1
Home ministry & office staff: 8
Countries: Belize; Liberia 4; Mexico; Uganda 1

European Christian Mission

1077 56th St., Ste 226
Delta, BC V4L 2A2 Canada
Phone: (604) 943-0211
Fax: (604) 943-0212
E-mail: ecmnainc@cs.com
Rev. Vincent Price, N. America Director

An interdenominational sending agency of
Evangelical tradition engaged in evange-
lism, broadcasting, literature distribution
and support of national churches. Financial
data from 1998.
Year founded in CAN: 1960
Income for Overseas Mins: $802,540
Personnel:
Home ministry & office staff: 4

Evangelical Covenant Church of Canada

P.O. Box 34025
Winnipeg, MB R3T 5T5 Canada
Phone: (204) 269-3437
Fax: (204) 269-3584
E-mail: ccc1@mts.net
Mr. Jeffrey Anderson, Superintendent

A denominational conference of covenantal
and evangelical tradition engaged in denominational funds transmission and mission mobilization for evangelism and
church planting. Statistics from 1996.
Year founded in CAN: 1904
Income for Overseas Mins: $52,280
Personnel:
Home ministry & office staff: 3

Evangelical Free Church of Canada Mission

Box 850 Langley Stn., LCD1
Langley, BC V3A 8S6 Canada
Phone: (604) 888-7772
Fax: (604) 888-3108
E-mail: efccm@twu.ca
Web Site: www.efccm.ca
Dr. David J. McKinley, Exec. Director

A denominational sending agency of Con-
gregational and Evangelical tradition en-
gaged in church planting, broadcasting,
theological education, evangelism, mobiliza-
tion for mission and short-term programs.
Purpose: "...exists to serve in the birth and
growth of healthy churches internationally."
Year founded in CAN: 1981
Income for Overseas Mins: $2,000,000
Fully Supported CAN Personnel Overseas:
Expecting to serve more than 4 years: 49
Expecting to serve 1 to 4 years: 3
Other Personnel:
Short-term less than 1 year from CAN: 1
Non-CAN serving in own/other country: 14
Home ministry & office staff: 10
Bivocational/Tentmaker from CAN: 1
Countries: Bolivia 8; China 2; Germany 2;
Hungary 3; Japan 2; Lithuania; Mexico 4;
Philippines 2; Romania 1; Russia 1; Thailand
2; Ukraine 17; Uzbekistan 2; Venezuela 3

Evangelical Lutheran Church in Canada, ELCIC Mission

302-393 Portage Ave.
Winnipeg, MB R3B 3H6 Canada
Phone: (204) 984-9150
Fax: (204) 984-9185
E-mail: vim@elcic.ca
Web Site: www.elcic.ca/mission
Rev. Paul Johnson, Mission in the World Exec.

The national mission office of a Lutheran
denomination engaged in support of over-
seas partner churches, missions in Canada
and campus ministry.
Purpose: "...to share the Gospel of Jesus
Christ with people in Canada and around
the world through the proclamation of the
Word, the celebration of the Sacraments
and through service in Christ's name."
Year founded in CAN: 1985
Income for Overseas Mins: $500,000
Fully Supported CAN Personnel Overseas:
Expecting to serve more than 4 years: 5
Expecting to serve 1 to 4 years: 6
Other Personnel:
Short-term less than 1 year from CAN: 3
Home ministry & office staff: 2
Countries: Argentina; Cameroon 2; Colom-

bia; El Salvador 1; Guyana; Hong Kong; Jordan; Papua New Guinea 1; Peru 1; Slovakia; Thailand

Evangelical Medical Aid Society

30 5155 Spectrum Way
Mississauga, ON L4W 5A1   Canada
Phone: (866) 438-7386
E-mail: main@cmds-emas.ca
Web Site: www.cmds-emas.ca
R. W. Elford, Exec. Director

A nondenominational specialized agency of Evangelical tradition engaged in medical work, disability assistance programs and extension education.

Purpose: "...to encourage and assist Christian medical work overseas."

Year founded in CAN: 1948

Income for Overseas Mins: $920,824

Gifts-in-Kind: 228,483

Fully Supported CAN Personnel Overseas:
  Expecting to serve more than 4 years: 1
  Expecting to serve 1 to 4 years: 2

Other Personnel:
  Short-term less than 1 year from CAN: 124
  Home ministry & office staff: 3

Countries: Angola 1; China; Cuba; India; Nigeria; Philippines; Romania; Ukraine; Vietnam

Evangelical Mennonite Conference

P.O. Box 1268
Steinbach, MB R0A 2A0 Canada
Phone: (204) 326-6401
Fax: (204) 326-1613
E-mail: emconf@mts.net
Web Site: www.emconf.ca
Mr. Len Barkman, Gen. Secretary

A denominational sending agency of Mennonite and Evangelical tradition engaged in church planting, TEE, evangelism, leadership development, medical work, support of national churches and services for other agencies.

Year founded in CAN: 1953

Income for Overseas Mins: $1,469,185

Fully Supported CAN Personnel Overseas:

Expecting to serve more than 4 years: 29
Expecting to serve 1 to 4 years: 2
Other Personnel:
  Home ministry & office staff: 2
Countries: Burkina Faso 2; Mexico 14; Paraguay 13

Evangelical Mennonite Mission Conf. Board of Missions & Service

Box 52059 Niakwa P.O.
Winnipeg, MB R2M 5P9 Canada
Phone: (204) 253-7929
Fax: (204) 256-7384
E-mail: emmc@mb.sympatico.ca
Mr. Len Sawatzky, Director

A denominational sending agency of Mennonite tradition engaged in church planting, broadcasting, evangelism, partnership development and support of national workers.

Year founded in CAN: 1959

Income for Overseas Mins: $482,380

Gifts-in-Kind: NA

Fully Supported CAN Personnel Overseas:
  Expecting to serve more than 4 years: 4
  Expecting to serve 1 to 4 years: 6

Other Personnel:
  Short-term less than 1 year from CAN: 23
  Home ministry & office staff: 15

Countries: Bolivia 2; Mexico 2

Evangelical Missionary Church of Canada World Partners

4031 Brentwood Road NW
Calgary, AB T2L 1L1 Canada
Phone: (403) 250-2759
Fax: (403) 291-4720
E-mail: evanmiss@emcc.ca
Web Site: www.emcc.ca
Rev. G. Keith Elliott, Exec. Dir. Missions & Adm.

A denominational sending agency of Evangelical tradition engaged in church planting, childcare/orphanage programs, development, theological education, leadership development and short-term programs.

Purpose: "...to win the lost, to build up believers and equip them to establish indigenous churches which participate in world-

wide outreach until Christ comes."
Year founded in CAN: 1998
Income for Overseas Mins: $19,945
Fully Supported CAN Personnel Overseas:
  Expecting to serve more than 4 years: 20
Other Personnel:
  Short-term less than 1 year from CAN: 63
  Home ministry & office staff: 7
  Bivocational/Tentmaker from CAN: 1
Countries: Brazil 7; Mexico 4; Nigeria 5;
Portugal 2; Spain 2

Evangelical Tract Distributors
12151 - 67th St.
Edmonton, AB T5B 1M6 Canada
Phone: (780) 477-1538
Fax: (780) 477-3795
E-mail: support@evangelicaltract.com
Web Site: www.evangelicaltract.com
Mr. John Harder, President
An interdenominational specialized agency
of Evangelical tradition engaged in litera-
ture distribution, evangelism and literature
production.
Purpose: "...to proclaim the Gospel of
Jesus Christ and His message of forgiveness
in as many languages as possible primarily
by the printing of gospel tracts and any
other appropriate media."
Year founded in CAN: 1935
Income for Overseas Mins: $30,000

FAIR (Fellowship Agency for International Relief)
679 Southgate Dr.
Guelph, ON N1G 4S2 Canada
Phone: (519) 821-4830
Fax: (519) 821-9829
E-mail: international@fellowship.ca
Web Site: www.febinternational.ca
Mr. Norman Nielsen, Coordinator
A denominational support agency of Bap-
tist tradition engaged in relief and/or reha-
bilitation and development. The relief arm
of FEBInternational.
Year founded in CAN: 1974
Income for Overseas Mins: $228,151

Far East Broadcasting Associates of Canada
6850 Antrim Ave.
Burnaby, BC V5J 4M4 Canada
Phone: (604) 430-8439
Fax: (604) 430-5272
E-mail: kenreeve@telus.net
Web Site: www.febcanada.ca
Mr. Don Patterson, Dir./Intl. Broadcast Support
An interdenominational specialized agency
of Evangelical tradition engaged in broadcasting, audio recording/distribution, evangelism and literature distribution. Financial
figure from 1998.
Purpose: "...to promote missions...to en-
courage evangelical Christians to partici-
pate in FEBCanada's ministries through
prayer, financial support and personal
involvement...to participate directly in FEB
Radio International's broadcast ministry
through the provision of staff, production
of programs and the funding of missionaries and special projects."
Year founded in CAN: 1964
Income for Overseas Mins: $1,142,719
Fully Supported CAN Personnel Overseas:
  Expecting to serve more than 4 years: 7
  Expecting to serve 1 to 4 years: 2
Other Personnel:
  Home ministry & office staff: 25
Countries: Cambodia 1; Hong Kong 2; N.
Mariana Isls 2; Philippines; Thailand 2

FEBInternational
679 Southgate Dr.
Guelph, ON N1G 4S2 Canada
Phone: (519) 821-4830
Fax: (519) 821-9829
E-mail: international@fellowship.ca
Web Site: www.febinternational.ca
Rev. Richard Flemming, Director
A denominational sending agency of Bap-
tist tradition engaged in church planting,
correspondence courses, evangelism, lead-
ership development, medical work, support
of national churches, support of national
workers and relief and/or rehabilitation.
Year founded in CAN: 1963
Income for Overseas Mins: $3,200,000
Fully Supported CAN Personnel Overseas:

Expecting to serve more than 4 years: 47
Expecting to serve 1 to 4 years: 12
Nonresidential mission personnel: 2
Other Personnel:
Short-term less than 1 year from CAN: 45
Non-CAN serving in own/other country: 2
Home ministry & office staff: 10
Countries: Belgium 6; Central Asia—General; Colombia 4; France 3; Italy 2; Japan 8; Kenya 2; Middle East 1; Pakistan 11; South Africa; Spain 4; Venezuela 6

Frontiers Canada

P.O. Box 9090
Edmonton, AB T5P 4K1 Canada
Phone: (780) 421-9090
Fax: (780) 421-9292
E-mail: info@frontiers.org

Rev. Nelson Wolf, Exec. Director

An interdenominational sending agency of Evangelical tradition engaged in church planting, evangelism, support of national workers and missionary training. Personnel information from 1996.

Purpose: "...working in close cooperation with local churches to see vital, worshipping witnessing churches established..."
Year founded in CAN: 1984
Income for Overseas Mins: NA
Fully Supported CAN Personnel Overseas:
Expecting to serve more than 4 years: 22
Nonresidential mission personnel: 3
Other Personnel:
Non-CAN serving in own/other country: 3
Home ministry & office staff: 50
Bivocational/Tentmaker from CAN: 2
Countries: Africa–General 2; Asia–General 3; Central Asia–General 10; Europe–General 3; Indonesia 4; Unspecified Country

Fundamental Baptist Mission of Trinidad and Tobago (Canada)

817 Kingston Rd.
Pickering, ON L1V 2R2 Canada
Phone: (905) 839-4621
Fax: (905) 839-4622
E-mail: godbless@ba.aien.com
Web Site: www.bayfairbaptist.com

Rev. Garry Francis, Secretary-Treasurer

A support agency of Baptist and Fundamental tradition engaged in funds transmission and support of national workers. Financial data included in USA sister agency.
Year founded in CAN: 1990
Income for Overseas Mins: NA
Personnel:
Home ministry & office staff: 1

Galcom International

115 Nebo Rd.
Hamilton, ON L8W 2E1 Canada
Phone: (905) 574-4626
Fax: (905) 574-4633
E-mail: galcom@galcom.org
Web Site: www.galcom.org

Rev. Allan T. McGuirl, Intl. Director

An interdenominational support agency of Evangelical and Baptist tradition engaged in designing, building and distributing high-tech communications equipment for other agencies used in evangelism and other ministries in 102 countries.

Purpose: "To provide durable technical equipment for communicating the Gospel worldwide...at the lowest possible price."
Year founded in CAN: 1989
Income for Overseas Mins: $1,145,271
Personnel:
Short-term less than 1 year from CAN: 3
Home ministry & office staff: 11

Glad Tidings Missionary Society

3456 Fraser St.
Vancouver, BC V5V 4C4 Canada
Phone: (604) 873-3621
Fax: (604) 876-1558
E-mail: info@gtchurch.ca
Web Site: www.gtchurch.ca

Pastor Rod Forrest, Director

A nondenominational sending agency of Independent tradition engaged in evangelism and church planting. Financial data from 1998.
Year founded in CAN: 1948
Income for Overseas Mins: $500,000
Fully Supported CAN Personnel Overseas:
Expecting to serve more than 4 years: 5

Other Personnel:
Non-CAN serving in own/other country: 2
Countries: Germany 1; Mexico 2; Philippines 1; Senegal 1

Global Outreach Mission

P.O. Box 1210
St. Catharines, ON L2R 7A7 Canada
Phone: (950) 684-1401
E-mail: glmissl@adelphia.net
Web Site:
www.globaloutreachmission.com
Dr. James O. Blackwood, President
A transdenominational sending agency of Evangelical and Independent tradition engaged in church planting, aviation services, broadcasting, theological education, evangelism and medical work.
Purpose: " ...sharing the gospel planting and encouraging his church, helping the hurting physically and serving in every area of Christian development."
Year founded in CAN: 1943
Income for Overseas Mins: $1,169,250
Fully Supported CAN Personnel Overseas:
Expecting to serve more than 4 years: 28
Expecting to serve 1 to 4 years: 2
Other Personnel:
Short-term less than 1 year from CAN: 4
Non-CAN serving in own/other country: 38
Home ministry & office staff: 13
Countries: Belgium; Bolivia; Brazil; Colombia 2; Democratic Republic of Congo 1; France 7; Ghana; Guatemala 2; Haiti 2; Hong Kong 2; India 4; Ireland 4; Kazakhstan 2; South Africa 2

Gospel for Asia

245 King St. E.
Stoney Creek, ON L8G 1L9 Canada
Phone: (888) 946-2742
E-mail: infocanada@gfa.org
Web Site: www.gfa.org
Pastor Wendell Leytham, Canadian Director
An interdenominational support agency of Evangelical tradition engaged in support of national workers, Bible distribution, evangelism and support of national churches. Financial figure from 1996.
Year founded in CAN: 1985

Income for Overseas Mins: $755,000
Personnel:
Home ministry & office staff: 10

Gospel Missionary Union of Canada

2121 Henderson Hwy.
Winnipeg, MB R2G 1P8 Canada
Phone: (204) 338-7831
Fax: (204) 339-3321
E-mail: amc@avmi.org
Web Site: www.avantministries.org
Mr. Grant Morrison, Canadian Director
An interdenominational sending agency of Baptist tradition engaged in church planting, theological education, broadcasting and leadership development. Name changing to Avant Ministries.
Year founded in CAN: 1949
Income for Overseas Mins: $2,751,681
Fully Supported CAN Personnel Overseas:
Expecting to serve more than 4 years: 49
Expecting to serve 1 to 4 years: 3
Other Personnel:
Home ministry & office staff: 21
Countries: Argentina 2; Austria 2; Bahamas, The 1; Belize 2; Bolivia 13; Brazil 1; Ecuador 7; Germany 2; Mali 9; Mexico 1; Panama 1; Spain 8

Greater Europe Mission (Canada)

100 Ontario St.
Oshawa, ON L1G 4Z1 Canada
Phone: (905) 728-8222
Fax: (905) 728-8958
E-mail: gemcanada@gemission.com
Web Site: www.gemission.org
Rev. Neil Rempel, Canadian Director
A nondenominational sending agency of Evangelical and Baptist tradition engaged in theological education, church planting, camping programs, evangelism and leadership development.
Purpose: "...to assist the peoples of Europe in building up the Body of Christ so every person in Europe is within reach of a witnessing fellowship."
Year founded in CAN: 1959

Income for Overseas Mins: $976,374
Fully Supported CAN Personnel Overseas:
Expecting to serve more than 4 years: 16
Expecting to serve 1 to 4 years: 2
Other Personnel:
Short-term less than 1 year from CAN: 27
Home ministry & office staff: 4
Countries: Austria 1; Croatia 2; France 3; Hungary 1; Ireland 1; Latvia 3; Luxembourg 2; Portugal 2; Ukraine 1

HCJB World Radio—Canada

6655 Kitimat Road, Unit #2
Mississauga, ON L5N 6J4 Canada
Phone: (905) 814-0176
Fax: (905) 814-6805
E-mail: hcjbcan@hcjb.org
Web Site: www.hcjb.org
Mr. Ian Leaver, Canadian Director
An interdenominational support agency of Evangelical tradition engaged in broadcasting, correspondence courses, development, evangelism, medical work, partnership development and video/film production/distribution.
Year founded in CAN: 1931
Income for Overseas Mins: $1,300,000
Fully Supported CAN Personnel Overseas:
Expecting to serve more than 4 years: 10
Expecting to serve 1 to 4 years: 6
Other Personnel:
Home ministry & office staff: 7
Countries: Ecuador 10

High Adventure Gospel Communication

P.O. Box 425, Station E
Toronto, ON M6H 4E3 Canada
Phone: (905) 898-5447
Fax: (905) 898-5447
E-mail: highadventure@sympatico.ca
Web Site: www.highadventure.org
Mr. Don McLaughlin, Dir. Outreach Mins.
A nondenominational agency of Evangelical tradition engaged in evangelism/Christian program placement on international radio.
Year founded in CAN: 1975
Income for Overseas Mins: NA
Personnel:
Home ministry & office staff: 4

HOPE International Development Agency

214 Sixth Street
New Westminster, BC V3L 3A2 Canada
Phone: (604) 525-5481
Fax: (604) 525-3471
E-mail: hope@hope-international.com
Web Site: www.hope-international.com
Mr. David S. McKenzie, Exec. Director
A service agency engaged in development, agricultural programs, leadership development, relief and/or rehabilitation and training.
Purpose: "...founded on Christian principles [to] provide alternate technological and educational support to people in developing countries where environmental, economic and/or social circumstances have interfered with the ability of local communities to sustain themselves..."
Year founded in CAN: 1975
Income for Overseas Mins: $14,512,985
Gifts-in-Kind: $11,000,000
Fully Supported CAN Personnel Overseas:
Expecting to serve more than 4 years: 2
Other Personnel:
Short-term less than 1 year from CAN: 20
Non-CAN serving in own/other country: 15
Home ministry & office staff: 8
Countries: Cambodia; Ethiopia; South Africa 2

International Child Care (Canada)

2476 Argentia Rd., #113
Mississauga, ON L5N 6M1 Canada
Phone: (888) 722-4453
Fax: (905) 821-6319
E-mail: canada@intlchildcare.org
Web Site: www.intlchildcare.org
Mr. Dana Osburn, Natl. Director
A Christian health agency working in Haiti and the Dominican Republic to change conditions which make people sick, hungry, umemployed and afraid. Statistics from 1996.
Year founded in CAN: 1972
Income for Overseas Mins: $998,040
Gifts-in-Kind: $144,756
Fully Supported CAN Personnel Overseas:
Expecting to serve more than 4 years: 2

Expecting to serve 1 to 4 years: 4
Other Personnel:
Home ministry & office staff: 1
Countries: Haiti 2

International Christian Aid Canada

P.O. Box 5090
Burlington, ON L7R 4G5 Canada
Phone: (905) 331-7799
Fax: (905) 331-7699
E-mail: icac@sympatico.ca
Mr. Kenneth D. Roe, Exec. Director

A support agency of Evangelical tradition engaged in relief and/or rehabilitation, agricultural programs, camping programs, children's programs, church planting, development and medical work.

Year founded in CAN: 1979
Income for Overseas Mins: $2,196,000
Gifts-in-Kind: $1,411,000
Personnel:
Non-CAN serving in own/other country: 78
Home ministry & office staff: 5
Bivocational/Tentmaker from CAN: 2
Countries: Africa—General, Honduras, Philippines

International Missions in Ontario
See: Christar

Inter-national Needs Network—Canada

P.O. Box 1288
Aldergrove, BC V9W 2V1 Canada
Phone: (604) 702-9805
Fax: (604) 702-9806
E-mail: inc@inter-nationalneeds.org
Web Site: www.inter-nationalneeds.org
Mr. John G. Dengok, Exec. Director

An interdenominational service agency of Evangelical tradition engaged in support of national workers, church planting, development, evangelism and leadership development.
Purpose: "...to link Canadian Christians and churches with overseas ministries of INC that seek to integrate evangelism, dis-

cipleship, and fulfillment of human needs through effective development."
Year founded in CAN: 1974
Income for Overseas Mins: $600,000
Personnel:
Short-term less than 1 year from CAN: 2
Non-CAN serving in own/other country: 804
Home ministry & office staff: 3
Countries: Bangladesh; Colombia; Czech Republic; Egypt; Eritrea; Ethiopia; Ghana; India; Morocco; Nepal; Philippines; Romania; Slovakia; Sri Lanka; Tanzania; Uganda; Vietnam; Zambia

International Teams of Canada

1 Union St.
Elmira, ON N3B 3J9 Canada
Phone: (519) 669-8844
Fax: (519) 669-5644
E-mail: ITCAN@iteams.org
Web Site: www.iteams.ca
Mr. Neil Ostrander, President

An interdenominational sending agency of Evangelical tradition engaged in evangelism, church planting, development, evangelism, leadership development, short-term programs and youth programs. Personnel information from 1998.

Purpose: "...engages in authentic partnerships with local churches and other missions to mobilize teams of people around the world to compassionate evangelism and training next generation leaders."
Year founded in CAN: 1966
Income for Overseas Mins: $958,348
Fully Supported CAN Personnel Overseas:
Expecting to serve more than 4 years: 18
Other Personnel:
Short-term less than 1 year from CAN: 500
Home ministry & office staff: 26
Countries: Australia 1; Austria 2; France 2; Germany 5; Italy 2; Poland 4; United Kingdom 2

INTERSERVE (Canada)

10 Huntingdale Blvd.
Scarborough, ON M1W 2S5 Canada
Phone: (416) 499-7511
Fax: (416) 499-4472

E-mail: info@hardplaces.ca
Web Site: www.interserve.org
Mr. Craig Shugart, Exec. Director

An interdenominational sending agency of Evangelical tradition engaged in evangelism, development, medical work, support of national churches and technical assistance. Statistics from 1998.

Purpose: "...recruiting, resourcing and deployment of Christian professionals and entrepreneurs for the establishment of the church among the Muslim, Hindu and Buddhist peoples of North Africa, the Middle East, Central and Southwest Asia."

Year founded in CAN: 1908

Income for Overseas Mins: $800,000

Fully Supported CAN Personnel Overseas:
Expecting to serve more than 4 years: 27

Other Personnel:
Short-term less than 1 year from CAN: 17
Home ministry & office staff: 10
Bivocational/Tentmaker from CAN: 6

Countries: Asia–General 7; Bangladesh 1; Cyprus 4; India 2; Nepal 10; Pakistan 3

InterVarsity Christian Fellowship of Canada

64 Prince Andrew Place
Toronto, ON M3C 2H4 Canada
Phone: (416) 443-1170
Fax: (416) 443-1499
E-mail: National@ivcf.ca
Web Site: www.ivcf.ca
Ms. Geri Rodman, President

An interdenominational support agency of Evangelical tradition engaged in evangelism, camping programs, leadership development and short-term programs.

Purpose: "...passionate about the transformation of youth, students and alumni into fully committed followers of Jesus."

Year founded in CAN: 1928

Income for Overseas Mins: NA

Fully Supported CAN personnel overseas:
Nonresidential mission personnel: 7

Other Personnel:
Short-term less than 1 year from CAN: 6
Home ministry & office staff: 155

Into All The World

51 Bond Court
Guelph, ON N1H 8N6 Canada
Phone: (519) 763-6147
Fax: (519) 763-1491
E-mail: iatw@sentex.net
Web Site: www.iatw.ca
Rev. Bill Lewis, CEO

An interdenominational sending agency of Charismatic tradition engaged in church planting, childcare/orphanage programs, theological education, leadership development, literature distribution and support of national workers.

Purpose: "A mission enabling agency that works with individuals and churches to fulfill the call of God on their life, with special concern about unreached and untargeted people in the 10-40 Window."

Year founded in CAN: 1981

Income for Overseas Mins: $120,000

Fully Supported CAN Personnel Overseas:
Expecting to serve 1 to 4 years: 3
Nonresidential mission personnel: 15

Other Personnel:
Short-term less than 1 year from CAN: 26
Non-CAN serving in own/other country: 16
Home ministry & office staff: 2

Countries: Benin; Cameroon; Djibouti; Eritrea; Ethiopia; India; Kenya; Nigeria; Uganda

Italian Pentecostal Church of Canada, The

6724 Fabre St.
Montreal, PQ H2G 2Z6 Canada
Phone: (514) 279-1100
Fax: (514) 279-1131
E-mail: IPCC@novalink.ca
Web Site: www.the-ipcc.org
Rev. David J. Mortelliti, General Superintendent

A denominational support agency of Pentecostal tradition engaged in support of national workers, childcare/orphanage programs, support of national churches, translation work and youth programs.

Year founded in CAN: 1912

Income for Overseas Mins: $53,017

Personnel:
Short-term less than 1 year from CAN: 2
Home ministry & office staff: 1

Janz Team Ministries

2121 Henderson Hwy.
Winnipeg, MB R2G 1P8 Canada
Phone: (204) 334-0055
Fax: (204) 339-3321
E-mail: jtm@janzteam.com
Web Site: www.janzteam.com
Mr. Jack Stenekes, N. American Director

An interdenominational sending agency of Evangelical tradition engaged in evangelism and music, camping programs, Christian education, and mobilization for mission.

Purpose: "...to be obedient to the Great Commission of Jesus Christ through evangelism and Christian education, contributing to the establishment and growth of vibrant churches."

Year founded in CAN: 1955

Income for Overseas Mins: $1,464,176

Fully Supported CAN Personnel Overseas:
Expecting to serve more than 4 years: 30

Other Personnel:
Short-term less than 1 year from CAN: 13
Non-CAN serving in own/other country: 3
Home ministry & office staff: 9

Countries: Austria 1; Brazil 2; Europe— General 3; Germany 17; Latin America— General 3; Portugal; Unspecified Country 4

Jusqu'aux Extremites de la Terre (JET)

29, ch. du Pied-de-Roi
Lac-Beauport, PQ G0A 2C0 Canada
Phone: (418) 849-3179
E-mail: jeffeettonda@videotron.ca
Mr. Jeff Street, Secretary/Director

An interdenominational service agency of Evangelical tradition engaged in support of national workers and leadership development in Francophone churches.

Purpose: "...A French language mission, JET exists to assist Francophone evangelical believers and churches to become directly involved in world missions and to raise up a generation of French speaking missionaries who will go out into the harvest."

Year founded in CAN: 2002

Language Recordings International

Unit 6, 120 Lancing Drive
Hamilton, ON L8W 3A1 Canada
Phone: (905) 574-8220
Fax: (905) 574-6843
E-mail: director@lricanada.ca
Web Site: www.lricanada.ca
Rev. Roy Grant, Exec. Director

An interdenominational specialized agency of Evangelical tradition engaged in audio recording/distribution, evangelism and support of national workers.

Purpose: "...committed to the preparation and distribution of audio-visual materials and related equipment for evangelism and discipleship purposes."

Year founded in CAN: 1967

Income for Overseas Mins: $94,384

Fully Supported CAN Personnel Overseas:
Expecting to serve 1 to 4 years: 3

Other Personnel:
Non-CAN serving in own/other country: 2
Home ministry & office staff: 7

Countries: Kenya; Nepal; Pakistan; United Kingdom

Latin America Mission (Canada) Inc.

14-3075 Ridgeway Dr.
Mississauga, ON L5L 5M6 Canada
Phone: (905) 569-0001
Fax: (905) 569-6990
E-mail: lam@idirect.com
Web Site: www.lam.org (for U.S. office)
Dr. Garth B. Wilson, Exec. Director

An interdenominational sending agency of Evangelical tradition engaged in theological education, camping programs, childcare/ orphanage programs, funds transmission, relief and/or rehabilitation and short-term programs.

Year founded in CAN: 1961

Income for Overseas Mins: $765,625

Gifts-in-Kind: $12,669

Fully Supported CAN Personnel Overseas:
Expecting to serve more than 4 years: 13
Nonresidential mission personnel: 10

Other Personnel:

Short-term less than 1 year from CAN: 5
Non-CAN serving in own/other country: 1
Home ministry & office staff: 3
Countries: Colombia 5; Costa Rica 8

Leprosy Mission Canada, The

75 The Donway West, Suite 1410
North York, ON M3C 2E9 Canada
Phone: (416) 441-3618
Fax: (416) 441-0203
E-mail: tlm@tlmcanada.org
Web Site: www.tlmcanada.org
Rev. Peter Derrick, Exec. Director
An interdenominational service agency of
Evangelical tradition engaged in medical
work, disability assistance programs and
specialized missionary training. Statistical
information from 1998.
Year founded in CAN: 1892
Income for Overseas Mins: NR
Fully Supported CAN Personnel:
Nonresidential mission personnel: 4
Other Personnel:
Short-term less than 1 year from CAN: 1
Non-CAN serving in own/other country: 100
Home ministry & office staff: 11

Liebenzell Mission of Canada

R.R. 1
Moffat, ON L0P 1J0 Canada
Phone: (519) 822-9748
Fax: (519) 767-1069
E-mail: jkoch@liebenzell.ca
Web Site: www.liebenzell.ca
Rev. Jakob Koch, Exec. Director
An interdenominational sending agency of
Evangelical Lutheran tradition engaged in
evangelism, TEE, medical work, support of
national churches, youth programs and
church planting.
Year founded in CAN: 1966
Income for Overseas Mins: $81,651
Fully Supported CAN Personnel Overseas:
Expecting to serve 1 to 4 years: 4
Other Personnel:
Home ministry & office staff: 2
Countries: Belau; Guam

Lutheran Bible Translators of Canada, Inc.

Box 934
Kitchener, ON N2G 4E3 Canada
Phone: (519) 742-3361
Fax: (519) 742-5989
E-mail: lbtc@golden.net
Web Site: www.lbtc.ca
Mr. Robert Schmitt, Exec. Director
A specialized agency of Lutheran tradition
engaged in Bible translation, linguistics, lit-
eracy work, Scripture in use, literature dis-
tribution, literature production, partnership
development and mobilization for mission.
Year founded in CAN: 1974
Income for Overseas Mins: $170,000
Gifts-in-Kind: $7,000
Fully Supported CAN Personnel Overseas:
Expecting to serve more than 4 years: 2
Other Personnel:
Home ministry & office staff: 4
Countries: Cameroon 2

MBMS International

2—169 Riverton Ave.
Winnipeg, MB R2L 2E5 Canada
Phone: (204) 669-6575
Fax: (204) 654-1865
E-mail: mbmsi@mbmsinternational.org
Web Site: www.mbmsinternational.org
Rev. Harold W. Ens, Gen. Director
A denominational sending agency of Mennonite tradition engaged in church planting, development, theological education,
evangelism, support of national workers
and youth programs. MBMS is a bi-national
organization and statistics cannot be separated into U.S. and Canadian. For statistical
information, see the U.S. listing.
Purpose: "...to participate in making disciples of all people groups, sharing the gospel of Jesus Christ cross-culturally and
globally, in Spirit-empowered obedience to
Christ's Commission and in partnership
with local Mennonite Brethren churches."
Year founded in CAN: 1878
Income for Overseas Mins: NA

Mennonite Brethren Missions Services

See: MBMS International

Mennonite Central Committee Canada

134 Plaza Dr.
Winnipeg, MB R3T 5K9 Canada
Phone: (204) 261-6381
Fax: (204) 269-9875
E-mail: mailbox@mcc.org
Web Site: www.mcc.org
Mr. Don Peters, Exec. Director
A denominational service agency of Mennonite tradition engaged in development, agricultural programs, relief and/or rehabilitation and technical assistance. Overseas personnel totals are consolidated in the Mennonite Central Committee International (USA) report. Financial figure from 1998.
Year founded in CAN: 1963
Income for Overseas Mins: $17,645,500
Gifts-in-Kind: $340,000

Mennonite Economic Development Associates

155 Frobisher Dr., Ste. I-106
Waterloo, ON N2V 2E1 Canada
Phone: (519) 725-1633
Fax: (519) 725-9083
E-mail: MEDA@meda.org
Web Site: www.meda.org
Mr. Allan Sauder, President, CEO
An interdenominational service agency of Mennonite tradition engaged in development, agricultural programs, management consulting/training and technical assistance.
Purpose: "...to address the needs of the disadvantaged through programs of economic development."
Year founded in CAN: 1953
Income for Overseas Mins: $4,637,128
Personnel:
Home ministry & office staff: 12

Mission Aviation Fellowship of Canada

P.O. Box 368
Guelph, ON N1H 6K5 Canada
Phone: (519) 821-3914
Fax: (519) 823-1650
E-mail: info@mafc.org
Web Site: www.mafc.org
Mr. Ron Epp, President
A nondenominational specialized agency of Evangelical tradition engaged in aviation services and technical assistance.
Year founded in CAN: 1972
Income for Overseas Mins: $1,800,000
Fully Supported CAN Personnel Overseas:
Expecting to serve 1 to 4 years: 45
Other Personnel:
Home ministry & office staff: 10
Countries: Angola; Botswana; Brazil; Chad; Haiti; Indonesia; Kenya; Lesotho; Papua New Guinea; Tanzania; Uganda

Mission of Mercy (Canada)

P.O. Box 65599
Vancouver, BC V5N 5K5 Canada
Phone: (877) 771-1808
Fax: (780) 424-8510
E-mail: info@missionofmercy.ca
Web Site: www.missionofmercy.ca
Mr. George C. Smith, President
A service agency of Pentecostal tradition engaged in relief and/or rehabilitation, childcare/orphanage programs, Christian education, medical work and youth programs.
Purpose: "...to provide for the basic human needs of less fortunate people without regard to gender, religion, social or ethnic origin."
Year founded in CAN: 1978
Income for Overseas Mins: $928,000
Gifts-in-Kind: $816,640
Fully Supported CAN Personnel Overseas:
Nonresidential mission personnel: 3
Other Personnel:
Home ministry & office staff: 3
Bivocational/Tentmaker from CAN: 5
Countries: India

Mission Possible Canada

P.O. Box 46047
London, ON N5W 3A1 Canada
Phone: (519) 285-2644
E-mail: Missionpossible@odyssey.on.ca

Web Site: www.mpint.org

Mr. James McKeegan, Board Chair

An interdenominational support agency of Charismatic and Evangelical tradition engaged in regular school programs, childcare/orphanage programs, church planting, Christian education, evangelism, leadership development, support of national workers and youth programs.

Year founded in CAN: 1994

Income for Overseas Mins: $96,000

Fully Supported CAN Personnel Overseas:
Expecting to serve more than 4 years: 1

Other Personnel:
Short-term less than 1 year from CAN: 4

Countries: Haiti 1

Missionary Ventures Canada

336 Speedvale Ave. W.
Guelph, ON N1H 7M7 Canada
Phone: (519) 824-9380
Fax: (519) 824-9452
E-mail: mvcanada@mvcanada.org
Web Site: www.mvcanada.org

Mr. John Verdone, President

An interdenominational service agency of Evangelical tradition engaged in short-term programs, evangelism, development, medical work, providing medical supplies and church construction. Financial information from 1996.

Purpose: "To encourage and support indigenous missions...through personal involvement, financial sponsorship, and ministry development."

Year founded in CAN: 1991

Income for Overseas Mins: $250,000

Personnel:
Short-term less than 1 year from CAN: 150
Home ministry & office staff: 1
Bivocational/Tentmaker from CAN: 2

MSC Canada

509-3950 14th Ave.
Markham, ON L3R 0A9 Canada
Phone: (905) 947-0468
Fax: (905) 947-0352
E-mail: msc@msc.on.ca
Web Site: www.msc.on.ca
Mr. William Yuille, President

A service agency for Brethren Assemblies missionaries sent by their local assemblies. Personnel totals are reported under Brethren Assemblies (Canada).

Purpose: "...to encourage and support service for the Lord by assembly-commended workers, in compliance with scriptural guidelines, government legislation and agreements with other organizations with which MSC is associated."

Year founded in CAN: 1940

Income for Overseas Mins: $4,419,551

Gifts-in-Kind: $8,499

Navigators of Canada, The

Box 27070
London, ON N5X 3X5 Canada
Phone: (519) 660-8300
Fax: (519) 660-4922
E-mail: navscanada@navigators.ca
Web Site: www.navigators.ca

Mr. Ross Rains, President

An interdenominational sending agency of Evangelical tradition engaged in literature distribution, evangelism, literature production and youth programs. Statistics from 1998.

Purpose: "...to reach the university campus and the community and to disciple believers intent on reproducing Christian values in following generations."

Year founded in CAN: 1960

Income for Overseas Mins: $1,677,730

Fully Supported CAN Personnel Overseas:
Nonresidential mission personnel: 2
Expecting to serve more than 4 years: 27
Expecting to serve 1 to 4 years: 1

Other Personnel:
Home ministry & office staff: 15
Bivocational/Tentmaker from CAN: 5

Countries: Bulgaria 1; Chile 4; China 2; Hungary 3; Lithuania 2; Mongolia 2; Russia; Saint Vincent and the Grenadines 2; Slovakia 4; Thailand 2; Turkey 2; Vietnam 3

New Tribes Mission of Canada

P.O. Box 707
Durham, ON N0G 1R0 Canada
Phone: (519) 369-2622
Fax: (519) 369-5828

E-mail: ntmc@ntmc.ca
Web Site: www.ntmc.ca

Mr. Raymond Jones, Chairman

A nondenominational sending agency of Fundamental and Independent tradition engaged in church planting, linguistics, literacy work, Bible translation and missionary training. Income figure from 1998.

Purpose: "...to assist the ministry of the local church through the mobilizing, equipping, and coordinating of missionaries to see indigenous New Testament churches established among unreached people groups..."

Year founded in CAN: 1950

Income for Overseas Mins: $3,943,909

Fully Supported CAN Personnel Overseas:
Expecting to serve more than 4 years: 300

Other Personnel:
Home ministry & office staff: 44

Countries: Africa–General; Asia–General; Greenland; Latin America–General; Oceania–General; Unspecified Country 300

OMF International—Canada

5155 Spectrum Way, Bldg. 21
Mississauga, ON L4W 5A1 Canada

Phone: (905) 568-9971
Fax: (905) 568-9974
E-mail: omfcanada@omf.ca
Web Site: www.omf.ca

Rev. William Fietje, National Director

A nondenominational sending agency of Evangelical tradition engaged in church planting, theological education, evangelism, support of national churches, relief and/or rehabilitation and development.

Purpose: "...to see an indigenous biblical church movement in each people group of East Asia, evangelizing their own people and reaching out in mission to other peoples."

Year founded in CAN: 1888

Income for Overseas Mins: $2,475,608

Fully Supported CAN Personnel Overseas:
Expecting to serve more than 4 years: 60
Expecting to serve 1 to 4 years: 6

Other Personnel:
Short-term less than 1 year from CAN: 58
Home ministry & office staff: 34
Bivocational/Tentmaker from CAN: 20

Countries: Indonesia 3; Japan 8; Philippines

18; Singapore 2; Taiwan 4; Thailand 19; Unspecified Country 6

OMS International—Canada

P.O. Box 10
Burlington, ON L7R 3Y3 Canada

Phone: (905) 639-3000
Fax: (905) 639-3433
E-mail: inform@omscanada.org

Mr. Gordon Morley, Exec. Director

A nondenominational sending agency of Evangelical tradition engaged in theological education, church planting, evangelism, evangelism and support of national churches.

Year founded in CAN: 1944

Income for Overseas Mins: $1,350,000

Personnel:
Home ministry & office staff: 7

Open Doors With Brother Andrew Canada

30-5155 Spectrum Way
Mississauga, ON L4W 5A1 Canada

Phone: (905) 602-6404
Fax: (905) 602-6477
E-mail: opendoorsca@od.org
Web Site: www.opendoorsca.org

Rev. Paul W. Johnson, Director for Canada

A nondenominational support agency of Evangelical tradition engaged in Bible distribution, correspondence courses, missions information service, leadership development, literature distribution and support of national workers. Statistics from 1998.

Year founded in CAN: 1977

Income for Overseas Mins: $450,000

Personnel:
Short-term less than 1 year from CAN: 68
Home ministry & office staff: 4

Operation Mobilization Canada

212 West St.
Port Colborne, ON L3K 4E3 Canada

Phone: (905) 835-2546
Fax: (905) 835-2533
E-mail: info@cdn.om.org
Web Site: www.omcanada.org

Mr. Gordon Abraham, Exec. Director

An interdenominational sending agency of Evangelical tradition engaged in evangelism, church planting, literature production/distribution, and support of national workers. Financial figure from 1998.

Purpose: "...to motivate, develop and equip people for world evangelization, and to strengthen and help plant churches, especially among the unreached in the Middle East, South and Central Asia and Europe."

Year founded in CAN: 1966

Income for Overseas Mins: $2,365,036

Fully Supported CAN Personnel Overseas:
Expecting to serve more than 4 years: 51
Expecting to serve 1 to 4 years: 15

Other Personnel:
Short-term less than 1 year from CAN: 50
Non-CAN serving in own/other country: 241
Home ministry & office staff: 35
Bivocational/Tentmaker from CAN: 5

Countries: Afghanistan 2; Albania 1; Asia—General 3; Central Asia—General 1; Czech Republic 2; India 1; Ireland 1; Israel 3; Lebanon 1; Malaysia 3; Middle East 3; Mozambique 2; Pakistan 1; South Africa 2; Spain 2; Sudan 2; Sweden 1; Turkey 3; Ukraine 2; United Kingdom 2; Uruguay 1; Unspecified Country 12

Outreach Canada
2 - 7201 72nd Street
Delta, BC V4G 1M5 Canada
Phone: (604) 952-0050
Fax: (604) 502-1667
E-mail: info@outreach.ca
Web Site: www.outreach.ca
Dr. Gerald Kraft, Exec. Director

An interdenominational support agency of Evangelical tradition engaged in church planting, evangelism, leadership development, management consulting/training, support of national churches and mission-related research.

Purpose: "...to assist the Body of Christ to make disciples of all peoples."

Year founded in CAN: 1977

Income for Overseas Mins: $50,000

Personnel:
Home ministry & office staff: 9

Overseas Council for Theological Education & Missions, Inc.
1275 W. 6th Ave., Ste. 348
Vancouver, BC V6H 1A6 Canada
Phone: (604) 737-7354
Fax: (604) 737-7384
E-mail: overseascouncil@telus.net
Web Site: www.overseascouncil.org
Mr. William H. Armerding, President

An interdenominational support agency of Evangelical tradition engaged in theological education, leadership development, management consulting/training, support of national churches and technical assistance. Personnel information from 1998.

Purpose: "To see men and women equipped to be excellent Christian leaders for the non-Western world through strong, evangelically and educationally sound training programs in their own cultures."

Year founded in CAN: 1979

Income for Overseas Mins: $1,170,000

Gifts-in-Kind: $50,000

Personnel:
Non-CAN serving in own/other country: 16

Countries: Croatia; Jamaica; Poland; Russia; Sri Lanka; Ukraine

Partners Intl. Canada
8500 Torbram Rd. #56
Brampton, ON L6T 5C6 Canada
Phone: (905) 458-1202
Fax: (905) 458-4339
E-mail: info@partnersinternational.ca
Web Site: www.partnersinternational.ca
Mr. Grant Waddell, President

A nondenominational support agency of Evangelical tradition engaged in support of national workers and churches, and funds transmission. Financial data from 1996.

Year founded in CAN: 1959

Income for Overseas Mins: $830,000

Personnel:
Home ministry & office staff: 13

Pentecostal Assemblies of Canada
2450 Milltower Court

Mississauga, ON L5N 5Z6 Canada
Phone: (905) 542-7044
Fax: (905) 542-7313
Web Site: www.paoc.org
Rev. Dr. William D. Morrow, Gen. Supt.

A denominational sending agency of Pentecostal tradition engaged in church planting, childcare/orphanage programs, theological education, TEE, leadership development and relief and/or rehabilitation. Personnel information from 1998.

Purpose: "To make disciples everywhere by the proclamation and practice of the gospel of Jesus Christ in the power of the Holy Spirit; to establish local congregations and train spiritual leaders."

Year founded in CAN: 1919

Income for Overseas Mins: $14,732,000

Gifts-in-Kind: $600,000

Fully Supported CAN Personnel Overseas:
Expecting to serve more than 4 years: 140
Expecting to serve 1 to 4 years: 25

Other Personnel:
Non-CAN serving in own/other country: 2
Home ministry & office staff: 13

Countries: Brazil 6; Bulgaria; Colombia; Cote d'Ivoire; Estonia 2; Ethiopia 7; Greece 2; Guatemala 2; Guinea-Bissau 4; Haiti 2; Hong Kong 14; India 4; Indonesia 7; Israel 4; Kenya 15; Latin America–General 2; Liberia 3; Macau 3; Malawi 10; Mozambique 4; Philippines 1; Poland 2; Russia 2; Rwanda 2; Senegal 4; South Africa 4; Sri Lanka 2; Tanzania 6; Thailand 7; Uganda 6; Ukraine 1; Serbia and Montenegro; Zambia 6; Zimbabwe 6

Persecuted Church Fellowship—See: Ukranian Children's Christian Fund

Pioneers
51 Byron Ave.
Dorchester, ON N0L 1G2 Canada
Phone: (519) 268-8778
Fax: (519) 268-2787
E-mail: picanada@wwdc.com
Web Site: www.pioneers.org
Mr. Donnie Scearce, Can. Exec. Director

A nondenominational sending agency of Evangelical tradition engaged in church planting, evangelism and mobilization for mission. Statistics from 1998.

Purpose: "...mobilizes teams to glorify God among unreached peoples by initiating church planting movements in partnership with local churches."

Year founded in CAN: 1981

Income for Overseas Mins: $686,589

Fully Supported CAN Personnel Overseas:
Expecting to serve more than 4 years: 13

Other Personnel:
Short-term less than 1 year from CAN: 30
Home ministry & office staff: 3

Countries: Asia—General 5; Belize 2; Bolivia 3; Bosnia and Herzegovina 1; Brazil 2

Presbyterian Church in Canada, Life and Mission Agency
50 Wynford Dr.
North York, ON M3C 1J7 Canada
Phone: (416) 441-1111
Fax: (416) 441-2825
E-mail: intmin@presbyterian.ca
Web Site: www.presbyterian.ca/international
Rev. Ian Morrison, Gen. Secretary

A denominational sending agency of Presbyterian and Reformed tradition engaged in support of national churches, development, theological education, leadership development and medical work. Statistical data from 1998.

Year founded in CAN: 1875

Income for Overseas Mins: $1,400,000

Fully Supported CAN Personnel Overseas:
Expecting to serve more than 4 years: 23
Expecting to serve 1 to 4 years: 8

Other Personnel:
Short-term less than 1 year from CAN: 20
Non-CAN serving in own/other country: 3
Home ministry & office staff: 4
Bivocational/Tentmaker from CAN: 1

Countries: Costa Rica; Cyprus 4; El Salvador 2; Ghana; Guatemala 4; Guyana 1; India; Israel; Japan 2; Kenya 1; Malawi 3; Mozambique; Nicaragua 2; Nigeria 2; Romania 1; Taiwan 1

Salvation Army Canada and Bermuda Territory, The

2 Overlea Blvd.
Toronto, ON M4H 1P4 Canada
Phone: (416) 425-2111
Fax: (416) 422-6201
Web Site: www.salvationarmy.ca
Ms. Christine MacMillan, Commissioner
A denominational sending agency of Methodist and Wesleyan tradition engaged in evangelism, development, Christian education, and relief and/or rehabilitation. Personnel information from 1998.
Year founded in CAN: 1882
Income for Overseas Mins: $4,170,000
Fully Supported CAN Personnel Overseas:
Expecting to serve more than 4 years: 35
Expecting to serve 1 to 4 years: 57
Nonresidential mission personnel: 2
Other Personnel:
Short-term less than 1 year from CAN: 6
Home ministry & office staff: 3
Countries: Australia; Bahamas, Bangladesh 2; Belgium; Brazil 2; Czech Republic; Finland; France 2; Germany 6; Ghana 2; Hong Kong 2; Hungary; Jamaica 1; Mexico; Mozambique; New Zealand; Pakistan; Papua New Guinea; Russia 5; Singapore; South Africa 6; Spain; Sri Lanka 1; Suriname; Tanzania; United Kingdom 4; Zambia; Zimbabwe 2

Samaritan's Purse—Canada

Box 20100, Calgary Pl.
Calgary, AB T2P 4J2 Canada
Phone: (403) 250-6565
Fax: (403) 250-6567
E-mail: canada@samaritan.org
Web Site: www.samaritanspurse.org
Dr. Sean P. Campbell, Exec. Director
A service agency of Evangelical tradition engaged in providing relief and/or rehabilitation, medical supplies, evangelism, children's programs, development and agricultural programs.
Purpose: "...providing spiritual and physical aid to hurting people around the world ...meeting the needs of people who are victims of war, poverty, natural disasters, disease and famine...serving the church worldwide to promote the Gospel..."

Year founded in CAN: 1973
Income for Overseas Mins: $35,989,859
Gifts-in-Kind: $27,681,401
Personnel:
Home ministry & office staff: 35

Scripture Gift Mission (Canada)

300 Steelcase Rd. W. #32
Markham, ON L3R 2W2 Canada
Phone: (905) 475-0521
E-mail: Can@sgm.org
Mr. Ted Bartlett, Exec. Director
A nondenominational support agency of Evangelical tradition engaged in literature distribution and literature production.
Year founded in CAN: 1973
Income for Overseas Mins: NA
Personnel:
Home ministry & office staff: 2

SEND Intl. of Canada

1-22423 Jefferies Rd., R.R. #3
London, ON N0L 1R0 Canada
Phone: (519) 657-6775
Fax: (519) 657-7027
E-mail: info@sendcanada.org
Web Site: www.send.org
Rev. Leander Rempel, Canadian Director
An interdenominational sending agency of Evangelical tradition engaged in church planting, camping programs, theological education, evangelism, leadership development and short-term programs.
Purpose: "...to start churches...evangelize the unreached... nurture disciples...develop leaders."
Year founded in CAN: 1963
Income for Overseas Mins: $1,878,406
Gifts-in-Kind: $26,151
Fully Supported CAN Personnel Overseas:
Expecting to serve more than 4 years: 39
Other Personnel:
Short-term less than 1 year from CAN: 30
Home ministry & office staff: 14
Countries: Asia–General 1; Czech Republic 4; Hong Kong 3; Japan 5; Macedonia 1; Philippines 9; Russia 13; Ukraine 3

SIM Canada

10 Huntingdale Blvd.
Scarborough, ON M1W 2S5 Canada
Phone: (416) 497-2424
Fax: (416) 497-2444
E-mail: postmast@sim.ca
Web Site: www.sim.ca
Mr. Pep Philpott, Director

An interdenominational sending agency of Evangelical tradition engaged in church planting, broadcasting, theological educa-tion, medical work, relief and/or rehabilita-tion and Bible translation.
Purpose: "...creatively partners with the Church to communicate and demonstrate powerfully to the world the whole Gospel of Jesus Christ."
Year founded in CAN: 1893
Income for Overseas Mins: $9,529,234
Gifts-in-Kind: $115,369
Fully Supported CAN Personnel Overseas:
  Expecting to serve more than 4 years: 128
  Expecting to serve 1 to 4 years: 13
  Nonresidential mission personnel: 3
Other Personnel:
  Short-term less than 1 year from CAN: 61
  Non-CAN serving in own/other country: 5
  Home ministry & office staff: 66
  Bivocational/Tentmaker from CAN: 2
Countries: Angola 7; Bangladesh 3; Benin 10; Bolivia 5; Botswana 3; Burkina Faso 9; Chile 2; Cote d'Ivoire 1; Eritrea 2; Ethiopia 18; Ghana 8; India 1; Niger 13; Nigeria 7; Para-guay 2; Peru 2; Senegal 2; South Africa 8; Sudan 2; Zambia 20; Unspecified Country 3

Slavic Gospel Association—Canada

6655 Kitimat Rd., Unit #2
Mississauga, ON L5N 6J4 Canada
Phone: (905) 814-5381
Fax: (905) 814-6805
E-mail: canada@sga.org
Web Site: www.sga.org
Rev. Allan W. Vincent, Exec. Director

An interdenominational support agency of Baptist tradition engaged in support of na-tional workers, childcare/orphanage pro-grams, theological education, literature distribution, support of national churches

and translation work.
Year founded in CAN: 1947
Income for Overseas Mins: $725,370
Gifts-in-Kind: $8,250
Fully Supported CAN Personnel Overseas:
  Expecting to serve more than 4 years: 2
Other Personnel:
  Short-term less than 1 year from CAN: 6
  Home ministry & office staff: 3
Countries: Ukraine 2

South American Missionary Society in Canada

Box 21082
Barrie, ON L4M 6J1 Canada
Phone: (705) 728-7151
Fax: (705) 728-6703
E-mail: sams_canada@on.aibn.com
Web Site: www.episcopalian.org/SAMS-canada

A denominational sending agency of Angli-can and Evangelical tradition engaged in mobilization for mission, evangelism, leader-ship development and support of national workers. Financial information from 1998.
Purpose: "...to find and send those whom God is calling to the mission field, and to widen and deepen the missionary vision of Canadian Anglicans."
Year founded in CAN: 1979
Income for Overseas Mins: $293,925

TEAM—The Evangelical Alliance Mission of Canada

Team Ministry Centre
Calgary, AB T3E 2R8 Canada
Phone: (403) 248-2344
Fax: (403) 207-6025
E-mail: team@teamcanada.org
Web Site: www.teamcanada.org
Mr. Lorne Strom, Director

An interdenominational sending agency of Evangelical tradition engaged in church planting, development, evangelism, medi-cal work, mobilization for mission, short-term programs and missionary training.
Purpose: "...to help [local] churches send missionaries to establish reproducing churches among the nations."

Year founded in CAN: 1890
Income for Overseas Mins: $2,113,713
Fully Supported CAN Personnel Overseas:
Expecting to serve more than 4 years: 50
Other Personnel:
Short-term less than 1 year from CAN: 19
Non-CAN serving in own/other country: 621
Home ministry & office staff: 58
Bivocational/Tentmaker from CAN: 5
Countries: Asia–General 21; Chad 5; Czech Republic 2; Europe–General; France 3; Germany 2; Italy 5; Latin America–General; Middle East 5; Peru 2; Spain 2; Venezuela 3

UFM Intl. in Canada

1020 Matheson Blvd. E. #11
Mississauga, ON L4W 4J9 Canada
Phone: (905) 238-0904
Fax: (905) 629-8439
E-mail: ufmcan@ufm.on.ca
Web Site: www.ufm.org
Mr. Dale Losch, Director
An interdenominational sending agency of Evangelical and Baptist tradition engaged in church planting, development, theological education, evangelism, support of national churches and short-term programs.
Year founded in CAN: 1931
Income for Overseas Mins: $884,000
Fully Supported CAN Personnel Overseas:
Expecting to serve more than 4 years: 13
Expecting to serve 1 to 4 years: 2
Nonresidential mission personnel: 15
Other Personnel:
Short-term less than 1 year from CAN: 20
Non-CAN serving in own/other country: 2
Home ministry & office staff: 16
Countries: Bosnia and Herzegovina 1; Brazil 6; Democratic Republic of Congo; Haiti 2; Ireland 2; Italy 1; Slovakia 1

Ukrainian Children's Christian Fund

15620 Westminster Hwy
Richmond, BC V6V 1A6 Canada
Phone: (604) 278-0692
Fax: (604) 279-9080
E-mail: pcf.lapka@shaw.ca
Mr. Michael S. Lapka, President
An interdenominational service agency of Evangelical tradition engaged in support of national workers, Bible distribution, evangelism and literature distribution. Country information from 1998.
Year founded in CAN: 1976
Income for Overseas Mins: $90,000
Personnel:
Non-CAN serving in own/other country: 28
Countries: Ukraine

United Church of Canada, Justice, Global & Ecumenical Unit

3250 Bloor St. W., Suite 300
Toronto, ON M8X 2Y4 Canada
Phone: (416) 231-5931
Fax: (416) 231-3103
E-mail: Info@united-church.ca
Web Site: www.united-church.ca
Mr. Chris Ferguson, Exec. Minister/Ecumenical Officer
A denominational sending agency of Ecumenical tradition engaged in development, agricultural programs, extension education, funds transmission and missionary training. Supports ministry, training, development and relief projects in more than 37 countries.
Year founded in CAN: 1925
Income for Overseas Mins: $9,688,000
Gifts-in-Kind: NR
Fully Supported CAN Personnel Overseas:
Expecting to serve more than 4 years: 48
Countries: Unspecified Country 48

Venture Teams International

#3A, 3023 - 21st St. NE
Calgary, AB T2E 7T1 Canada
Phone: (403) 777-2970
Fax: (403) 777-2973
E-mail: info@vti.ca
Web Site: www.vti.ca
Mr. Mark Sorell, Acting Director
An interdenominational service agency of Evangelical tradition engaged in missionary training, evangelism, leadership development, mobilization for mission, short-term programs and children's programs. Statistical information from 1998.
Purpose: "Training young adults for ministry in order to bridge the gap between

classroom learning and life experience."
Year founded in CAN: 1978
Income for Overseas Mins: $400,000
Personnel:
  Short-term less than 1 year from CAN: 78
  Home ministry & office staff: 4

Voice of the Martyrs, The
Box 117, Port Credit
Mississauga, ON L5G 4L5 Canada
Phone: (905) 602-4832
Fax: (905) 602-4833
E-mail: thevoice@persecution.net
Web Site: www.persecution.net
Mr. Klaas Brobbel, Exec. Director
A nondenominational support agency of Evangelical tradition engaged in Bible distribution, broadcasting, development, missions information service, relief and/or rehabilitation and short-term programs.
Purpose: "...to be an effective source of information and support of persecuted Christians around the world."
Year founded in CAN: 1971
Income for Overseas Mins: $600,000
Personnel:
  Short-term less than 1 year from CAN: 1
  Home ministry & office staff: 5

WEC International (Canada)
37 Aberdeen Ave.
Hamilton, ON L8P 2N6 Canada
Phone: (905) 529-0166
Fax: (905) 529-0630
E-mail: wec-int@canada.com
Web Site: www.hwcn.org/link/wec
Mr. Henry Bell, Canadian Director
An interdenominational sending agency of Evangelical tradition engaged in church planting, evangelism, support of national churches, mobilization for mission, missionary training and children's programs. Financial information from 1998.
Purpose: "...to evangelize the unreached peoples...to establish fully discipled, self-governing, self-supporting and reproducing churches able to fulfill their part in the Great Commission."
Year founded in CAN: 1936
Income for Overseas Mins: $1,327,740

Fully Supported CAN Personnel Overseas:
  Expecting to serve more than 4 years: 62
  Expecting to serve 1 to 4 years: 3
  Nonresidential mission personnel: 2
Other Personnel:
  Short-term less than 1 year from CAN: 10
  Home ministry & office staff: 16
  Bivocational/Tentmaker from CAN: 30
Countries: Africa–General 13; Asia–General 9; Brazil 2; Cambodia 2; Central Asia–General 8; Cote d'Ivoire 1; Equatorial Guinea 3; Fiji 2; Gambia, The 3; Ghana 2; India 1; Mexico 3; Nepal 2; Senegal 6; Sierra Leone; South Africa 1; Spain 2; Thailand 2

Western Tract Mission, Inc.
401 - 33rd St., West
Saskatoon, SK S7L 0V5 Canada
Phone: (306) 244-0446
Fax: (306) 242-6115
E-mail: astobbe@sk.sympatico.ca
Web Site: www.westerntractmission.org
Mr. Arnold Stobbe, Acting Director
An interdenominational service agency of Evangelical and Mennonite tradition engaged in literature distribution, correspondence courses and literature production. Staff figure from 1998.
Year founded in CAN: 1941
Income for Overseas Mins: NA
Personnel:
  Home ministry & office staff: 10

White Fields Missionary Society (Canada)
P.O. Box 242
Edmonton, AB T5J 2J1 Canada
Phone: (780) 483-5750
E-mail: canada@whitefields.org
Web Site: www.whitefields.org
Rev. Stephen Lonetti, General Director
Year founded in CAN: 1971
A service agency of Evangelical tradition engaged in support of national churches, support of national workers and leadership development.
Purpose: "...assisting national church planters working with experienced missionaries in reaching their own people with the gospel of Christ."

World Gospel Mission (Canada)

26 Clark Street
Hartland, NB E7P 1L1 Canada
Phone: (506) 375-8262
Fax: (506) 375-8220
Rev. Brian Murray, Director Canada
An interdenominational support agency of Wesleyan tradition engaged in evangelism, church planting and theological education. Statistical data consolidated in U. S. report.
Year founded in CAN: 1982
Income for Overseas Mins: NA

World Mission Prayer League

5408 49th Ave.
Camrose, AB T4V 0N7 Canada
Phone: (780)672-0464
Fax: (780) 672-0464
E-mail: wmplcdn@cable-lynx.net
Web Site: www.wmpl.org
Rev. Rob Lewis, Exec. Director
A denominational sending agency of Lutheran tradition engaged in church planting, medical work, development, TEE, evangelism and leadership development. Statistics from 1998.
Year founded in CAN: 1969
Income for Overseas Mins: $83,433
Fully Supported CAN Personnel Overseas:
Expecting to serve more than 4 years: 4
Expecting to serve 1 to 4 years: 2
Other Personnel:
Home ministry & office staff: 3
Countries: Central Asia–General 4; Mexico

World Relief Canada

600 Alden Rd., Suite 310
Markham, ON L3R 0E7 Canada
Phone: (905) 415-8181
Fax: (905) 415-0287
E-mail: worldrelief@wrcanada.org
A nondenominational specialized agency of Evangelical tradition engaged in relief and/or rehabilitation, agricultural programs, development, literacy work and partnership development in 17 countries.
Purpose: "...partners with the evangelical church in Canada and overseas to respond

to the basic needs of the world's most oppressed, poor and suffering people, empowering them to meet their own needs in the name of Jesus Christ."
Year founded in CAN: 1970
Income for Overseas Mins: $2,234,000
Personnel:
Home ministry & office staff: 10

World Team

7575 Danbro Cres.
Mississauga, ON L5N 6P9 Canada
Phone: (905) 821-6300
Fax: (905) 821-6325
E-mail: infocanada@worldteam.org
Web Site: www.worldteam.org
Rev. Ernie Dyck, Canadian Director
A nondenominational sending agency of Evangelical tradition engaged in church planting, Bible translation and theological education. Statistical information from 1998.
Purpose: "...to establish reproducing churches among the least-evangelized peoples of the world."
Year founded in CAN: 1948
Income for Overseas Mins: $2,217,265
Fully Supported CAN Personnel Overseas:
Expecting to serve more than 4 years: 44
Nonresidential mission personnel: 4
Other Personnel:
Short-term less than 1 year from CAN: 20
Home ministry & office staff: 24
Bivocational/Tentmaker from CAN: 2
Countries: Cameroon 8; Haiti 4; Indonesia 7; Italy 1; Mexico 2; Peru 8; Philippines 10; Singapore 2; Spain 2

World Vision Canada

1 World Drive
Mississauga, ON L5T 2Y4 Canada
Phone: (905) 565-6100
Fax: (905) 696-2162
E-mail: Info@worldvision.ca
Web Site: www.worldvision.ca
Mr. Dave Toycen, President
A transdenominational service agency of Evangelical tradition engaged in relief and/or rehabilitation, childcare/orphanage programs, development and leadership development.

Purpose: "...a Christian humanitarian relief and development organization inviting Canadians to share their resources to empower people living in poverty."
Year founded in CAN: 1954
Income for Overseas Mins: $150,000,000
Gifts-in-Kind: $43,000,000
Fully Supported CAN Personnel Overseas:
Nonresidential mission personnel: 5
Other Personnel:
Short-term less than 1 year from CAN: 121
Non-CAN serving in own/other country: 12
Home ministry & office staff: 418
Countries: Burundi; Costa Rica; Ghana; Guatemala; Honduras; India; Kenya; Malawi; Rwanda; South Africa

Wycliffe Bible Translators of Canada

4316 - 10 St. NE
Calgary, AB T2E 6K3 Canada
Phone: (403) 250-5411
Fax: (403) 250-2623
E-mail: info@wycliffe.ca
Web Site: www.wycliffe.ca
Dr. Roger Gilstrap, Exec. Director
A nondenominational sending agency of Evangelical tradition engaged in Bible translation, linguistics, literacy work, support of national workers, training and agricultural programs.
Purpose: "[To] challenge, train and assist Canadians to serve indigenous peoples through Bible translation and literacy-based development."
Year founded in CAN: 1968
Income for Overseas Mins: $9,800,000
Fully Supported CAN Personnel Overseas:
Expecting to serve more than 4 years: 212
Nonresidential mission personnel: 212
Other Personnel:
Short-term less than 1 year from CAN: 40
Home ministry & office staff: 26
Countries: Asia–General 38; Brazil 9; Burkina Faso 5; Cameroon 25; Caribbean–General 2; Central African Republic 1; Chad 3; Colombia 1; Democratic Republic of Congo 2; Ecuador 2; Ghana 2; Guatemala 8; Guyana 2; Honduras 1; Indonesia 7; Kenya 3; Malaysia 3; Mali 3; Mexico 12;

Mozambique 4; Niger 3; Nigeria 4; Papua New Guinea 25; Peru 8; Philippines 16; Sudan 6; Suriname 2; Togo 2; Uganda 2; United Kingdom 1; Unspecified Country 10

Young Life of Canada

1155 W. Pender St., Suite 610
Vancouver, BC V6E 2P4 Canada
Phone: (604) 688-7622
Fax: (604) 688-3125
E-mail: YLife@younglife.ca
Web Site: www.younglife.ca
Mr. Harold J. Merwald, Natl. Director
An interdenominational support agency of Evangelical tradition engaged in teenage evangelism and camping programs.
Year founded in CAN: 1954
Income for Overseas Mins: $10,000
Personnel:
Home ministry & office staff: 75

Youth for Christ—Canada

7337-137th St., STE. #100
Surrey, BC V3W 1A4 Canada
Phone: (604) 507-9712
E-mail: info@yfccanada.com
Web Site: www.yfccanada.com
Mr. Barry Bowater, National Director
A transdenominational support agency of Evangelical tradition engaged in youth programs, camping programs, evangelism and mobilization for mission. Statistics from 1998.
Purpose: "To participate in the body of Christ in responsible evangelism of youth, presenting them with the person, work and teachings of Christ and discipling them into the Church."
Year founded in CAN: 1944
Income for Overseas Mins: $500,000
Personnel:
Short-term less than 1 year from CAN: 7
Home ministry & office staff: 251
Bivocational/Tentmaker from CAN: 5

Youth With A Mission (Canada)

2718 Robinson Rd.
Winfield, BC V4V 1G6 Canada
Phone: (250) 766-3838

Fax: (250) 766-2387
E-mail: ywam@disciples.com
Web Site: www.ywam.ca

Mr. Paul Martinson, Canada Representative

An interdenominational sending agency of Charismatic and Evangelical tradition engaged in short-term programs, extension education, leadership development, services for other agencies, missionary training, training and youth programs. Countries of service from 1998.

Purpose: "...presenting Jesus Christ personally to this generation, to mobilize as many as possible to help in this task and to the training and equipping of believers for their part in fulfilling the Great Commission."

Year founded in CAN: 1966

Income for Overseas Mins: $3,000,000

Fully Supported CAN Personnel Overseas:
Expecting to serve more than 4 years: 134
Nonresidential mission personnel: 12

Other Personnel:
Short-term less than 1 year from CAN: 400
Home ministry & office staff: 450

Countries: Argentina 1; Australia 16; Barbados 4; Belize 4; Chile 1; Denmark 1; Dominican Republic 2; Fiji 2; Greenland 2; Guyana 2; India 8; Indonesia 1; Jamaica 2; Japan 2; Jordan 2; Kenya 1; Lithuania 3; Mexico 4; Mozambique 2; Netherlands 8; New Zealand 2; Northern Mariana Islands 1; Norway 2; Oceania–General 1; Philippines 8; Russia 10; Switzerland 1; Taiwan 2; Thailand 2; Ukraine 7; United Kingdom 24; Unspecified Country 4; Venezuela 1; Zimbabwe 1

Chapter 6
Indices to Canadian Protestant Agencies

M
any *Handbook* users find it valuable to locate agencies by particular categories of church tradition or ministry activity. This chapter provides the user with those indices. Agency responses on the *Mission Handbook* survey questionnaire helped define the listed categories. The organizations in each category appear in alphabetical order by organization name.

Index by Church Tradition

If an agency needed more than one generic or denominational category to describe its traditional doctrinal and/or ecclesiastical stance, the agency may appear under as many as two of the given categories. We have arranged the list alphabetically by category and within each category by agency name. See question #7 of the survey questionnaire reproduced in the Appendix for the actual wording of the question and the check-off list of choices.

Index by Ministry Activity

Almost all agencies are involved in several types of ministry activities. Each agency may be listed under as many as six primary categories of activity. We asked those with more than six primary activities to indicate the six activities toward which they had committed the largest amount of resources.

We have divided the broad activities of education and evangelism into subcategories. For example, the evangelism category appears as "evangelism, mass" and "evangelism, student," and so on. See question #8 of the survey questionnaire in the Appendix for the actual wording of the question and the check-off list of activities.

Agencies sometimes have written in new categories under the "other" choice in previous surveys. Some of these, if used often enough, may be included in the check-off list for the next edition's survey questionnaire. Sometimes categories are dropped because of lack of use. The most used categories, however, have remained the same over the years.

Seven new categories added during this edition (which will appear as options on the next survey) are: adoption, apologetics, discipleship, justice & related, tentmaking & related, TESOL, and urban ministry.

Church Tradition

Anglican
S. American Missionary Society in Canada

Baptist
ABWE–Canada
Baptist Gen. Conf. of Canada
BGCC Global Ministries
Canadian Baptist Ministries
Canadian Conv. of Southern Baptists
Canadian South America Mission
Czechoslovak Evangelical Mission
FAIR
FEBInternational
Fundamental Bapt. Mission–Trinidad/Tobago
Galcom
Gospel Missionary Union of Canada
Slavic Gospel Association–Canada

Charismatic
Into All The World
Mission Possible Canada
Youth With A Mission (Canada)

Christian/Plymouth Brethren
Brethren Assemblies (Canada)
MSC Canada

Congregational
Evangelical Free Church of Canada Mission

Ecumenical
Canadian Bible Society
Canadian Churches' Forum for Global Mins.
United Church of Canada

Evangelical
Action International Ministries
Africa Inland Mission (Canada)
African Enterprise Association of Canada
Apostolic Church in Canada
Arab World Ministries (Canada)
Associated Gospel Churches
Back to the Bible Missionary Agency
Baptist General Conference of Canada
Barry Moore Ministries
BCM International (Canada), Inc.
Bible League of Canada, The
Campus Crusade for Christ of Canada
Canadian South America Mission
Centre for World Mission—British Columbia
Child Evangelism Fellowship of Canada
Christar
Christian Aid Mission
Christian and Missionary Alliance in Canada

Christian Blind Mission Intl. (Canada)
Christian Indigenous Development Overseas
Christian Studies International of Canada
Compassion Canada
Croisade du Livre Chretien
Crossroads Christian Communications Inc.
Emmanuel Relief and Rehabilitation Intl.
Equip, Canada
European Christian Mission
Evangelical Covenant Church of Canada
Evangelical Medical Aid Society
Evangelical Free Church of Canada Mission
Evang. Missionary Ch. CAN World Partners
Evangelical Mennonite Conference
Evangelical Tract Distributors
Far East Broadcasting Associates of Canada
Frontiers Canada
Galcom International
Global Outreach Mission
Gospel for Asia
Greater Europe Mission (Canada)
HCJB World Radio–Canada
High Adventure Gospel Communication Mins.
International Child Care (Canada)
International Christian Aid Canada
Inter-national Needs Network–Canada
International Teams of Canada
INTERSERVE (Canada)
InterVarsity Christian Fellowship of Canada
Janz Team Ministries
Language Recordings International
Latin America Mission (Canada) Inc.
Leprosy Mission Canada, The
Mission Aviation Fellowship of Canada
Missionary Ventures Canada
Navigators of Canada
OMF International–Canada
OMS International–Canada
Open Doors With Brother Andrew Canada
Operation Mobilization Canada
Outreach Canada
Overseas Council for Theol. Ed. & Msns., Inc.
Partners International Canada
Pioneers
Samaritan's Purse–Canada
Scripture Gift Mission (Canada)
SEND International of Canada
SIM Canada
South American Missionary Society–Canada
TEAM–Canada
UFM International in Canada
Ukrainian Children's Christian Fund
Venture Teams International
Voice of the Martyrs, The
WEC International (Canada)
Western Tract Mission, Inc.

World Relief Canada
World Team
World Vision Canada
Wycliffe Bible Translators of Canada
Young Life of Canada
Youth for Christ—Canada
Youth With a Mission (Canada)

Fundamental
Barry Moore Ministries
BCM International Inc. (Canada)
Centre for World Mission–British Columbia
Fundamental Baptist Msn.–Trinidad/Tobago
New Tribes Mission of Canada

Holiness
Bible Holiness Movement
Ch. of God (Anderson, Ind.), Canadian Bd.

Independent
ABWE–Canada
Glad Tidings Missionary Society
Global Outreach Mission
New Tribes Mission of Canada

Lutheran
Evang. Lutheran Ch. in Canada, ELCIC
Liebenzell Mission of Canada
Lutheran Bible Translators of Canada, Inc.
World Mission Prayer League

Mennonite
Evangelical Mennonite Conference
Evangelical Mennonite Mission Conf. Bd.
MBMS International
Mennonite Central Committee Canada
Mennonite Economic Development Assoc.
Western Tract Mission, Inc.

Methodist
Salvation Army Canada and Bermuda

Pentecostal
Apostolic Church In Canada, The
Apostolic Ch. of Pentecost of Canada, Inc.
Italian Pentecostal Church of Canada, The
Mission of Mercy (Canada)
Pentecostal Assemblies of Canada

Presbyterian
Presbyterian Church in Canada

Reformed
Christian Ref. World Relief Committee, Can.
Presbyterian Church in Canada

Wesleyan
Bible Holiness Movement
Ch. of God (Anderson, IN), Canadian Bd.
Salvation Army Canada and Bermuda
World Gospel Mission (Canada)

Ministry Activity

Agricultural programs
Apostolic Ch. of Pentecost of Canada, Inc.
Canadian Convention of Southern Baptists
Canadian Food for the Hungry
Christian Ref. World Relief Comte. of Can.
Crossroads Christian Communications Inc.
Emmanuel Relief and Rehabilitation Intl.
HOPE International Development Agency
International Christian Aid Canada
Mennonite Central Committee Canada
Mennonite Economic Dev. Assoc.
Samaritan's Purse–Canada
United Church of Canada
World Relief Canada
Wycliffe Bible Translators of Canada

Audio recording/distribution
Canadian Bible Society
Far East Broadcasting Associates of Canada
Language Recordings International

Aviation services
Canadian South America Mission
Global Outreach Mission
Mission Aviation Fellowship of Canada

Bible distribution
Apostolic Church In Canada, The
Apostolic Ch. of Pentecost of Canada, Inc.
Bible Holiness Movement
Bible League of Canada, The
Canadian Bible Society
Croisade du Livre Chretien
Gospel for Asia
Open Doors With Brother Andrew Canada
Ukrainian Children's Christian Fund
Voice of the Martyrs, The

Broadcasting, radio and/or TV
Arab World Ministries (Canada)
Back to the Bible Missionary Agency
Crossroads Christian Communications Inc.
European Christian Mission
Evangelical Free Church of Canada Mission
Evangelical Mennonite Mission Conf. Bd.
Far East Broadcasting Associates of Canada
Galcom International
Global Outreach Mission

Gospel Missionary Union of Canada
HCJB World Radio–Canada
High Adventure Gospel Communication Mins.
SIM Canada
Voice of the Martyrs, The

Camping programs
Associated Gospel Churches
Greater Europe Mission (Canada)
International Christian Aid Canada
InterVarsity Christian Fellowship of Canada
Janz Team Ministries
Latin America Mission (Canada) Inc.
SEND International of Canada
Young Life of Canada
Youth for Christ–Canada

Childcare/orphanage
Christian Aid Mission
Compassion Canada
Emmanuel Relief and Rehabilitation Intl.
Evang. Missionary Church of Canada
International Child Care (Canada)
International Christian Aid Canada
Into All The World
Italian Pentecostal Church of Canada
Latin America Mission (Canada) Inc.
Mission of Mercy (Canada)
Mission Possible Canada
Pentecostal Assemblies of Canada
Slavic Gospel Association–Canada
World Vision Canada

Childrens programs
Action International Ministries
BCM International (Canada), Inc.
Canadian Food for the Hungry
Child Evangelism Fellowship of Canada
Compassion Canada
Samaritan's Purse–Canada
Venture Teams International
WEC International (Canada)

Church construction
Apostolic Ch. of Pentecost of Canada, Inc.
Ch. of God (Anderson, Ind.), Canadian Bd.
Missionary Ventures Canada

Church establishing/planting
ABWE
Apostolic Church In Canada, The
Arab World Ministries (Canada)
Associated Gospel Churches
Baptist General Conf. Canada (Global Mins.)
BCM International (Canada), Inc.
BGCC Global Ministries

Bible Holiness Movement
Brethren Assemblies (Canada)
Canadian Baptist Ministries
Canadian Convention of Southern Baptists
Canadian South America Mission
Christar
Christian Aid Mission
Christian and Missionary Alliance in Canada
Ch. of God (Anderson, Ind.), Canadian Bd.
Evangelical Covenant Ch. of Canada
Evangelical Free Church of Canada Mission
Evangelical Mennonite Conference
Evangelical Mennonite Mission Conf. Bd.
Evang. Msny. Ch. of Can. World Partners
FEBInternational
Frontiers Canada
Glad Tidings Missionary Society
Global Outreach Mission
Gospel Missionary Union of Canada
Greater Europe Mission (Canada)
International Christian Aid Canada
International Needs Network–Canada
International Teams of Canada
Into All The World
Liebenzell Mission of Canada
MBMS International
Mission Possible Canada
MSC Canada
New Tribes Mission of Canada
OMF International–Canada
OMS International–Canada
Operation Mobilization Canada
Outreach Canada
Pentecostal Assemblies of Canada
Pioneers
SEND International of Canada
SIM Canada
TEAM–Canada
UFM International in Canada
WEC International (Canada)
World Gospel Mission (Canada)
World Mission Prayer League
World Team

Correspondence courses
Arab World Ministries (Canada)
Bible League of Canada
FEBInternational
HCJB World Radio–Canada
MSC Canada
Open Doors With Brother Andrew Canada
Western Tract Mission, Inc.

**Development, community
and/or other**
Action International Ministries

Africa Inland Mission (Canada)
Baptist General Conf. Canada (Global Mins.)
BGCC Global Ministries
Canadian Baptist Ministries
Canadian Food for the Hungry
Christian Blind Mission Intl. (Canada)
Christian Ref. Wld. Relief Committee Canada
Compassion Canada
Crossroads Christian Communications Inc.
Emmanuel Relief and Rehabilitation Intl.
Equip, Canada
Evang. Msny. Ch. Canada World Partners
FAIR (Fellowship Agency for Intl. Relief)
HCJB World Radio—Canada
HOPE International Development Agency
International Christian Aid Canada
International Needs Network—Canada
International Teams of Canada
INTERSERVE (Canada)
Leprosy Mission Canada, The
MBMS International
Mennonite Central Committee Canada
Mennonite Economic Dev. Assoc.
Missionary Ventures Canada
OMF International–Canada
Presbyterian Ch. in Canada, Life and Msn.
Salvation Army Canada/Bermuda Territory
Samaritan's Purse–Canada
TEAM–Canada
UFM International in Canada
United Church of Canada
Voice of the Martyrs
World Mission Prayer League
World Relief Canada
World Vision Canada

Disability assistance programs
BCM International (Canada), Inc.
Christian Blind Mission Intl. (Canada)
Evangelical Medical Aid Society
Leprosy Mission Canada, The

Education, church/sch.
general Christian
BCM International (Canada), Inc.
Canadian Convention of Southern Baptists
Evangelical Covenant Church of Canada
Janz Team Ministries
Mission of Mercy (Canada)
Mission Possible Canada
Salvation Army Canada/Bermuda Territory

Education, extension (other)
Evangelical Medical Aid Society
Leprosy Mission Canada, The
United Church of Canada

Youth With A Mission (Canada)

Education, missionary
(certificate/degree)
Canadian Churches' Forum for Global Mins.
Christian Studies International of Canada

Education, theological
ABWE—Canada
Africa Inland Mission (Canada)
Apostolic Ch. of Pentecost of Canada, Inc.
Baptist Gen. Conf. of Canada (Global Mins.)
Canadian Baptist Ministries
Canadian South America Mission
Christian Studies International of Canada
Evangelical Free Church of Canada Mission
Evangelical Lutheran Church in Canada
Evang. Missionary Ch. Can. World Partners
Galcom International
Global Outreach Mission
Gospel Missionary Union of Canada
Greater Europe Mission (Canada)
Into All The World
Latin America Mission (Canada) Inc.
MBMS International
OMF International–Canada
OMS International–Canada
Overseas Council for Theol. Ed. & Missions
Pentecostal Assemblies of Canada
Presb. Ch. in Canada, Life/Mission Agency
SEND International of Canada
SIM Canada
Slavic Gospel Association–Canada
UFM International in Canada
World Gospel Mission (Canada)
World Team

Education, theological
by extension (TEE)
ABWE–Canada
Christian and Missionary Alliance in Canada
Evangelical Mennonite Conference
Liebenzell Mission of Canada
Pentecostal Assemblies of Canada
World Mission Prayer League

Evangelism, mass
African Enterprise Association of Canada
Campus Crusade for Christ of Canada
Christian Aid Mission
Christian and Missionary Alliance in Canada
Evangelical Lutheran Church in Canada
Evangelical Mennonite Mission Conf. Bd.
Evangelical Tract Distributors
Far East Broadcasting Associates of Canada
Galcom International

Gospel for Asia
HCJB World Radio–Canada
High Adventure Gospel Communication Mins.
International Teams of Canada
Janz Team Ministries
OMS International–Canada
Operation Mobilization Canada
Salvation Army Canada/Bermuda Territory
Samaritan's Purse–Canada
Youth for Christ–Canada

Evangelism, personal and small group
ABWE–Canada
Action International Ministries
Africa Inland Mission (Canada)
African Enterprise Association of Canada
Apostolic Church In Canada
Arab World Ministries (Canada)
Associated Gospel Churches
Barry Moore Ministries
BCM International (Canada), Inc.
BGCC Global Ministries
Bible Holiness Movement
Bible League of Canada, The
Campus Crusade for Christ of Canada
Canadian Convention of Southern Baptists
Child Evangelism Fellowship of Canada
Christar
European Christian Mission
Evangelical Covenant Church of Canada
Evangelical Free Church of Canada Mission
Evangelical Mennonite Conference
FEBInternational
Frontiers Canada
Glad Tidings Missionary Society
Global Outreach Mission
Greater Europe Mission (Canada)
Inter-national Needs Network–Canada
International Teams of Canada
INTERSERVE (Canada)
InterVarsity Christian Fellowship of Canada
Language Recordings International
Liebenzell Mission of Canada
MBMS International
Missionary Ventures Canada
MSC Canada
Navigators of Canada, The
OMF International–Canada
OMS International–Canada
Operation Mobilization Canada
Outreach Canada
Pioneers
SEND International of Canada
South American Msny. Society in Canada
TEAM–Canada
UFM International in Canada

Ukrainian Children's Christian Fund
Venture Teams International
WEC International (Canada)
World Gospel Mission (Canada)
World Mission Prayer League

Evangelism, student
Campus Crusade for Christ of Canada
InterVarsity Christian Fellowship of Canada
Mission Possible Canada
Navigators of Canada, The
Young Life of Canada
Youth for Christ–Canada

Funds transmission
African Enterprise Association of Canada
Apostolic Church In Canada, The
Compassion Canada
Evangelical Lutheran Church in Canada
Fundamental Bapt. Msn. of Trinidad/Tobago
Latin America Mission (Canada) Inc.
Partners International Canada
United Church of Canada

Furloughed missionary support
Canadian Churches' Forum for Global Mns.

Information services
African Enterprise Association of Canada
Centre for World Mission–British Columbia
Open Doors With Brother Andrew Canada
Voice of the Martyrs, The

Leadership development
Africa Inland Mission (Canada)
Associated Gospel Churches
Barry Moore Ministries
BGCC Global Ministries
Canadian Baptist Ministries
Canadian South America Mission
Christian Ref. World Relief Comte. of CAN
Christian Studies International of Canada
Ch. of God (Anderson, Ind.), Canadian Bd.
Evangelical Mennonite Conference
Evangelical Msny. Ch. of CAN World Partners
FEBInternational
Gospel Missionary Union of Canada
Greater Europe Mission (Canada)
HOPE International Development Agency
Inter-national Needs Network–Canada
International Teams of Canada
InterVarsity Christian Fellowship of Canada
Into All The World
Mission Possible Canada
Open Doors With Brother Andrew Canada
Outreach Canada

Overseas Council for Theol. Ed. & Missions
Pentecostal Assemblies of Canada
Presbyterian Ch. in Canada, Life and Msn.
SEND International of Canada
South American Msny. Society in Canada
Venture Teams International
World Mission Prayer League
World Vision Canada
Youth With A Mission (Canada)

Linguistics
Canadian Bible Society
Lutheran Bible Translators of Canada, Inc.
New Tribes Mission of Canada
Wycliffe Bible Translators of Canada

Literacy
Bible League of Canada, The
Christian Ref. World Relief Comte. of CAN
Emmanuel Relief and Rehabilitation Intl.
Lutheran Bible Translators of Canada, Inc.
New Tribes Mission of Canada
World Relief Canada
Wycliffe Bible Translators of Canada

Literature distribution
Action International Ministries
Back to the Bible Missionary Agency
BCM International (Canada), Inc.
Bible Holiness Movement
Canadian Bible Society
Child Evangelism Fellowship of Canada
Croisade du Livre Chretien
Czechoslovak Evangelical Mission
European Christian Mission
Evangelical Tract Distributors
Far East Broadcasting Associates of Canada
Into All The World
Lutheran Bible Translators of Canada, Inc.
MSC Canada
Navigators of Canada, The
Open Doors With Brother Andrew Canada
Operation Mobilization Canada
Scripture Gift Mission (Canada)
Slavic Gospel Association–Canada
Ukrainian Children's Christian Fund
Western Tract Mission, Inc.

Literature production
Bible Holiness Movement
Canadian Bible Society
Child Evangelism Fellowship of Canada
Czechoslovak Evangelical Mission
Evangelical Tract Distributors
Lutheran Bible Translators of Canada, Inc.

Navigators of Canada, The
Operation Mobilization Canada
Scripture Gift Mission (Canada)
Western Tract Mission, Inc.

Management consulting/training
Christian Reformed. Wld. Relief Committee
Mennonite Economic Development Assoc.
Outreach Canada
Overseas Council for Theol. Ed. & Missions

Medical supplies
Apostolic Church In Canada, The
Canadian Food for the Hungry
Crossroads Christian Communications Inc.
International Child Care (Canada)
Missionary Ventures Canada
Samaritan's Purse–Canada

Medicine, including dental and public health
ABWE–Canada
Africa Inland Mission (Canada)
Baptist Gen. Conf. of Canada (Global Mins.)
Christian Blind Mission Intl. (Canada)
Crossroads Christian Communications Inc.
Evangelical Lutheran Church in Canada
Evangelical Medical Aid Society
Evangelical Mennonite Conference
FEBInternational
Global Outreach Mission
HCJB World Radio–Canada
International Christian Aid Canada
INTERSERVE (Canada)
Leprosy Mission Canada, The
Liebenzell Mission of Canada
Mission of Mercy (Canada)
Missionary Ventures Canada
Presbyterian Church in Canada
SIM Canada
TEAM–Canada
World Mission Prayer League

Member Care
Associated Gospel Churches

National church nurture/support
Action International Ministries
Arab World Ministries (Canada)
Back to the Bible Missionary Agency
Baptist Gen. Conf. of Canada (Global Mins.)
Barry Moore Ministries
BGCC Global Ministries
Bible Holiness Movement
Christian Aid Mission

Ch. of God (Anderson, Ind.), Canadian Bd.
Compassion Canada
Emmanuel Relief and Rehabilitation Intl.
European Christian Mission
Evangelical Lutheran Church in Canada
Evangelical Mennonite Conference
FEBInternational
Gospel for Asia
INTERSERVE (Canada)
Italian Pentecostal Church of Canada
Liebenzell Mission of Canada
OMF International–Canada
OMS International–Canada
Outreach Canada
Overseas Council for Theol. Ed. & Missions
Partners International Canada
Presbyterian Church in Canada
Slavic Gospel Association - Canada
UFM International in Canada
WEC International (Canada)

Partnership development
Associated Gospel Churches
Baptist Gen. Conf. of Canada (Global Mins.)
Canadian South America Mission
Evangelical Mennonite Mission Conf. Board
Galcom International
HCJB World Radio–Canada
Lutheran Bible Translators of Canada, Inc.
World Relief Canada

Recruiting/Mobilizing
Action International Ministries
African Enterprise Association of Canada
Centre for World Mission—British Columbia
Evangelical Covenant Church of Canada
Evangelical Free Church of Canada Mission
Janz Team Ministries
Pioneers
South American Msny. Society in Canada
TEAM–Canada
Venture Teams International
WEC International (Canada)
Youth for Christ–Canada

Relief and/or rehabilitation
Canadian Baptist Ministries
Canadian Convention of Southern Baptists
Canadian Food for the Hungry
Christian Aid Mission
Christian Ref. World Relief Comte. of CAN
Crossroads Christian Communications Inc.
Emmanuel Relief and Rehabilitation Intl.
FAIR (Fellowship Agency for Intl. Relief)
FEBInternational
HOPE International Development Agency

International Christian Aid Canada
Latin America Mission (Canada) Inc.
Leprosy Mission Canada
Mennonite Central Committee Canada
Mission of Mercy (Canada)
MSC Canada
OMF International–Canada
Pentecostal Assemblies of Canada
Salvation Army Canada/Bermuda Territory
Samaritan's Purse–Canada
SIM Canada
Voice of the Martyrs
World Relief Canada
World Vision Canada

Research
Centre for World Mission–British Columbia
Outreach Canada

Services for other agencies
Canadian Churches' Forum for Global Mins.
Centre for World Mission–British Columbia
Evangelical Mennonite Conference
Youth With A Mission (Canada)

Short-term programs coordination
Canadian Food for the Hungry
Evangelical Free Church of Canada Mission
Evang. Msny. Ch. of CAN World Partners
International Teams of Canada
InterVarsity Christian Fellowship of Canada
Latin America Mission (Canada) Inc.
Missionary Ventures Canada
MSC Canada
SEND International of Canada
TEAM–Canada
UFM International in Canada
Venture Teams International
Voice of the Martyrs, The
Youth With A Mission (Canada)

Support of national workers
Apostolic Church of Pentecost of Canada
Christian Aid Mission
Evangelical Mennonite Mission Conf. Bd.
FEBInternational
Frontiers Canada
Fundamental Bapt. Msn.–Trinidad/Tobago
Gospel for Asia
International Needs Network–Canada
Into All The World
Italian Pentecostal Church of Canada
Language Recordings International
MBMS International
Mission Possible Canada
Open Doors With Brother Andrew Canada

Operation Mobilization Canada
Partners International Canada
Slavic Gospel Association–Canada
South American Msny. Society in Canada
Ukrainian Children's Christian Fund
Wycliffe Bible Translators of Canada

Technical assistance
Christian Indigenous Development Overseas
Equip, Canada
Galcom International
INTERSERVE (Canada)
Mennonite Central Committee Canada
Mennonite Economic Development Assoc.
Mission Aviation Fellowship of Canada
Overseas Council for Theol. Ed. & Missions

Campus Crusade for Christ of Canada
HCJB World Radio–Canada

Youth programs
BCM International (Canada), Inc.
International Teams of Canada
Italian Pentecostal Church of Canada
Liebenzell Mission of Canada
MBMS International
Mission of Mercy (Canada)
Mission Possible Canada
Navigators of Canada, The
Youth for Christ–Canada
Youth With A Mission (Canada)

Training, other
Action International Ministries
Apostolic Ch. of Pentecost of Canada, Inc.
Barry Moore Ministries
Child Evangelism Fellowship of Canada
Equip, Canada
Galcom International
HOPE International Development Agency
Leprosy Mission Canada, The
Wycliffe Bible Translators of Canada
Youth With A Mission (Canada)

Training/Orientation, missionary
Bible League of Canada
Canadian Churches' Forum for Global Mins.
Christian Aid Mission
Equip, Canada
Frontiers Canada
New Tribes Mission of Canada
TEAM–Canada
United Church of Canada
Venture Teams International
WEC International (Canada)
Youth With A Mission (Canada)

Translation, Bible
Canadian Bible Society
Lutheran Bible Translators of Canada, Inc.
New Tribes Mission of Canada
SIM Canada
World Team
Wycliffe Bible Translators of Canada

Translation, other
Italian Pentecostal Church of Canada
Slavic Gospel Association–Canada

Video/Film production/distribution
Arab World Ministries (Canada)

Chapter 7

Countries of Activity for
Canadian Protestant Agencies

I n this chapter you will find the countries where agencies reported field personnel in answer to question #12 of the Survey Questionnaire (see the Appendix for details). The few exceptions to this are agencies whose whole program supports (with funds raised in Canada, but which may not be designated to specific personnel on a regular basis) churches or other initiatives in a country.

All countries are listed in alphabetical order according to the name most commonly recognized in North America. Countries that are part of the Commonwealth of Independent States (most of the former Soviet Union) have been listed separately. Examples of this include Armenia, Kyrgyzstan and Belarus. In a few cases we have listed a territory or other administrative district of a country because it is commonly viewed as a separate entity and mission agencies report it that way. An example would be the Azores, located in the Atlantic Ocean 900 miles west of mainland Portugal.

We have separated the personnel totals for all agencies into five categories. Under the "personnel from Canada" heading, the term of expected service has been divided into three categories: 4+ years, 2-4 years and 1-2 years for fully supported personnel. For non-Canadian personnel in the "other countries" heading, the categories are those who are citizens of that ministry country and those who are not citizens, and are fully or partially supported by funds raised in Canada by the associated agency. For example, a Korean with specific mission/ministry duties serving in Korea would be included in an agency's "citizens" column of the Korea section. A Korean serving in Russia would be listed in the "not citizen" column of the Russia section.

At the end of each country section, totals of each category for that country are given. Please note that the totals for the "other countries" heading do not necessarily reflect all non-Canadian mission personnel who draw support from Canadian agencies. Some agencies give grants for ongoing institutions and other programs without specifying individual recipients. This may be in addition to Canadian mission personnel based in that country or the agency may not have Canadian personnel living in that country.

Please note also that the totals will be minimum numbers only because of the bigger number of large agencies in this edition that reported their personnel only by general regions and not by specific countries. Therefore, their numbers are not included in this "countries of activity" section.

	Personnel from Canada				Other Countries	
	First Year	4+ yrs.	2-4 yrs.	1-2 yrs.	Citizens	Not Citizens
Afghanistan						
Operation Mobilization Canada		2	-	-	-	-
Totals:		2	-	-	-	-
Africa—General						
Apostolic Church of Pentecost of Canada Inc.	1955	2	-	-	-	-
Arab World Ministries (Canada)		3	-	-	-	-
Campus Crusade for Christ of Canada		2	-	-	-	-
Christian Aid Mission		-	-	-	-	1
Frontiers Canada		2	-	-	-	-
International Christian Aid Canada	1980	-	-	-	10	-
New Tribes Mission of Canada		-	-	-	-	-
WEC International (Canada)		6	-	-	-	-
Totals:		15	-	-	10	1
Albania						
Canadian Baptist Ministries	1993	2	-	-	-	-
Child Evangelism Fellowship of Canada		2	-	-	-	-
Operation Mobilization Canada		1	-	-	-	-
Totals:		5	-	-	-	-
Angola						
Africa Inland Mission (Canada)		-	-	-	-	-
Brethren Assemblies (Canada)	1958	1	-	-	-	-
Canadian Baptist Ministries	1956	2	-	-	-	-
Evangelical Medical Aid Society	1988	1	-	-	-	-
Mission Aviation Fellowship of Canada		-	4	-	-	-
SIM Canada	1917	7	-	-	-	-
Totals:		11	4	-	-	-
Argentina						
Brethren Assemblies (Canada)	1987	4	-	-	-	-
Christian and Missionary Alliance in Canada		2	-	-	-	-
Evangelical Lutheran Church in Canada		-	-	-	-	-
Gospel Missionary Union of Canada	1911	2	-	-	-	-
Youth With A Mission (Canada)		1	-	-	-	-
Totals:		9	-	-	-	-
Asia—General						
Arab World Ministries (Canada)		6	-	-	-	-
BGCC Global Ministries		4	-	-	-	-
Campus Crusade for Christ of Canada		-	9	3	-	-
Canadian Baptist Ministries	1985	3	2	-	-	-
Christar		13	-	-	-	40
Christian Aid Mission		-	-	-	-	1
Frontiers Canada		3	-	-	-	-
INTERSERVE (Canada)	1975	7	-	-	-	-
New Tribes Mission of Canada		-	-	-	-	-
Operation Mobilization Canada		3	-	-	-	-
Pioneers		5	-	-	-	-
SEND International of Canada	2001	1	-	-	-	-
TEAM–Canada		21	-	-	-	236

	First Year	4+ yrs.	2-4 yrs.	1-2 yrs.	Personnel from Canada — Citizens	Other Countries — Not Citizens
WEC International (Canada)		9	-	-	-	-
Wycliffe Bible Translators of Canada	2001	38	-	-	-	-
Totals		113	11	3	-	277

Australia

Child Evangelism Fellowship of Canada		-	2	-	-	-
International Teams of Canada		1	-	-	-	-
Salvation Army Canada/Bermuda Territory	1996	-	4	-	-	-
Youth With A Mission (Canada)		16	-	-	-	-
Totals:		17	6	-	-	-

Austria

Brethren Assemblies (Canada)	1983	4	-	-	-	-
Gospel Missionary Union of Canada	1966	2	-	-	-	-
Greater Europe Mission (Canada)	1964	1	-	-	-	-
International Teams of Canada		2	-	-	-	-
Janz Team Ministries		1	-	-	-	-
Totals		10	-	-	-	-

Bahamas, The

Gospel Missionary Union of Canada	1956	1	-	-	-	-
Salvation Army Canada/Bermuda Territory	1997	-	4	-	-	-
Totals		1	4	-	-	-

Bangladesh

Inter-national Needs Network–Canada	1974	-	-	-	93	-
INTERSERVE (Canada)	1952	1	-	-	-	-
Salvation Army Canada/Bermuda Territory	1994	2	-	-	-	-
SIM Canada	1957	3	-	-	-	-
Totals		6	-	-	93	-

Barbados

Youth With A Mission (Canada)		4	-	-	-	-
Totals:		4	-	-	-	-

Belau

Liebenzell Mission of Canada	2001	-	-	2	-	-
Totals		-	-	2	-	-

Belgium

Brethren Assemblies (Canada)	1970	6	-	-	-	-
Canadian Baptist Ministries	1985	6	-	5	-	-
FEBInternational	1978	6	-	-	-	-
Global Outreach Mission		-	1	-	-	-
Salvation Army Canada/Bermuda Territory	1997	-	2	-	-	-
Totals		18	3	5	-	-

Belize

Equip, Canada	2003	-	-	2	-	-
Gospel Missionary Union of Canada	1955	2	-	2	-	-
Pioneers		2	-	-	-	-
Youth With A Mission (Canada)		4	-	-	-	-
Totals		8	-	4	-	-

	First Year	Personnel from Canada 4+ yrs.	2-4 yrs.	1-2 yrs.	Other Countries Citizens	Not Citizens
Benin						
Christian and Missionary Alliance in Canada		3	-	-	-	-
Into All The World	1998	-	-	-	-	2
SIM Canada	1946	10	-	-	-	-
	Totals:	13	8	-	-	2
Bolivia						
Brethren Assemblies (Canada)	1976	10	-	-	-	-
Campus Crusade for Christ of Canada		-	-	-	-	-
Canadian Baptist Ministries	1898	5	-	-	-	-
Canadian Food for the Hungry	1999	1	1	-	-	-
Canadian South America Mission	1922	2	-	-	-	-
Child Evangelism Fellowship of Canada		1	-	-	-	-
Evangelical Free Church of Canada Mission		8	-	1	-	2
Evangelical Mennonite Mission Conf. Board	1969	2	2	-	-	-
Global Outreach Mission		-	-	-	4	-
Gospel Missionary Union of Canada	1928	13	-	-	-	-
Pioneers		3	-	-	-	-
SIM Canada	1907	5	-	-	-	-
	Totals:	50	3	1	4	2
Bosnia and Herzegovina						
Pioneers		1	-	-	-	-
UFM International in Canada		1	-	-	-	-
	Totals:	2	-	-	-	-
Botswana						
Brethren Assemblies (Canada)	1991	2	-	-	-	-
Mission Aviation Fellowship of Canada		-	2	-	-	-
SIM Canada	1973	3	-	-	-	-
	Totals	5	2	-	-	-
Brazil						
Action International Ministries		4	-	-	-	-
Apostolic Church In Canada, The	1980	-	-	-	6	-
Apostolic Church of Pentecost of Canada	1995	2	-	-	-	-
Brethren Assemblies (Canada)	1948	3	-	-	-	-
Canadian Food for the Hungry	2000	1	-	-	-	-
Canadian South America Mission	1913	-	-	1	-	-
Child Evangelism Fellowship of Canada		2	-	-	-	-
Christian and Missionary Alliance in Canada		3	-	-	-	-
Emmanuel Relief and Rehabilitation Intl.	1985	-	-	-	2	-
Evangelical Missionary Church of Canada	1969	7	-	-	-	-
Global Outreach Mission		-	1	-	-	-
Gospel Missionary Union of Canada	1911	1	-	-	-	-
Janz Team Ministries	1968	2	-	-	2	-
Mission Aviation Fellowship of Canada		-	4	-	-	-
Pentecostal Assemblies of Canada	1965	6	-	-	-	-
Pioneers		2	-	-	-	-
Salvation Army Canada /Bermuda Territory	1991	2	3	-	-	-
UFM International in Canada		6	-	-	-	-
WEC International (Canada)	1957	2	-	-	-	-

	Personnel from Canada				Other Countries	
	First Year	4+ yrs.	2-4 yrs.	1-2 yrs.	Citizens	Not Citizens
Wycliffe Bible Translators of Canada	1968	9	-	-	-	-
Totals:	52	8	1	10	-	

Bulgaria

	First Year	4+ yrs.	2-4 yrs.	1-2 yrs.	Citizens	Not Citizens
Navigators of Canada, The		1	-	-	-	-
Pentecostal Assemblies of Canada	1998	-	-	1	-	-
Totals:	1	-	1	-	-	

Burkina Faso

	First Year	4+ yrs.	2-4 yrs.	1-2 yrs.	Citizens	Not Citizens
Apostolic Church of Pentecost of Canada	1990	4	-	-	-	-
Christian and Missionary Alliance in Canada		2	-	-	-	-
Evangelical Mennonite Conference		2	2	-	-	-
SIM Canada	1930	9	-	1	-	-
Wycliffe Bible Translators of Canada	1946	5	-	-	-	-
Totals	22	2	1	-	-	

Burundi

	First Year	4+ yrs.	2-4 yrs.	1-2 yrs.	Citizens	Not Citizens
World Vision Canada		-	-	-	-	1
Totals	-	-	-	-	1	

Cambodia

	First Year	4+ yrs.	2-4 yrs.	1-2 yrs.	Citizens	Not Citizens
Canadian Food for the Hungry	2000	-	1	-	-	-
Christian and Missionary Alliance in Canada		6	-	-	-	-
Christian Reformed World Relief Committee		1	-	-	-	-
Far East Broadcasting Associates of Canada	1993	1	-	-	-	-
HOPE International Development Agency	1992	-	-	-	4	-
WEC International (Canada)	1992	2	-	-	-	-
Totals	10	1	-	4	-	

Cameroon

	First Year	4+ yrs.	2-4 yrs.	1-2 yrs.	Citizens	Not Citizens
Evangelical Lutheran Church in Canada	1999	2	2	-	-	-
Into All The World	1999	-	-	-	1	1
Lutheran Bible Translators of Canada, Inc.	1981	2	-	-	-	-
World Team	1985	8	-	-	-	-
Wycliffe Bible Translators of Canada	1971	25	-	-	-	-
Totals:	37	2	-	1	1	

Caribbean—General

	First Year	4+ yrs.	2-4 yrs.	1-2 yrs.	Citizens	Not Citizens
Wycliffe Bible Translators of Canada	2001	2	-	-	-	-
Central African Republic		-	-	-	-	-
Africa Inland Mission (Canada)		-	-	-	-	-
Wycliffe Bible Translators of Canada	2000	1	-	-	-	-
Totals:	3	-	-	-	-	

Central Asia - General

	First Year	4+ yrs.	2-4 yrs.	1-2 yrs.	Citizens	Not Citizens
BGCC Global Ministries		1	-	-	-	-
FEBInternational	2000	-	2	-	-	-
Frontiers Canada		10	-	-	-	-
Operation Mobilization Canada		1	-	-	-	-
WEC International (Canada)		8	-	-	-	-
World Mission Prayer League	1945	4	-	-	-	-
Totals:	24	2	-	-	-	

		Personnel from Canada			Other Countries	
	First Year	4+ yrs.	2-4 yrs.	1-2 yrs.	Citizens	Not Citizens
Chad						
Africa Inland Mission (Canada)		-	-	-	-	-
Mission Aviation Fellowship of Canada		-	2	-	-	-
TEAM–Canada		5	-	-	-	-
Wycliffe Bible Translators of Canada	1994	3	-	-	-	-
Totals:		8	2	-	-	-
Chile						
Brethren Assemblies (Canada)	1952	14	-	-	-	-
Christian and Missionary Alliance in Canada		2	-	-	-	-
Navigators of Canada, The		4	-	-	-	-
SIM Canada	1986	2	-	-	-	-
Youth With A Mission (Canada)		1	-	-	-	-
Totals:		23	-	-	-	-
China						
Canadian Baptist Ministries	1990	-	2	-	-	-
Christian Aid Mission		-	-	-	-	2
Christian Studies International of Canada	2000	-	1	-	-	-
Evangelical Free Church of Canada Mission		2	-	-	-	2
Evangelical Medical Aid Society	2000	-	2	-	-	-
Navigators of Canada, The		2	-	-	-	-
Totals:		4	5	-	-	4
Colombia						
Action International Ministries		3	-	-	-	-
Brethren Assemblies (Canada)	1972	1	-	-	-	-
Canadian South America Mission	1934	-	-	-	-	-
Christian and Missionary Alliance in Canada		3	-	-	-	-
Evangelical Lutheran Church in Canada		-	-	-	-	-
FEBInternational	1969	4	-	1	2	-
Global Outreach Mission		2	-	-	-	-
Inter-national Needs Network–Canada	1994	-	-	-	8	-
Latin America Mission (Canada) Inc.		5	-	-	1	-
Pentecostal Assemblies of Canada	1996	-	1	-	-	-
Wycliffe Bible Translators of Canada	1963	1	-	-	-	-
Totals:		19	1	1	11	-
Comoros						
Africa Inland Mission (Canada)		-	-	-	-	-
Totals		-	-	-	-	-
Congo, Democratic Republic of						
Africa Inland Mission (Canada)		-	-	-	-	-
Brethren Assemblies (Canada)	1952	3	-	-	-	-
Canadian Baptist Ministries	1961	8	-	-	-	-
Global Outreach Mission		1	-	-	-	-
UFM International in Canada		-	-	-	-	2
Wycliffe Bible Translators of Canada	1990	2	-	-	-	-
Totals:		14	-	-	-	2

	First Year	4+ yrs.	2-4 yrs.	1-2 yrs.	Other Countries Citizens	Not Citizens
Congo, Republic of the						
Christian and Missionary Alliance in Canada		4	-	-	-	-
Totals:		4	-	-	-	-
Costa Rica						
Brethren Assemblies (Canada)	1956	2	-	-	-	-
Christian and Missionary Alliance in Canada		1	-	-	-	-
Latin America Mission (Canada) Inc.		8	-	-	-	-
Presbyterian Church in Canada		-	-	-	1	-
World Vision Canada	2001	-	-	-	-	1
Totals		11	-	-	1	1
Cote d'Ivoire						
Christian and Missionary Alliance in Canada		13	1	-	-	-
Pentecostal Assemblies of Canada	1986		-	-	-	-
SIM Canada	1968	1	-	-	-	-
WEC International (Canada)	1934	1	-	1	-	-
Totals		15	1	1	-	-
Croatia						
Canadian Baptist Ministries	1991	-	2	-	-	-
Greater Europe Mission (Canada)	1974	2	-	-	-	-
Overseas Council for Theol. Ed & Msns.	1990	-	-	-	3	-
Totals:		2	2	-	3	-
Cuba						
Evangelical Medical Aid Society		-	-	-	-	-
Totals:		-	-	-	-	-
Cyprus						
INTERSERVE (Canada)	1965	4	-	-	-	-
Presbyterian Church in Canada	1990	4	-	-	-	-
Totals		8	-	-	-	-
Czech Republic						
Inter-national Needs Network–Canada	1993	-	-	-	6	-
Operation Mobilization Canada		2	-	-	-	-
Salvation Army Canada and Bermuda	1998	-	2	-	-	-
SEND International of Canada	1984	4	-	-	-	-
TEAM–Canada		2	-	-	-	-
Totals:		8	2	-	6	-
Denmark						
Youth With A Mission (Canada)		1	-	-	-	-
Totals:		1	-	-	-	-
Djibouti						
Into All The World		-	-	-	-	-
Totals:		-	-	-	-	-
Dominican Republic						
Brethren Assemblies (Canada)	1947	2	-	-	-	-

		Personnel from Canada			Other Countries	
	First Year	4+ yrs.	2-4 yrs.	1-2 yrs.	Citizens	Not Citizens
Youth With A Mission (Canada)		2	-	-	-	-
Totals:		4	-	-	-	-
Ecuador						
Action International Ministries		2	-	-	-	-
Brethren Assemblies (Canada)	1983	5	-	-	-	-
Campus Crusade for Christ of Canada		-	-	-	-	-
Christian and Missionary Alliance in Canada		8	1	-	-	-
Gospel Missionary Union of Canada	1896	7	-	-	-	-
HCJB World Radio–Canada		10	6	-	-	-
Wycliffe Bible Translators of Canada	1970	2	-	-	-	-
Totals:		34	7	-	-	-
Egypt						
Inter-national Needs Network–Canada	1997	-	-	-	2	-
Totals:		-	-	-	2	-
El Salvador						
Apostolic Church of Pentecost of Canada	1971	2	-	-	-	-
Brethren Assemblies (Canada)	1991	3	-	-	-	-
Evangelical Lutheran Church in Canada	1988	1	-	-	-	-
Presbyterian Church in Canada	1999	2	-	-	-	-
Totals:		8	-	-	-	-
Equatorial Guinea						
WEC International (Canada)	1933	3	-	-	-	-
Totals:		3	-	-	-	-
Eritrea						
Inter-national Needs Network–Canada	1980	-	-	-	-	-
Into All The World		-	-	-	-	-
SIM Canada	1952	2	-	-	-	-
Totals:		2	-	-	-	-
Estonia						
Apostolic Church of Pentecost of Canada	1985	6	-	-	-	-
Pentecostal Assemblies of Canada	1991	2	-	-	-	-
Totals:		8	-	-	-	-
Ethiopia						
Baptist General Conference of Canada		1	-	2	-	-
BGCC Global Ministries		3	-	-	-	-
HOPE International Development Agency	1985	-	-	-	9	-
Inter-national Needs Network–Canada	1996	-	-	-	50	-
Into All The World	1999	-	1	-	2	-
Pentecostal Assemblies of Canada	1958	7	-	-	-	-
SIM Canada	1927	18	-	-	-	-
Totals:		29	1	2	61	-
Europe - General						
Frontiers Canada		3	-	-	-	-
Janz Team Ministries		3	-	-	-	-

	First Year	Personnel from Canada 4+ yrs.	2-4 yrs.	1-2 yrs.	Other Countries Citizens	Not Citizens
TEAM - Canada		-	-	-	-	188
Totals:		6	-	-	-	188
Fiji						
WEC International (Canada)	1986	2	-	-	-	-
Youth With A Mission (Canada)		2	-	-	-	-
Totals:		4	-	-	-	-
Finland						
Brethren Assemblies (Canada)	1982	2	-	-	-	-
Salvation Army Canada/Bermuda Territory	1997	-	-	1	-	-
Totals:		2	-	1	-	-
France						
Arab World Ministries (Canada)	1960	6	-	-	-	-
Brethren Assemblies (Canada)	1949	19	-	-	-	-
Canadian Baptist Ministries	1992	2	-	-	-	-
Christar		1	-	-	-	-
Christian and Missionary Alliance in Canada		4	-	-	-	-
FEBInternational	1982	3	-	2	-	-
Global Outreach Mission		7	-	-	6	-
Greater Europe Mission (Canada)	1949	3	-	1	-	-
International Teams of Canada		2	-	-	-	-
Salvation Army Canada/Bermuda Territory	1994	2	-	-	-	-
TEAM - Canada		3	-	-	-	-
Totals:		52	-	3	6	-
Gabon						
Christian and Missionary Alliance in Canada		9	-	-	-	-
Totals:		9	-	-	-	-
Gambia, The						
WEC International (Canada)	1965	3	-	-	-	-
Totals:		3	-	-	-	-
Germany						
Christian and Missionary Alliance in Canada		10	8	-	-	-
Evangelical Free Church of Canada Mission		2	-	-	-	-
Glad Tidings Missionary Society		1	-	-	-	-
Gospel Missionary Union of Canada	1961	2	-	-	-	-
International Teams of Canada		5	-	-	-	-
Janz Team Ministries	1955	17	-	-	-	-
Salvation Army Canada/Bermuda Territory	1991	6	2	-	-	-
TEAM - Canada		2	-	-	-	-
Totals:		45	10	-	-	-
Ghana						
Bible Holiness Movement	1987	-	-	-	-	-
Global Outreach Mission		-	-	-	2	-
Inter-national Needs Network–Canada	1986	-	-	-	91	-
Presbyterian Church in Canada		-	-	-	1	-
Salvation Army Canada/Bermuda Territory	1995	2	-	-	-	-

| | Personnel from Canada | | | | Other Countries |
	First Year	4+ yrs.	2-4 yrs.	1-2 yrs.	Citizens	Not Citizens
SIM Canada	1956	8	-	1	-	1
WEC International (Canada)	1940	2	-	-	-	-
World Vision Canada	2001	-	-	-	-	1
Wycliffe Bible Translators of Canada	1986	2	-	-	-	-
Totals:		14	-	1	94	2
Greece						
Pentecostal Assemblies of Canada	1965	2	-	-	-	-
Totals:		2	-	-	-	-
Greenland						
New Tribes Mission of Canada		-	-	-	-	-
Youth With A Mission (Canada)		2	-	-	-	-
Totals:		2	-	-	-	-
Guam						
Ch. of God (Anderson, IN), Canadian Bd.		-	-	-	-	-
Liebenzell Mission of Canada	2001	-	-	2	-	-
Totals:		-	-	2	-	-
Guatemala						
Brethren Assemblies (Canada)	1998	2	-	-	-	-
Canadian Food for the Hungry	1999	2	-	-	-	-
Christian and Missionary Alliance in Canada		4	-	-	-	-
Global Outreach Mission		2	-	-	11	-
Pentecostal Assemblies of Canada	1990	2	4	-	-	-
Presbyterian Church in Canada	1992	4	-	-	-	-
World Vision Canada	2001	-	-	-	-	1
Wycliffe Bible Translators of Canada	1960	8	-	-	-	-
Totals:		24	4	-	11	1
Guinea						
Christian and Missionary Alliance in Canada		9	-	-	-	-
Totals:		9	-	-	-	-
Guinea-Bissau						
Pentecostal Assemblies of Canada	1988	4	-	-	-	-
Totals		4	-	-	-	-
Guyana						
Canadian Baptist Ministries	1992	-	-	6	-	-
Evangelical Lutheran Church in Canada		-	-	-	-	-
Presbyterian Church in Canada	1997	1	-	-	-	-
Wycliffe Bible Translators of Canada	1994	2	-	-	-	-
Youth With A Mission (Canada)		2	-	-	-	-
Totals:		5	-	6	-	-
Haiti						
Christian Reformed World Relief Committee		2	-	-	-	-
Emmanuel Relief and Rehabilitation Intl.	1988	-	-	-	1	-
Global Outreach Mission		2	-	-	2	-
International Child Care (Canada)		2	4	-	-	-

	Personnel from Canada				Other Countries	
	First Year	4+ yrs.	2-4 yrs.	1-2 yrs.	Citizens	Not Citizens
Mission Aviation Fellowship of Canada		-	2	-	-	-
Mission Possible Canada	1979	1	-	-	-	-
Pentecostal Assemblies of Canada	1996	2	-	-	-	-
UFM International in Canada		2	-	2	-	-
World Team	1936	4	-	-	-	-
Totals:		15	6	2	3	-

Honduras

	First Year	4+ yrs.	2-4 yrs.	1-2 yrs.	Citizens	Not Citizens
Christian Reformed World Relief Committee		3	-	-	-	-
International Christian Aid Canada	1974	-	-	-	41	1
World Vision Canada	2001	-	-	-	-	1
Wycliffe Bible Translators of Canada	1989	1	-	-	-	-
Totals:		4	-	-	41	2

Hong Kong

	First Year	4+ yrs.	2-4 yrs.	1-2 yrs.	Citizens	Not Citizens
Brethren Assemblies (Canada)	1994	2	-	-	-	-
Canadian Baptist Ministries	1992	-	2	-	-	-
Christian and Missionary Alliance in Canada		4	-	-	-	-
Evangelical Lutheran Church in Canada	2000	-	2	-	-	-
Far East Broadcasting Associates of Canada	1986	2	-	-	-	-
Global Outreach Mission		2	-	-	-	-
Pentecostal Assemblies of Canada	1908	14	-	4	-	-
Salvation Army Canada/Bermuda Territory	1996	2	-	-	-	-
SEND International of Canada	1986	3	-	-	-	-
Totals:		29	4	4	-	-

Hungary

	First Year	4+ yrs.	2-4 yrs.	1-2 yrs.	Citizens	Not Citizens
Child Evangelism Fellowship of Canada		2	-	-	-	-
Christian and Missionary Alliance in Canada		6	-	-	-	-
Evangelical Free Church of Canada Mission		3	-	-	1	-
Greater Europe Mission (Canada)	1996	1	-	-	-	-
Navigators of Canada, The		3	-	-	-	-
Salvation Army Canada/Bermuda Territory	1997	-	2	-	-	-
Totals:		15	2	-	1	-

India

	First Year	4+ yrs.	2-4 yrs.	1-2 yrs.	Citizens	Not Citizens
Action International Ministries		2	-	2	-	-
Apostolic Church In Canada, The	1994	-	-	-	1	1
Apostolic Church of Pentecost of Canada	1998	2	-	-	-	-
Bible Holiness Movement	1990	-	-	-	-	-
Brethren Assemblies (Canada)	1982	2	-	-	-	-
Campus Crusade for Christ of Canada		2	-	-	-	-
Canadian Baptist Ministries	1870	4	-	-	-	-
Christian Aid Mission		-	-	-	2	1
Evangelical Medical Aid Society		-	-	-	-	-
Global Outreach Mission		4	-	-	12	-
Inter-national Needs Network–Canada	1979	-	-	-	202	-
INTERSERVE (Canada)	1952	2	-	-	-	-
Into All The World	1986	-	-	-	2	-
Mission of Mercy (Canada)		-	-	-	-	-
Operation Mobilization Canada		1	-	-	-	-
Pentecostal Assemblies of Canada	1911	4	1	-	-	-

	First Year	4+ yrs.	2-4 yrs.	1-2 yrs.	Personnel from Canada Citizens	Other Countries Not Citizens
Presbyterian Church in Canada	1959	-	1	-	-	-
SIM Canada	1893	1	-	2	2	-
WEC International (Canada)	1926	1	-	-	-	-
World Vision Canada	1997	-	-	-	-	1
Youth With A Mission (Canada)		8	-	-	-	-
Totals:		33	2	4	221	3

Indonesia

	First Year	4+ yrs.	2-4 yrs.	1-2 yrs.	Citizens	Not Citizens
Canadian Baptist Ministries	1973	3	-	1	-	-
Christian Aid Mission		-	-	-	-	2
Christian and Missionary Alliance in Canada		18	1	-	-	-
Christian Reformed World Relief Committee		1	-	-	-	-
Frontiers Canada		4	-	-	-	-
Mission Aviation Fellowship of Canada		-	8	-	-	-
OMF International–Canada	1952	3	-	-	-	-
Pentecostal Assemblies of Canada	1982	7	-	-	-	-
World Team	1954	7	-	-	-	-
Wycliffe Bible Translators of Canada	1977	7	-	-	-	-
Youth With A Mission (Canada)		1	-	-	-	-
Totals		51	9	1	-	2

Ireland

	First Year	4+ yrs.	2-4 yrs.	1-2 yrs.	Citizens	Not Citizens
Baptist General Conference of Canada		1	-	-	-	-
Brethren Assemblies (Canada)	1968	12	-	-	-	-
Global Outreach Mission		4	-	-	1	-
Greater Europe Mission (Canada)	1974	1	-	-	-	-
Operation Mobilization Canada		1	-	-	-	-
UFM International in Canada		2	-	-	-	-
Totals:		21	-	-	1	-

Israel

	First Year	4+ yrs.	2-4 yrs.	1-2 yrs.	Citizens	Not Citizens
Christian and Missionary Alliance in Canada		-	2	-	-	-
Operation Mobilization Canada		3	-	-	-	-
Pentecostal Assemblies of Canada	1989	4	-	-	-	-
Presbyterian Church in Canada		-	-	-	1	-
Totals:		7	2	-	1	-

Italy

	First Year	4+ yrs.	2-4 yrs.	1-2 yrs.	Citizens	Not Citizens
BCM International (Canada), Inc.	1960	-	-	-	-	2
Brethren Assemblies (Canada)	1987	4	-	-	-	-
FEBInternational	1980	2	-	-	-	-
International Teams of Canada		2	-	-	-	-
TEAM–Canada		5	-	-	-	-
UFM International in Canada		1	-	-	-	-
World Team	1970	1	-	-	-	-
Totals:		15	-	-	-	2

Jamaica

	First Year	4+ yrs.	2-4 yrs.	1-2 yrs.	Citizens	Not Citizens
Apostolic Church In Canada, The	1949	-	-	-	14	-
Overseas Council for Theol. Ed. & Msns.	1990	-	-	-	2	-
Salvation Army Canada/Bermuda Territory	1994	1	4	-	-	-
Youth With A Mission (Canada)		2	-	-	-	-
Totals:		3	4	-	16	-

	Personnel from Canada				Other Countries	
	First Year	4+ yrs.	2-4 yrs.	1-2 yrs.	Citizens	Not Citizens

Japan

Brethren Assemblies (Canada)	1949	7	-	-	-	-
Child Evangelism Fellowship of Canada		2	-	-	-	-
Christian and Missionary Alliance in Canada		4	-	-	-	-
Evangelical Free Church of Canada Mission		2	-	-	-	-
FEBInternational	1963	8	2	1	-	-
OMF International–Canada	1951	8	-	-	-	-
Presbyterian Church in Canada	1962	2	-	2	-	-
SEND International of Canada	1988	5	-	-	-	-
Youth With A Mission (Canada)		2	-	-	-	-
	Totals:	40	2	3	-	-

Jordan

Evangelical Lutheran Church in Canada	-	-	-	-	-	-
Youth With A Mission (Canada)		2	-	-	-	-
	Totals:	2	-	-	-	-

Kazakhstan

Global Outreach Mission		2	-	-	-	-
	Totals:	2	-	-	-	-

Kenya

Africa Inland Mission (Canada)	-	-	-	-	-	-
Brethren Assemblies (Canada)	1963	4	-	-	-	-
Canadian Baptist Ministries	1970	6	4	2	-	-
Christian Reformed World Relief Committee		2	-	-	-	-
FEBInternational	1998	2	-	-	-	-
Into All The World	1981	-	1	-	2	-
Language Recordings International	1977	-	1	-	2	-
Mission Aviation Fellowship of Canada		-	4	-	-	-
Pentecostal Assemblies of Canada	1939	15	-	2	-	-
Presbyterian Church in Canada	1979	1	-	-	-	-
World Vision Canada	2000	-	-	-	-	2
Wycliffe Bible Translators of Canada	2000	3	-	-	-	-
Youth With A Mission (Canada)		1	-	-	-	-
	Totals:	34	10	4	4	2

Korea, South

Bible Holiness Movement	1985	-	-	-	-	-
	Totals:	-	-	-	-	-

Laos

Christian and Missionary Alliance in Canada		2	-	-	-	-
	Totals:	2	-	-	-	-

Latin America—General

Christian Aid Mission	-	-	-	-	-	1
Janz Team Ministries		3	-	-	-	-
New Tribes Mission of Canada	-	-	-	-	-	-
Pentecostal Assemblies of Canada		2	-	-	-	-
TEAM–Canada		-	-	-	-	91
	Totals:	5	-	-	-	92

	First Year	4+ yrs.	2-4 yrs.	1-2 yrs.	Personnel from Canada Citizens	Other Countries Not Citizens
Latvia						
Canadian Baptist Ministries	1995	2	-	-	-	-
Greater Europe Mission (Canada)	1992	3	-	1	-	-
Totals:		5	-	1	-	-
Lebanon						
Christian and Missionary Alliance in Canada		2	-	-	-	-
Operation Mobilization Canada		1	-	-	-	-
Totals:		3	-	-	-	-
Lesotho						
Africa Inland Mission (Canada)		-	-	-	-	-
Mission Aviation Fellowship of Canada		-	2	-	-	-
Totals:		-	2	-	-	-
Liberia						
Equip, Canada	1996	4	-	-	-	-
Pentecostal Assemblies of Canada	1915	3	-	1	-	-
Totals:		7	-	1	-	-
Lithuania						
Evangelical Free Church of Canada Mission		-	-	-	2	-
Navigators of Canada, The		2	-	-	-	-
Youth With A Mission (Canada)		3	-	-	-	-
Totals:		5	-	-	2	-
Luxembourg						
Greater Europe Mission (Canada)	1989	2	-	-	-	-
Totals:		2	-	-	-	-
Macau						
Pentecostal Assemblies of Canada	1953	3	-	-	-	-
Totals:		3	-	-	-	-
Macedonia						
SEND International of Canada	1999	1	-	-	-	-
Totals:		1	-	-	-	-
Madagascar						
Africa Inland Mission (Canada)		-	-	-	-	-
Brethren Assemblies (Canada)	1997	2	-	-	-	-
Totals:		2	-	-	-	-
Malawi						
Bible Holiness Movement	1990	-	-	-	-	-
Emmanuel Relief and Rehabilitation Intl.	1980	2	-	9	-	-
Pentecostal Assemblies of Canada	1980	10	1	-	-	-
Presbyterian Church in Canada	1995	3	-	-	-	-
World Vision Canada	1999	-	-	-	-	1
Totals:		15	1	9	-	1

		Personnel from Canada				Other Countries
	First Year	4+ yrs.	2-4 yrs.	1-2 yrs.	Citizens	Not Citizens

Malaysia
Christian and Missionary Alliance in Canada		-	2	1	-	-
Operation Mobilization Canada	1978	3	-	-	-	-
Wycliffe Bible Translators of Canada		3	-	-	-	-
Totals:		6	2	1	-	-

Mali
Christian and Missionary Alliance in Canada		5	-	-	-	-
Christian Reformed World Relief Committee		1	-	-	-	-
Gospel Missionary Union of Canada	1919	9	-	1	-	-
Wycliffe Bible Translators of Canada	2001	3	-	-	-	-
Totals:		18	-	1	-	-

Mexico
Action International Ministries		-	2	-	-	-
Apostolic Church of Pentecost of Canada	1983	2	-	-	-	-
Baptist General Conference of Canada		-	-	-	-	-
Brethren Assemblies (Canada)	1988	6	-	-	-	-
Campus Crusade for Christ of Canada		-	-	-	-	-
Christian and Missionary Alliance in Canada		14	2	-	-	-
Equip, Canada	2001	-	-	2	-	-
Evangelical Free Church of Canada Mission		4	-	1	-	-
Evangelical Mennonite Conference		14	-	-	-	-
Evangelical Mennonite Mission Conf. Board	1982	2	2	2	-	-
Evangelical Missionary Ch. of Canada	1994	4	-	-	-	-
Glad Tidings Missionary Society		2	-	-	-	2
Gospel Missionary Union of Canada	1956	1	-	-	-	-
Salvation Army Canada/Bermuda Territory	1997	-	-	1	-	-
WEC International (Canada)	1991	3	-	1	-	-
World Mission Prayer League	1950	-	2	-	-	-
World Team	1994	2	-	-	-	-
Wycliffe Bible Translators of Canada	1949	12	-	-	-	-
Youth With A Mission (Canada)		4	-	-	-	-
Totals:		70	8	7	-	2

Middle East
Christian Aid Mission		-	-	-	-	1
FEBInternational	1990	1	-	-	-	-
Operation Mobilization Canada		3	-	-	-	-
TEAM–Canada		5	-	-	-	106
WEC International (Canada)		7	-	-	-	-
Totals:		16	-	-	-	107

Mongolia
Navigators of Canada, The		2	-	-	-	-
Totals:		2	-	-	-	-

Morocco
Inter-national Needs Network–Canada	1983	-	-	-	6	-
Totals:		-	-	-	6	-

		Personnel from Canada			Other Countries	
	First Year	4+ yrs.	2-4 yrs.	1-2 yrs.	Citizens	Not Citizens

Mozambique

Africa Inland Mission (Canada)		-	-	-	-	-
Operation Mobilization Canada		2	-	-	-	-
Pentecostal Assemblies of Canada	1927	4	-	-	-	2
Presbyterian Church in Canada	1997	-	1	-	-	-
Salvation Army Canada/Bermuda Territory	1997	-	1	-	-	-
Wycliffe Bible Translators of Canada	1994	4	-	-	-	-
Youth With A Mission (Canada)		2	-	-	-	-
Totals:		12	2	-	-	2

Myanmar/Burma

Canadian Food for the Hungry	1995	2	-	-	-	-
Totals:		2	-	-	-	-

N. Mariana Isls

Far East Broadcasting Associates of Canada	1995	2	-	-	-	-
Totals:		2	-	-	-	-

Namibia

Africa Inland Mission (Canada)		-	-	-	-	-
Totals:		-	-	-	-	-

Nepal

Christian Aid Mission		-	-	-	-	2
Inter-national Needs Network–Canada	1975	-	-	-	65	-
INTERSERVE (Canada)	1952	10	-	-	-	-
Language Recordings International	2000	-	-	-	-	-
WEC International (Canada)	1967	2	-	-	-	-
Totals:		12	-	-	65	2

Netherlands

BCM International (Canada), Inc.	1950	-	-	-	-	1
Youth With A Mission (Canada)		8	-	-	-	-
Totals:		8	-	-	-	1

New Zealand

Salvation Army Canada/Bermuda Territory	1998	-	2	-	-	-
Youth With A Mission (Canada)		2	-	-	-	-
Totals:		2	2	-	-	-

Nicaragua

Presbyterian Church in Canada	1985	2	-	-	-	-
Totals:		2	-	-	-	-

Niger

Christian Reformed World Relief Committee		2	-	-	-	-
SIM Canada	1924	13	-	2	-	2
Wycliffe Bible Translators of Canada	1989	3	-	-	-	-
Totals:		18	-	2	-	2

Nigeria

Bible Holiness Movement	1959	-	-	-	-	-

	First Year	4+ yrs.	2-4 yrs.	1-2 yrs.	Other Countries Citizens	Not Citizens
Brethren Assemblies (Canada)	1954	4	-	-	-	-
Campus Crusade for Christ of Canada		2	-	-	-	-
Evangelical Medical Aid Society		-	-	-	-	-
Evangelical Missionary Ch. of Canada	1974	5	-	-	-	-
Into All The World	1985	-	-	-	6	-
Presbyterian Church in Canada	1980	2	-	1	-	-
SIM Canada	1893	7	-	1	-	-
Wycliffe Bible Translators of Canada	1991	4	-	-	-	-
Totals:		24	-	2	6	-

Northern Mariana Islands

	First Year	4+ yrs.	2-4 yrs.	1-2 yrs.	Citizens	Not Citizens
Youth With A Mission (Canada)		1	-	-	-	-
Totals:		1	-	-	-	-

Norway

	First Year	4+ yrs.	2-4 yrs.	1-2 yrs.	Citizens	Not Citizens
Youth With A Mission (Canada)		2	-	-	-	-
Totals:		2	-	-	-	-

Oceania - General

	First Year	4+ yrs.	2-4 yrs.	1-2 yrs.	Citizens	Not Citizens
New Tribes Mission of Canada		-	-	-	-	-
Youth With A Mission (Canada)		1	-	-	-	-
Totals:		1	-	-	-	-

Pakistan

	First Year	4+ yrs.	2-4 yrs.	1-2 yrs.	Citizens	Not Citizens
Baptist General Conference of Canada		1	-	-	-	-
Christian Aid Mission		-	-	-	-	1
FEBInternational	1969	11	-	-	-	-
INTERSERVE (Canada)	1952	3	-	-	-	-
Language Recordings International	2000	-	-	-	-	-
Operation Mobilization Canada		1	-	-	-	-
Salvation Army Canada/Bermuda Territory	1997	-	-	1	-	-
Totals:		16	-	1	-	1

Panama

	First Year	4+ yrs.	2-4 yrs.	1-2 yrs.	Citizens	Not Citizens
Gospel Missionary Union of Canada	1953	1	-	-	-	-
Totals:		1	-	-	-	-

Papua New Guinea

	First Year	4+ yrs.	2-4 yrs.	1-2 yrs.	Citizens	Not Citizens
Evangelical Lutheran Church in Canada	2000	1	-	-	-	-
Mission Aviation Fellowship of Canada		-	13	-	-	-
Salvation Army Canada/Bermuda Territory	1998	-	2	-	-	-
Wycliffe Bible Translators of Canada	1957	25	-	-	-	-
Totals:		26	15	-	-	-

Paraguay

	First Year	4+ yrs.	2-4 yrs.	1-2 yrs.	Citizens	Not Citizens
Canadian South America Mission	1990	-	-	-	-	-
Evangelical Mennonite Conference		13	-	-	-	-
SIM Canada	1987	2	-	-	-	-
Totals:		15	-	-	-	-

Peru

	First Year	4+ yrs.	2-4 yrs.	1-2 yrs.	Citizens	Not Citizens
Brethren Assemblies (Canada)	1977	4	-	-	-	-

		Personnel from Canada			Other Countries	
	First Year	4+ yrs.	2-4 yrs.	1-2 yrs.	Citizens	Not Citizens
Canadian Food for the Hungry	2000	-	2	-	1	-
Canadian South America Mission	1926	2	-	3	-	-
Christian and Missionary Alliance in Canada		5	-	-	-	-
Evangelical Lutheran Church in Canada	1994	1	-	-	-	-
SIM Canada	1965	2	-	-	-	-
TEAM–Canada		2	-	-	-	-
World Team	1906	8	-	-	-	-
Wycliffe Bible Translators of Canada	1979	8	-	-	-	-
Totals:		32	2	3	1	-

Philippines

Action International Ministries		8	2	-	-	-
Baptist General Conference of Canada		2	-	-	-	-
Bible Holiness Movement	1961	-	-	-	-	-
Brethren Assemblies (Canada)		4	-	-	-	-
Campus Crusade for Christ of Canada		2	-	-	-	-
Christian and Missionary Alliance in Canada		12	3	-	-	-
Emmanuel Relief and Rehabilitation Intl.	1981	3	-	-	-	-
Evangelical Free Church of Canada Mission		2	-	1	-	-
Evangelical Medical Aid Society		-	-	-	-	-
Far East Broadcasting Associates of Canada	1996	-	2	-	-	-
Glad Tidings Missionary Society		1	-	-	-	-
International Christian Aid Canada	1988	-	-	-	26	-
Inter-national Needs Network–Canada	1977	-	-	-	71	-
OMF International–Canada	1954	18	2	2	-	-
Pentecostal Assemblies of Canada	1992	1	-	-	-	-
SEND International of Canada	1987	9	-	-	-	-
World Team	1981	10	-	-	-	-
Wycliffe Bible Translators of Canada	1955	16	-	-	-	-
Youth With A Mission (Canada)		8	-	-	-	-
Totals:		96	9	3	97	-

Poland

Brethren Assemblies (Canada)	1996	2	-	-	-	-
Christian and Missionary Alliance in Canada		4	-	-	-	-
International Teams of Canada		4	-	-	-	-
Overseas Council for Theol. Ed. & Msns.	1990	-	-	-	4	-
Pentecostal Assemblies of Canada	1999	2	-	-	-	-
Totals:		12	-	-	4	-

Portugal

Baptist General Conference of Canada		1	-	-	-	-
BGCC Global Ministries		1	-	-	-	-
Brethren Assemblies (Canada)	1959	6	-	-	-	-
Evangelical Missionary Church of Canada	1998	2	-	-	-	-
Greater Europe Mission (Canada)	1971	2	-	-	-	-
Janz Team Ministries		-	-	-	-	1
Totals:		12	-	-	-	1

Puerto Rico

Brethren Assemblies (Canada)	1967	1	-	-	-	-
Totals:		1	-	-	-	-

	First Year	4+ yrs.	2-4 yrs.	1-2 yrs.	Other Countries Citizens	Not Citizens
Romania						
Evangelical Free Church of Canada Mission		1	-	-	1	-
Evangelical Medical Aid Society		-	-	-	-	-
Inter-national Needs Network–Canada	1992	-	-	-	11	-
Presbyterian Church in Canada, Life and Msn.	1994	1	-	-	-	-
Totals:		2	-	-	12	-
Russia						
Brethren Assemblies (Canada)	1998	3	-	-	-	-
Campus Crusade for Christ of Canada		1	-	-	-	-
Christian and Missionary Alliance in Canada		8	-	-	-	-
Christian Studies International of Canada	1995	2	-	-	-	-
Evangelical Free Church of Canada Mission		1	-	-	-	-
Navigators of Canada, The		-	1	-	-	-
Overseas Council for Theol. Ed. & Msns.	1993	-	-	-	2	-
Pentecostal Assemblies of Canada	1993	2	-	-	-	-
Salvation Army Canada/Bermuda Territory	1990	5	1	-	-	-
SEND International of Canada	1986	13	-	-	-	-
Youth With A Mission (Canada)		10	-	-	-	-
Totals:		45	2	-	2	-
Rwanda						
Canadian Food for the Hungry	1999	-	1	-	-	-
Pentecostal Assemblies of Canada	1998	2	2	-	-	-
World Vision Canada	2001	-	-	-	-	1
Totals:		2	3	-	-	1
Saint Vincent/Grenadines						
Brethren Assemblies (Canada)	1990	1	-	-	-	-
Navigators of Canada, The		2	-	-	-	-
Totals:		3	-	-	-	-
Senegal						
Christian Reformed World Relief Committee		2	-	-	-	-
Glad Tidings Missionary Society		1	-	-	-	-
Pentecostal Assemblies of Canada	1989	4	-	-	-	-
SIM Canada	1984	2	-	-	-	-
WEC International (Canada)	1936	6	-	-	-	-
Totals:		15	-	-	-	-
Serbia and Montenegro						
Campus Crusade for Christ of Canada		2	-	-	-	-
Christian and Missionary Alliance in Canada		2	-	-	-	-
Pentecostal Assemblies of Canada	1995	-	-	-	3	-
Totals:		4	-	-	3	-
Seychelles						
Africa Inland Mission (Canada)		-	-	-	-	-
Totals:		-	-	-	-	-
Sierra Leone						
WEC International (Canada)	2001	-	-	-	1	-
Totals:		-	-	-	1	-

	First Year	4+ yrs.	2-4 yrs.	1-2 yrs.	Citizens	Not Citizens
		Personnel from Canada			Other Countries	

Singapore
	First Year	4+ yrs.	2-4 yrs.	1-2 yrs.	Citizens	Not Citizens
OMF International–Canada	1950	2	-	-	-	-
Salvation Army Canada/Bermuda Territory	1997	-	4	-	-	-
World Team	1997	2	-	-	-	-
Totals:		4	4	-	-	-

Slovakia
	First Year	4+ yrs.	2-4 yrs.	1-2 yrs.	Citizens	Not Citizens
Canadian Baptist Ministries	1989	2	-	-	-	-
Evangelical Lutheran Church in Canada	2001	-	-	1	-	-
Inter-national Needs Network–Canada	1993	-	-	-	6	-
Navigators of Canada, The		4	-	-	-	-
UFM International in Canada		1	-	-	-	-
Totals:		7	-	1	6	-

South Africa
	First Year	4+ yrs.	2-4 yrs.	1-2 yrs.	Citizens	Not Citizens
Brethren Assemblies (Canada)	1957	1	-	-	-	-
Campus Crusade for Christ of Canada		4	-	-	-	-
Emmanuel Relief and Rehabilitation Intl.	2003	-	1	-	-	-
FEBInternational	2002	-	-	2	-	-
Global Outreach Mission		2	-	-	-	-
HOPE International Development Agency	1983	2	-	-	-	2
Operation Mobilization Canada		2	-	-	-	-
Pentecostal Assemblies of Canada	1908	4	-	-	-	-
Salvation Army Canada/Bermuda Territory	1991	6	4	-	-	-
SIM Canada	1989	8	-	1	-	-
WEC International (Canada)	1955	1	-	-	-	-
World Vision Canada	2000	-	-	-	-	2
Totals:		30	5	3	-	4

South America—General
	First Year	4+ yrs.	2-4 yrs.	1-2 yrs.	Citizens	Not Citizens
Christian Aid Mission		-	-	-	-	1
Totals:		-	-	-	-	1

Spain
	First Year	4+ yrs.	2-4 yrs.	1-2 yrs.	Citizens	Not Citizens
Apostolic Church of Pentecost of Canada	1969	1	-	-	-	-
BCM International (Canada), Inc.	1950	-	-	-	-	2
Brethren Assemblies (Canada)	1975	4	-	-	-	-
Christian and Missionary Alliance in Canada		2	-	-	-	-
Evangelical Missionary Church of Canada	1996	2	-	-	-	-
FEBInternational	1980	4	-	-	-	-
Gospel Missionary Union of Canada	1966	8	-	-	-	-
Operation Mobilization Canada		2	-	-	-	-
Salvation Army Canada/Bermuda Territory	1998	-	2	-	-	-
TEAM–Canada		2	-	-	-	-
WEC International (Canada)	1968	2	-	-	-	-
World Team	1972	2	-	-	-	-
Totals:		29	2	-	-	2

Sri Lanka
	First Year	4+ yrs.	2-4 yrs.	1-2 yrs.	Citizens	Not Citizens
Inter-national Needs Network–Canada	1976	-	-	-	29	-
Overseas Council for Theol. Ed. & Msns.	1997	-	-	-	1	-
Pentecostal Assemblies of Canada	1982	2	-	-	-	-

	First Year	Personnel from Canada 4+ yrs.	2-4 yrs.	1-2 yrs.	Other Countries Citizens	Not Citizens
Salvation Army Canada /Bermuda Territory	1994	1	2	-	-	-
Totals:		3	2	-	30	-
Sudan						
Africa Inland Mission (Canada)	-	-	-	-	-	-
Operation Mobilization Canada		2	-	-	-	-
SIM Canada	1938	2	-	3	-	-
Wycliffe Bible Translators of Canada	1994	6	-	-	-	-
Totals:		10	-	3	-	-
Suriname						
Salvation Army Canada/Bermuda Territory	1996	-	2	-	-	-
Wycliffe Bible Translators of Canada	1994	2	-	-	-	-
Totals:		2	2	-	-	-
Sweden						
Child Evangelism Fellowship of Canada		2	-	-	-	-
Operation Mobilization Canada		1	-	-	-	-
Totals:		3	-	-	-	-
Switzerland						
Youth With A Mission (Canada)		1	-	-	-	-
Totals:		1	-	-	-	-
Taiwan						
Apostolic Church of Pentecost of Canada	1963	2	-	-	-	-
Christian and Missionary Alliance in Canada		4	-	-	-	-
OMF International–Canada	1951	4	-	-	-	-
Presbyterian Church in Canada	1958	1	-	3	-	-
Youth With A Mission (Canada)		2	-	-	-	-
Totals:		13	-	3	-	-
Tanzania						
Africa Inland Mission (Canada)	-	-	-	-	-	-
Bible Holiness Movement	1998	-	-	-	-	-
Campus Crusade for Christ of Canada	-	-	-	-	-	-
Christian Reformed World Relief Committee		3	-	-	-	-
Emmanuel Relief and Rehabilitation Intl.	1993	2	-	1	-	-
Inter-national Needs Network–Canada	1997	-	-	-	21	-
Mission Aviation Fellowship of Canada		-	2	-	-	-
Pentecostal Assemblies of Canada	1914	6	-	-	-	-
Salvation Army Canada/Bermuda Territory	1998	-	2	-	-	-
Totals:		11	4	1	21	-
Thailand						
Christian and Missionary Alliance in Canada		3	2	-	-	-
Evangelical Free Church of Canada Mission		2	-	-	1	-
Evangelical Lutheran Church in Canada	2000	-	1	-	-	-
Far East Broadcasting Associates of Canada	1994	2	-	-	-	-
Navigators of Canada, The		2	-	-	-	-
OMF International–Canada	1951	19	-	-	-	-
Pentecostal Assemblies of Canada	1961	7	-	-	-	-

		Personnel from Canada			Other Countries	
	First Year	4+ yrs.	2-4 yrs.	1-2 yrs.	Citizens	Not Citizens
WEC International (Canada)	1947	2	-	-	-	-
Youth With A Mission (Canada)		2	-	-	-	-
Totals:		39	3	-	1	-
Togo						
Wycliffe Bible Translators of Canada	1981	2	-	-	-	-
Totals:		2	-	-	-	-
Trinidad and Tobago						
Apostolic Church of Pentecost of Canada	2001	1	-	-	-	-
Totals:		1	-	-	-	-
Turkey						
Christian Aid Mission	-	-	-	-	-	2
Navigators of Canada, The		2	-	-	-	-
Operation Mobilization Canada		3	-	-	-	-
Totals:		5	-	-	-	2
Uganda						
Africa Inland Mission (Canada)	-	-	-	-	-	-
Christian Reformed World Relief Committee		1	-	-	-	-
Ch. of God (Anderson, IN), Canadian Bd.	-	-	-	-	-	-
Emmanuel Relief and Rehabilitation Intl.	2002	-	1	1	-	1
Equip, Canada	2000	1	-	-	1	-
Inter-national Needs Network–Canada	1994	-	-	-	74	-
Into All The World	2003	-	1	-	-	-
Mission Aviation Fellowship of Canada	-	2	-	-	-	-
Pentecostal Assemblies of Canada	1955	6	-	-	-	-
Wycliffe Bible Translators of Canada	2000	2	-	-	-	-
Totals:		10	4	1	75	1
Ukraine						
Campus Crusade for Christ of Canada		2	2	-	-	-
Canadian Baptist Ministries	1987	4	-	-	-	-
Christian Aid Mission	-	-	-	-	2	1
Evangelical Free Church of Canada Mission		17	-	-	1	4
Evangelical Medical Aid Society	-	-	-	-	-	-
Greater Europe Mission (Canada)	1993	1	-	-	-	-
Operation Mobilization Canada		2	-	-	-	-
Overseas Council for Theol. Ed. & Msns.	1997	-	-	-	4	-
Pentecostal Assemblies of Canada	1993	1	3	-	-	-
SEND International of Canada	1996	3	-	-	-	-
Slavic Gospel Association - Canada		2	-	-	-	-
Ukrainian Children's Christian Fund	-	-	-	-	28	-
Youth With A Mission (Canada)		7	-	-	-	-
Totals:		39	5	-	35	5
United Kingdom						
Arab World Ministries (Canada)	1984	1	-	-	-	-
Christar		2	-	-	-	-
International Teams of Canada		2	-	-	-	-
Language Recordings International	1998	-	2	-	-	-

	First Year	Personnel from Canada 4+ yrs.	2-4 yrs.	1-2 yrs.	Other Countries Citizens	Not Citizens
Operation Mobilization Canada		2	-	-	-	-
Salvation Army Canada/Bermuda Territory	1985	4	4	-	-	-
Wycliffe Bible Translators of Canada	1988	1	-	-	-	-
Youth With A Mission (Canada)		24	-	-	-	-
Totals:		36	6	-	-	-

Unspecified Country

	First Year	4+ yrs.	2-4 yrs.	1-2 yrs.	Citizens	Not Citizens
ABWE		24	8	-	-	-
BGCC Global Ministries		3	-	-	-	-
Christian Blind Mission Intl. (Canada)		122	-	-	-	-
Frontiers Canada		-	-	-	3	-
Janz Team Ministries		4	-	-	-	-
New Tribes Mission of Canada		300	-	-	-	-
OMF International–Canada		6	2	-	-	-
Operation Mobilization Canada		12	15	-	88	153
SIM Canada		3	-	-	-	-
United Church of Canada		48	-	-	-	-
Wycliffe Bible Translators of Canada	1992	10	-	-	-	-
Youth With A Mission (Canada)		4	-	-	-	-
Totals:		536	25	-	91	153

Uruguay

	First Year	4+ yrs.	2-4 yrs.	1-2 yrs.	Citizens	Not Citizens
Brethren Assemblies (Canada)	1974	5	-	-	-	-
Operation Mobilization Canada		1	-	-	-	-
Totals:		6	-	-	-	-

Uzbekistan

	First Year	4+ yrs.	2-4 yrs.	1-2 yrs.	Citizens	Not Citizens
Evangelical Free Church of Canada Mission		2	-	-	-	-
Totals:		2	-	-	-	-

Venezuela

	First Year	4+ yrs.	2-4 yrs.	1-2 yrs.	Citizens	Not Citizens
Brethren Assemblies (Canada)	1947	6	-	-	-	-
Canadian Baptist Ministries	1992	2	-	-	-	-
Christian and Missionary Alliance in Canada		9	-	-	-	-
Evangelical Free Church of Canada Mission		3	-	-	-	-
FEBInternational	1990	6	-	2	-	-
TEAM–Canada		3	-	-	-	-
Youth With A Mission (Canada)		1	-	-	-	-
Totals:		30	-	2	-	-

Vietnam

	First Year	4+ yrs.	2-4 yrs.	1-2 yrs.	Citizens	Not Citizens
Baptist General Conference of Canada		2	-	-	-	-
Evangelical Medical Aid Society		-	-	-	-	-
Inter-national Needs Network–Canada	1991	-	-	-	57	-
Navigators of Canada, The		3	-	-	-	-
Totals:		5	-	-	57	-

Zambia

	First Year	4+ yrs.	2-4 yrs.	1-2 yrs.	Citizens	Not Citizens
Apostolic Church of Pentecost of Canada	1999	2	-	-	-	-
Bible Holiness Movement	1990	-	-	-	-	-
Brethren Assemblies (Canada)		29	-	-	-	-
Christian Reformed World Relief Committee		2	-	-	-	-

| | Personnel from Canada | | | Other Countries | |
	First Year	4+ yrs.	2-4 yrs.	1-2 yrs.	Citizens	Not Citizens
Ch. of God (Anderson, IN), Canadian Bd.		-	-	-	-	-
Inter-national Needs Network–Canada	1985	-	-	-	12	-
Pentecostal Assemblies of Canada	1955	6	-	2	-	-
Salvation Army Canada/Bermuda Territory	1998	-	2	-	-	-
SIM Canada	1910	20	-	2	-	-
Totals:		59	2	4	12	-
Zimbabwe						
Pentecostal Assemblies of Canada	1947	6	-	-	-	-
Salvation Army Canada/Bermuda Territory	1988	2	3	-	-	-
Youth With A Mission (Canada)		1	-	-	-	-
Totals:		9	3	-	-	-

Selective Bibliography

Prepared by Ferne Lauraine Weimer, Billy Graham Center Library
with Andrew Culbertson

As background to the study of contemporary mission activities, this bibliography seeks to introduce several types of materials to readers of the *Mission Handbook*. Categories include General Reference Works, Directories, Books on Mission in the Twenty-First Century, and Journals. Selections emphasize empirical or reasonably objective data, with most having global or regional coverage. The Directory section adds a sampling of single country sources that were selected because they included multiple denominations.

General Reference Works

The majority of works in this section are recently published dictionaries, encyclopedias, atlases, handbooks, or other reference tools in the field of mission. A few historical works give context and perspective to statistics in the current *Mission Handbook*.

Anderson, Gerald H., ed. *Biographical Dictionary of Christian Missions.* New York: Simon & Schuster Macmillan, 1998; Grand Rapids, Michigan: Eerdmans, 1999. Web: www.omsc.org

Barrett, David B., George T. Kurian, and Todd M. Johnson, eds. *World Christian Encyclopedia: A Comparative Survey of Churches and Religions,* 2nd Edition. Two volume set. New York: Oxford University Press, 2001. Web: www.oup-usa.org

Barrett, David B., and Todd M. Johnson. *World Christian Trends, AD 30-AD 2200.* Pasadena, California: William Carey Library, 2001. Web: www.gospelcom.net/wclbooks/

Brierley, Peter, and Heather Wraight. *Atlas of World Christianity: 2000 Years.* Nashville, Tennessee: Thomas Nelson, 1998. Web: www.christian-research.org.uk

Brierley, Peter, ed. *World Churches Handbook.* London, England: Christian Research, 1997. Based on the *Operation World* database by Patrick Johnstone, WEC International, 1993. Web: www.christian-research.org.uk

Evangelism and Missions Information Service. *Mission Handbook: U.S. and Canadian Christian Ministries Overseas, 2001-2003,* 18th ed. Wheaton, Illinois: EMIS, 2000.

_____. *Mission Handbook: U.S. and Canadian Protestant Ministries Overseas, 2004-2006,* 19th ed. Wheaton, Illinois: EMIS, 2004.

Fahlbusch, Erwin, et al., eds. *The Encyclopedia of Christianity.* 5 vols. Grand Rapids, Michigan: Eerdmans; Leiden, The Netherlands: E.J. Brill, 1999-   . Work in progress. Web: www.eerdmans.com

Goddard, Burton L., ed. *The Encyclopedia of Modern Christian Missions: The Agencies.* Camden, New Jersey: Thomas Nelson & Sons, 1967.

Grimes, Barbara F., ed. *Ethnologue: Languages of the World.* 14th ed. Dallas, Texas: Summer Institute of Linguistics, 2000. CD-ROM and/or 2-volume print versions available at: www.ethnologue.com/print.asp. Searchable online at: www.ethnologue.com/web.asp

Johnstone, Patrick. *Operation World.* 21st century edition. Carlisle, Cumbria, UK: Paternoster Lifestyle, 2001. CD-ROM and print editions available from Gabriel Resources at: www.gabriel-resources.com or print only at www.paternoster-publishing.com.

Linder, Eileen W., ed. *Yearbook of American & Canadian Churches.* Nashville, Tennessee: Abingdon Press, 2003. Annual. Web: www.abingdon.org

Missionary Research Library. Various predecessor titles to the *Mission Handbook.* Editions 1-7. New York: Missionary Research Library, 1953-1966.
· 1953: *Foreign Missionary Agencies in the United States*
· 1956: *Directory of Foreign Missionary Agencies in North America,* Revised ed.
· 1958: *Directory of North American Protestant Foreign Missionary Agencies,* 3rd ed.
· 1960: *Directory of North American Protestant Foreign Missionary Agencies,* 4th ed.
· 1962: *North American Protestant Foreign Mission Agencies,* 5th ed.
· 1964: *North American Protestant Foreign Mission Agencies,* 6th ed.
· 1966: *North American Protestant Foreign Mission Agencies,* 7th ed.

Missionary Research Library and MARC. *Mission Handbook.* Editions 8-9. New York: Missionary Research Library; Pasadena, CA: MARC, 1968-1970.
· 1968: *North American Protestant Foreign Mission Agencies,* 8th ed.
· 1970: *North American Protestant Ministries Overseas,* 9th ed.

Mission Advanced Research and Communication Center (MARC). *Mission Handbook.* Editions 10-17. Pasadena, CA: MARC, 1973-1997.
· 1973: *Mission Handbook: North American Protestant Ministries Overseas,* 10th ed.
· 1976: *Mission Handbook: North American Protestant Ministries Overseas,* 11th ed.
· 1979: *Mission Handbook: North American Protestant Ministries Overseas,* 12th ed.
· 1986: *Mission Handbook: North American Protestant Ministries Overseas,* 13th ed.
· 1989: *Mission Handbook: USA/Canada Protestant Ministries Overseas,* 14th ed.
· 1993: *Mission Handbook: USA/Canada Christian Ministries Overseas,* 15th ed.
· 1995: *Mission Handbook.* Directory Edition, 16th ed.
· 1997: *Mission Handbook, 1998-2000: U.S. and Canadian Christian Ministries Overseas,* 17th ed.
· See Evangelism and Missions Information Service for 18th and 19th editions.

Moreau, A. Scott, ed. *Evangelical Dictionary of World Missions.* Grand Rapids, Michigan: Baker Book House, 2000. Web: www.bakerbooks.com

Müller, Karl, Theo Sundermeier, Stephen B. Bevans, and Richard H. Bliese, eds. *Dictionary of Mission: Theology, History, Perspectives.* (American Society of Missiology Series, 24). Maryknoll, New York: Orbis Books, 1997. Web: www.orbisbooks.com

National Association of Evangelicals. *National Evangelical Directory, 1999-2000.* Carol Stream, Illinois: National Association of Evangelicals, 1999.

United States Catholic Mission Association. *Mission Statistics, 2000-2001.* Web: www.uscatholicmission.org/misstats.htm

Welliver, Dotsey, and Minnette Smith, eds. *Directory of Schools and Professors of Mission and Evangelism in the USA and Canada, 2002-2004.* Wheaton, Illinois:

Evangelism and Missions Information Service, 2002. Web: www.billygraham center.org/emis

Published Mission and Church Directories beyond the United States and Canada

The entries in this section offer a sampling of printed directories from around the world. Some directories focus on mission agencies while others cover multiple types of Christian organizations. Specifically excluded are directories limited to specific denominations or traditions.

Bentley, Peter, and Philip J. Hughes. *A Directory of Australian Religious Organizations: 1999.* Kew, Victoria, Australia: Christian Research Association, 1999.

Brierley, Peter, and Boyd Myers. *Irish Christian Handbook = Lámhleabhar Chríostaí na hEireann, 1995/96.* Eltham, London: Christian Research, 1994.

Brierley, Peter, Heather Wraight, and David Longley. *UK Christian Handbook, 2002/2003.* London: Christian Research; HarperCollins Religious, 2001. Web: www.christian-research.org.uk ; www.ukchristianhandbook.org.uk

Chao, Jonathan. *The China Mission Handbook: a Portrait of China and its Church.* Hong Kong: Chinese Church Research Center, 1989.

Downes, D. R. *Directory of Kenya's Missionary-Sending Ministries.* Nairobi, Kenya: Daystar University College, 2000.

European Churches Handbook. London: MARC Europe, 1992. Contents: Vol. 1.— Denmark, Finland, France, Norway, Switzerland (French), United Kingdom. Vol. 2—Austria, Netherlands, Northern Ireland, Republic of Ireland, Spain.

Froise, Marjorie. *Lesotho Christian Handbook, 1992-93.* Johannesburg: Christian Info, 1992.

Froise, Marjorie. *South African Christian Handbook 1999/2000.* Welkom, South Africa: Christian Info, [1999?].

Froise, Marjorie. *Swaziland Christian Handbook 1994.* Welkom, South Africa: Christian Info, 1994.

Guillermo, Merlyn L., and L. P. Verora. *Protestant Churches and Missions in the Philippines.* [Philippines]: World Vision Philippines, 1982.

Japan Evangelical Missionary Association. *JEMA Directory for 2003.* Tokyo, Japan: The Association, 2003. 53rd ed. Web: jema.org

Korea Research Institute for Missions and Communication. *Directory of Korean Missionaries & Mission Societies.* [South Korea]: Korea Research Institute for Missions and Communication, 1992. Note: Text in Korean, with some English. [See also: Korean World Missions Association website: www.kwma.org and Korean World Mission Council for Christ: www.kwmc.com]

Lazarus, Sam. *Proclaiming Christ: a Handbook of Indigenous Missions in India.* Madras, Tamil Nadu, India: Church Growth Association of India, 1992.

Linzey, Sharon, ed. *Christianity in Russia and Post Communist Europe: Directory 2003.* Pasadena, California: William Carey Library, 2003.

Linzey, Sharon, and Peter Kuzmic. *Directory of Indigenous Christian Organizations of the Former Soviet Union and East Central Europe; Between Two Worlds: the Challenges of Ministry in Eastern Europe.* Evanston, Illinois: Berry Publishing Services, 1996.

Linzey, Sharon, M. Holt Ruffin, and Mark R. Elliot. *East-West Christian Organizations: a Directory of Western Christian Organizations Working in East Central Europe and the Newly Independent States Formerly Part of the Soviet Union.* Evanston, Illinois: Berry Publishing Services, 1993.

Malaysia & Brunei Church Directory 1986-1987. Singapore: Singapore Every Home Crusade, Ltd., 1986.

National Evangelical Christian Fellowship Malaysia Missions Commission. *Missions Agencies Handbook.*

Pate, Larry D. *From Every People: A Handbook of Two-Thirds World Missions with Directory/Histories/Analysis.* Monrovia, CA: MARC, 1989.

Shane, John. *The Nairobi Networker: A Christian Worker's Directory.* 2nd ed. Nairobi, Kenya: Urban Ministries Support Group, 1997.

Tumusiime, Ephraim N. *Uganda Christian Missions Directory 1995-96.* [Kampala, Uganda]: Published by the Directory of Uganda Christian Mission Agencies, 1995.

Mission Directories on the Web

The websites listed in this section contain electronic directories of mission agencies. In most cases the directories contain full contact information for the organizations which are included.

WORLDWIDE

Missions Commission of the World Evangelical Alliance (formerly World Evangelical Fellowship). www.globalmission.org

REGIONS

Europe

World Mission Directory of The European Missionary Association. www.mission.org

European Evangelical Alliance. Includes links to the associations of individual countries. europeanea.org

Ibero-America (Latin America, Spain and Portugal).

The Ibero-American Missions Handbook of COMIBAM Internacional. www.comibam.org/catalogo2002

INDIVIDUAL COUNTRIES

Australia

Missions Interlink of the Australian Evangelical Alliance. www.evangelicalalliance.org.au/commissions/mi/list.asp

Evangelical Missionary Alliance, NSW (New South Wales) www.pastornet.net.au/scwm/ema_html.htm

Brazil

InfoBrasil. www.infobrasil.org

Canada
Global Mission Roundtable of the Evangelical Fellowship of Canada.
www.globalmission.org/canada/index.htm

Hong Kong
Hong Kong Association of Christian Missions. www.hkacm.org.hk (Site
in Chinese)

India
India Missions Association of the Evangelical Fellowship of India.
iyesu.com/missions/Ima

Japan
Japan Evangelical Missionary Association. www.keikyo.com/jema

New Zealand
Centre for Mission Direction. www.cmd.org.nz/agencies.html

United Kingdom
Global Connections. www.globalconnections.co.uk/directory.asp

United States of America
AERDO: www.AERDO.org

AIMS: Accelerating International Mission Strategies. www.aims.org

Catholic Mission Association. www.uscatholicmission.org

EFMA: Evangelical Fellowship of Mission Agencies.
www.efmamissions.org

FOM: The Fellowship of Missions. www.fellowshipofmissions.org/
members.html

IFMA: Interdenominational Foreign Mission Association of North
America. www.ifmamissions.org/member.htm

Orthodox Christian Mission Center. www.ocmc.org

Books on Mission in the Twenty-First Century

These monographs and collected essays discuss the future of global evangelization and selected issues in missiology. They focus on the thinking of the church
in the 1990s and encourage examination of new approaches to mission in the
new millennium.

Bible Translation and the Spread of the Church: the Last 200 Years. Leiden; New York:
E. J. Brill, 1990.
Bonk, Jonathan, ed. *Between Past and Future: Evangelical Mission Entering the
Twenty-first Century.* Evangelical Missiological Society Series, no. 10. Pasadena,
California: William Carey Library, 2003.

Bosch, David. *Believing in the Future: Toward a Missiology of Western Culture.* Valley Forge, Pennsylvania: Trinity Press International; Leominster, England: Gracewing, 1995.

Brierley, Peter. *Future Church: A Global Analysis of the Christian Community to the Year 2010.* London, England: Christian Research, 1998.

Bryant, David. *The Hope at Hand: National and World Revival for the 21st Century.* Grand Rapids, Michigan: Baker Books, 1995.

Bush, Luis, ed. *AD 2000 & Beyond Handbook: a Church for Every People and the Gospel for Every Person by AD 2000.* 3rd Edition. [San Jose, Calif.]: AD 2000 & Beyond Movement, 1995.

Elmer, Duane H., and Lois McKinney, general eds. *With an Eye on the Future: Development and Mission in the 21st Century: Essays in Honor of Ted W. Ward.* Monrovia, California: MARC, 1996.

Engel, James F. *A Clouded Future? Advancing North American World Missions.* Milwaukee, Wisconsin: Christian Stewardship Association, 1996. Note: "A study of parachurch financing underwritten by the Lilly Endowment Inc."

Engel, James F., and William A. Dyrness. *Changing the Mind of Missions: Where Have We Gone Wrong?* Downers Grove, Illinois: InterVarsity Press, 2000.

Guthrie, Stan. *Missions in the Third Millennium: 21 Key Trends for the 21st Century.* Carlisle, Cumbria; Waynesboro, Georgia: Paternoster Publishing, 2000.

Jenkins, Philip. *The Next Christendom: The Coming of Global Christianity.* New York: Oxford University Press, 2002.

Johnstone, Patrick J. *The Church is Bigger than You Think: Structures and Strategies for the Church in the 21st Century.* Pasadena, California: William Carey; Fearn, Ross-shire, Great Britain: Christian Focus Publications; Gerrards Cross, Bucks, Great Britain: WEC, 1998.

Martinson, Paul Varo, ed. *Mission at the Dawn of the 21st Century: A Vision for the Church.* Minneapolis, MN: Kirk House Publishers, 1999. Note: Chiefly papers from the Congress on the World Mission of the Church, held at the Luther Theological Seminary in St. Paul in 1998.

McKaughan, Paul, Dellanna O'Brien, and William R. O'Brien. *Choosing a Future for U. S. Missions.* Monrovia, California: MARC, 1998.

Phillips, James M., and Robert T. Coote, eds. *Toward the Twenty-First Century in Christian Mission.* Grand Rapids, Michigan: Eerdmans, 1993. Festschrift in honor of Gerald H. Anderson.

Samuel, Vinay, and Chris Sugden, eds. *A.D. 2000 and Beyond: A Mission Agenda.* Oxford, UK: Regnum Books, 1991. Festschrift for John Stott's 70th birthday.

Shenk, Wilbert R. *Changing Frontiers of Mission.* Maryknoll, New York: Orbis Books, 1999.

Taylor, William D., ed. *Global Missiology for the 21st Century: The Iguassu Dialogue.* World Evangelical Fellowship Globalization of Mission Series. Grand Rapids, Michigan: Baker Book House, 2000.

Telford, Tom, with Lois Shaw. *Missions in the 21st Century: Getting Your Church into the Game.* Wheaton, Illinois: Harold Shaw Publishers, 1998.

Wuthnow, Robert. *Christianity in the Twenty-First Century: Reflections on the Challenges Ahead.* New York: Oxford University Press, 1993.

Mission Journals and Newsletters

The following are important journals and news sources for mission research. Whenever known, subscription addresses are included.

Section 1 contains a core list of English language titles of highest interest to readers of the *Mission Handbook*; annotations note specific reasons for inclusion. Section 2 offers additional titles, emphasizing the international research community.

Section 1: Core English Language Periodicals

Bibliographia Missionaria. Vatican City: Pontifical Missionary Library, 1987-   . Annual. Pontifical Urbaniana University, 00120 Vatican City, Italy.

This annual bibliography covers a wide range of Catholic and Protestant literature from multiple language sources. The topical section, "Present State and Future of Mission," offers both articles and books of interest.

Connections. Hyderabad, India: World Evangelical Alliance Missions Commission, 2002-   . 3 issues per year. $10.00. WEA Missions Commission, c/o World Evangelical Alliance Secretariat, PO Box 1839, Edmonds, WA 98020, USA. Web: www.globalmission.org.

Connections aims to express the core values of the WEA Missions Commission and to communicate its perspective on contemporary mission issues. Each issue contains articles related to the issue's central theme along with book reviews and news and announcements concerning WEA activities in various areas of the world.

Evangelical Missions Quarterly. Wheaton, IL: Evangelism and Missions Information Service, 1964-   . 4 issues per year. $24.95. Evangelical Missions Quarterly, Box 794, Wheaton, IL 60189, USA. E-mail: emis@wheaton.edu; Web: www.gospelcom.net/bgc/emis.

Using both academic and missionary authors, EMQ tackles contemporary issues from a conservative perspective. Readers can keep up-to-date in research by reading the book reviews, highlights from periodicals, listings of conferences and seminars, and the internet resource guide, "Missions on the Web."

International Bulletin of Missionary Research. New Haven, CT: Overseas Ministries Study Center, 1981-   . Quarterly. $27.00/year., International Bulletin of Missionary Research, P.O. Box 3000, Denville, NJ 07834 USA. E-mail: ibmr@omsc.org; Web: www.omsc.org.

Beyond its many fine articles, several features are noteworthy. In each January issue, David B. Barrett and Todd M. Johnson publish the "Annual Statistical Table on Global Mission," and the editors issue their "Fifteen Outstanding Books of [the previous year] for Mission Studies." Each issue contains book reviews, and "Dissertation Notices" appear periodically.

International Journal of Frontier Missions. El Paso, TX: International Student Leaders Coalition for Frontier Missions, 1984-   . Quarterly. $15.00. IJFM, 1539 East Howard Street, Pasadena, CA 91104, USA. E-mail: ijfm_subscriptions@wciu.edu;

Web: www.ijfm.org.
The editors seek to be "forerunners in missions to the frontiers."

International Review of Mission. Geneva, Switzerland: Commission on World Mission and Evangelism of the World Council of Churches, 1912- . Quarterly. $50.00. WCC Office, Rm 1062, 475 Riverside Drive, New York, NY 10115, USA. E-mail: cm@wcc-coe.org; Web: www.wcc-coe.org/wcc/what/mission/irm.html.

Covering a broad ecumenical spectrum, each issue contains 10-12 scholarly articles on one topic. Of particular interest is the ongoing "Bibliography on Mission Studies." Section 02.00.00 contains citations to "Surveys of the Christian Situation" with Section 02.04.00 specifically featuring "Mission Futures."

Missiology. Scottdale, PA: American Society of Missiology, 1973- . Quarterly. Individual subscription for one year = $21.00. Missiology, American Society of Missiology, 616 Walnut Avenue, Scottdale, PA 15683, USA. Web: www.asmweb. org

As the official publication of the ASM, *Missiology* is a "forum for the exchange of ideas" among scholars in the field of missiology. Besides lengthy book reviews and brief sketches on "books and media resources received," each issue contains a highly selective list of "Essential Books on Missiology" for a $100 budget and a secondary list of "Important Books on Missiology" for an additional $200 budget.

Missionalia. Menlo Park, South Africa: Southern African Missiological Society, 1973- . 3 issues per year. Individual subscription for one year (airmail) = $40.00. The Editor, Missionalia, P. O. Box 35704, Menlo Park 0102, South Africa. E-mail: missionalia@bigfoot.com; Web: www.geocities.com/Athens/Parthenon/ 8409/missalia.htm.

Missionalia is of particular interest to missionaries and scholars working in Africa. A significant portion of each issue is devoted to "Missiological Abstracts" with an annual index compiled in the last issue of each volume. The editors also provide a list of journals abstracted in each volume.

World Pulse. Wheaton, IL: Evangelism and Missions Information Service, 1984- . 20 issues per year. $29.95/year; online subscription $14.95/year. World Pulse, P.O. Box 794, Wheaton, IL 60189, USA. E-mail: emis@wheaton.edu; Web: www.gospelcom.net/bgc/emis/index.htm.

World Pulse reports and analyzes mission news, interviews key leaders, and offers an "Information Corner" highlighting newsmakers and calendar of future events.

Section 2: International Mission Journals

Evangelikale Missiologie. Korntal, Germany: Arbeitskreis für Evangelikale Missiologie, 1985- . 4 issues per year. AfeM - Geschäftsstelle, Kristina Weirich, Postfach 1360, D-51691 Bergneustadt, Germany. E-mail: afem.em@t-online.de; Web: www.afem-em.de

Exchange: Journal of Missiological and Ecumenical Research. Leiden, The Netherlands: Brill Academic Publishers in cooperation with the Interuniversity Institute for Missiological and Ecumenical Research, 1972- . 4 issues per year. Brill Academic Publishers Inc., 112 Water Street, Suite 400, Boston, MA 02109. E-mail: cs@brillusa.com; Web: www.brill.nl

Mission: Journal of Mission Studies = Revue des Sciences de la Mission. Ottawa, Ontario, Canada: Institut des Sciences de la Mission = Institute of Mission Studies, 1994- . 2 issues per year. Mission, Saint Paul University, 223 Main Street, Ottawa, ON, Canada K1S 1C4.

Mission Studies: Journal of the International Association for Mission Studies. Leiden, Netherlands: IAMS, 1984- . 2 issues per year. IAMS Secretariat, Peter Bangs Vej 1 D, DK-2000 Frederiksberg, Copenhagen, Denmark. E-mail: iams@mission studies.org; Web: www.missionstudies.org

Missionsforum: en tidskrift från Svenska Missionsrådet. (formerly known as *Tidskriften Missionsforum*) Stockholm, Sweden: Svenska Missionsradet, 1995- . 4 issues per year. Svenska Missionsradet, Starrbäcksgatan 11, se - 172 99 Sund byberg, Sweden. E-mail: info@missioncouncil.se; Web: www.missioncouncil.se

Neue Zeitschrift für Missionswissenschaft. Nouvelle Revue de Science Missionaire. Immensee, [Switzerland]: Verein zur Förderung der Missionswissenschaft, etc., 1945- . 4 issues per year. Verlag NZM, Postfach 62, Calendariaweg 4, CH-6405 Immensee, Switzerland. E-mail: vlgnzm@bluewin.ch; Web: mypage.bluewin.ch/nzm

Norsk Tidsskrift for Misjon. Oslo, Norway: Egede Institute in cooperation with Tapir Publishers, 1948- . 4 issues per year. NTM, Tapir Forlag, Nardovn. 14, 7005 Trondheim, Norway. E-mail: forlag@tapir.no

South-Pacific Journal of Mission Studies. North Turramurra, NSW, Australia: South Pacific Association of Mission Studies, 1989- . Irregular. SPJMS, Jim Mulroney, SPAMS, Columban Mission Institute, 420 Bobbin Head Road, North Turramurra, NSW 2074, Australia. E-mail: cmi@columban.org.au; Web: www.columban.org.au

Swedish Missiological Themes/Svensk Missionstidskrift. Uppsala, Sweden: Swedish Institute of Missionary Research, 1913- . 4 issues per year. Swedish Institute of Missionary Research, P.O. Box 1526, SE-751 45 Uppsala, Sweden. E-mail: gustafbjorck@teol.uu.se; Web: www.teol.uu.se/hemsidor/simeng/index.html

Third Millennium: Indian Journal of Evangelization. Gujarat, India: Third Millennium, 1998- . Quarterly. The Managing Editor, Third Millennium, Bishop's House, P.B. No. 1, Kalavad Road, Rajkot 360005, Gujarat, India. E-mail: bishoprajkot@sify.com

Transformation: An International Evangelical Dialogue on Mission and Ethics. Oxford, England: Oxford Centre for Mission Studies, 1984- . 4 issues per year. Transformation, Vanguard University, 55 Fair Drive, Costa Mesa, CA 92626, USA. E-mail: transformation@vanguard.edu; Web: www.ocms.ac.uk

Wereld en Zending: Oecumenisch tijdschrift voor missiologie en missionaire Praktijk, voor Nederland en Belgie. Kampen, The Netherlands: Uitgeverij Kok, [1972]- . 4 issues per year. Uitgeverij Kok, Postbus 130, 8260 GA, Kampen, The Netherlands. E-mail: abonnementen@kok.nl.

Zeitschrift für Mission. Stuttgart, Germany; Basel, Switzerland: Deutschen Gesellschaft für Missionswissenschaft und der Basler Mission, 1975- . 4 issues per year. Verlag Otto Lembeck, Gärtnerweg 16, D-60322 Frankfurt/Main, Germany. E-mail: verlag@lembeck.de; Web: www.lembeck.de

Zeitschrift für Missionswissenschaft und Religionswissenschaft. Münster, Germany: Internationales Institut für missionswissenschaftliche Forschungen e. V., 1911- . 4 issues per year. ZMR, Institut für Missionswissenschaft, Hufferstr. 27, D-48149 Münster, Germany.

Appendix A
Association Members

AERDO Agencies
For information on AERDO agencies, please check their web site at www.AERDO.org

AFMA Agencies
Abundant Life Association
Abundant Lifestyle Ministries, Inc.
Accountability First
Adams & Associates International
African Intercontinental Missions
Agape Gospel Mission
AIMS
Apostolic Team Ministries
Asian Ministry Teams
Bible League (The)
Calvary Commission
Calvary International
Calvary Ministries Inc. International
CBN International
China Ministries International
Christ for India, Inc.
Christ for the Nations
Christian Aid Mission
Christian Fellowship Union
Christian Layman's Msny. Evangelism Assoc.
Christianity.Com
Church Planting International
Evangel Bible Translators
Faith Network International
Fellowship Travel International Inc.
Food for the Hungry
Foreign Missions Foundation
Forward Edge International
Global Advance
Globe Missionary Evangelism
Good Shepherd Ministries International
Gospel Team Outreach
Hands for Christ
Health Teams International
Hearts of the Father Outreach
Hope for Africa
In His IMAGE, Inc.
Indonesian Harvest Outreach
INTERDEV
Int'l Health Services Foundation
Int'l Leadership Seminars, Inc.
International Outreach Ministries
James Financial Services
Jesus Film Project
Kingdom Expansion Ministries

Leadership Training International
Literacy & Evangelism International
Living Faith, Inc. (The)
Mahesh Chavda Ministries Int'l
Marriage Ministries Int'l
Mission Possible Foundation, Inc.
Mission to Unreached Peoples
Missionary Action Inc./FLAME
Missionary Revival Crusade
New Life League International
Operation Blessing
Int'l Pentecostal Holiness Church
Precious Seed Ministries
PROJECT: World International
Straightway Inc.
Supreme Task
Teen Mania Ministries
Vista Medical Clinic
Weiner Ministries International
World Harvest Now, Inc.
World Indigenous Missions
World Outreach
WorldWide Frontier Mission Crusade Inc.

EFMA Agencies
Advent Christian Gen. Conf., Dept. World Msns.
Africa Inter-Mennonite Mission
African Enterprise, Inc.
Assemblies of God World Missions
Baptist General Conference
Barnabas International
Bethany Fellowship Missions
Bible Literature International
Bibles For The World, Inc.
Brethren in Christ World Missions
Calvary Evangelistic Mission, Inc.
Campus Crusade for Christ, Intl.
CBInternational
Children's Cross Connection USA
Christ for the City International
Christian and Missionary Alliance
Christian Church of North America Missions
Christian Reformed World Missions
Church of God (Cleveland, TN) World Missions
Church of the Nazarene, World Mission Dept.
Ch. of the United Brethren in Christ, Global Mins.
Church Resource Ministries
Churches of God, General Conference
Citireach International

CLC Mins. Intl. (Christian Literature Crusade)
Compassion International, Inc.
Dayspring Enterprises International
Development Associates International (DAI)
Eastern Mennonite Missions
Edwin L. Hodges Ministries
EQUIP
Evangelical Congregational Church, Global
Ministries Commission
Evangelical Free Church Mission
Evangelical Friends Mission
Evangelical Mennonite Conference Bd.
Msns.
Evangelical Presbyterian Ch.—World
Outreach
Evangelism Explosion International
Evangelistic Faith Missions
Far East Broadcasting Company, Inc.
Food for the Hungry, Inc.
Foursquare Missions International
Free Methodist World Missions
Free Will Baptists, Inc., National Assoc.,
Board of Foreign Mission
Frontier Mission Fellowship
Frontiers
General Baptists International
Global Focus
Global Mapping International
Grace Brethren International Missions
Grace Ministries International
Great Commission Ministries, Inc.
International Institute for Christian Studies
Intl. Pentecostal Holiness Ch. World Msns.
International Teams, U.S.A.
InterVarsity Christian Fellowship/USA
Leadership Ministries Worldwide
LIFE Ministries
Link Care Foundation
Lutheran Bible Translators
Lutheran Brethren World Missions
MBMS International
Medical Ambassadors International
Middle East Media—USA
Mission Aviation Fellowship
Mission Possible Foundation, Inc.
Mission to the World (PCA), Inc.
Mission To Unreached Peoples
Mission Training Intl. (Missionary Internship)
Mission: Moving Mountains, Inc.
Navigators, U.S. International Missions
Group
New Directions International
New Life League International
N. American Baptist Conf. Intl. Missions
Dept.
OC International, Inc.

OMS International, Inc.
Open Bible Standard Churches, Intl. Mins.
Operation Mobilization, Inc.
Outreach Incorporated
Overseas Council International
Paraclete, Inc.
Partners International
Perimeter Church, Global Outreach
Peter Deyneka Russian Ministries
SAT-7 North America
Seed International
South American Missionary Society of the
Episcopal Church
Southern Baptist Convention Intl. Mission
Board
STEM (Short-Term Evangelical Missions) Intl.
Teen Missions International
The Mission Society for United Methodists
Third World Baptist Missions
Walk Thru The Bible Ministries
WEC International
Wesleyan World Missions
World Concern
World Gospel Mission
World Harvest Mission
World Help
World Mission Prayer League Inc.
World Missions and Evangelism, Inc.
World Partners USA (Missionary Church)
World Relief Corporation
World Thrust International, Inc.
World Vision Inc.
World Witness, Foreign Mission Board of the
Associate Reformed Presbyterian Church
WorldTeach
Wycliffe Bible Translators USA

IFMA Agencies
Africa Inland Mission Canada
Africa Inland Mission International
American Missionary Fellowship
AmeriTribes
AMF International
Arab World Ministries
Audio Scripture Ministries
Avant Ministries
Back to the Bible International
BCM International
Biblical Literature Fellowship
Cadence International
CAM International Canada
CAM International
Chosen People Ministries Canada
Chosen People Ministries International
Christar
Christar Canada

Crossover Communications, International
European Christian Mission NA, Inc.
Fellowship International Mission
Galcom International
Galcom International (U.S.)
Global Outreach Mission
Global Outreach Mission Canada
Gospel Missionary Union Canada
Gospel Recordings
Great Commission Ministries
Greater Europe Mission
Greater Europe Mission Canada
HCJB World Radio
HCJB World Radio Canada
Impact International
InterAct Ministries
InterAct Ministries Canada
InterDev
InterServe/USA
Janz Team Ministries Canada
Janz Team Ministries USA
Jews for Jesus
Jews for Jesus Canada
Kids Alive International
Language Recordings International (Gospel
    Recordings Canada)
Latin America Mission
Liebenzell Mission Canada
Liebenzell Mission USA
Media Associates International
Missionary Tech Team
Navigators of Canada
New Tribes Mission (NTM)
Network of Intl. Christian Schools (NICS)
North America Indian Ministries
North America Indian Ministries USA
Northern Canada Evangelical Mission
OMF International
OMF International Canada
Outreach to Asia Nationals
Partners International Canada
Pioneers Canada
Pioneers International
Pioneers USA
Ramabai Mukti Mission
Rio Grande Bible Institute
Romanian Missionary Society
SEND International
SEND International Canada
SEND International USA
Shalom Outreach Ministries
SIM Canada
SIM International
SIM USA
Slavic Gospel Association
Slavic Gospel Association Canada

South America Mission
South America Mission Canadian
TEAM of Canada
TEAM (The Evangelical Alliance Mission)
Trans World Radio Canada
Trans World Radio International
Trans World Radio USA
U.S. Center for World Mission (Frontier
    Mission Fellowship)
UFM Canada
UFM International
United World Mission
White Fields
World Missions Fellowship
World Reach, Inc.
World Team Canada
World Team International
World Team USA
Zion Evangelical Ministries of Africa

Appendix B

Mission Handbook
USA Protestant Ministries Overseas Questionnaire

Please return to: EMIS, P. O. Box 794, Wheaton, IL 60189-9908

1. What is your organization's name as you are known and would like to be listed in the Mission Handbook?

_____

2. Mailing Address:

_____
(P. O. Box or Street)   (City)   (State)   (Zip)

3. Telephone number: (_____) _____
Fax number: (_____) _____
E-mail _____
Web Site _____

4. Chief Executive Officer in the USA:

_____
(Name)   (Title of Position)

5. Year organization founded in USA: _____

6. Which **one** of the following is most used in describing your organization's denominational orientation?
   - ❏ Denominational
   - ❏ Nondenominational
   - ❏ Interdenominational
   - ❏ Transdenominational
   - ❏ Prefer that denominational orientation not be used
   - ❏ Other _____

7. Which **one** (or two if needed) of the following terms describes the traditional doctrinal and/or ecclesiastical stance of your organization (or that of your supporters if more appropriate)?

   - ❏ Adventist
   - ❏ Anglican
   - ❏ Baptist
   - ❏ Brethren
   - ❏ Christian ("Restoration Movement"
   - ❏ Christian/Plymouth Brethren
   - ❏ Charismatic
   - ❏ Congregational
   - ❏ Ecumenical
   - ❏ Episcopal
   - ❏ Evangelical
   - ❏ Friends
   - ❏ Fundamentalist
   - ❏ Holiness
   - ❏ Independent
   - ❏ Lutheran
   - ❏ Mennonite
   - ❏ Methodist
   - ❏ Pentecostal
   - ❏ Presbyterian
   - ❏ Reformed
   - ❏ Wesleyan
   - ❏ Other

   _____

   _____

   _____

8. Select **up to six** descriptors from the following list which are **primary** activities of your organization. If actively involved in more than six, please indicate only the six for which the most resources are currently committed.

❑ Agricultural programs
❑ Association of Missions
❑ Audio recording/distribution
❑ Aviation services
❑ Bible distribution
❑ Bible memorization
❑ Broadcasting, radio and/or TV
❑ Camping programs
❑ Childcare/orphanage
❑ Children's programs
❑ Church construction/financing
❑ Church establishing/planting
❑ Correspondence courses
❑ Development, community/ other
❑ Disability assistance programs
❑ Education, church/sch. general Christian
❑ Education, missionary (certificate)
❑ Education, theological education by extension (TEE)
❑ Education, extension (other)
❑ Education, theological
❑ Evangelism, mass
❑ Evangelism, personal & small group
❑ Evangelism, student
❑ Funds transmission
❑ Furloughed missionary support
❑ Information service (mission related)
❑ Leadership development

❑ Linguistics
❑ Literacy
❑ Literature distribution
❑ Literature production
❑ Management consulting/training
❑ Medical supplies
❑ Medicine, incl. dental & public health
❑ Member care
❑ National church nurture/support
❑ National worker support
❑ Partnership development
❑ Psychological counseling
❑ Purchasing services
❑ Recruiting/mobilizing
❑ Relief and/or rehabilitation
❑ Research (missions related)
❑ Services for other agencies
❑ Short-term programs coordination
❑ Supplying equipment
❑ Technical assistance
❑ Training/orientation, missionary
❑ Training, other
❑ Translation, Bible
❑ Translation, other
❑ Video/film production/distribution
❑ Youth programs
❑ Other

_____

_____

_____

Which **one** of the above activities above is most commonly associated with your organization?

_____

Is your organization a member of an association of missions?

❑ ANAM   ❑ AERDO   ❑ AFMA   ❑ EFMA   ❑ IFMA   ❑ CWS

❑ Other:_____

Your organization's electronic mail (E-mail) and Internet Web address can be included in the new Handbook if you so desire.

E-mail address: _____

Internet Web address: _____

9. What was your organization's **grand total income for all ministries in the USA and overseas**, raised in the USA in calendar or fiscal 2001 (Denominations should report their board total)? $_____

10. Of the grand total for all ministries reported in Question 9, what was the amount of **income for overseas ministries**? $ _____

11. Of the amount reported in Question 10, what, if any, was the **dollar amount of gifts-in-kind** commodities and/or services that were donated for overseas activities to your organization?

_____

12. **COUNTRIES OF SERVICE AND FIELD PERSONNEL**
For personnel from USA: Include those engaged in **cross-cultural ministry and fully supported** under your organization as of Jan. 1, 2002. Include those on furlough and those on loan to another organization if they are fully supported by your organization. Include those on loan to your organization only if fully supported by you. Include spouses, even if they don't have "official" ministry status but serve in a ministry or support role.

** **Please report missionaries serving in the United States in Question #16 and not below.**

For **personnel from non-USA countries**: Include personnel with specific mission/ministry duties who are fully or partially supported by/through your organization from funds raised in the USA.

Please make additional copies of the page if needed.

Note: Indicate a region only if a specific counry is not suitable.	Year Work Began	From USA: Fully supported personnel with length of service expected to be			From non-USA countries: Fully or partially supported personnel. Show the number on the appropriate country of service line.	
Country of Service		1, up to 2 years	2 to 4 years	More than 4 years	Citizens of their country of service	Not citizens of their country of service

OTHER PERSONNEL (Categories other than those reported in Question 12)

13. Number of **nonresidential mission personnel** from the USA (persons not residing in the country(s) of their ministry focus but assigned to overseas duties and traveling overseas at least 12 weeks per year on operational aspects of the ministry) who are supported by your organization.

_____ Fully supported by your organization
_____ Partially supported

14. Number of **short-term personnel** from the USA who went on overseas service projects or mission trips **less than 1 year, but at least 2 weeks**, in 2001 through your organization, either fully or partially supported including those raising their own support: _____

If you have a short-term program, where are **initial contacts** usually made with potential participants?

_____ Churches   _____Conferences (other than in churches)

_____ Individually _____ Schools   Other: _____

How many of your regular staff in the USA and overseas have **duties related to short-term programs?**

_____ Full-time on S-T program   Part-time on S-T program:

50%+ of total time _____ 10–49% _____

15. **Number of USA bi-vocational or "tentmaker" personnel sponsored or supervised by your organization** (persons who support themselves partially or fully through non-church/mission vocations and live overseas for the purpose of Christian witness, evangelism, and/or encouraging believers). _____

If you relate to "tentmakers," do you have staff assigned to maintain such contacts? _____ Yes   _____ No

Note: If countries of service for personnel in Items 13–15 are not already listed in the table in Item 12, please add the countries to the list. Also list countries with no personnel but with regular ongoing programs you support.

16. Number of **staff** and/or other employees assigned to office duties **in the USA.**

_____ Full-time paid staff   _____ Part-time paid staff/associates

_____ Volunteer (ongoing) helpers

If your organization has a board-adopted short **purpose or mission statement, please enclose a copy** from a brochure, letterhead, newsletter, or other copy that you share with others.

Please list any periodicals published by your organization: _____

Please give the name and title of the person in your organization in charge of one or all of the following departments: Recruiting, Training and Member Care.

Name: _____

Title:_____

If you have **additional comments** about your organization or this survey that you would like us to be aware of, please indicate here or enclose an additional sheet.

THANK YOU for responding to this survey! We appreciate it.

Submitted by: _____   Date: _____

Position:_____

BV 2050 .D55 2004-2006

Welliver, Dotsey

Mission handbook. U.S. and Canadian
Protestant ministries overseas.